Science In Your World

SENIOR AUTHORS
Dr. Jay K. Hackett
University of Northern Colorado

Dr. Richard H. Moyer
University of Michigan-Dearborn

CONTRIBUTING AUTHORS
Stephen C. Blume
Elementary Science Curriculum Specialist
St. Tammany Public School System
Slidell, Louisiana

Ralph M. Feather, Jr.
Teacher of Geology, Astronomy, and Earth Science
Derry Area School District
Derry, Pennsylvania

Edward Paul Ortleb
Science Supervisor
St. Louis Board of Education
St. Louis, Missouri

Dr. Barbara Swanson Thomson
Associate Professor in Science Education
The Ohio State University
Columbus, Ohio

CONTRIBUTING WRITER
Ann H. Sankey
Science Specialist
Educational Service District 121
Seattle, Washington

READING CONSULTANT
Barbara S. Pettegrew, Ph.D.
Director of the Reading/Study Center
Assistant Professor of Education
Otterbein College, Westerville, Ohio

SAFETY CONSULTANT
Gary E. Downs, Ed.D.
Professor
Iowa State University
Ames, Iowa

GIFTED AND MAINSTREAMING CONSULTANTS
George Fichter
Educational Consultant
Programs for Gifted
Ohio Department of Education
Worthington, Ohio

Timothy E. Heron, Ph.D.
Professor
Department of Human Services, Education
The Ohio State University
Columbus, Ohio

CONTENT CONSULTANTS
Robert T. Brown, M.D.
Associate Professor of Clinical Pediatrics
Director, Section for Adolescent Health
The Ohio State University/Children's Hospital
Columbus, Ohio

Henry D. Drew, Ph.D.
Chemist
U.S. FDA, Division of Drug Analysis
St. Louis, Missouri

Judith L. Doyle, Ph.D.
Physics Teacher
Newark High School
Newark, Ohio

Todd F. Holzman, M.D.
Child Psychiatrist
Harvard Community Health Plan
Wellesley, Massachusetts

Knut J. Norstog, Ph.D.
Research Associate
Fairchild Tropical Garden
Miami, Florida

James B. Phipps, Ph.D.
Professor, Geology/Oceanography
Grays Harbor College
Aberdeen, Washington

R. Robert Robbins, Ph.D.
Associate Professor of Astronomy
Astronomy Department, University of Texas
Austin, Texas

Sidney E. White, Ph.D.
Professor
Department of Geology & Mineralogy
The Ohio State University
Columbus, Ohio

REVIEWERS: Teachers and Administrators
Joan Achen, General Herkimer Elementary School, Utica, NY; **Mary Alice Bernreuter,** Mae Walters Elementary School, Hialeah, FL; **Betty Cermin,** Inez Foster Elementary, San Antonio, TX; **Jane Doane,** Blanton Elementary, Odessa, TX; **Jack Finger,** Waukesha Public Schools, Waukesha, WI; **Sister Teresa Fitzgerald,** CSJ, Office of Catholic Education, Brooklyn, NY; **Janice Gritton,** Gavin H. Cochran Elementary School, Louisville, KY; **Ann Hanacik,** Blair Elementary School, Waukesha, WI; **Barbara Kmetz,** Trumbull High School, Trumbull, CT; **Mary Jo Kreidler,** Riverside Park Elementary, San Antonio, TX; **Yolanda V. Lopez,** J.T. Canales Elementary, Brownsville, TX; **Waltina Mroczek,** Beachwood Elementary School, Beachwood, OH; **Edith Mueller,** Northview Elementary School, Waukesha, WI; **Phyllis S. Murphy,** Wilson Elementary, San Antonio, TX; **Melissa Orr,** Goliad Elementary, Odessa, TX; **Cari Richter,** Colonies North Elementary, San Antonio, TX; **Peggy Smith,** Special Education Resource Teacher, Fort Worth, TX; **Frank Stone,** Floranada Elementary School, Fort Lauderdale, FL; **John Varine,** Kiski Area School District, Vandergrift, PA; **Sue Ann Whan,** Greece Central School District, Rochester, NY; **Dr. Rosa White,** Cutler Ridge Elementary School, Miami, FL

CREDITS
Series Editor: Jane Parker,
Design Coordinator: Kip Frankenberry,
Series Production Editor: Helen Mischka,
Teacher Edition Coordinator: Judy Kinney,
Level Editor: Priscilla Zilling
Contributing Editors: Barbara A. Everett, Ava Stinnett, Beverlee Jobrack

Macmillan/McGraw-Hill School Division
866 Third Avenue
New York, New York 10022

Printed in the United States of America

ISBN 0-675-16254-8

9 8 7 6 5 4 3 2

What's inside...

Pupil Edition Unit and Chapter Titles

Science In Your World
Designed for you _and_ your student.

Core Components

- Pupil Edition
- Teacher Edition
- Teacher Resource Book

Optional Components

- Activity Book, Pupil Edition
- Activity Book, Teacher Edition
- Transparency Package
- Posters
- Software Package
- Videotapes
- Science Fair Handbook
- Activity Center
- Activity Center, Teacher Edition
- Activity Materials Management System Handbook
- Activity Materials Kit
- Safety Kit
- Stickers
- Safety Cards

TEACHER EDITION

3

SCIENCE

In Your World

Macmillan/McGraw-Hill

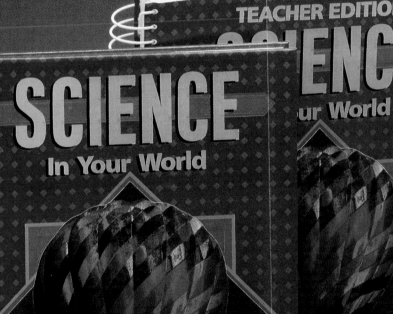

SCIENCE

In Your World

Macmillan/McGraw-Hill

TEACHER RESOURCE MASTERS

TEACHER RESOURCE MASTERS

TEACHER RESOURCE MASTERS

TEACHER RESOURCE MASTERS

SCIENCE

In Your World

ANSWER BOOKLET

BOOKLET 4

BOOKLET 3

BOOKLET 2

BOOKLET 1

Macmillan/McGraw-Hill

We designed Science In Your World to hold your students' attention and make reading about science fun.

From the literature excerpts that begin every unit, to the carefully developed questions in every unit review, *Science In Your World* makes reading about science fun. A colorful and motivating format entices students to read and keep reading. Before they know it, they're learning something new about science!

1 Active voice keeps narrative moving

2 Questions get students involved

3 Examples relate science to students

4 Second person speaks directly to students

The Water Cycle

2 **3**

4

1

Think of all the ways you will use water today. Will you wash your hands? Will you brush your teeth? Will you have a drink of water after recess or before you go to bed? Will you give your plants or your pets a drink, too? Chances are you will use water and not even think about it. Suppose there was no water in your home or school for one day. How would your life change?

Water is Earth's most important resource. Every living thing on Earth needs water to survive. Without drinking water in some form, you would not be able to live for more than a few days. Think of all the people, plants, and animals near your home. They all need water to survive.

LESSON 1 GOALS
You will learn
● that water is important to living things.
● the four stages of the water cycle.

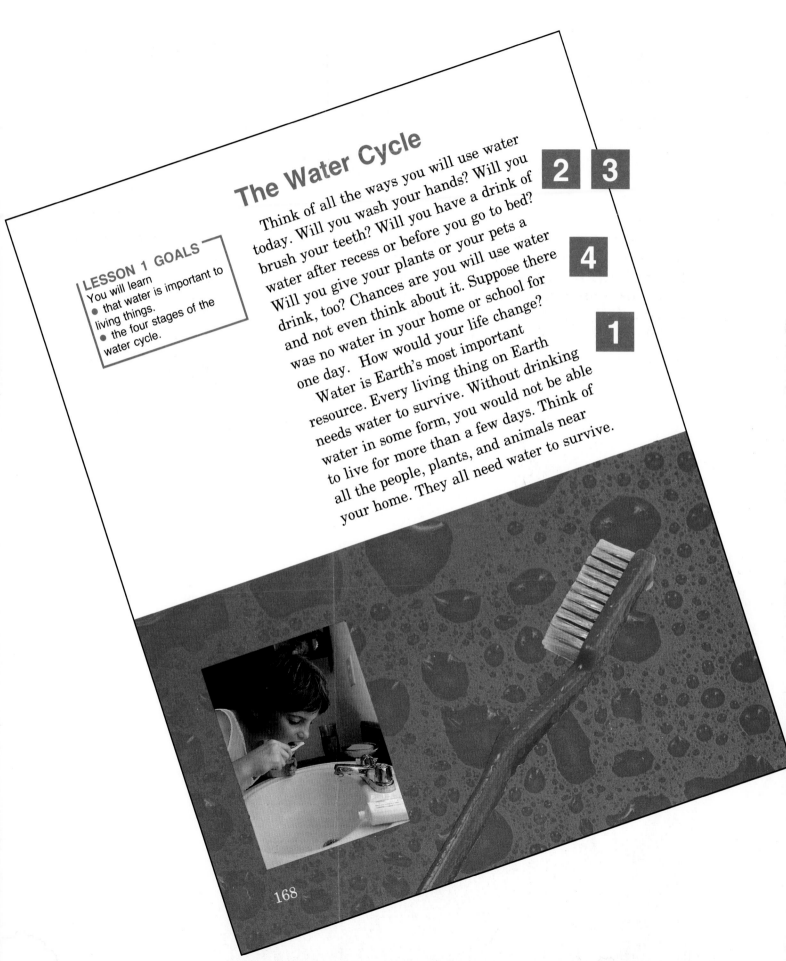

168

Science In Your World helps you reinforce the work you've done in reading, math, and writing.

LANGUAGE CONNECTION

Writing: Have students **work in cooperative groups** to explain in writing why they can slide down a playground slide. Is gravity necessary? Is friction necessary? Is any work done?

Language Connections in your Teacher Edition help you spend more time on language arts *and* science — by using science content to teach and reinforce concepts and skills from reading, writing, grammar, spelling, and oral language.

Our program will help you when time runs short.

Your students are more motivated to learn science when they see connections to other curriculum areas. Science and Reading, Science and Math notes bring out important ideas on the student page. Additional teaching tips for integrating science with other subjects offer interesting suggestions for combining lessons.

Friction

Friction

Friction (FRIHK shun) is the force that slows down or stops objects in motion. Imagine that you are riding a bike on level ground. If you stop pedaling, think about what happens. Friction between your bike tires and the ground slows you. Now imagine the same bike ride, but this time use the brakes. Think about what happens now. The friction that slows you this time is friction between your bike tires and the brake pads.

Friction happens whenever one object moves over another. The amount of friction depends on the kind of surfaces that touch each other. There is more friction when an object moves over a rough surface than when it moves over a smooth surface. For example, you are able to ride a sled very fast down a hill covered with snow. You could not ride a sled as easily on a grassy hill. Because the grass is not as smooth as snow, there is more friction.

What is friction?

SCIENCE AND . . .
Reading

Why is it safer to wear shoes with rough rubber soles than smooth leather soles on a wet, slippery day?
A. Rubber doesn't get wet.
B. Rubber has more friction.
C. Rubber cost

SCIENCE AND . . .
Math

Lance and Maria carried boxes of supplies. Lance's box had a mass of 73 kg. Maria's had a mass of 39 kg. What was the mass of both boxes?
A. 112 kg.
B. 34 kg.
C. 102 kg.
D. 44 kg.

Friction is less on a smooth surface.

Hands-on activities are simple and easy to do for both you and your students.

Science is fun when it's done right. These activities bring science to life using only the simplest materials. They don't take much time. They're a snap to organize, simple to perform, and fascinating to observe. Appealing and motivating opportunities build skills such as classifying, measuring, interpreting data, and forming hypotheses. Hands-on and cooperative grouping symbols in every lesson help support your teaching strategy.

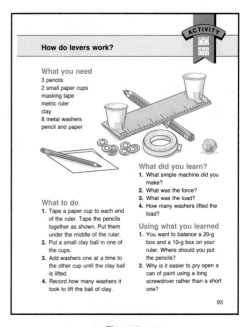

ACTIVITY

How do levers work?

What you need
3 pencils
2 small paper cups
masking tape
metric ruler
clay
8 metal washers
pencil and paper

What to do
1. Tape a paper cup to each end of the ruler. Tape the pencils together as shown. Put them under the middle of the ruler.
2. Put a small clay ball in one of the cups.
3. Add washers one at a time to the other cup until the clay ball is lifted.
4. Record how many washers it took to lift the ball of clay.

What did you learn?
1. What simple machine did you make?
2. What was the force?
3. What was the load?
4. How many washers lifted the load?

Using what you learned
1. You want to balance a 20-g box and a 10-g box on your ruler. Where should you put the pencils?
2. Why is it easier to pry open a can of paint using a long screwdriver rather than a short one?

93

Doing science in the classroom can be fun! Kids love these activities because they bring science to life right before their eyes. You'll love them because they use only the simplest materials. They're a snap to organize.

You Can...
Make a Chart

Scientists must know how to organize their data. One way to organize data is to use a chart. This chart shows how the height of two plants changed. You can make your own chart. Talk to ten friends. Find out how many brothers and sisters each friend has. Put your data into a chart. Who has the most brothers? Who has the most sisters?

Height of Plants		
Day	Plant A	Plant B
1	5 cm	5 cm
2	5½ cm	6 cm
3	6 cm	7 cm
4	6½ cm	7 cm
5	7 cm	9 cm

Have You Ever...
Experimented With the Space in a Cup?

Fill the cup with water. Put it on a paper towel. What do you think will happen when you try to put something else into the space that is filled with water? Try it and see. Put a marble in the cup. What happens? What do you think will happen if you put another marble in the cup? Why do you think it will happen?

Teaching cycles help you shape up lessons quickly.

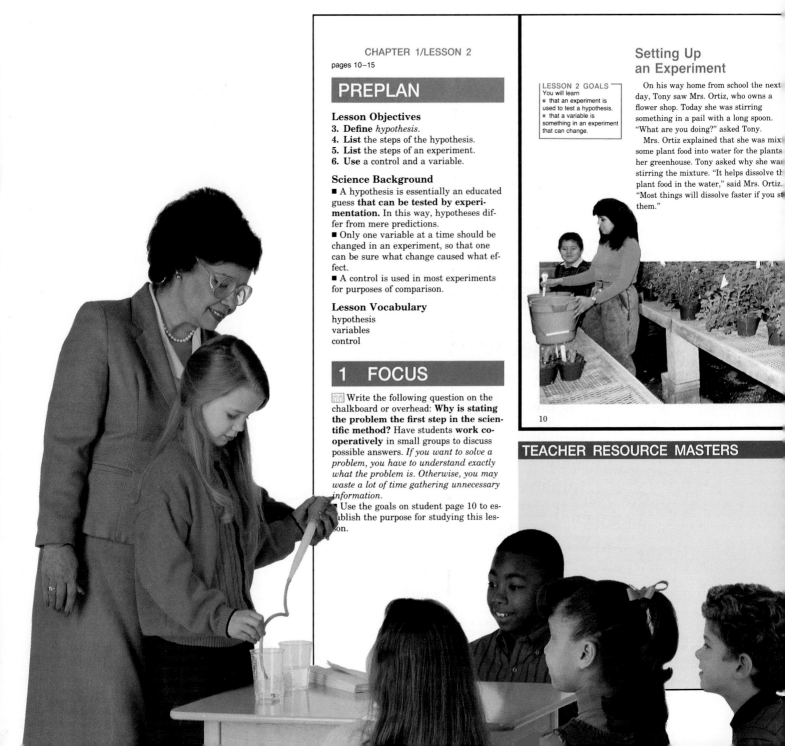

PREPLAN

Lesson Objectives
3. **Define** *hypothesis*.
4. **List** the steps of the hypothesis.
5. **List** the steps of an experiment.
6. **Use** a control and a variable.

Science Background
■ A hypothesis is essentially an educated guess **that can be tested by experimentation.** In this way, hypotheses differ from mere predictions.
■ Only one variable at a time should be changed in an experiment, so that one can be sure what change caused what effect.
■ A control is used in most experiments for purposes of comparison.

Lesson Vocabulary
hypothesis
variables
control

1   FOCUS

Write the following question on the chalkboard or overhead: **Why is stating the problem the first step in the scientific method?** Have students **work cooperatively** in small groups to discuss possible answers. *If you want to solve a problem, you have to understand exactly what the problem is. Otherwise, you may waste a lot of time gathering unnecessary information.*
Use the goals on student page 10 to establish the purpose for studying this lesson.

LESSON 2 GOALS
You will learn
● that an experiment is used to test a hypothesis.
● that a variable is something in an experiment that can change.

Setting Up an Experiment

On his way home from school the next day, Tony saw Mrs. Ortiz, who owns a flower shop. Today she was stirring something in a pail with a long spoon. "What are you doing?" asked Tony.

Mrs. Ortiz explained that she was mixing some plant food into water for the plants in her greenhouse. Tony asked why she was stirring the mixture. "It helps dissolve the plant food in the water," said Mrs. Ortiz. "Most things will dissolve faster if you stir them."

10

TEACHER RESOURCE MASTERS

Each teaching cycle is a three-step lesson plan you can see at a glance. Just open your Teacher Edition to the first two pages of any lesson. Refer to the numbered teaching steps in the margins. Check out the other options, if you wish, on the pages that follow. Now you're ready to go!

The three teaching steps — Focus, Teach, and Apply — include strategies from a widely recognized teaching model.

1 Focus: How do I start?

2 Teach: How do I guide students to understanding?

3 Apply: How do I close?

...hought about what Mrs. Ortiz said ...d, "Do you want to do an ...nt?" ...lained that they were studying ...entific methods at school. First, ...ded to state the problem they were ...solve. Tony wrote the problem on ...f paper.

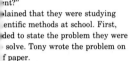

Problem: How can we make plant food dissolve in water faster?

11

TEACHER RESOURCE MASTERS

Independent Practice   11

CHAPTER 1/LESSON 2
pages 10–15

2 TEACH

■ Discuss the idea of a fair test, and ask students why it is important to have the same amount of water in each pail.
■ Ask students why Tony stirred only one pail. Point out that the pail not stirred is called the control.
■ Note that at each step throughout the experiment Tony is careful to write things down. Ask: **Why is it important to write things down as you go?** *A careful record of observations is important when it is time to think about results.*

Guided Practice
■ Check students' understanding of lesson concepts by discussing the Lesson Review questions on student page 15. If necessary, use the **reteaching strategy** in OPTIONS.

Independent Practice
■ Assign the Lesson 2 section of the Teacher Resource Master **Independent Practice,** page 11.

3 APPLY

■ Suggest these hypothetical experiments and have students identify the variables.
1. A man wants to find out how to make his homemade cookies crisper, so he tries baking them at different temperatures. (oven temperature)
2. A girl wanted to see which paper towel would soak up the most water. She tested three brands. (amount of water absorbed, paper towel brands)

Close
■ Use Summary statements on student page 15 to review lesson concepts.

OPTIONS

Reteaching Strategy
■ Ask students to explain the difference between a hypothesis and a wild guess. Have them devise an experiment to test a wild guess.

Chapter 1   11

Science In Your World

TEACHER REFERENCE GUIDE

FEATURING:
ABOUT THE
AUTHORS

SCOPE AND
SEQUENCE

PROGRAM
PHILOSOPHY
AND GOALS

THINKING
IN SCIENCE

TEACHING
STRATEGIES

READING
STRATEGIES

SCIENCE AT
HOME

SCIENCE FAIR

MATERIALS
LIST

RESOURCES

ABOUT THE AUTHORS

SENIOR AUTHORS

Dr. Jay K. Hackett is a professor of Earth Science Education at the University of Northern Colorado. He holds a B.S. in General Science, an M.N.S. in Physical Science, and an Ed.D. in Science Education with support in Earth Science. A resource teacher for elementary schools, he conducts numerous workshops and professional seminars. With over 30 years of teaching experience, he has taught and consulted on science programs across all levels and remains active in local, state, and national science professional organizations.

Dr. Richard H. Moyer is a professor of Science Education at the University of Michigan, Dearborn. He holds a B.S. in Chemistry and Physics Education, an M.S. in Curriculum and Instruction, and an Ed.D. in Science Education. With more than 20 years of teaching experience on all levels, he is currently involved in teacher training. He is the recipient of two Distinguished Faculty Awards. He conducts numerous workshops and in-service training programs for science teachers. Dr. Moyer is also the author of Merrill Publishing Company's *General Science* textbook.

CONTRIBUTING AUTHORS

Stephen C. Blume serves as the Elementary Science Specialist for the St. Tammany Public School System in Slidell, LA. Mr. Blume holds a B.A. from St. Mary's University and an M.A. from Southeastern Louisiana University in elementary education. He is a member of the National Science Teachers Association, the Louisiana Science Teachers Association, and the Council for Elementary Science International. He is the author of several articles related to teaching science, as well as Macmillan/McGraw Hill's *Science Fair Handbook* and Merrill Publishing Company's *Science Connections*.

Ralph M. Feather, Jr., is a teacher of geology, astronomy, and earth science and serves as Science Department Chair in the Derry Area School District in Derry, PA. He holds a B.S. in Geology and a M.Ed. in Geoscience from the Indiana University of Pennsylvania. He is a member of the Geological Society of America, the National Science Teachers Association, and the Association for Supervision and Curriculum Development, as well as many other professional organizations. Mr. Feather is co-author of Merrill Publishing Company's *Science Connections* and the Teacher Resource Package for *Focus on Earth Science*.

Edward Paul Ortleb is the Science Supervisor for the St. Louis Board of Education. He holds an A.B. in Education from Harris Teachers College and a M.A. in Education and an Advanced Graduate Certificate in Science Education from Washington University, St. Louis. Mr. Ortleb is a lifetime member of NSTA, having served as its president in 1978-79. He is a contributing author for the Teacher Resource Books for Merrill Publishing Company's *Accent on Science* and *General Science* and is co-author of Merrill Publishing Company's *Science Connections*.

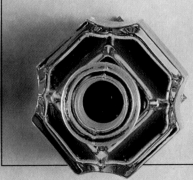

Dr. Barbara Swanson Thomson is an associate professor in science education at The Ohio State University in Columbus, Ohio. Dr. Thomson received a B.S. from Michigan State University, an M.A. in reading and linguistics from The Ohio State University, and a Ph.D. in Science Education with a specialty in botany from The Ohio State University. She has held numerous national and local leadership positions in educational organizations. She conducts numerous workshops and inservice programs for teachers and has had teaching experience at all levels.

Jay Hackett

Richard H. Moyer

Stephen C. Blume

Ralph M. Feather

Edward Ortleb

Barbara S. Thomson

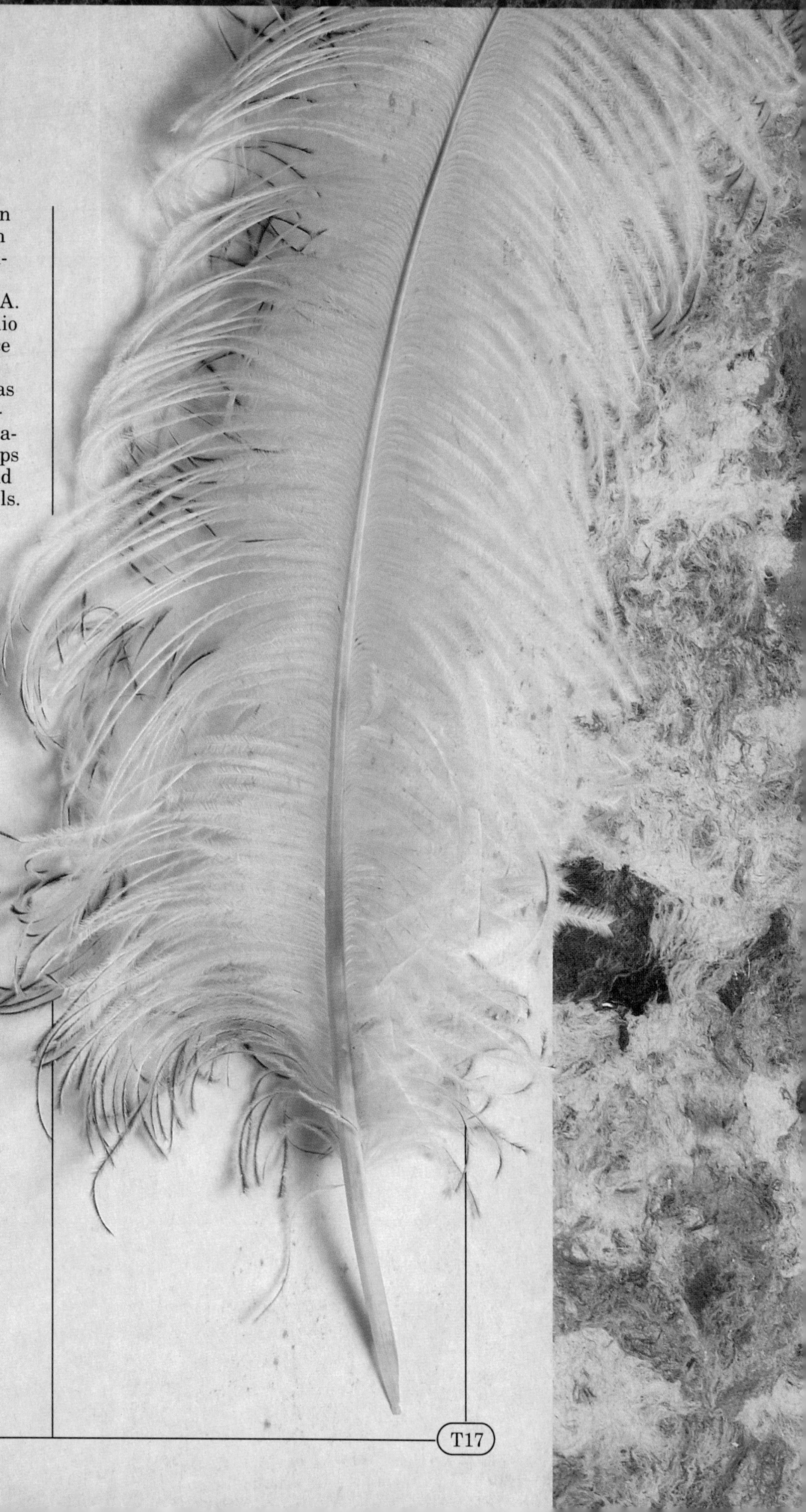

SCOPE & SEQUENCE

PROGRAM PHILOSOPHY AND GOALS

PHILOSOPHY

SCIENCE In Your World is designed to offer a variety of meaningful experiences to develop children's natural curiosity about themselves and everything around them.

Appropriate learning experiences encourage children to explore and develop explanations for phenomena in the world. These experiences provide a framework that helps children make informed choices and decisions today and in the future.

Effective engagement in science enables children to understand and appreciate the impact of science and technology on society.

GOALS

Active involvement in the ***SCIENCE In Your World*** philosophy, approach, and experiences will prepare children to do the following:

- Use critical-thinking process skills to solve problems and develop concepts.

- Integrate reading, writing, and mathematical thought processes to develop understandings in science.

- Recognize and explain cause-and-effect relationships in the world around them.

- Make informed choices and decisions that affect their environment and daily lives.

- Value the nature of science in its objectivity, limitations, and tentativeness.

- Understand and respect the impact of science on society and its use of technology.

THINKING IN SCIENCE

Cognitive Development
Learning involves both awareness and judgement. *Cognitive development* is the process of development by which knowledge is acquired. Most of what science knows about cognitive development has come from observing children and finding similar patterns in the ways in which they think and acquire knowledge. Teachers and parents who know what to expect from children have a basis for developing appropriate and meaningful learning experiences.

At one time, scientists thought that children and adults learned in the same way. In this view, a child's mind was seen simply as an empty bucket into which a teacher could pour knowledge. A Swiss psychologist, Jean Piaget (1896-1980), is the person most responsible for advancements in researching cognitive development. We now know that cognitive development affects a child's learning to speak, read, and understand mathematical concepts and abstract ideas.

Piaget observed that people seem to go through four stages of cognitive development in the same order at approximately the same age ranges.

In 1972 Piaget said, "Children should be able to do their own experimenting and their own research. Teachers, of course, can guide them by providing appropriate materials, but the essential thing is that in order for a child to understand something, he must construct it himself, he must re-invent it."

SCIENCE In Your World applies our understanding of cognitive development in the following ways.

1. Experiences are designed to be appropriate to the general cognitive abilities of children at each age group.

2. Questions and experiences facilitate the development of certain operations at each grade level, including serial ordering, conservation, classification, and the formation of simple hypotheses.

3. Multiple exposure to certain types of thinking operations is provided throughout each grade level.

4. New concepts are introduced by providing familiar and concrete references.

5. Students learn and understand new concepts through motivating, hands-on activities.

By doing these things in education, we can appeal to children's strengths and stimulate the development of more advanced thinking patterns.

kog nish´ ən

Four Stages of Cognitive Development

Birth to two years   Sensory-Motor   A child is self-centered and learns by senses. Young children like to play peek-a-boo. They think that if you can't see them, they don't exist. A young child has to sense something by sight, sound, taste, smell, or touch to know it.

Two to seven years   Preoperational   Children tend to focus on only one aspect of an issue. As a teacher, you may have met children who found it impossible to believe that you were also a parent. This is because a child in the preoperational stage focuses on only one aspect of an issue.

Six to eleven years   Concrete-Operational Children can see two sides of an issue but have difficulty with abstract thought. "That's not fair." "You cheated!" Rules, at this stage, become very important. Rules are concrete and should not change. Children are frustrated by exceptions in spelling or in games. To wonder about the appropriateness of a rule or a procedure is not part of the thinking process at this time.

Eleven and older   Formal-Operational   People have the ability to reason on an abstract level.

THINKING IN SCIENCE

CRITICAL THINKING

Critical-Thinking Science Process Skills

What are *critical* thinking skills? The word *critical* can mean *evaluative,* and it can mean *crucial.* In education both definitions apply. Learning involves a crucial awareness and judgment. Our goal in education is to encourage the development of critical-thinking skills and to expand the potential for learning at each stage of cognitive development.

In 1956, Benjamin Bloom of the University of Chicago published a classification system for intellectual tasks that

specific listing of critical-thinking skills below.

Throughout the program, *SCIENCE In Your World* has conscientiously included experiences that help students develop, practice, and apply critical-thinking process skills. The process skills are carefully introduced and developed through the use of higher-level divergent questions, controlled experiments, and problem-solving and creative activities at each grade level. In addition, the *Application Activities,* all formal activities, and the *You Can…* activities

Observing	Students use their sense of sight, sound, taste, smell, or touch to learn more about objects and events.
Classifying	Students sort or group objects or events based on common properties and/or categorize objects or events based on existing relationships among them.
Inferring	Students interpret, explain, and identify causes based on observed events and collected data.
Communicating	Students convey information in oral and written forms and visually through the use of graphs, charts, pictures, and diagrams.
Recognizing and Using Spatial Relationships	Students estimate the relative positions of both moving and nonmoving objects.
Measuring	Students identify and order length, area, volume, mass, and temperature to describe and quantify objects or events.
Predicting	Based on observations and inferences, students propose possible results or outcomes of future events.
Using Numbers	Students transfer or apply ordering, counting, adding, subtracting, multiplying, and dividing to quantify data where appropriate in investigations or experiments.
Interpreting Data	Students explain the meaning of information gathered in scientific situations.
Forming Hypotheses	Students first make an assumption and then draw out and test its logical consequences.
Separating and Controlling Variables	Students recognize the many factors that affect the outcomes of events. They understand the relationship of the factors to one another so that one factor (variable) can be manipulated while the others are controlled.
Experimenting	Students test hypotheses or predictions under conditions in which variables are both controlled and manipulated.
Formulating Models	Students construct mental, verbal, or physical representations of ideas, objects, or events. They then use the models to clarify explanations or to demonstrate relationships.
Defining Operationally	Students form a working definition that is based upon their actual experiences.

has become known as Bloom's Taxonomy. The levels of thought he identified from simple to complex are **Knowledge, Comprehension, Application, Analysis, Synthesis,** and **Evaluation.** Bloom's Taxonomy forms the basis for the more

are specifically designed to practice critical-thinking process skills. This careful attention provides stimulation for your students to develop more advanced thinking patterns.

THINKING IN SCIENCE

We know that competency in content is only one part of success in learning. When asked to *apply* a concept or to *interpret* an everyday situation in light of the concepts they have learned, many students become confused. Problem solving must be an integral part, as it is a natural part, of education.

A Problem-Solving Process or Model may be helpful to many students who do not know where to begin in solving a problem. Identifying the problem and then planning an effective strategy to solve it are the crucial steps in problem solving. You may want to suggest these nine steps as one way to attack a problem.

In 1949, Albert Einstein wrote, "There is not a single concept of which I am convinced that it will stand firm, and I feel uncertain whether I am in general on the right track." Solving difficult problems is one of the most complex things we do. Often we come to realize that the real problem is different from what we had originally thought. Or we discover that the solution we've derived does not really solve the problem. We do not always reach successful solutions on the first try. At any stage in the problem-solving process, we may need to go back to the beginning and start again.

SCIENCE In Your World offers students multiple opportunities to practice problem-solving skills as they read and actively participate in the activities in the student book. Activity suggestions in the teacher edition and the *Application Activities* in the back of each student edition are specifically designed as problems to solve.

As educators we can encourage students to try to solve problems. We can include problem solving in daily teaching, not only in science but in every area. If we focus on helping students use the process rather than merely get the right answer, we can help build the confidence needed to develop more advanced thinking skills.

PROBLEM SOLVING

1 Verbalize the problem.
State the problem aloud and believe that you can solve it.

2 Define the problem.
Analyze the information given and determine what you still need to know to solve the problem.

3 Explore.
Brainstorm strategies for collecting and organizing information to solve the problem. Strategies for collecting data may be to observe, survey, or research known information. Strategies for organization might be to construct a table or graph, look for a pattern, talk to an expert, make a model, guess and check, work backwards, or use a process of elimination.

4 Plan.
Decide on a strategy or group of strategies and list the steps needed to complete the plan.

5 Collect information.
Using the plan, gather the data needed to solve the problem.

6 Organize and analyze data.
According to your plan, complete the strategies needed to organize the information gathered into a usable form. Then analyze the data to find out what they tell you about the problem.

7 Generate potential solutions.
Using the analysis of the data, brainstorm a list of possible solutions for the problem.

8 Choose and explain the solution.
Review the procedures, data, and thought processes that led to your particular solution of the problem.

9 Implement the solution.
Solve the problem.

COOPERATIVE LEARNING

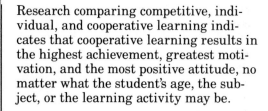

Research comparing competitive, individual, and cooperative learning indicates that cooperative learning results in the highest achievement, greatest motivation, and the most positive attitude, no matter what the student's age, the subject, or the learning activity may be.

What Is Cooperative Learning?

Just putting students together to do something is *not* necessarily cooperative learning. Cooperative learning groups *learn* things together, not just do things together.

1. Cooperative learning requires more than individual accountability for mastering the assigned materials. Individuals are responsible for everyone else, as well.

2. Cooperative learning requires face-to-face interaction among group members.

3. Cooperative learning requires shared leadership responsibilities.

4. Cooperative learning requires students to use appropriate interpersonal and small-group skills that will be valuable in working in groups throughout their lives.

The Teacher's Role in Cooperative Learning

1. Form the groups and assign a diverse group of students to each group.

2. Explain the roles of members in a group.

3. Explain the task and its goals.

4. Explain the criteria for success.

5. Monitor the cooperative behavior in the group and share your observations with the group.

6. Provide assistance with the task: give feedback, redirect questions, encourage thinking, manage conflict, and supply resources.

7. Provide closure for the lesson. Have students summarize what they've learned, and have them relate it to previous learning.

8. Evaluate the group process. Have groups rate themselves and write specific ways to improve.

9. Evaluate student learning. You might use individual or group tests and systems of extra points for groups achieving high marks overall.

Student Roles in Cooperative Learning

In small groups, each group member may have more than one role. Among the tasks that need to be carried out are the following:

1. Facilitator—the person responsible for making sure the group stays on task and uses positive, cooperative learning strategies.

2. Recorder—the person who documents the group's observations, data, and answers to activity questions.

3. Gatherer of materials—the person responsible for getting the materials from the teacher.

4. Reader—the person responsible for reading the instructions to the group.

5. Performer—the person responsible for carrying out the activity procedures.

6. Interpreter/Observer—the person who explains what happens during the activity.

7. Custodian/Cleaner—the person responsible for returning all unused materials to the proper place and returning the group's working space to its original condition.

Using Cooperative Strategies

To prepare students for cooperative learning, the following rules may be helpful.

1. Stay with your group. Moving around hinders progress.

2. To get ideas for procedures, use a brainstorming technique in which each person in the group takes turns coming up with an idea. During brainstorming no one can criticize another's idea.

3. Make group decisions by consensus.

4. Encourage each other to participate.

5. Use each other's names. Use eye contact.

INTEGRATING SCIENCE

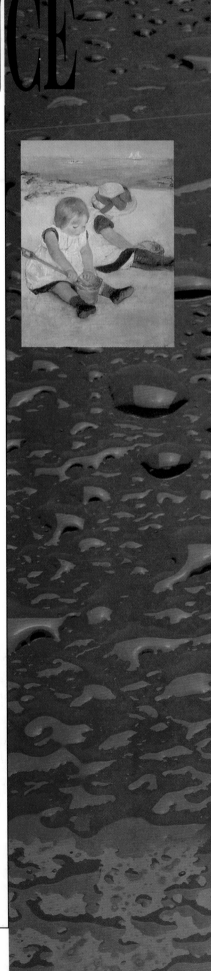

6. Ask the teacher for help only after you have decided as a group that you need help.

7. Don't make negative personal remarks.

How Is Cooperative Learning Used in *SCIENCE In Your World?*

Virtually all the activities in the student edition and the suggested activities in the teacher edition will work in a cooperative learning situation. Many of the activity pages make specific suggestions for working in a cooperative learning situation. In many cases, a cooperative learning group can be formed as students participate in the *Whole Class Projects* or *Science Fair Projects* that are listed on the teacher edition interleaf pages before each chapter.

You may also choose to form cooperative groups to read, study, or demonstrate knowledge of the concepts and methods explained in the text itself. ■

Integrating Science

We hear a lot about purposeful integration of the *language* arts: listening, speaking, reading, thinking, and writing. The language arts complement one another. When a student uses one, the others are reinforced. Language arts are the tools of thinking and learning across the curriculum. By the same token, no skill or subject can be taught in isolation. Subject areas interweave and overlap, and all learning involves an integration of the language arts. But what does integration mean specifically for science?

Science is truly integrated in the world. When children play in snow, when they help bake cookies, when they dig in sand, when they pick flowers, when they take care of their pets, they are engaged in scientific discovery, concepts, and methods.

Additionally, science naturally involves all of the language arts. Children practice reading, writing, listening, speaking, and critical thinking when they encounter scientific text, ideas, and activities. Science is a natural for developing interactive, cooperative group skills as students work in teams to complete activities. Science is particularly suited to the practice of critical-thinking skills as students encounter and solve problems.

Science is encountered constantly in social studies, math, and other curriculum areas. For example, scientific discoveries have changed the course of history. The study of geography goes hand in hand with the study of life, earth, and physical science. Science frequently relies on mathematic principles. And it is difficult to participate in physical education or learn about health without a scientific knowledge of the human body.

Literature, both fiction and nonfiction, complements your science curriculum, as well. Think of all you learned about spiders by reading *Charlotte's Web,* about deer from *The Yearling,* or about wild horses from *Misty of Chincoteague.*

SCIENCE In Your World is specifically designed to develop a student's understanding of science in human experience and the individual's role in the community and in society. The text involves real examples of the scientific phenomena that are explained. The activities and concepts are meant to be applied in real life.

In addition, throughout the teacher edition are specific ideas for math, language arts, social studies, art, physical education, home economics, and other curriculum integration in the *Connection* features. The student edition includes features such as *Science and… Math* that draw concrete analogies between science and other areas. The program also includes references in *Books to Read* at the end of each unit in the student and teacher editions and cross-disciplinary ideas in the Teacher Resource Books.

TEACHING MODEL

SCIENCE In Your World makes it easy for you to develop your lesson plans for each part of your lesson cycle. Strategies for the achievement of each step in the cycle can be found in specific areas of the teacher edition. The Teaching Model below identifies these sections. It may be used in a variety of ways to meet the needs of different teaching situations and different lessons. The flexibility of **SCIENCE In Your World** allows for the use of this model in its entirety on a daily basis, allowing for all steps to be incorporated while you are involved in a single activity. It can also be adapted for a weekly structure or a structure determined by individual classroom needs.

Step	Goal	SCIENCE In Your World
Focus	Focus students' attention. State goal or objective.	*Focus: Motivation strategies.* Student Edition: *Lesson Goals.*
Explanation	Input information. Teach to the objectives.	*Teach:* Teaching Tips.
Check Understanding	Make sure students understand the objective.	*Checking for Understanding; Reteaching Strategy.*
Guided Practice Check for Mastery	Guide students to make sure initial learning is successful. Observe and evaluate student performance.	Student in-text questions; Margin questions; Margin strategies; *Lesson Review*
Independent Practice Assess Mastery	Allow students to gain fluency through practice. Observe and evaluate student performance.	Use of *Independent Practice Masters* in the *Teacher Resource Book* for each lesson.
Closure	Make sure students understand and can apply what has been taught.	*Apply:* Application of lesson concepts. Summary statements to review concepts.
Extension	Build upon skills.	All Teacher Resource Book Activities; *Unit Review: Challenging Project, Books to Read; Lesson and Feature Options; Application Activities.*

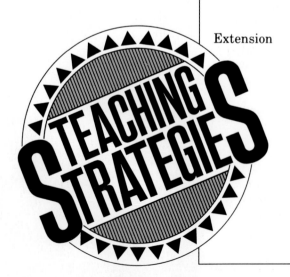

HINTS FOR CLASSROOM MANAGEMENT

by Dr. Richard H. Moyer

There is no one right way to manage a science classroom just as there is no one right way to manage a classroom studying any subject. There are, of course, a few guidelines that are helpful to keep in mind regarding the smooth operation of an activity-oriented subject area like science.

Preplan
Preplanning is probably the most important part of a successful lesson. Studying the Planning Guide at the beginning of each chapter in *SCIENCE In Your World* and skimming the student text and teacher margin material is essential for a smooth lesson that offers the teacher few "surprises."

Next, preview the activities you plan to have students do. It has been said often that science experiments always work—just not always the way you thought they would! Working through the activities and experiments ahead of time is the easiest way for teachers to be aware of how materials will work. In this way, you can also prepare your students for their subsequent experience.

Organize Materials
Be sure you have adequate supplies of materials before you begin an activity. It is also valuable to think about how (and when) you will distribute materials to the class. You may wish to assign roles to group members in class. One role could be gatherer of materials: the person responsible for equipment and supplies.

It is also helpful to package small materials together to ease distribution. Plastic containers or food bags, shoe boxes, and egg cartons often work well for this purpose. Remember, it is also important to get materials back in an orderly manner. The use of containers and assigned students will be helpful for this task as well.

Make Students Aware of Expectations
Be sure the students know what you expect of them. Discuss rules for appropriate behavior during science.

Make Students Aware of Lesson Goals
A science activity will be more effective if students know why they are engaged in it. Before beginning an activity, review procedures with the class. Be sure students have well in mind *what it is they are trying to find out.*

Make Effective Use of Human Resources
Peer Tutoring can enhance student understanding and retention. Peer tutoring is most effective when students of differing abilities are paired. Your role in peer tutoring is to train tutors to use positive reinforcement and good questioning strategies while maintaining their own language and learning styles as they teach each other.

Reciprocal Teaching is another method for making effective use of resources. Call on teachers, principals, parents, members of the community, and students who have specific expertise to help with particular lessons or activities. Make yourself available, as well, for lessons that require your expertise.

Time on Science
Many teachers wonder about how much time they should spend on science every day. Each chapter introduction and formal activity in *SCIENCE In Your World* provides a Time Allotment for your planning purposes. Lessons were developed based on a daily 30-minute science period. However, depending on your state, district, or school guidelines or your personal preferences, the total amount of time you spend on science will vary. You may wish to extend some lessons and shorten others. You may wish to integrate some science chapters or activities with other curriculum areas. *SCIENCE In Your World* is designed to be adapted to your needs.

TEACHING EXCEPTIONAL

The chart below provides you with general help in teaching exceptional students. In each chapter interleaf section in the teacher edition,

SCIENCE In Your World also provides a *For Your Exceptional Students* feature that offers specific suggestions for help.

	Description	Sources Of Help/Information
Learning Disabled	All learning disabled students have an academic problem in one or more areas, such as academic learning, language, perception, social-emotional adjustment, memory, or attention.	*Journal of Learning Disabilities* *Learning Disability Quarterly*
Behaviorally Disabled	Children with behavior disorders deviate from standards for expectations of behavior and impair the functioning of others and themselves. These children may also be gifted or learning disabled.	*Exceptional Children* *Journal of Special Education*
Physically Disabled	Children who are physically disabled fall into two categories –those with orthopedic impairments and those with other health impairments. Orthopedically impaired children have the use of one or more limbs severely restricted, so the use of wheelchairs, crutches, or braces may be necessary. Children with other health impairments may require the use of respirators or other medical equipment.	Batshaw, M.L., and M.Y. Perset. *Children with Handicaps: A Medical Primer.* Baltimore: Paul H. Brooks, 1981. Hale, G. (Ed.). *The Source Book for the Disabled.* New York: Holt, Rinehart & Winston, 1982. *Teaching Exceptional Children*
Visually Disabled	Children who are visually disabled have partial or total loss of sight. Individuals with visual impairments are not significantly different from their sighted peers in ability range or personality. However, blindness can affect cognitive, motor, and social development, especially if early intervention is lacking.	*Journal of Visual Impairment and Blindness* *Education of Visually Handicapped* American Foundation for the Blind
Developmentally Handicapped	A student with a developmental handicap experiences significant subaverage intellectual functions along with deficits in adaptive behavior. The deficits in both of these areas have significant impact on a student's developmental period of maturation.	Gearhart, B., Weishahn, M., and Gearhart, C. *The Exceptional Student in the Regular Classroom.* Columbus, Ohio: Merrill Publishing Company, 1988.
Hearing Impaired	Children who are hearing impaired have partial or total loss of hearing. Individuals with hearing impairments are not significantly different from their hearing peers in ability range or personality. However, deafness can affect cognitive, motor, and social development if early intervention is lacking. Speech development also is often affected.	*American Annals of the Deaf* *Journal of Speech and Hearing Research* *Sign Language Studies*
Multicultural and/or Bilingual	Multicultural and/or bilingual children often speak English as a second language or not at all. Customs and behaviors of people in the majority culture may be confusing for some of these students. Cultural values may inhibit some of these students from full participation.	*Teaching English as a Second Language Reporter* R.L. Jones, ed., *Mainstreaming and the Minority Child.* Reston, VA: Council for Exceptional Children, 1976.
Gifted	Although no formal definition exists, these students can be described as having above average ability, task commitment, and creativity. Gifted students rank in the top 5% of their class. They usually finish work more quickly than other students, and are capable of divergent thinking.	*Journal for the Education of the Gifted* *Gifted Child Quarterly* *Gifted/Creative/Talented*

STUDENTS

In addition, many *Options* are labeled as basic, average, or advanced to guide you in your assignments.

Tips For Instruction

1. Provide support and structure: clearly specify rules, assignments, and duties.
2. Establish situations that lead to success: use simple vocabulary.
3. Practice skills frequently–use games and drills to help maintain student interest.
4. Allow students to record answers on tape and allow extra time to complete tests and assignments.
5. Provide outlines or tape lecture material.
6. Pair students with peer helpers, and provide classtime for pair interaction.

1. Provide a carefully structured environment with regard to scheduling, rules, and room arrangement.
2. Clearly outline objectives and how you will help students obtain objectives. Seek input from them about their strengths, weaknesses, and goals.
3. Reinforce appropriate behavior and model it for students.
4. Do not expect immediate success. Instead, work for long-term improvement.
5. Balance individual needs with group requirements.

1. Assume that students understand more than they may be able to communicate.
2. Openly discuss with students any uncertainties you have about when to offer aid.
3. Ask parents or therapists what special devices or procedures are needed, and if any special safety precautions need be taken.
4. Allow physically disabled students to do everything their peers do, including participating in field trips, special events, and projects.
5. Help nondisabled students and adults understand the characteristics of physically disabled students.

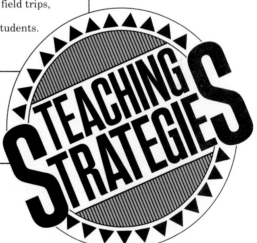

1. Help the student become independent–make the student accountable for assignments.
2. Teach classmates how to serve as guides.
3. Eliminate unnecessary noise in the classroom.
4. Encourage students to use their sense of touch. Provide tactile models whenever possible.
5. Describe people and events as they occur in the classroom.
6. Provide taped lectures and reading assignments.
7. Team the student with a sighted peer for laboratory work.

1. Seat students away from distracting noises and outside activities.
2. Actively involve students with hands-on activities of short duration.
3. Sequence information from simple to complex.
4. Emphasize concrete, relevant experiences.
5. Provide immediate feedback.
6. Use frequent and continuing progress checks.
7. Use oral tests whenever possible.

1. Seat students where they can see your lip movements easily, and avoid visual distractions.
2. Avoid standing with your back to a window or light source.
3. Avoid moving around the room or writing on the board while speaking. Instead, use an overhead projector, which allows you maintain eye contact while writing.
4. Encourage students to face the speaker, even if students must move around during class discussions.
5. Write all assignments on the board, or provide written instructions.
6. If the student has a manual interpreter, allow both student and interpreter to select the most favorable seating arrangements.

1. Do not allow the language students bring to school to influence your expectations of their academic performances; however, beware of reverse discrimination.
2. Try to incorporate students' languages into your instruction. The help of a bilingual aide may be effective.
3. Include information on different cultures in the curriculum to aid students' self-image–avoid cultural stereotypes.
4. Encourage students to share their culture in the classroom.

1. Make arrangements for students to take selected subjects early.
2. Let students express themselves in art forms such as drawing, creative writing, or acting.
3. Make public services available through a catalog of resources, such as agencies providing free and inexpensive materials, community services and programs, and people in the community with specific expertise.
4. Ask "what if" questions to develop high-level thinking skills.
5. Emphasize concepts, theories, ideas, relationships, and generalizations.

EFFECTIVE USE OF ACTIVITIES

by Dr. Jay K. Hackett

Guided Discovery

The heart of the elementary school science curriculum is involvement in meaningful guided discovery. This active participation in hands-on activities, guided by relevant thought-provoking questions, involves children in thought processes that help them develop problem-solving skills, reasoning, and understanding. Guided-discovery investigations emphasize science process skills such as observing, classifying, inferring, measuring, predicting, interpreting data, and drawing appropriate conclusions to develop higher-level thinking skills.

The effective use of guided-discovery investigations makes it possible for children to reconstruct previously developed explanations or concepts. Children develop explanations for common scientific phenomena observed in daily living experiences before they are exposed to formal science instruction in school. These explanations are often very different from what teachers expect. Surprisingly, these naive or mixed ideas often persist even after listening to more sophisticated explanations from the teacher and reading well-developed scientific explanations in textbooks.

Many learning theorists and researchers believe these misconceptions can be restructured by involving children in new experiences that can't be explained using their previously developed ideas. Good guided-discovery activities can provide these experiences as well as the verbal interaction with peers and the teacher to help children recognize new relationships and construct more accurate generalizations.

Guided-Discovery Activities in Science

Both the formal and supplemental activities in *SCIENCE In Your World* provide experiences through which students develop and reinforce or restructure concepts, as well as develop the ability to use process skills. The activity format, used consistently throughout the program, provides structure at the beginning of each investigation with some flexibility towards the close. This guided discovery focuses the attention of students on specific outcomes and at the same time stimulates intrinsic motivation so often provided by discovery.

Pre- and Post-Lab Discussions

One of the genuine "secrets of success" employed by truly effective elementary school science teachers is the mastery of what some call pre-lab and post-lab discussion. In other words, both the proper introduction and the effective conclusion of the science activity are crucial to its success. A good pre-lab will accomplish the following:

- Stimulate interest or engage the student.

- Provide clues as to what is expected and set the purpose.

- Establish relevance to the learner.

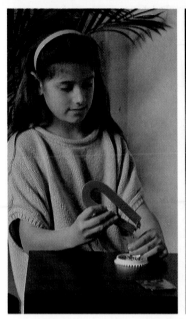

In *SCIENCE In Your World* the problem statement that appears as the title of each activity in the student edition and the *Focus* section in the margin guide of the teacher edition provide suggestions for effective pre-lab discussion.

An effective post-lab discussion should accomplish these goals:

- Clearly identify a conclusion.

- Help students summarize or draw conclusions using their own words.

- Reveal how the conclusion applies to the everyday world of the child.

In *SCIENCE In Your World, What Did You Learn?* and *Using What You Learned* in the student edition and the *Apply/Close* section in the margin guide of the teacher edition provide ideas to accomplish the post-lab goals.

Activities and Different Types of Students

Guided-discovery activities provide a variety of experiences to enhance learning through a variety of modes. Examples are summarized below.

Visual Learners   Students with a visual-learning preference are able to make first-hand observations, to compare and contrast, and to study charts, graphs, and pictorial representations.

Auditory Learners   Peer discussions in small groups coupled with post activity discussion to summarize findings and reach conclusions benefit students with an auditory preference for learning.

Kinesthetic Learners   Kinesthetic learners are aided by hands-on manipulation of equipment and materials during investigations.

Active involvement in hands-on activities also benefits students with certain learning disabilities. Many special students are quite capable of learning through participation in activities, but they can't read well or express their thoughts in writing. A number of research studies have shown that engagement in good activity-centered science programs has enhanced or even accelerated the language development of these students.

Activities often provide a vehicle to extend and enrich learning experiences for gifted and talented students. Participation in inquiry activities may bring out other questions and problems to pursue. These questions and problems are often excellent pursuits for gifted students. Extension of activities make excellent homework assignments to challenge gifted students.

Involvement in meaningful science investigations is participation in the nature of science itself. Experiences such as these help students appreciate the role of science and technology in our society and enhance the scientific literacy of our citizens.

TEACHING STRATEGIES

LEARNING CENTERS IN THE CLASSROOM

by Dr. Jay K. Hackett

Many teachers who actively engage their students in guided discovery utilize learning centers as an integral part of their instruction. They have found that well-designed learning center activities provide motivation and help students become more self-directed and responsible. They also can provide for individual differences among students.

Students may work at centers individually or in small, cooperative groups as a part of your regular ongoing science instruction. They may also use a learning center to pursue special interests and needs.

How can you set up a science learning center? One way is to set aside an area of your classroom to create a particularly rich learning environment. Use posters, pictures, collections, and other interesting materials to decorate this area. In this type of learning center, students can work on activities that you design to introduce or reinforce specific science concepts. Activities to develop process or problem-solving skills can also be effectively carried out. In addition, you can design science center activities for children to explore creative endeavors such as inventions, science poetry, and creative drama.

The teacher's role in the learning center is to organize the space, provide materials, and explain what students are to do and how to function in a learning center. To work independently, students need clear goals and directions for each activity. You may want to include a log at the learning center for students to record their progress. You may also want to confer with them to discuss their work at the learning center.

Many regular features found in the **SCIENCE In Your World** program lend themselves to science center activities. The *Application Activities* section at the back of every level of the student edition provides sixteen activities that could become part of the center. Suggestions provided in the *Unit Review* for projects and trade books suggested to enhance unit concepts also can become part of the center.

The *Planning Resources* page before each unit in the teacher edition of **SCIENCE In Your World** contains a *Science Center* feature. Each feature includes stated goals, a listing of necessary materials, and a well-developed procedure to assist you with implementation. Other features that make excellent science center activities include suggestions found in *Reinforcement, Enrichment,* and *Challenge*. All hands-on margin activities are preceded by a hands-on symbol that will alert you to their suitability for use in the science center.

Give science learning centers a try. You will find they broaden your instructional base and allow you to work more effectively with each of your students.

TEACHING STRATEGIES

LIFE IN THE CLASSROOM

by Dr. Jay K. Hackett

Elementary students have a natural curiosity and interest in living organisms. For this reason, teaching science should include opportunities to develop a respect for life and all living things. Students need to understand the importance of providing humane care for pets, animals housed in the classroom, and animals used in science projects. In addition, teaching science provides an opportunity to demonstrate a noninvasive approach to the environment as students study plants and animals in their natural habitats.

You may be interested in setting up an aquarium or a terrarium for your class. In addition, students often wish to bring their own live plants and animals to share with the rest of the class. With plants and animals in the classroom, students can learn the importance and responsibilities of providing proper food, sufficient space, fresh water, and adequate light and ventilation for life to thrive. Additionally, observation of natural living patterns, such as growth rates or activity and rest patterns of plants, pets, fish, or domestic animals can be educational. Life in the classroom can be a valuable and stimulating educational experience for children providing certain conditions are met.

1. First, it is important to check school, local, and state guidelines regarding regulations on housing plants and animals in the classroom.

2. Secondly, in making assignments, such as leaf or bug collections, consider the impact that the assignment will have on the environment. Assignments can be adapted so that students will develop a conscientious attitude toward the environment.

3. All animal studies should be carefully supervised by the teacher. Experimental procedures must be ones that don't subject animals to pain or discomfort. Any behavioral studies or training should use only positive reinforcement.

4. Care of living things in the classroom must be directly supervised by a teacher experienced in proper care.

5. For animals in the classroom, animal quarters should be able to be cleaned easily. Proper temperature must also be maintained.

6. Weekends and vacation periods can create problems if there has been no formal planning for the care of animals in the class. Some type of schedule with school custodians or responsible students should be pre-arranged for those days when school is not in session. Some custodians may volunteer to care for animals during weekends or short vacation periods.

7. If it becomes necessary during long vacation periods, responsible students may be allowed to take the animals or plants home to care for them after parental permission has been obtained.

8. Copies of state and local regulations regarding animal care can be obtained from local veterinarians, the Humane Society, and the National Science Teachers Association, 1742 Connecticut Avenue N.W., Washington DC 20009.

Studying living organisms is not a small responsibility. However, with careful teacher planning, students can develop a respect for life as they learn the responsibility and cooperation required when caring for living things.

SAFETY IN SCIENCE

Safety is of prime importance in every classroom, but science demands particular safety awareness. To aid in safety awareness, *SCIENCE In Your World* has carefully screened photographs to prevent showing potential safety hazards. References to specific safety practices appear in the written text and are often keyed to illustrations. Activities in which safety is a concern are identified by cautionary safety symbols. These symbols and an explanation for them appear on the following page. In addition, the material that accompanies each activity highlights teacher safety considerations and also includes tips on safety with plants, animals, fire, and other areas when appropriate.

The following safety guidelines are not inclusive but are meant to provide some general information for you in the science classroom.

SAFETY RULES

1. Inspect materials and equipment for defects or potential hazards prior to the school year, and discard those that are unsafe.

2. Store all equipment and materials properly. Store potentially hazardous materials under lock and key.

3. Demonstrate the proper use of all materials used in the science classroom. Be familiar with any potential hazards. Use all appropriate safeguards.

4. Use the appropriate materials and equipment specified for each activity. Give clear, complete directions **BEFORE** students begin any activity.

5. Take appropriate precautions when using fire and/or heat sources. Be sure that you perform as a teacher demonstration all activity steps involving the use of a heat source.

6. Instruct students not to taste or touch substances or materials without your permission.

7. Stress the importance of not touching eyes, mouth, face, or other body parts while working with plants, animals, or chemicals. Instruct students to wash their hands thoroughly after each activity.

8. Stress the importance of appropriate behavior during all activities.

9. Provide supervision during each activity.

10. Familiarize students with first-aid, fire-drill, and other emergency procedures. Post instructions for these procedures in a prominent place.

SAFETY SYMBOLS

Below are the safety symbols used throughout SCIENCE In Your World to alert you and your students to possible danger. Be sure that you review each symbol with the students and that they understand each symbol before beginning any activity. A blackline master with these symbols and their meanings also appears in the Appendix of the accompanying Teacher Resource Book.

DISPOSAL ALERT
This symbol appears when care must be taken to dispose of materials properly.

BIOLOGICAL SAFETY
This symbol appears when there is danger involving bacteria, fungi, and protists.

OPEN FLAME ALERT
This symbol appears when use of an open flame could cause a fire or an explosion.

THERMAL SAFETY
This symbol appears as a reminder to use caution when handling hot objects

SHARP OBJECT SAFETY
This symbol appears when a danger of cuts or puncture caused by the use of sharp objects exists.

FUME SAFETY
This symbol appears when chemicals or chemical reactions could cause dangerous fumes.

ELECTRICAL SAFETY
This symbol appears when care should be taken when using electrical equipment.

PLANT SAFETY
This symbol appears when poisonous plants or plants with thorns are handled.

ANIMAL SAFETY
This symbol appears whenever live animals are studied and the safety of the animals and the students must be ensured.

RADIOACTIVE SAFETY
This symbol appears when radioactive materials are used.

CLOTHING PROTECTION SAFETY
This symbol appears when substances used could stain or burn clothing.

FIRE SAFETY
This symbol appears when care should be taken around open flames.

EXPLOSION SAFETY
This symbol appears when the misuse of chemicals could cause an explosion.

EYE SAFETY
This symbol appears when a danger to the eyes exists. Safety goggles should be worn when this symbol appears.

POISON SAFETY
This symbol appears when poisonous substances are used.

CHEMICAL SAFETY
This symbol appears when chemicals used can cause burns or are poisonous if absorbed through the skin.

TEACHING STRATEGIES

EVALUATION

Evaluation is a vital part of the teaching process, but it is often the most difficult thing to do. In many cases, teachers are insecure about assigning projects, activities, or writing because they are not sure of the best way to evaluate them. In science, as in other disciplines, there are a variety of evaluative strategies that a teacher can use. Different activities can be evaluated by different methods. The important thing is for you to decide which evaluative method you will use and to let the students know how their work will be evaluated when it is assigned.

Summative Evaluation
Usually when teachers first think of evaluation, they think about tests and grades. These tests are intended to sum up what the student knows about a subject. **Summative Evaluation** is normally conducted after formal study of a lesson, chapter, or unit. Summative Evaluation in *SCIENCE In Your World* includes the formal end-of-chapter tests provided in the student text. Here, test items are provided to help you ascertain student mastery of all objectives for each lesson. Activities in *SCIENCE In Your World* can also be summatively evaluated by assigning a grade to student activity worksheets from the *Teacher Resource Book*.

Formative Evaluation
Of course, evaluation involves much more than merely assigning grades. Evaluation is an ongoing process that can be used to guide student learning and diagnose difficulties students may be having. This type of evaluation is known as **Formative Evaluation**. Made *during* the course of study, it guides and promotes student learning.

Much of what teachers do informally in the classroom as they interact with their students is actually a type of formative evaluation. In the margin guide of *SCIENCE In Your World,* you will find many suggestions that will assist you in the formative evaluation of your students. These include suggested discussion questions as well as answers to student-text questions. Each lesson also includes a section entitled *Guided Practice*. This is designed to offer a mid-lesson check of student understanding of lesson concepts. If you determine the need, a *Reteaching Strategy* follows each of these checks.

Teachers may also wish to evaluate student performance on activities and process skills in science. As indicated above, the student activity worksheets can be used when completing the formal activities in the text. Formative evaluation of activities should also be accomplished through observation and discussion while students are

engaged in the activities. Ask students why they are doing certain steps of an activity while they are working. Be sure students are aware of what they are trying to find out. In other words, be sure students are aware of the goal of an activity before they begin and while they work through activities.

The evaluation component of the *Activity Book* can also be extremely helpful in evaluating process skill development. For each process skill, you will find a formal test (summative evaluation). Also included is an observational checklist for each process skill (formative evaluation). This checklist breaks down each process skill into component parts that are observable by the teacher.

In addition, it is also important for teachers to periodically assess students' attitudes toward science. Discuss with students what they like about science. In this way, you will gain insights into student interests.

BY DR. RICHARD H. MOYER

Holistic Evaluation

Holistic Evaluation is a method by which you can assess an activity or project as a whole. Holistic evaluation may be a general impression of the work and may require only a short observation. In some cases, you may wish to simply acknowledge completion of the assignment. In others, you may want to measure a student's work against certain general features, such as creativity, effort, or conformance to requirements. You need not individually analyze every bit of a student's work in order to evaluate it.

Peer Evaluation/ Response Groups

Peer Evaluation can be of particular value especially if much of your classwork is done in cooperative groups. In many ways, peer evaluation goes on without any formal acknowledgement. For this reason, it is helpful to establish guidelines for peer evaluation even when cooperative groups are not used. These are some suggestions you may find helpful in explaining how to make a peer evaluation.

1. Listen carefully to the assignment explanation or description.

2. Comment on the best part of the work after the explanation is complete.

3. Ask questions about things you do not understand.

4. Give specific, constructive feedback.

In some cases, you may wish to form cooperative response groups for the purpose of sharing student work. As teacher, you should take an active role in setting up and monitoring these groups. They should consist of a mix of students who know and practice the guidelines above. The methods of sharing can vary. In some instances demonstrating or reading aloud may be appropriate. Circulating the assignment or making a copy and attaching an evaluation sheet for written comments may also be appropriate.

Self-Evaluation

A major goal in education is to encourage children to become self-disciplined and eager to learn. We want students to internalize knowledge and skills. Having students make self-evaluations can demonstrate the responsibility each person has for his or her own work. It can develop greater self-reliance and independence. But self-evaluation is among the most difficult things people do because it requires critical-thinking skills and is so intertwined with self-concept and personality. There are, however, some guidelines that may help students organize their thoughts about themselves.

1. Develop a concrete checklist of items you want to evaluate before you begin an assignment. They may be based on the requirements for the assignment. Take the checklist out when the assignment is complete and evaluate each item.

2. Write a short paragraph before you turn in any assignment to evaluate how you think you did. Give yourself a grade if you want to.

3. Keep a record of your improvement on each assignment.

4. Establish your own goals for improvement for the next assignment.

5. Discuss your self-evaluation and goals for improvement with your teacher.

Whether you use summative, formative, holistic, peer, or self-evaluations, feedback is necessary for optimal student development.

TEXT STRUCTURE

SCIENCE In Your World has been carefully designed and written to make it as easy as possible for your students to read.

Logic

Each *SCIENCE In Your World* text is divided into four units: Life Science, Earth Science, Physical Science, and the Human Body. Each unit is sub-divided into chapters, which are divided into lessons of study. The units, chapters, and lessons are of varying lengths, dependent on the information in them. Each lesson leads logically to the next, increasing a child's knowledge, interest, and confidence, and taking students to higher and higher levels of learning and understanding.

Organization of Prose

A variety of expository text structures has been employed in *SCIENCE In Your World* depending on the subject matter in a particular lesson. For example, the lesson may be organized in time order if a historical context is called for. The text may also be organized in inductive order with the description of a cause and its effect, a problem and its solution, or a comparison and contrast.

Research has shown that reading comprehension improves when common text structures such as these are used.

Readability

Several relevant factors concerning readability were considered in the writing of this program.

For one thing, careful attention was given to the concepts taught at each level. Our understanding of cognitive development served as the basis for selecting and planning experiences appropriate to the general cognitive abilities of each group at each grade level.

In addition, each lesson begins by relating the text to what the student already knows. This may mean using a poison ivy example to introduce a lesson on poisons or Magellan to introduce a chapter on oceans and seas. Throughout the text, real-life examples are used. For example, writing with a rock on the sidewalk is a streak test, and mushroom pizza describes a form of fungi. These features make the concepts interesting and easy for students to read, understand, and retain.

Format

To facilitate reading, each page is attractively and simply laid out with clear titles and labels and bite-sized chunks of information.

To establish a purpose for reading, a list of goals that function as learning objectives begins each lesson in levels 3-6. After each lesson, summary statements are listed followed by review ques-tions that zero in on the lesson goals.

The vocabulary chosen for each lesson complements the development of concepts. As each vocabulary word is introduced, it is boldfaced and, when appropriate, phonetically respelled.

Questions in the text have been directed to students to help them rethink the information they have read and to personalize the text material. In the margin of the intermediate texts, questions are included as guides for teachers and students to check reading comprehension and retention of information.

Student Reference Material

SCIENCE In Your World provides students with a comprehensive Table of Contents, Index, Glossary, and Chapter and Unit Review to help them locate information in the text quickly.

Photographs, Illustrations, Charts, and Graphs

Research has shown that visual representation of text material dramatically increases comprehension. For this reason, *SCIENCE In Your World* has been elaborately illustrated with attractive visual examples of science concepts and procedures. The pictures selected were also chosen with the student in mind. A variety of people are shown engaged in scientific discovery.

PRIOR KNOWLEDGE AND EMERGENT LITERACY

Prior Knowledge

People don't easily retain isolated bits of information. Piaget believed that people of all ages learn either by *assimilating* new information into a structure that we have already created or by changing our established structure to *accommodate* new information that doesn't fit. Either way, we activate prior knowledge when we learn something new.

An awareness of and an attempt to activate prior knowledge can help students make the connection between what is known and what is new. It reassures students that they already have a basic understanding of new concepts, and it gives them reference points for assimilating or accommodating new material.

Teachers can activate a student's prior knowledge simply by asking what he or she already knows about a topic. But *SCIENCE In Your World* has built-in features that allow students to do this independently. Each unit, chapter, and lesson begins by relating the upcoming text to what the student already knows. In addition, throughout the text, real-life examples are used. Furthermore, each lesson leads logically to the next, increasing a child's knowledge, interest, and confidence along the way.

By activating and developing their own knowledge on every page, *SCIENCE In Your World* enables students to comprehend science with ease, interest, and success.

Emergent Literacy

Learning to read doesn't happen in one day. *Emergent literacy* is a term that is often used to describe the period of growth before children begin to read. It includes the language and print experiences children have before coming to school. It refers to the skills that mark the onset of reading: turning pages, moving eyes from left to right, developing awareness of the forms and functions of print, distinguishing between text and pictures, identifying logos and signs,

scribbling, and playing with language rhymes and rhythms.

In *SCIENCE In Your World,* kindergartners and first graders are not expected to read everything in the text. But science provides an opportunity to develop this important skill while learning scientific content, concepts, and methods. *SCIENCE In Your World* encourages emergent literacy by activating students' prior knowledge, providing opportunities for whole-group reading with the *Big Books* for grades K-2, providing attractive, stimulating illustrations in the student texts, and offering writing and hands-on activities that make young students *want* to read more.

READING
S·T·R·A·T·E·G·I·E·S

WRITING FOR SCIENCE

Writing, a reading strategy? Yes! Research shows that the process of writing is really a process of thinking. Writing helps activate prior knowledge, generate new ideas, organize thoughts, synthesize ideas, summarize learning, and apply language conventions. Writing promotes student thinking and improves reading comprehension. It enhances learning in every discipline, including science.

Writing for Comprehension
Writing something down can aid comprehension immediately. The following ideas show how writing can help some specific problems.

When students cannot understand a verbal description of a process, have them
- draw a picture or series of pictures and label the parts of the process.
- write down each stage of the process, and number the consecutive stages.

When students have trouble remembering vocabulary words, have them
- draw a semantic map of the word. Write the word in the center of a paper. In bubbles or with lines around the word, write examples or synonyms of the word.
- find a sentence that contains the word. Rewrite the sentence in their own words. Ask a question about the sentence. Then read the sentence to someone else to see if the meaning of the word is clear.
- make a direct comparison chart listing the confusing word and words like it down the side. Across the top, list characteristics or meanings of each of the words. Then mark the characteristics or meanings that apply to each word.

Types of Writing for Science
When people think of scientific writing, they generally think of written lab reports that state the following:

Description of Problem
Hypothesis
Background Information
Methods Used
Analysis of Results
Discussion
Summary
Conclusions

But this is not the only form of writing scientists do. All types of writing can help develop scientific literacy. Below are examples of the scientific application of each form of writing.

Expressive Writing   A daily or weekly personal journal can record a student's thoughts, ideas, and observations.

Descriptive Writing   Description is the stuff scientific investigation is made of. Descriptive writing is in all other forms of writing.

Expository Writing   Expository writing is transfer of information. Reports, summaries, and instructions enable students to communicate what they have learned.

Persuasive Writing   As in lab reports, persuasive writing enables students to present their knowledge in a factual, logical, and persuasive manner.

Narrative Writing   Narrative writing can be a biography of a famous scientist or can tell the story of how a student arrived at a particular conclusion.

Poetry   Especially in the early grades, poetry can be used to sum up or describe an experience.

Teaching Writing for Science
Writing for science is no different from any other type of writing instruction. The writing process provides the best method for planning, executing, and evaluating writing for the greatest number of students.

Prepare   Identify the purpose and audience for your writing. Do any necessary research and make an outline or plan for writing.

Write   Follow your plan to write. Don't worry about making mistakes. Just get your thoughts down on paper.

Revise   Read your writing. Check for logic, clarity of ideas, missing or unnecessary information, rhythm, and flow.

Edit   Proofread your writing for errors in spelling, punctuation, grammar, and vocabulary.

Share   Share your work with other people: your teacher, a response group, your friends, or family. Ask for feedback.

DISCUSSION

Scientists are well aware of the importance of discussion when they write reports of their experiments. Discussion involves consideration of a problem or question. Factors that affect the data one way or another can be brought out and considered.

In the classroom, discussion can be one of the most valuable tools a teacher can use to help students learn. A good discussion offers students opportunities to verbalize what they know and find out what others discovered. It is a vehicle for bringing up questions and problems and getting help to solve them. Discussion also provides the teacher with a good way to evaluate student progress and understanding.

A discussion can also be a horrible experience for students who are not prepared, for students who don't trust their classmates or teacher, or in classrooms in which a particular student or the teacher dominates every discussion.

Good discussions occur when everyone speaks, normally quiet people are fluent, people listen to each other and are flexible, original ideas are generated, problems are solved, and the group doesn't want the discussion to end.

There are certain rules that can be applied to encourage good discussions.

1. Discussion should be limited to groups of students who are prepared to discuss a particular topic.

2. The agenda for the discussion should be specific and understood by all participants.

3. A time limit should be set for the discussion.

4. A facilitator, the teacher or a student, should be assigned to keep the group on the topic, discourage negative comments, and make sure everyone gets an adequate chance to speak.

5. At the end of the discussion, the group should come to a consensus about what was accomplished.

Throughout *SCIENCE In Your World* there are multiple opportunities for discussion groups. On pages T30 and T31 are suggestions for pre- and post-lab discussions. But the completion of any activity, chapter review, or even a failed experiment can provide fodder for a good discussion.

READING
S·T·R·A·T·E·G·I·E·S

THE ART OF QUESTIONING IN SCIENCE

by Dr. Richard H. Moyer

READING STRATEGIES

It has been said that the greatest potential for learning comes when a teacher asks the right question. Asking good questions is indeed an art. Good questioning strategies can lead to much more effective lessons and a higher-level understanding of science concepts.

Educators classify classroom questions in many ways. On these pages we will look at three common ways to classify classroom questions. We find these are helpful for teachers interested in fostering higher-level and critical-thinking skills among their students.

Divergent and Convergent Questions
One of the simplest ways to classify questions is by whether they are open-ended or closed. Open-ended questions are usually referred to as **divergent** and closed-ended questions as **convergent**. Divergent questions have many possible answers, while convergent questions have few (or only one) possible correct response. "How could you group these objects?" is an example of a divergent question. There are, of course, multiple possible appropriate responses. The value of such a question is that it stimulates classroom discussion and involvement of students.

On the other hand, "Is this a correct grouping of the objects?" is an example of a convergent question. There is only one possible correct response: yes or no. Since it requires only that the student be able to recognize whether the grouping is correct or not, it requires lower-level thought on the student's part.

Neither type of question is necessarily "better" than the other. However, you should strive for a mix of the two. Unfortunately, convergent questions most often dominate classroom discussions. This generally results in lower-level discussions and the active involvement of few students.

Divergent questions should be used to stimulate higher-level thinking as well as inquiry and creative thinking in the classroom. Convergent questions, on the other hand, are helpful to focus on a single answer or to direct students' attention to certain events or ideas.

Literal, Interpretive, Critical, and Creative Questions
Another way to classify questions is to think of them as requiring a literal, interpretive, critical, or creative response. Below is a description of each type of question.

Literal Requires simple regurgitation of information. Literal questions, like convergent questions, have right or wrong answers. They can be used to ascertain if a student is aware of some information. "What color was the litmus paper?" is an example of a literal question.

Interpretive Requires some analysis on the part of the student, who must show that information has been comprehended. Students may have to put pieces of information together or interpret data to answer the question. "How might salt affect perspiration?" is an example of an interpretive question.

Critical Requires students to evaluate information or procedures. They must rely on their own knowledge and judgment to answer this type of question. "What is wrong with this procedure?" is an example of a critical question.

Creative Requires students to use their imaginations to create a solution to a problem. They must use their knowledge and critical judgment to develop an adequate solution. "How can we make this procedure work?" is an example of a creative question.

Again, the important thing to do when asking questions is to mix them up. Science does not have only right and wrong answers to phenomena, but it does have some. So a variety of types of science questions is not only good for students, but also is highly appropriate.

Levels of Critical-Thinking Questions
It is also helpful to think about classifying classroom questions in terms of Bloom's Taxonomy of Educational Objectives. The levels of thought Bloom identified from simple to complex are summarized below.[1]

It is important to consider the *level* of the questions we ask in the classroom. Again, a mix of levels is in order. Lower-level questions are useful to focus attention on specific details or events, but are not appropriate to develop critical-thinking or inquiry skills. To that end, you should try to ask questions that reflect the higher levels from Bloom's Taxonomy. Keep in mind that lower-level questions are not bad or undesirable. What is undesirable is to only ask lower-level questions.

More specifically, asking questions that require students to perform the Critical-Thinking Science Process Skills described on page T22 would also engage them in a variety of levels of thinking. Are you asking questions related to the science processes that students use to analyze the results of activities or draw inferences from their observations? Such questions are important to help students gain the experiences necessary to develop inquiry and critical-thinking skills.

Developing better classroom questioning skills requires much practice. It is easier to think about than to actually do. However, the positive results of carefully thinking about and analyzing our questioning techniques pays off in countless ways.

Throughout the program, *SCIENCE In Your World* has provided all types of questions for students and teachers. From the *Lesson Review, Chapter Review,* and margin questions in the student text to the numerous questions in the teacher edition, *SCIENCE In Your World* provides a unique blend of thoughtful questions to develop advanced thinking skills in science.

Bloom's Taxonomy Of Educational Objectives

Knowledge	Recalling facts or memorizing.
Comprehension	Describing in your own words, interpreting, translating from one medium to another.
Application	Problem solving, applying information to produce a result.
Analysis	Finding underlying structure, breaking down a process, identifying motives.
Synthesis	Creating unique and original products.
Evaluation	Resolving differences of opinion or controversies; making value decisions about issues.

[1]Carin and Sund. 1989. *Teaching Science Through Discovery,* 6th ed., p.159. Columbus, OH: Merrill Publishing Company.

SCIENCE AT HOME

by Dr. Jay K. Hackett

Teachers have long been aware of the positive relationship between student success in school and the interest and involvement of parents in support of the education of their children. This interest and support are carried out in a variety of ways.

There are many excellent opportunities for home-school collaboration and cooperation in using *SCIENCE In Your World.* Each of these has much potential for improving the performance of students as well as increasing the scientific literacy of both students and parents. In addition, cooperative efforts such as these can establish strong positive reinforcement and support among teachers, students, and parents.

Let's look at several suggested home-school activities and how they might be conducted.

1. Inform parents that you will be asking their child to take home the activity worksheets completed in daily science activities. Ask them to find a convenient time for their child to tell another family member what was done and what was learned.

2. Establish a regular practice of sending home the *Family Science* activity found in your *Teacher Resource Book.* Encourage both students and family members to do the hands-on activities at home and discuss the results. Send a letter home encouraging parents to take part in these home activities.

3. Solicit help from parents when needed. For example, send a science materials scavenger hunt list to help build your inventory of common equipment, materials, and supplies such as candles, paper cups, flashlight batteries, liquid soap, baby food jars, waxed paper, and so on.

4. Ask for volunteer family aids to help you with a science materials inventory, investigations, and other tasks.

5. Ask parents to encourage their child to bring home science trade books from the school resource center or public library. Encourage them to read with their child or have the child share what was read with other family members.

6. Hold a special after-school, hands-on science workshop for family members and their children. Conduct several interesting hands-on activities with the student and a family member participating as a team. Use activities that utilize common household materials and supplies. Workshops such as these could be particularly helpful for parents hesitant to do the *Family Science* activity with their child.

7. Send a letter home asking parents to encourage their child to watch science-related television programs such as *Mr. Wizard, 3-2-1 Contact, National Geographic Specials, Nova,* and others. Suggest that they provide a short period of time at dinner or before bedtime to have the child tell what was learned from the program.

8. Encourage parents during school visitations or by letter to make family visits to local museums, the zoo, a botanical garden, or planetarium.

Cooperative activities between school and home such as these will require initial planning and follow through on your part. But the potential rewards for all involved will be worth it. Activities such as these offer special encouragement and benefits for females and minority students and family members. Give some of these suggestions, or others you create, a try. Share the positive results with your colleagues and encourage them to try similar activities, too.

SCIENCE FAIR

by Dr. Jay K. Hackett

Every year science fairs are held at class, school, district, state, and national levels. If you are not aware of your school's science fair schedule, ask your principal about it because participation in science fair projects is one of the most motivating and meaningful learning experiences your students can have. When involved in science fair projects, students actively experience the nature of science itself. Students get first-hand experience in designing and using an organized procedure for solving a problem. They use scientific methods and develop critical-thinking process skills as they add to their knowledge about the world in which they live.

Many students are frightened by the idea of entering a science fair. But all science fair projects simply begin with questions. Why do some balls bounce higher than others? Why are plants green? What do ants eat? What would happen if…? When students become accustomed to asking questions and seeking answers, they are ready to identify problems and set up procedures for seeking solutions.

To help students develop questioning minds, you can encourage them to ask questions about their observations. You can set up interesting classroom displays, collections, pictures, and bulletin boards. You can even set up a questions corner where students can write down questions about the displays, and, of course, you could contribute your own questions to the list. Talk about all of your questions in class, and have students help you decide which ones need further investigation.

To get students used to the idea of a science fair, particularly in primary grades, it is helpful to conduct a class science project. Help students pose several interesting questions. Decide on one interesting question and the resultant problem. Ask students, "What do you want to know? How can you find out?" Using the problem-solving process, help them design a logical procedure for conducting the experiment. Allow small groups of students to assume responsibility for different parts of the investigation. Interpret the results and cooperatively arrive at a conclusion. Now each student has participated in a model science project and has become more confident in his or her own ability to identify and successfully complete an individual science fair project.

SCIENCE In Your World provides a variety of features to assist you in using science projects as a regular part of your science instruction. Each unit review provides a selected list of science fair project ideas. Chapter interleaf pages provide suggestions for whole-class science projects as well as additional science fair project ideas. In addition, the program provides you with a *Science Fair Handbook.* This handbook provides guidelines and ideas for developing science fair projects along with helpful tips for organizing and conducting a science fair in your school. Blackline masters of entry forms, judging criteria, and award certificates are also provided. *SCIENCE In Your World* makes it easy for your students to think of themselves as scientists as they develop successful science fair projects.

MATERIALS LIST

LEVEL THREE

Includes Item—Qty.—Page No.

Nonconsumables

animals, small—6—p. 201,223*
apron—15—as needed***
asphalt, pieces—6—p. 125
balances—6—p. 33, 347, 353**
ball, baseball—1—p. 337**
ball, table tennis—1—p. 337**
ball, tennis—1—p. 337**
blocks, wood—6—p. 69**
blocks, triangular wooden—10—p. 347**
boards (approx. 12″ × 30″)—6—p. 97**
books—64—p. 87, 97, 141, 353
books, reference (nonfiction, animal tracks, animal pictures, health)—as needed—p. 125, 217, 237, 239, 319
books, telephone—6—p. 161
bottles, soft drink—6—p. 55
boxes, cardboard—6—p. 87
cages, glass/wire—3—p. 201**
charts/tables—30 (a variety)—p. 17, 339
clay, modeling—1 box—p. 93**
clothespins, clip-type—10—p. 347
concrete, pieces—6—p. 125
coverslips—1 box—p. 253**
cups/glasses, clear plastic—1 package—p. 5, 27, 173, 341**
dimes—6—p. 55
dish towels—10—p. 77
dishes, clear baking—6—p. 61
dishes, flat plastic—12—p. 170, 173**
dishes, shallow—3—p. 201, 223**
dishpans, plastic—6—p. 279**
droppers—30—p. 22, 55, 253**
erasers, chalkboard—10—p. 77
forks, plastic—30—p. 36
freezer compartment, refrigerator—1—p. 55, 139
gram masses—10 sets—p. 347, 353**
hair dryer—1—p. 353
hand lens—15—p. 119, 125, 128, 143**
jars, small glass—30—p. 9
jars, large plastic widemouthed—20—p. 49, 179, 223, 279, 337**
jars, small widemouthed—12—p. 9, 119, 337
knives, plastic—30—p. 36, 113
lamps—6—p. 333
lids with holes—3—p. 223
marbles—2 bags (50)—p. 27, 69, 76, 97**
margarine tubs with lids—30—p. 22**
materials, tinker toys/erector set—1 set—p. 103
mealworms—15—p. 270**
measuring cups—10—p. 9, 22**
meter stick—1—p. 337**
microscopes—6—p. 253**
nickels—2 rolls—p. 33
objects, small classroom—30 (a variety)—p. 33, 73
oven mitts—6 pairs—p. 173***
pans, loaf—6—p. 113**
pans, 9 × 13—6—p. 141, 353

paper clips, large—1 box—p. 347**
paper clips, small—3 boxes—p. 33, 73**
paper punches—15—p. 209**
pitchers, quart—8—p. 147
play money—a variety—p. 361**
popcorn poppers, hot-air—3—p. 335
rakes—6—p. 237
refrigerator—1—p. 113
rocks—1 bag—p. 133, 353
rubber bands, large thin—6—p. 73**
rulers, metric—10—p. 93, 97, 143, 197, 223, 347**
safety goggles—30—p. 55, 73, 77***
screws—10—p. 347
scissors—30—p. 193, 209, 239, 359
shoes, students' own—1 per student—p. 29
slides, glass—1 box—p. 253**
slides, prepared for micro-viewer (animal cells)—a variety—p. 283**
spoons, plastic—10—p. 22, 341
spray bottles—15—p. 345, 355**
stopwatch—1—p. 9, 57, 153, 179**
stirrers—8—p. 147, 377
table, long—5—p. 77
thermometers—12—p. 9, 147, 333, 337**
toys, wagon or truck—8—p. 87
tweezers—6 pairs—p. 253**
viewers, micro slide—6—p. 283**
watch, with second hand—1—p. 170, 270, 293, 333, 341
watering cans, small—6—p. 141, 197, 353

Consumables

bags, large plastic—10—p. 153
bags, small plastic—6—p. 341
balloons—1 bag (30)—p. 296**
bananas—8—p. 113*
bedding, animal—2 bags—p. 201**
birdseed, mixed—1 bag—p. 201, 237
bread crumbs—1 bag—p. 237*
cardboard (20 cm × 30 cm)—15—p. 239**
cardboard, thin (6 cm × 30 cm)—30—p. 73**
cardboard, thin (10 cm × 10 cm)—8—p. 279**

cards, index—4 packages—p. 209, 270**
carrots, cooked—6—p. 36*
carrots, raw—2 bags—p. 201, 237
clay—2 kg bags—p. 349
clay, modeling—7 boxes—p. 93, 351
cloth, cotton (64 sq. cm)—36—p. 355, 359
clothing, old—a variety—p. 359
cornstarch—2 boxes—p. 44
crayons—30 boxes—p. 119, 125, 209, 239, 245, 309, 324
cups, paper (90 mL)—1 box—p. 44, 61, 93, 143, 153, 179, 223, 347, 353**
cups, paper (150 mL)—1 box—p. 128**
detergent, liquid—3 brands—p. 22
envelopes—6—p. 161
Epsom salts—1 box—p. 128**
film containers (35mm with lids)—10—p. 139**
fish scales—6 each of 2 different kinds—p. 253**
flour—2 bags—p. 237
food, animal—as needed—p. 223
gelatin (3 flavors)—8 boxes each—p. 113
glue, white—1 large bottle—p. 239
grass, cuttings—1 bag—p. 268*
gravel—3 bags—p. 119, 141, 223, 349**
hose, rubber/plastic—4 meters—p. 279
ice cubes—5 trays—p. 57, 147, 173*
juice, fruit—1 carton—p. 5*
juice, lemon—1 jar—p. 341*
labels, blank—78—p. 143, 193, 197
labels, food (a variety)—32—p. 305, 339**
labels, medicine—30 (a variety)—p. 363
leaves—2 bags—p. 268, 349, 353*
lettuce—1 head—p. 201*
magazines, advertisements—a variety—p. 339, 361
magazines, animal pictures—a variety—p. 239
materials, scenery—a variety—p. 239
milk—1 qt.—p. 341*
milk cartons—6—p. 97
mosses—1 bag—p. 353*
newspaper—120 sheets—p. 44, 119, 128, 268
newspaper, advertisements—a variety—p. 339
paint, tempera—6 boxes—p. 324**
paint—1 small can—p. 345
pans, aluminum—60—p. 349, 355
paper clips, metal—1 box—p. 345
paper, drawing (8″ × 10″)—1 package—p. 17, 103, 133, 139, 143, 253, 270, 283, 333

paper, notebook—as needed—all activities
paper plates—36—p. 36, 309*
paper towels—2 rolls—p. 27, 44, 153
peanuts—1 large bag—p. 237
pebbles—1 bag—p. 141**
pencils—1 box—all activities
pencils, unsharpened—30—p. 93
pens, felt-tip (black)—20—p. 179, 197
plants, young potted—as needed—p. 223, 353*
plants, young bean—30—p. 197*
plates, paper—1 package—p. 36, 309
plastic knives—6—p. 36, 113
plastic forks—6—p. 36
popcorn, kernels—3 bags—p. 335
posterboard—30—p. 324
rocks—42 (a variety)—p. 223, 351, 353
salt—2 cartons—p. 49, 341
sand—1 bag—p. 119, 128, 141, 349, 351**
sandpaper—10 pieces—p. 77**
sawdust—1 bag—p. 349
seeds, lima bean—36—p. 143**
silt—1 bag—p. 349
soap, liquid—1 bottle—p. 76
soil, clayrich—3 bags—p. 143, 179, 268, 349**
soil, humus—2 bags—p. 119, 141, 143, 353**
soil, potting—3 bags—p. 49, 179, 223**
soil, sandy—1 bag—p. 143, 179**
stamps, postage—6—p. 161
sticks, twigs—large bundles—p. 268, 353
straws, bendable drinking—32—p. 5**
straws, straight drinking—42—p. 5, 347**
string—2 balls—p. 73, 77, 347, 359**
sugar, cubes—1 box—p. 9, 341**
tape, masking—2 rolls—p. 73, 93, 139, 179, 345
tape, transparent—1 roll—p. 61
thread—1 spool—p. 87**
toothpicks—1 box—p. 347**
twist ties—6—p. 341**
vegetable oil—1 bottle—p. 22, 345
washers, steel—11—p. 93, 345**
water, tap (hot and cold)—as needed—p. 9, 22, 27, 44, 49, 61, 119, 128, 139, 141, 143, 147, 153, 170, 173, 179, 197, 201, 223, 253, 268, 279, 333, 337, 341, 349, 353
wrap, plastic—1 box—p. 61
yarn—2 skeins—p. 193, 209**

*perishable
**included in Materials Kit
***included in Safety Kit

RESOURCES

Film/Filmstrip Suppliers

Academy Films
Box 1023
Venice, CA 90291

Agency for Instructional Technology (AIT)
Box A
Bloomington, IN 47401

AIMS Media
6901 Woodley Avenue
Van Nuys, CA 91406

American Forest Institute
1250 Connecticut Avenue, NW
Suite 320
Washington, DC 20036

Barr Films
P.O. Box 5667
3490 East Foothill Boulevard
Pasadena, CA 91107

Beacon Films
1250 Washington Street
Box 575
Norwood, MA 02062

Benchmark Films, Inc.
145 Scarborough Road
Briarcliff Manor, NY 10510

Bullfrog Films, Inc.
Oley, PA 19547

Carolina Biological Supply Co.
2700 York Road
Burlington, NC 27215

Centre Productions, Inc.
1800 30 Street, Suite 307
Boulder, CO 80301

Centron Educational Films
Div. of Simon & Schuster
108 Wilmot Road
Deerfield, IL 60015

Clearvue, Inc.
5711 N. Milwaukee
Chicago, Il 60646

Coronet/MTI Film & Video
Distributors of LCA
108 Wilmot Road
Deerfield, IL 60015

Counselor Films
1728 Cherry Street
Philadelphia, PA 19103

CRM/McGraw-Hill
P.O. Box 641
Del Mar, CA 92014

Davidson Films, Inc.
231 "E" Street
Davis, CA 95616

Educational Media International
Box 1288
175 Margaret Place
Elmhurst, IL 60126

Encyclopaedia Britannica Educational Corporation
425 N. Michigan Avenue
Chicago, IL 06011

Filmakers Library, Inc.
133 E. 58th Street, 703A
New York, NY 10022

Films for the Humanities, Inc.
Box 2053
Princeton, NJ 08540

Films, Inc.
1213 Wilmette Avenue
Wilmette, IL 60091

Gateway (now Coronet)

Handel Film Corporation
8730 Sunset Boulevard
West Hollywood, CA 90069

Hawaii State Dept. of Education
1390 Miller Street
Honolulu, HA 96813

Indiana University Audiovisual Center
Bloomington, IN 47405-5901

International Film Bureau, Inc.
332 S. Michigan Avenue
Chicago, IL 60604

Journal Films, Inc.
930 Pitner Avenue
Evanston, IL 60202

Knowledge Unlimited
Box 52
Madison, WI 53701

Learning Corp. of America
(now Coronet)

Library Filmstrip Center
205 E. Locust Street
Bloomington, IL 61701

Mar/Chuk Film Industries, Inc.
P.O. Box 61
Mount Prospect, IL 60056

Macmillan Video
Macmillan Publishing Co.
866 Third Avenue
New York, NY 10022

MTI Teleprograms (now Coronet)

National Audiovisual Center
8700 Edgeworth Drive
Capitol Heights, MD 20743

National Film Board of Canada
1251 Avenue of the Americas
New York, NY 10020

National Geographic Society Educational Services
17th and "M" Streets, NW
Washington, DC 20036

New World Video
1888 Century Park E
Los Angeles, CA 90067

Paramount (now AIMS Media)

Phoenix/BFA Educational Media
Division of Phoenix Films
468 Park Avenue S
New York, NY 10016

Professional Research, Inc.
930 Pitner Avenue
Evanston, IL 60202

PBS Video
475 L'Enfant Plaza, SW
Washington, DC 20024

Pyramid Film & Video
Box 1048
Santa Monica, CA 90406

Society for Visual Education, Inc.
1345 Diversey Parkway
Chicago, IL 60614

Stanton Films
2417 Artesia Boulevard
Redondo Beach, CA 90278

Sterling Education Films, Inc.
241 E. 34th Street
New York, NY 10016

Walt Disney Educational Media Co.
500 S. Buena Vista Street
Burbank, CA 91521

Weston Woods Studios, Inc.
389 Newtown Turnpike
Weston, CT 06883

Wombat Productions, Inc.
250 W 57 St., Suite 916
New York, NY 10019

film film film

RESOURCES

VIDEOTAPE

Videotape Suppliers

Agency for Instructional Technology (AIT)
Box A
Bloomington, IN 47401

AIMS Media
6901 Woodley Avenue
Van Nuys, CA 91406

Barr Films
P.O. Box 5667
3490 East Foothill Boulevard
Pasadena, CA 91107

Beacon Films
1250 Washington Street
Box 575
Norwood, MA 02062

Bullfrog Films
Oley, PA 19547

Carolina Biological Supply Co.
2700 York Road
Burlington, NC 27215

Centre Productions, Inc.
1800 30th Street, Suite 207
Boulder, CO 80301

Centron Educational Films
Division of Simon & Schuster
108 Wilmot Road
Deerfield, IL 60015

Coronet/MTI Film & Video
Distributors of LCA
108 Wilmot Road
Deerfield, IL 60015

Educational Media International
Box 1288
175 Margaret Place
Elmhurst, IL 60126

Encyclopaedia Britannica Educational Corporation (EBEC)
425 N. Michigan Avenue
Chicago, IL 60611

Filmakers Library, Inc.
133 E. 58th St., 703A
New York, NY 10022

Films for the Humanities, Inc.
Box 2053
Princeton, NJ 08540

Films, Inc.
733 Green Bay Road
Wilmette, IL 60091

Handel Film Corp.
8730 Sunset Boulevard
Los Angeles, CA 90069

Hawkhill Associates, Inc.
125 E. Gilman Street
Madison, WI 53703

International Film Bureau, Inc.
332 S. Michigan Avenue
Chicago, IL 60604

Learning Corp. of America
(now Coronet)

Macmillan Video
866 Third Avenue
New York, NY 10022

Media Projects, Inc.
P.O. Box 2008
Portland, OR 97208

National Audiovisual Center
8700 Edgeworth Drive
Capitol Heights, MD 20743

National Film Board of Canada
1251 Avenue of the Americas
New York, NY 10020

National Geographic Society Educational Services
17th and M Street, NW
Washington, DC 20036

New World Video
1888 Century Park, East
Los Angeles, CA 90067

Perennial Education, Inc.
930 Pitner Avenue
Evanston, IL 60202

Phoenix/BFA Educational Media
Division of Phoenix Films
468 Park Avenue S
New York, NY 10016

Professional Research Inc.
930 Pitner Avenue
Evanston, IL 60202

Pyramid Film & Video
Box 1048
Santa Monica, CA 90406

Society for Visual Education
1345 W. Diversey Parkway
Chicago, IL 60614

Time-Life Video
Time-Life Building
1271 Avenue of the Americas
New York, NY 10020

University of California Extension Media Center
2223 Fulton Street
Berkeley, CA 94720

University of Texas
Audiovisual Unit
7703 Floyd Curl Drive
San Antonio, TX 78274

University of Utah Instructional Media Services
207 Milton Bennion Hall
Salt Lake City, UT 84112

University of Wisconsin Bureau of Audio Visual Instruction
1327 University Avenue
P.O. Box 2093
Madison, WI 53701

Walt Disney Educational Media Co.
500 S. Buena Vista Street
Burbank, CA 91521

Wombat Productions, Inc.
250 W. 57 Street, Suite 916
New York, NY 10019

RESOURCES

tv

TV Programs

Public Broadcasting Service

"All About You"
30—15 minute lessons
Primary—Health
Teacher Guide

"Community of Living Things"
15—15 minute lessons
Intermediate—Science
Teacher Guide

"Discovering"
20—15 minute lessons
Intermediate—Science
Teacher Guide

"Dragons, Wagons & Wax"
30—15 minute lessons
Primary—Science
Teacher Guide

"Human Community"
15—15 minute lessons
Intermediate—Life,
Environmental
Teacher Guide

"The Inside Story with Slim Goodbody"
8-15 minute lessons
Primary—Health
Teacher Guide

"L-4" (Man's relationship with environment—Earth and Space)
16—15 minute lessons
Intermediate—Science
Teacher Guide

"Owl TV"
30 minutes
Primary/Intermediate

"Search for Science"
30—15 minute lessons
Intermediate—Science
Teacher Guide

"3-2-1 Contact"
30 minutes
Intermediate/Jr. High—
Science
Write: Children's TV
Workshop for teacher guides.

"Up Close & Natural"
15—15 minute lessons
Primary—Science
Teacher Guide

"Zoo Zoo Zoo"
16—15 minute lessons
Primary—Natural Science
Teacher Guide

Nickelodeon

"Mr. Wizard's World"
30 minutes
Intermediate/Jr. High

RESOURCES

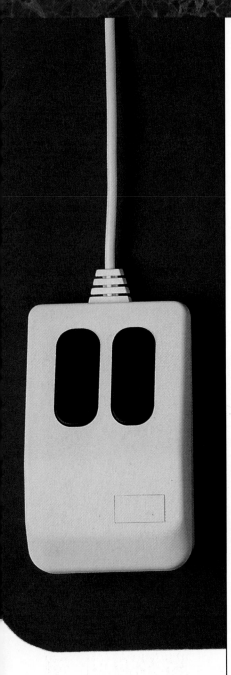

Software Suppliers

Activision, Inc.
2350 Bayshore Parkway
Mountain View, CA 94043

AIMS Media
6901 Woodley Avenue
Van Nuys, CA 91406

Bantam Books
666 Fifth Avenue
New York, NY 10103

BrainBank, Inc.
220 Fifth Avenue
New York, NY 10001

Collamore Educational Publishing
125 Spring Street
Lexington, MA 02173

Diversified Educational Enterprises
725 Main Street
Lafayette, IN 47901

Educational Activities, Inc.
1937 Grand Avenue
Baldwin, NY 11510

Educational Materials & Equipment Co.
P.O. Box 17
Pelham, NY 10803

Educational Technology
6150 N. 16th Street
Phoenix, AZ 85016

Focus Media, Inc.
839 Stewart Avenue
Garden City, NY 11530

Grolier Electronic Publishing, Inc.
95 Madison Avenue
New York, NY 10016

Intellectual Software
562 Boston Avenue
Bridgeport, CT 06610

January Productions
249 Goffle Road
P.O. Box 66
Hawthorne, NJ 07507

K–12 MicroMedia
6 Arrow Rd.
Ramsey, NJ 07446

Learning Well
200 South Service Road
Roselyn Heights, NY 11577

Marshfilm/Marshware, Inc.
P.O. Box 8082
Shawnee Mission, KS 66208

MECC
3490 Lexington Avenue, North
St. Paul, MN 55126

Micro Power & Light Co.
12810 Hillcrest Rd., Suite 120
Dallas, TX 75230

Mindscape
3444 Dundee Road
Northbrook, IL 60062

Orange Cherry Software
P.O. Box 427
Bedford Hills, NY 10507

Right On Programs
1737 Veterans Highway
Central Islip, NY 11722

Simon & Schuster
P.O. Box 2987
New York, NY 10185

Spectrum Software
75 Todd Pond Road
Lincoln, MA 01773

Teach Yourself by Computer Software, Inc.
2128 West Jefferson Road
Pittsford, NY 14534

T.H.E.S.I.S.
P.O. Box 147
Garden City, MI 48135

Unicorn Software
2950 East Flamingo Road, #B
Las Vegas, NV 89121

World Book Discovery, Inc.
510 Merchandise Mart Plaza
Chicago, IL 60654

software

RESOURCES

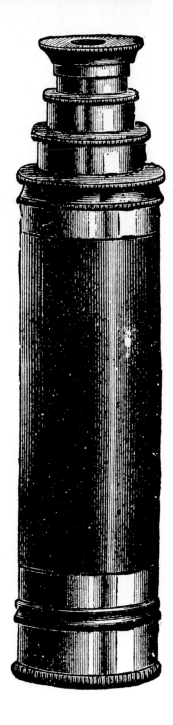

Scientific Equipment Suppliers

Aquarium and Science Supply Co.
1610 North Kings Highway
Cherry Hill, NJ 08034
(609) 795-5302/5303

Carolina Biological Supply Co.
2700 York Road
Burlington, NC 27215
(919) 584-0381

Central Scientific Co.
(CENCO)
11222 Melrose Avenue
Franklin Park, IL 60131
(312) 451-0150

Connecticut Valley Biological Supply Co., Inc.
82 Valley Road
P.O. Box 326
Southampton, MA 01073
(800) 628-7748

Delta Education, Inc.
P.O. Box M
Nashua, NH 03061-6012
(800) 258-1302

Edmund Scientific Co.
101 E. Gloucester Pike
Barrington, NJ 08007
(609) 547-3488

Fisher Scientific Co.
Educational Materials Div.
4901 W. LeMoyne St.
Chicago, IL 60651
(800) 621-4769

Frey Scientific Co.
905 Hickory Lane
Mansfield, OH 44905
(419) 589-9905

Grau-Hall Scientific Corp.
6501 Elvas Avenue
Sacramento, CA 95819
(916) 455-5258

Kons Scientific Co., Inc.
P.O. Box 3
Germantown, WI 53022-0003
(800) 242-5667

Learning Things, Inc.
68A Broadway
P.O. Box 436
Arlington, MA 02174
(617) 646-0093

McKilligan Supply Corp.
435 Main Street
Johnson City, NY 13790
(607) 729-6511

Nasco
901 Janesville Avenue
Fort Atkinson, WI 53538
(414) 563-2446

Sargent-Welch Scientific Co.
7300 N. Linder Avenue
Skokie, IL 60077
(312) 677-0600

Schoolmasters Science
745 State Circle
P.O. Box 1941
Ann Arbor, MI 48106
(313) 761-5072

Science Kit and Boreal Laboratories
777 East Park Drive
Tonawanda, NY 14150
(800) 828-7777

Ward's Natural Science Establishment, Inc.
5100 W. Henrietta Road
P.O. Box 92912
Rochester, NY 14692-9012
(800) 962-2660

RESOURCES

INSTRUCTIONAL AIDS··PERIODICALS

Instructional Aids

American Geophysical Union
2000 Florida Avenue, NW
Washington, D.C. 20009
(202) 462-6903

American Nuclear Society
555 N. Kensington Avenue
LaGrange Park, IL 60525
(312) 352-6611

Astro Media
Div. of Kalmbach Pub. Co.
1027 N. Seventh Street
Milwaukee, WI 53233
(414) 272-2060

Astronomical Society of the Pacific
1290 24th Avenue
San Francisco, CA 94122
(415) 661-8660

Cambridge Development Lab
1696 Massachusetts Avenue
Cambridge, MA 02138
(800) 637-0047

Creative Dimensions
P.O. Box 1393
Bellingham, WA 98227
(206) 733-5024

Hansen Publications
1098 South 200 West
Salt Lake City, UT 84101
(800) 321-2369

H. S. Center for Educational Resources
T-281 HSB SB-56
University of Washington
Seattle, WA 98195
(206) 545-1186

Hubbard Scientific Company
P.O. Box 104
1946 Raymond Drive
Northbrook, IL 60062
(800) 323-8368

Ideal School Supply Company
11000 S. Lavergne Avenue
Oak Lawn, IL 60453
(312) 425-0800

Lawrence Hall of Science
Discovery Corner
University of California
Berkeley, CA 94720
(415) 642-1016

MMI Corp.
2950 Wyman Parkway
P.O. Box 19907
Baltimore, MD 21211
(301) 366-1222

NASA
National Aeronautics & Space
Administration
Washington, DC 20546

National Dairy Council
6300 North River Road
Rosemont, IL 60018-4233
(312) 696-1020

National Geographic Educational Services
Dept. 76, P.O. Box 1640
Washington, DC 20013

Nystrom
3333 Elston Avenue
Chicago, IL 60618
(800) 621-8086

Scavenger Scientific Supply Company
P.O. Box 211328
Auke Bay, AK 99821

The Science Man Co.
A Div. of TSM Marketing, Inc.
4738 N. Harlem Avenue
Harwood Heights, IL 60656
(312) 867-4441

Scott Resources/ESNR Division
P.O. Box 2121
401 Hickory Street
Fort Collins, CO 80522
(303) 484-7445

Society for Nutrition Education
2140 Shattuck Ave., Suite 1110
Berkeley, CA 94704

Society for Visual Education, Inc.
1345 Diversey Parkway
Chicago, IL 60614
(312) 525-1500

Science Periodicals for Students

Primary
Animal Kingdom
New York Zoological Society
Bronx, NY 10460

Chickadee
Young Naturalist Foundation
59 Front Street
Toronto, Ontario M5E 1B3,
Canada

Scienceland
Scienceland, Inc.
501 Fifth Avenue
New York, NY 10017

Your Big Backyard
National Wildlife Federation
8925 Leesburg Pike
Vienna, VA 22184-0001

Elementary
Animals
Massachusetts Society for the
Prevention of Cruelty
to Animals
350 S. Huntington Avenue
Boston, MA 02130

Current Science
Xerox Education Publications
1250 Fairwood Avenue
Columbus, OH 43216

Dolphin Log
Cousteau Society
Membership Center
930 West 21st Street
Norfolk, VA 23517

Kind
The Humane Society
of the U.S.
Youth Membership Division
2100 L Street, NW
Washington, DC 20037

National Geographic World
National Geographic Society
17th and M Street, NW
Washington, DC 20036

Odyssey
1027 N. 7th Street
Milwaukee, WI 53233

Owl
P.O. Box 2878
Des Moines, IA 50320

Ranger Rick
National Wildlife Federation
8925 Leesburg Pike
Vienna, VA 22184-0001

Science World
Scholastic, Inc.
P.O. Box 644
Lyndhurst, NJ 07071

3-2-1 Contact
Box 53051
Boulder, CO 80322-2933

Zoo Books
Wildlife Education, Inc.
P.O. Box 85271
San Diego, CA 92138

Zoonooz
Zoological Society of
San Diego, Inc.
Box 551
San Diego, CA 92112

RESOURCES

Elementary Science Methods Books

Abruscato, Joseph. *Teaching Children Science.* Englewood Cliffs, NJ: Prentice-Hall, 1982.

Building Basic Skills in Science. Chicago, IL: Contemporary Books, Inc., 1982.

Carin, Arthur and Robert Sund. *Teaching Science Through Discovery.* Columbus, OH: Merrill Publishing Co., 1985.

Friedl, Arthur. *Teaching Science to Children: An Integrated Approach.* Westminster, MD: Random House, 1986.

Gega, Peter C. *Science in Elementary Education.* New York: John Wiley & Sons, 1986.

Harlan, Jean. *Science Experiences for the Early Childhood Years.* Columbus, OH: Merrill Publishing Co., 1984.

Iatridis, Mary D. *Teaching Science to Young Children: A Resource Book.* New York: Garland Publishing, 1986.

Kintsch, W. *Methods & Tactics in Cognitive Science.* Hillsdale, NJ: Erlbaum, Assoc., 1984.

McGill, Ormond. *Science Magic: One Hundred One Experiments You Can Do.* New York: Arco Publishing, Inc., 1984.

Stull, Elizabeth C. and Carol L. Price. *Science and Math Enrichment Activities for the Primary Grades.* West Nyack, NY: The Center for Applied Research in Education, Inc., 1987.

Earth Science Resource Books

Bakker, Robert T. *The Dinosaur Heresies.* New York: William Morrow & Co., 1986.

Ballard, Robert D. *Exploring Our Living Planet.* Washington, DC: National Geographic Society, 1983.

Cattermole, Peter and Patrick Moore. *The Story of the Earth.* New York: Cambridge University Press, 1985.

Cooke, Donald A. *The Life and Death of Stars.* New York: Crown Pubs., Inc., 1985.

Darling, David J. *Discovering Our Universe.* Minneapolis: Dillon Press, Inc., 1985.

Dietrich, R.V. and Reed Wicander. *Minerals, Rocks and Fossils.* New York: John Wiley and Sons, 1983.

Forrester, Frank. *1001 Questions Answered About the Weather.* New York: Dover Publications, 1981.

Giovanelli, Ronald G. *Secrets of the Sun.* New York: Cambridge University Press, 1984.

Preiss, Bryon, Editor. *The Planets.* New York: Bantam Books Inc., 1985.

Redfern, Ron. *The Making of a Continent.* New York: Times Books, 1983.

Turk, Jonathan. *Introduction to Environmental Studies,* 2nd Edition. New York: Saunders College Publishing, 1985.

Life Science Resource Books

Beller, Joel. *Experimenting with Plants.* Simon & Schuster, 1985.

Bodanis, David. *The Body Book: A Fantastic Voyage to the World Within.* Boston: Little, Brown & Co., 1984.

Department of the Interior, United States Fish and Wildlife Service. *Endangered and Threatened Wildlife and Plants.* Washington, DC: United States Government Printing Office, 1986.

Dowden, Anne. *From Flowers to Fruit.* New York: Crowell Junior Books, 1984.

Ferry, Georgina, Editor. *The Understanding of Animals.* New York: Basil Blackwell, 1984.

Gardner, Eldon J. *Human Heredity.* New York: John Wiley & Sons, 1983.

Gibbons, Bob. *How Flowers Work: A Guide to Plant Biology.* New York: Sterling Publishing Co., 1984.

Hoage, R.J., Editor. *Animal Extinction: What Everyone Should Know.* Washington, DC: Smithsonian, 1985.

Scheeler, Phillip and Donald E. Bianchi. *Cell Biology: Structure, Biochemistry, and Function.* New York: John Wiley & Sons, 1983.

Tributsch, Helmut, translated by Miriam Varon. *How Life Learned to Live: Adaptation in Nature.* Cambridge, MA: MIT Press, 1985.

Waldrop, Victor, Editor. *Incredible Animals A to Z.* Vienna, VA: National Wildlife Federation, 1985.

Physical Science Resource Books

Dobbs, Roland. *Electricity and Magnetism.* Boston: Routledge and K. Paul, 1984.

Feynman, Richard P. *QED: The Strange Theory of Light and Matter.* Princeton, NJ: Princeton University Press, 1985.

Hess, Fred C. *Chemistry Made Simple.* New York: Doubleday and Co., 1984.

Holden, Alan and Phyllis Morrison. *Crystals and Crystal Growing.* Cambridge, MA: MIT Press, 1982.

Levine, Ira N. *Physical Chemistry.* New York: McGraw-Hill, 1983.

Milne, Lorus J. and Margery Milne. *Nature's Great Carbon Cycle.* New York: Atheneum Publishers, 1983.

Pierce, John R. *The Science of Musical Sound.* New York: W.H. Freeman, 1983.

Ramage, Janet. *Energy: A Guidebook.* New York: Oxford University Press, 1983.

Segre, Emile. *From Falling Bodies to Radio Waves.* New York: W.H. Freeman, 1984.

Walton, Alan J. *Three Phases of Matter,* 2nd Edition. New York: Clarendon Press, 1983.

Books

SCIENCE
In Your World

SENIOR AUTHORS
Dr. Jay K. Hackett
Dr. Richard H. Moyer

Macmillan/McGraw-Hill
School Publishing Company

ACKNOWLEDGMENTS

For permission to reprint copyrighted material, grateful acknowledgment is made to the following authors, publishers, and agents. All possible care has been taken to trace the ownership of every selection included and to make full acknowledgment of its use. If any errors have inadvertently occurred, they will be corrected in subsequent editions, provided notification is sent to the publisher.

Jonathan Cape Ltd.: From *The Poetry of Robert Frost* edited by Edward Connery Lathem. Copyright 1928, 1939, © 1967, 1969 by Holt, Rinehart and Winston. Copyright © 1956 by Robert Frost. Reprinted by permission of Robert Frost, the editor.

Eleanor Farjeon: Text excerpt from "Bedtime" from *Eleanor Farjeon's Poems for Children* by Eleanor Farjeon. Reprinted by permission of David Higham Associates, Ltd.

Harper & Row, Publishers, Inc.: Text excerpt from "Bedtime" from *Eleanor Farjeon's Poems for Children* by Eleanor Farjeon.

Lippincott: "Bedtime" originally appeared in *Over the Garden Wall* by Eleanor Farjeon. Copyright 1933, renewed 1961 by Eleanor Farjeon.

Harold Ober Associates, Incorporated: From "Bedtime" from *Over the Garden Wall*, reprinted by permission of Harold Ober Associates Incorporated, copyright © 1933, 1961 by Eleanor Farjeon.

Henry Holt and Company, Inc.: From "Keepsakes" from *Is Somewhere Always Far Away?* by Leland B. Jacobs, copyright © 1967 by Leland B. Jacobs. Reprinted by permission of Henry Holt and Company, Inc. "Lodged" from *The Poetry of Robert Frost*, edited by Edward Connery Lathem. Copyright 1928, 1939, © 1967, 1969 by Holt, Rinehart and Winston. Copyright © 1956 by Robert Frost. Reprinted by permission of Henry Holt and Company, Inc.

CREDITS

Series Editor: Jane Parker
Design Coordinator: Kip Frankenberry
Series Production Editor: Helen Mischka
Level Editors: Patricia Morooka-Barr, Patricia A. Evans
Contributing Editors: Barbara A. Everett, Beverlee Jobrack
Production Editor: Jillian C. Yerkey
Designer: Brent Good
Artist: Lynda Kae Harper
Photo Editor: Mark Burnett

Macmillan/McGraw-Hill School Division
866 Third Avenue
New York, New York 10022
Printed in the United States of America
ISBN 0-675-16227-0

9 8 7 6 5 4 3 2

SENIOR AUTHORS

Dr. Jay K. Hackett
University of Northern Colorado

Dr. Richard H. Moyer
University of Michigan-Dearborn

CONTRIBUTING AUTHORS

Stephen C. Blume
Elementary Science Curriculum Specialist
St. Tammany Public School System
Slidell, Louisiana

Edward Paul Ortleb
Science Supervisor
St. Louis Board of Education
St. Louis, Missouri

Ralph M. Feather, Jr.
Teacher of Geology, Astronomy, and Earth Science
Derry Area School District
Derry, Pennsylvania

Dr. Barbara Swanson Thomson
Associate Professor in Science Education
The Ohio State University
Columbus, Ohio

CONTRIBUTING WRITER

Ann H. Sankey
Science Specialist
Educational Service District 121
Seattle, Washington

READING CONSULTANT

Barbara S. Pettegrew, Ph.D.
Director of the Reading/Study Center
Assistant Professor of Education
Otterbein College, Westerville, Ohio

SAFETY CONSULTANT

Gary E. Downs, Ed.D.
Professor
Iowa State University
Ames, Iowa

GIFTED AND MAINSTREAMED CONSULTANTS

George Fichter
Educational Consultant
Programs for Gifted
Ohio Department of Education
Worthington, Ohio

Timothy E. Heron, Ph.D.
Professor
Department of Human Services, Education
The Ohio State University
Columbus, Ohio

CONTENT CONSULTANTS

Robert T. Brown, M.D.
Assoc. Prof. Clinical
Pediatrics Dir., Section for
Adolescent Health The Ohio State Univ.
Children's Hosp. Columbus, Ohio

Henry D. Drew, Ph.D.
Chemist, U.S. FDA
Div. of Drug Analysis
St. Louis, Missouri

Judith L. Doyle, Ph.D.
Physics Teacher
Newark High School
Newark, Ohio

Todd F. Holzman, M.D.
Child Psychiatrist
Harvard Com. Health Plan
Wellesley, Massachusetts

Knut J. Norstog, Ph.D.
Research Associate
Fairchild Tropical Garden
Miami, Florida

James B. Phipps, Ph.D.
Prof., Geol./Oceanography
Grays Harbor College
Aberdeen, Washington

R. Robert Robbins, Ph.D.
Assoc. Professor
Astronomy Department
University of Texas
Austin, Texas

Sidney E. White, Ph.D.
Professor
Dept. of Geology/Mineralogy
The Ohio State Univ.
Columbus, Ohio

REVIEWERS: Teachers and Administrators

Joan Achen, General Herkimer Elementary School, Utica, NY; **Mary Alice Bernreuter,** Mae Walters Elementary School, Hialeah, FL; **Jack Finger,** Waukesha Public Schools, Waukesha, WI; **Sister Teresa Fitzgerald,** CSJ, Office of Catholic Education, Brooklyn, NY; **Janice Gritton,** Gravin H. Cochran Elementary School, Louisville, KY; **Ann Hanacik,** Blair Elementary School, Waukesha, WI; **Barbara Kmetz,** Trumbull High School, Trumbull, CT; **Waltina Mr'oczek,** Beachwood Elementary School, Beachwood, OH; **Edith Mueller,** Northview Elementary School, Waukesha, WI; **Peggy Smith,** Special Education Resource Teacher, Fort Worth, TX; **Frank Stone,** Floranada Elementary School, Fort Lauderdale, FL; **John Varine,** Kiski Area School District, Vandergrift, PA; **Sue Ann Whan,** Greece Central School District, Rochester, NY; **Dr. Rosa White,** Cutler Ridge Elementary School, Miami, FL

Table of Contents

denotes ACTIVITY.
See page x for ACTIVITIES TABLE OF CONTENTS.

v

Unit 2 — Earth Science 110

🐦 denotes ACTIVITY.

denotes ACTIVITY.
See page x for ACTIVITIES TABLE OF CONTENTS.

Activities

Have You Ever...

You Can...

Activities

Process Skill Models

Problem Solving Activities

SCIENCE IS . . . UNDERSTANDING

Students need to be scientifically literate to be prepared to contribute to the world of today and tomorrow. **SCIENCE In Your World** introduces students to famous scientists and accepted scientific facts, concepts, theories, and laws.

Marie Curie, a French chemist and physicist, was known for her work on radioactivity and radium. She shared a Nobel Prize in physics in 1903 with her husband, Pierre. She was the first person to be awarded a second Nobel Prize when she was honored in 1911 in chemistry for her discovery of radium. In 1935, her daughter, Irene Joliot-Curie, continued the family tradition when she shared a Nobel Prize in chemistry with her husband.

The questions on the student page involve things students will study this year in science. You may wish to ask them what they already know about how fire is made, how things dissolve, and how skateboards work. You might have them draw a picture of a fire and ask them to explain how a scientific understanding of fire can help people use and control it.

Science is...
Understanding

"All my life through, the new sights of Nature made me rejoice like a child."

Marie Curie   French chemist (1867–1934)

What happens in a fire?
Where do things go when they dissolve?
How do skateboards work?
Science has some answers for you.

Science is...

Discovering

"That's one small step for a man, one giant leap for mankind."

Neil A. Armstrong
American astronaut (July 21, 1969)

Neil Armstrong discovered what it was like to be the first person to step on the moon.
Discover science!

xiii

SCIENCE In Your World puts students in the role of scientists as they understand and use scientific methods to question, observe, describe, classify, measure, predict, hypothesize, and draw conclusions to solve problems in their world. Students will engage in literal, interpretive, critical, and creative thinking skills as they rediscover their world through scientific eyes.

Born in 1930, Neil A. Armstrong was the first human to walk on the moon.

You may wish to lead a discussion about discoveries your students have made. They may have realized how much an ant can carry, how dogs sweat, or how fish breathe. They may have dug into sand at a beach and found water. All of these are incidents in which your students are acting as scientists.

SCIENCE IS . . . DECIDING

Science is more than concepts and discovery. **SCIENCE In Your World** recognizes that science involves important decision-making skills as well. Students can work to solve today's and tomorrow's problems by learning how to make responsible decisions. The scientific decisions made in the realms of life, earth, and physical science affect our lives today and the lives of many future generations.

Born in 1944, Richard E. Leakey is a member of a family of anthropologists and archaeologists whose work in East Africa has indicated that human evolution centered there. His parents, Louis and Mary Leakey, discovered stone tool and fossil evidence older than that previously found in Asia. Richard Leakey has made discoveries of his own.

In this quote, Richard Leakey explains one major difference between people and animals. You may wish to ask students what choices they can make to stay healthy or to help, rather than hurt, people, animals, and nature.

Science is ...

Deciding

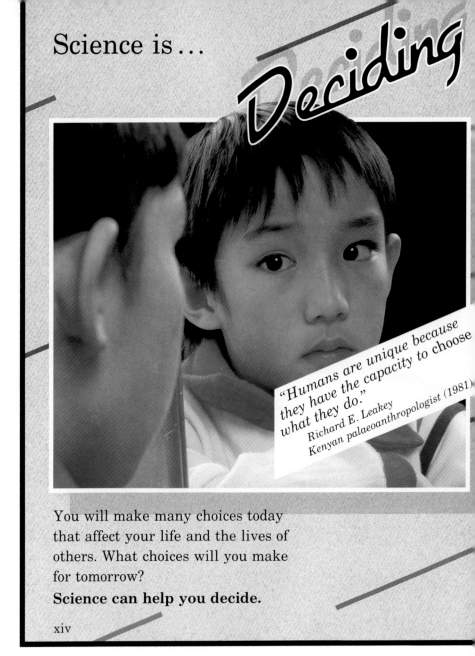

"Humans are unique because they have the capacity to choose what they do."
Richard E. Leakey
Kenyan palaeoanthropologist (1981)

You will make many choices today that affect your life and the lives of others. What choices will you make for tomorrow?
Science can help you decide.

xiv

Science is...

Applying

"I just invent, then wait until man comes around to needing what I've invented."
R. Buckminster Fuller
American engineer (1895–1983)

In about 1900, a Connecticut pie company found that people enjoyed playing catch with empty pie pans. Who ran the pie company? Joseph R. Frisbie! Have you thrown a Frisbee today?

xv

Scientific knowledge can affect all aspects of students' lives at home, in school, in the community, in the world, and in the universe. Applying the scientific principles they learn in **SCIENCE In Your World,** students can better understand and make decisions about the world around them.

R. Buckminster Fuller was an American architect and engineer famous for his technological designs, like the geodesic dome, aimed at getting maximum output from minimum material and energy.

You may wish to have students use the library to investigate some famous inventions and to report on how inventors begin their work. Some possibilities might be Velcro, microwave cooking, lip balm, new types of packaging, or cellular telephones.

Or you may wish to have students write a description or draw a picture of an invention they think might solve a problem.

SCIENCE IS . . . THINKING SCIENTIFICALLY

This year in **SCIENCE In Your World,** students will go far beyond learning facts and understanding established scientific methods. Like scientists, they will use their minds to think about their world in new ways, solve problems, and develop ideas.

To help them think scientifically, the six critical thinking process skills listed here on the student pages are taught in **Process Skill Models** on student pages 333-343. These models introduce students to process skills that are appropriate to their developmental cognitive stage and are practiced over and over in the formal activities. In each model, a process skill is explained, described in a sample, and practiced in specific activities.

These models immediately precede the Problem Solving Activities that are correlated with individual lessons. To aid your students in thinking like scientists from the beginning of the school year, you may wish to assign all of the models during the first several days of science class.

The Process Skill Models also appear in the *Activity Book,* pages 1-12.

Science is...

Measuring

Using Numbers

Controlling Variables

xvi

Interpreting Data

Predicting

Hypothesizing

in your world...

Find out all about these process skills on pages 333-343 of this science book.

1

Science is everywhere! What makes a plant grow? How high is the sky? Why is it blue? How do fish breathe? How do animals communicate? How does a TV work? How deep is the sea? How does bread rise? How do babies learn to talk? All the questions that people wonder about the world involve science. Using the scientific knowledge we have today and the scientific methods we can learn in **SCIENCE In Your World,** we can seek the answers to the wonders of the world.

You may wish to make a list of questions children have about the world and show how their questions involve science. Many of their questions may have complex answers that scientists have not yet been able to discover. Have students think of themselves as the scientists of the future who will be able to understand more than ever before.

Physical Science

I have no time to plan! Where can I find ideas for bulletin boards, audio visuals, and so on? Look no further!

Classroom Centers

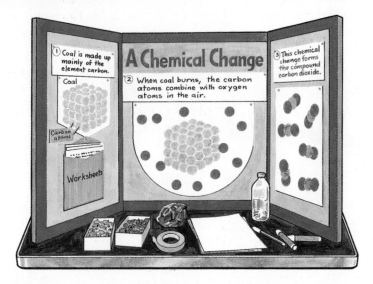

Bulletin Board

Goals: This bulletin board will reinforce the concept of pushes and pulls as forces.

Materials: 16 drawings of people using pushes and pulls

2 larger drawings: representing the "push" force and the "pull" force

2 small paper cups   scissors
letters   cellophane tape
                                    pins
construction paper (2 sheets—1 red, 1 blue)

Procedure: Position the two large drawings at the center of the bulletin board. Tack a paper cup at the base of each drawing. Make flags by taping small strips of red or blue construction paper to the top of straight pins. Place the blue flags in one cup and the red flags in the other. These flags will be used to represent pushes and pulls. Position the 16 smaller drawings on each side of the push or pull drawings. Ask students to use the pins to show the kind of force used in each of the 16 drawings. Some drawings represent both pushes and pulls. Suggested responses include boy flying kite = pull; girl playing marbles = push; carpenter pounding nail = push; girl having hair braided = pull; girl hitting softball = push; leaves of tree falling to ground = pull; tug-o-war = pull; boy vacuuming carpet = push.

Science Center

Goals: Students will make models of chemical change, using materials to represent atoms of elements combining to form a compound, and relate the process to the change in observable properties of the actual substances.

Materials: pop beads, two colors   lump of coal
drawing paper   markers
containers   sealed bottle
gummed labels

Procedure: Label one color of beads "carbon atoms." Label the beads of another color "oxygen atoms." Label the coal "carbon" and the empty, sealed bottle "carbon dioxide." Prepare a worksheet and point out that when we burn fuels, a chemical change occurs and heat is released. When fuels burn thoroughly, each carbon atom unites with two oxygen atoms from the air to form the compound carbon dioxide. Point out that coal is made of carbon atoms. The container of oxygen "atoms" represents oxygen in the air. When coal burns, each of its carbon atoms combines with two oxygen atoms from the air, producing carbon dioxide. Have students **work cooperatively** to carry out this reaction using models and describe the properties of carbon dioxide. Finally, have students draw what takes place in the total chemical change and tell how they know the process is a chemical change.

Places to Go, People to See

Field Trip Ideas

Have students study the school grounds to find examples of simple machines such as a seesaw (lever), flagpole (pulley), wheelchair ramp (inclined plane), and so on.

Speakers and Visitors

Contact a chemist or physicist to discuss the makeup of matter and the changes that occur in the states of matter.

Audiovisuals for the Students

 ### Films and Filmstrips

Behavior of Matter, 16 mm, 15 min., color, EBEC.
Simple Machines—Using Mechanical Advantage, 16 mm, 16 min., color, Barr Films.

 ### Videotapes

Behavior of Matter, 15 min., color, EBEC.
Matter & Motion, seventeen 15-minute programs, color, Agency for Instructional Technology.
Mr. Wizard's World of Science Video Library, Merrill Publishing Company: Tape 1, "Simple Machines"; Tape 2, "Inertia"; Tape 3, "Gravity"; Tape 4, "Action and Reaction"; Tape 6, "Fluid Flow"; Tape 12, "Heat Transfer"; Tape 16, "Change of State"; Tape 17, "Chemistry in the Kitchen"; Tape 19, "Chemical Reactions"; Tape 20, "Combustion."

 ### Computer Software

Physical or Chemical? Students learn to recognize differences between physical and chemical properties of matter in a two-part program. Includes lists of resources.
Type: Tutorial, Quiz
Hardware: Apple II+, IIe, IIc
Supplier: Educational Materials and Equipment Co.
Physical Science Series: Machines, Work, and Energy Introduces the workings of six basic machines and defines work, energy, and force.
Type: Tutorial, Simulation, Quiz
Hardware: Apple II+, IIe, IIc
Supplier: Educational Activities, Inc.

Resources for the Teacher

 ### Materials at Little/No Cost

USGS
Book & Report Sales
Box 25425
Denver, CO 80225
"The Interior of the Earth" is a booklet that describes Earth's crust, mantle, and core.

 ### Resource Books

Christianson, Gale E. *In the Presence of the Creator: Isaac Newton and His Times.* New York: Free Press, 1984.
Hess, Fred C. *Chemistry Made Simple.* New York: Doubleday and Co., 1984.
Weinberg, Steven. *The Discovery of Subatomic Particles.* New York: W. H. Freeman and Co., 1983.
Wheeler, Gerald and Larry Kirkpatrick. *Physics: Building a World View.* Englewood Cliffs, NJ: Prentice-Hall, 1983.

UNIT CONCEPTS

Chapter 1
- The first step of a scientific method is to decide on the problem.
- Variables change in an experiment. A control is a standard for comparison.
- A chart is helpful in comparing the results of an experiment with the hypothesis.

Chapter 2
- Matter is described by its properties. Mass and space are two properties common to all matter.
- Matter is made of atoms.
- The pattern and space between particles determines a matter's state–solid, liquid, or gas.

Chapter 3
- A change in the physical properties of matter is a physical change.
- Matter changes state when it gains or loses heat.
- Matter can be combined in mixtures, where each type of matter keeps its physical properties, or in compounds, where elements combine during a chemical change.

Chapter 4
- The force needed to move an object depends on the object's mass.
- Gravity and friction affect the amount of force needed to move an object.
- Energy is the ability to do work.

Chapter 5
- Simple machines make work seem easier by changing the direction or amount of force needed to do work.
- Wedges and screws are made up of inclined planes.
- Using a wheel and axle reduces the force needed to turn the axle. A pulley reduces a force or changes its direction.
- Compound machines are made of two or more simple machines.

Physical Science

2

Be prepared! Chapter concepts appear in one neat package right here.

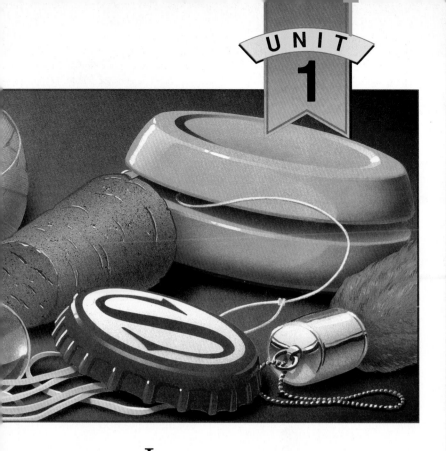

UNIT 1

I keep bottle caps,
    I keep string,
I keep keys and corks
    And all such things.

from "Keepsakes"
Leland B. Jacobs

Literature in a science book? You bet! Relate science to what students are reading.

3

Understanding the Selection

■ Have students talk about things people might save. Tell students that you are going to read a poem about some things that someone kept.
■ Read the poem aloud. Then have students read the poem aloud with you.
■ Ask: **What kinds of things did the poet keep?** *bottle caps, string, keys, corks*
Ask: **Why do you think the poet saved these things?** Possible answers: *The poet liked the color or feel of these things; they brought back memories of happy times.*

Relating the Selection to Unit Concepts

■ Ask students to describe the shape of the things talked about in the poem. Possible answers: *round, straight, oblong.* Ask students to describe how they think the things that are talked about in the poem feel to the touch. Possible answers: *soft, hard, rough, smooth.*
■ Discuss how people describe objects. Ask: **What other words could you use to describe the things talked about in the poem?** Lead students to discover that they could talk about the color of the things and the size of the things.

Relating the Selection to the Student's World

■ Have students look at the photograph and tell what things they see. *cork, keys, bottle caps, paper clips, yarn, marbles, yo-yo, and so on.*
■ Ask: **How could you use shape, color, size, and texture to describe the things in the picture?** Accept all answers that convey shape, color, size, and texture of the things.
■ Have students choose something in the room to describe to the class using shape, color, size, and texture. Other students in the class should try to guess what is being described.

ACTIVITY CENTER

For fun, hands-on, independent activities that integrate reading, writing, math, and technology with the chapters in this unit, have students complete some or all of the Activity Center Activities below. Look for specific chapter references in the Lesson Planning Guides.

Reading: 1 Who's Afraid of the Big Bad Wolf? **2** Wings of Wax, **3** Mixing It Up, **4** Toyland
Writing: 1 Day of Discovery, **2** Ice Is Nice, **3** Floating Through Space, **4** New and Improved
Math: 1 Mission Possible, **2** Block Busters, **3** Treasure Hunt, **4** Playing With Play Dough
Technology: 1 Water on Ice, **2** Fire! **3** Fancy Footwear, **4** As the Wheel Turns

CHAPTER 1

Think Like a Scientist

*Plan ahead—
See each lesson
in the chapter
at a glance:
objectives, vocabulary,
materials, and all
program supplements.*

Planning Guide

Lessons	Objectives	Vocabulary
Chapter Introduction pp. 4, 5		
Lesson 1 Using a Scientific Method pp. 6–9	1. **Operationally define** a *scientific method.* 2. **Decide** on a problem.	scientific method problem
Lesson 2 Setting Up an Experiment pp. 10–15	3. **Define** *hypothesis.* 4. **List** the steps of the hypothesis. 5. **List** the steps of an experiment. 6. **Use** a control and a variable.	hypothesis variables control
Lesson 3 Recording and Discussing Data pp. 16–23	7. **Discuss** the results from the experiment. 8. **Compare** the outcome with the hypothesis.	
Chapter Review pp. 24, 25		

Planning Guide

Text Activities		Teacher Resource Masters	Other Components
Title/Skill	Materials per Group		
Have You Ever . . . Experimented With Straws? p. 5 Observing Time Allotment: 30 minutes	juice glasses drinking straws (one bendable, one straight)		**Activity Center:** "Who's Afraid of the Big Bad Wolf?"; "Wings of Wax"; "Day of Discovery"; "Mission Possible"
How Fast Will Sugar Dissolve? p. 9 Measuring/Observing Time Allotment: 30 minutes	3 small, clear jars measuring cup water (ice, room temperature, warm) thermometer 3 sugar cubes watch pencil and paper	Independent Practice, pp. 11, 12 Activity Worksheet, pp. 3, 4 Language Arts Connection, p. 9 Health Connection, p. 10	
		Independent Practice, pp. 11, 12	
You Can . . . Make a Chart, p. 17 Communicating/Interpreting Data Time Allotment: 20 minutes	examples of completed charts paper and pencil	Independent Practice, pp. 11, 12 Activity Worksheet, pp. 5, 6 Transparency Master, p. 1 ◆ Family Science, p. 2 Critical Thinking, p. 7 ▲ Critical Thinking, p. 8 ◆ Reteaching Activity, p. 13	
How Can You Find the Best Soap? p. 22 Hypothesizing/Observing, Time Allotment: 30 minutes	3 margarine bowls with lids 3 brands liquid dish soap 3 droppers warm water measuring cup vegetable oil small spoon pencil and paper		
		Test A, p. 14 Test B, pp. 15, 16	Software, "Hunting With A Camera"

◆ Basic / ▲ Advanced / All other masters are for use by all students.

Think Like a Scientist

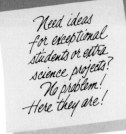

Need ideas for exceptional students or extra science projects? No problem! Here they are!

For Exceptional Students

ESL/LEP

Chapter 1/Lesson 1, Page 8

Ask students to think of a problem they had to solve recently. Help them by relating a hypothetical problem that you had to solve recently. As an example, tell students your family life had become very hectic in the morning. The children couldn't find their assignments at the last minute and lunches were not ready when it was time for family members to leave the house. The result: Everyone was upset. Tell students that you and the other family members tried to pinpoint the problem: Too many chores had been postponed until morning.

Have students state their problems. Ask them to list three or four choices.

Chapter 1/Lesson 3, Page 10

Ask students to think of a hypothesis for how they might solve the problem of why one of the classroom plants is not growing well. Have them list two or three hypotheses. Discuss their ideas. Help the students plan an experiment to test their hypotheses. Work with them to decide on controls.

Chapter 1/Lesson 3, Page 16

Have students consider the following hypothesis: **The plant did not grow well because it did not receive the right amount of water.** Have students assume that an experiment yielded the results shown in the chart below.

Plant	Watering Frequency	Description
1	every day	had many dark spots
2	every two days	had some dark spots
3	once a week	was all green

Ask students to discuss what they learned from the chart. Have them write sentences about how to care for the plant in question.

Gifted

Chapter 1/Lesson 2, Page 15

Have students make up a hypothesis to solve this problem: What kinds of food stick to your teeth? Ask them to plan an experiment, determine the variable, and state what will be the control in their experiment. Allow students to carry out their experiment and make a chart to record the results. Students may extend their project by finding a relationship between sticky foods and tooth decay.

Mainstreamed

Chapter 1/Lesson 2, Page 15

Physical Impairment: After reviewing text material related to forming hypotheses, give students a goldfish in a jar of water. Have them observe the behavior of the fish, especially how the fish breathes. Ask them to write a sentence about their observations. Tell students you want them to think about this problem: What makes fish breathe faster or slower at times? Direct them to observe the fish and make up a hypothesis about this. Have them share their hypotheses. If they wish, let them test their hypotheses.

Projects to Do

Whole Class Science Project

Have students brainstorm in **cooperative groups** to plan a science project to study what mealworms like to eat. Have each group form a hypothesis and design an experiment, using an appropriate variable and controls. Have the groups carry out the experiment and record their data. Finally, have the groups share their data and publish the results on the bulletin board.

Science Fair Projects

Individual students could do one of the following projects, using scientific methods:

1. Find out what plants need to grow.
2. Investigate which kind of popcorn pops best.
3. Find out what can be done to keep lettuce crispy.
4. Design an experiment to determine what kind of bread stays fresh longest.

pages 4–25

Chapter Concepts

■ The first step of a scientific method is to decide on the problem.

■ Variables change in an experiment, while a control is a standard for comparison that shows what happens when nothing is changed.

■ A chart is helpful in comparing the results of an experiment with the hypothesis.

Chapter Background

■ Science is what people have learned in the past and what they are still learning about the world around them.

■ Scientists use certain methods to solve problems.

■ By using the steps of a scientific method, people can find answers to many questions that puzzle them.

■ A scientific method does not need to be rigid. It does, however, make use of the basic processes of science, such as stating a problem, observing, hypothesizing, experimenting, recording data, and making a conclusion.

Look for These Symbols

   —Hands-on activity

   —Cooperative learning

   —Overhead transparency

♦ —Basic/Reinforcement

● —Average/Enrichment

▲ —Advanced/Challenge

   —Calculator Practice

SCIENCE
In Your World

4

Watch for these easily recognizable symbols that tell you at a glance what type of learning experience is described.

CHAPTER

1

Think Like a Scientist

Have you ever had a drink of cold juice on a hot day? These children are both drinking juice, but the straws they are using are different. How are they different? Why does one child need a straw that bends?

Have You Ever...

Experimented With Straws?

Scientists are close observers. Look closely at a straight straw and a bendable straw. How are they different, and how are they the same? Scientists make changes to see what will happen. Make a change. Bend each straw. Try drinking out of each one and record what happens. Why do you think a bendable straw works? What part of your body bends like a bendable straw?

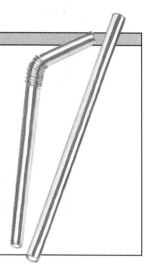

Use this short, quick, fun activity to spark student interest and tap prior knowledge.

What are the four parts of every effective lesson? PREPLAN, FOCUS, TEACH, APPLY.

PREPLAN

Time Allotment: 30 minutes

Objectives
1. **Compare** an ordinary and a bendable straw.
2. **Observe** the differences in drinking through a bendable and a straight straw.

Setup
■ You will need the following materials for each student or activity group:
glass of water   1 bendable and 1 straight straw

1 FOCUS

■ Ask a student to describe what is happening in the picture on page 4.

2 TEACH

■ Ask: **Why do you think one child has a straw that bends?** *The child is too small to reach the glass on the table.*

Have You Ever . . .
Have students **work cooperatively** in groups of four.
■ Ask students to think about why the ridges make a straw bend more easily.
■ **Student Responses**
1. The folds in the straw make many little bends so that the straw curves instead of bending at a right angle.
2. The spinal column bends like a bendable straw.

3 Apply

■ Ask students to think like a scientist and invent a straw that does something special. Encourage them to draw pictures of their inventions and write them.

Close
■ Ask: **What problems have you solved today?** Accept reasonable answers and discuss problem-solving techniques.

PREPLAN—
What do you need?
Lesson objectives
and science
background, of
course.

PREPLAN

Lesson Objectives
1. **Operationally define** a *scientific method*.
2. **Decide** on a problem.

Science Background
■ This lesson is designed to introduce students to the methods scientists use to solve problems. It is important to keep two things in mind throughout the teaching of this chapter. First, methods of science are not limited to the laboratory. Scientific methods can be used to solve day-to-day problems, as shown in this chapter. Second, the scientific method referred to in this chapter involves several steps, including identifying a problem, forming a hypothesis, conducting an experiment, and so on.

Lesson Vocabulary
scientific method   problem

Note: The activity on student page 9 may be used for guided discovery before you begin this lesson.

1 FOCUS

■ Display several different brands of flashlight batteries. Engage students by asking: **Which type of battery would be best for use in a flashlight? Which would be best for other uses? How could you find out?** Through discussion, have students conclude that there are many questions of this nature that people encounter every day. Point out that problems of this kind usually begin with a question. Read the text until students have discovered the problem faced by Tony.

■ Use the goals on student page 6 to establish the purpose for studying this lesson.

Using a Scientific Method

LESSON 1 GOALS
You will learn
● that people can use scientific methods to solve problems in everyday life.
● about the first steps in a scientific method.

Establish the purpose for reading with goals that are conveniently correlated to lesson objectives.

Tony and his family were just finishing their supper. Tony was proud because he had helped cook. After dinner all of the family helped clear the dirty dishes. Tony and his sister Anne started washing the dishes. They were having trouble getting the greasy pots and pans clean. Anne said, "We should be using the new dish soap I saw advertised on TV. The TV ad said it's the best dish soap for greasy pots and pans!"

1. Focus—Engage your students and prepare them for what's to come!

TEACHER RESOURCE MASTERS

Language Arts Connection 9

LANGUAGE ARTS CONNECTION Composition   Chapter 1

Name _____

WRITING ABOUT EXPERIMENTS

When you solve problems in science, you use the scientific method. When you write, you also use an orderly process. These are the steps you follow:
1. Think about what you would like to say.
2. Organize what you want to say.
3. Write your first draft.
4. Make changes and rewrite.
5. Share your writing with others.

Think about an experiment that you enjoyed doing. Use the steps of the writing process to tell what you did and why you had fun doing it.

Answers will vary.

And what's more, find reduced Teacher Resource Master pages right when you want them.

Tony's mother smiled and said, "Our dish soap is fine. Just get finished!"

Tony and Anne finished the pots and pans, while Tony thought, "They're probably pretty much the same. It probably doesn't matter which one we use." Still, Tony wondered if there was a way to find out which dish soap was really best.

Tony didn't realize it, but he was beginning to think like a scientist. **Scientific methods** are lists of steps that scientists use to solve problems. You, too, can use a scientific method to find the answers to everyday problems.

2. TEACH—
Use one or more of these stimulating teaching suggestions. Guided and independent practice make checking for understanding a snap.

3. APPLY—
No lesson is complete without applying what has been learned. Lesson closure ties up any loose ends.

7

2 TEACH

■ Ask students to suggest problems in their everyday lives that might be solved by conducting an experiment.

Guided Practice

■ Check students' understanding of lesson concepts by discussing the Lesson Review questions on student page 8. If necessary, use the **reteaching strategy** in OPTIONS.

Independent Practice

■ Assign the Lesson 1 section of the Teacher Resource Master **Independent Practice,** page 11.

3 APPLY

■ Tell students that the door to the classroom is hard to open at certain times of the year. Ask them if they have ever observed a door sticking like that. Ask them to think like a scientist and state what the problem with the door may be.

Close

■ Use the summary statements on student page 8 to review the lesson concepts.

OPTIONS

Reteaching Strategy

Divide the class into small **cooperative groups** to make up skits that show why stating a problem is a help to scientists and other people in solving their problems.

Students having trouble? Reteaching Suggestions give them another chance.

TEACHER RESOURCE MASTERS

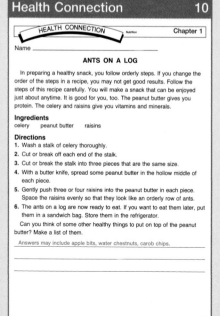

Health Connection 10

HEALTH CONNECTION — Nutrition — Chapter 1

Name _____

ANTS ON A LOG

In preparing a healthy snack, you follow orderly steps. If you change the order of the steps in a recipe, you may not get good results. Follow the steps of this recipe carefully. You will make a snack that can be enjoyed just about anytime. It is good for you, too. The peanut butter gives you protein. The celery and raisins give you vitamins and minerals.

Ingredients
celery   peanut butter   raisins

Directions
1. Wash a stalk of celery thoroughly.
2. Cut or break off each end of the stalk.
3. Cut or break the stalk into three pieces that are the same size.
4. With a butter knife, spread some peanut butter in the hollow middle of each piece.
5. Gently push three or four raisins into the peanut butter in each piece. Space the raisins evenly so that they look like an orderly row of ants.
6. The ants on a log are now ready to eat. If you want to eat them later, put them in a sandwich bag. Store them in the refrigerator.

Can you think of some other healthy things to put on top of the peanut butter? Make a list of them.

Answers may include apple bits, water chestnuts, carob chips.

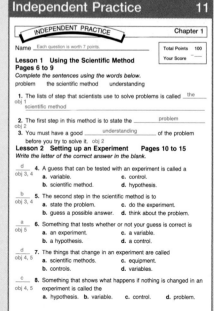

Independent Practice 11

INDEPENDENT PRACTICE — Chapter 1

Name ___ Each question is worth 7 points. ___   Total Points 100   Your Score ___

Lesson 1   Using the Scientific Method
Pages 6 to 9
Complete the sentences using the words below.
problem   the scientific method   understanding

1. The lists of step that scientists use to solve problems is called ___the scientific method___
obj 1

2. The first step in this method is to state the ___problem___
obj 2

3. You must have a good ___understanding___ of the problem before you try to solve it. obj 2

Lesson 2   Setting up an Experiment   Pages 10 to 15
Write the letter of the correct answer in the blank.

___d___ 4. A guess that can be tested with an experiment is called a
obj 3, 4
  a. variable.   c. control.
  b. scientific method. d. hypothesis.

___b___ 5. The second step in the scientific method is to
obj 3, 4
  a. state the problem.   c. do the experiment.
  b. guess a possible answer. d. think about the problem.

___a___ 6. Something that tests whether or not your guess is correct is
obj 5
  a. an experiment.   c. a variable.
  b. a hypothesis.   d. a control.

___d___ 7. The things that change in an experiment are called
obj 4, 5
  a. scientific methods. c. equipment.
  b. controls.   d. variables.

___c___ 8. Something that shows what happens if nothing is changed in an
obj 4, 5 experiment is called the
  a. hypothesis. b. variable.   c. control.   d. problem.

OPTIONS

LANGUAGE CONNECTION

Reading: Have students **work co-operatively in pairs** to discuss and respond to the following questions. Describe how the problem stated in this lesson began. Who started Tony thinking about the best dish soap? (Anne mentioned a new dish soap. Mother said their current dish soap is fine.) When and where does the story take place? (The story takes place after supper in the kitchen of Tony and Anne's house.) Think of other everyday problems that may have begun in a similar way in your own life. (Responses will vary.)

♦ **Reinforcement:** Ask students to state the problem to be solved in understanding each of the following natural phenomena:
1. You see your breath on a cold day.
2. The car windows get fogged up on a cold day.

● **Enrichment:** Ask students to think about rainbows, sunsets, or the color of the sky. Have them think of something about these phenomena that they would like to understand better. Have them state their problem as a question.

▲ **Challenge:** Have interested students keep track of problems that arise during a twenty-four-hour period that they would like to resolve by using the scientific method. Ask them to state each problem as a question.

LESSON REVIEW ANSWERS

1. scientific methods
2. to have a good understanding of what the problem is

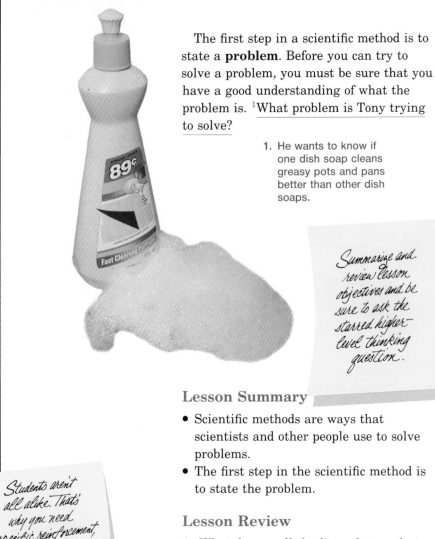

The first step in a scientific method is to state a **problem**. Before you can try to solve a problem, you must be sure that you have a good understanding of what the problem is. [1]What problem is Tony trying to solve?

> 1. He wants to know if one dish soap cleans greasy pots and pans better than other dish soaps.

Summarize and review lesson objectives and be sure to ask the starred higher-level thinking question.

Lesson Summary

- Scientific methods are ways that scientists and other people use to solve problems.
- The first step in the scientific method is to state the problem.

Lesson Review

1. What do we call the lists of steps that scientists use to solve problems?
★2. Why would a scientist first state the problem?

Students aren't all alike. That's why you need specific reinforcement, enrichment, and challenge ideas.

8

TEACHER RESOURCE MASTERS

How fast will sugar dissolve?

How? Where? When? Why? Scientific discoveries begin with questions. Use the formal activities to foster inquiry and advanced thinking skills.

What you need

3 small, clear jars
   (labeled A, B, and C)
measuring cup
water (ice, room temperature,
   warm)
thermometer
3 sugar cubes
watch
pencil and paper

What to do

1. Pour 125 mL of ice water into cup A.
2. Pour 125 mL of room-temperature water into cup B and 125 mL of warm water into cup C.
3. Record the temperature of the water in each cup.
4. Guess which cup of water will dissolve the sugar cube first.
5. Drop a sugar cube into each cup.
6. Observe each cup for 10 minutes. Record your observations.

What did you learn?

1. In which cup did it take the longest time for the sugar to dissolve? the shortest?
2. How does water temperature affect the time needed to dissolve sugar?

Using what you learned

1. Would it be easier to make hot tea or iced tea sweet? Why?
2. What else might affect how long it takes to dissolve a sugar cube?

9

ACTIVITY RESPONSES

What did you learn?
1. The sugar in the ice water (cup A) took the longest to dissolve. It may not have been totally dissolved even after ten minutes. The sugar in the warm water (cup C) dissolved first.
2. Sugar dissolves faster as the temperature of the water increases.

Using what you learned
1. It would be easier to sweeten hot tea. Sugar dissolves faster in hot liquids.
2. Some answers students may suggest are stirring the water, amount of water, number of sugar cubes, grinding the cubes, and so on.

Don't forget to use the Activity Worksheet in the Teacher Resource Book and watch out for those safety symbols

---

Employ the tried and true lesson approach of PREPLAN, FOCUS, TEACH, and APPLY.

PREPLAN

Time Allotment: 30 minutes
Process Skill: Measuring, Observing

Objectives
1. **Utilize** the scientific method.
2. **Infer** that temperature affects solubility.
3. **Record** and **interpret** data.
4. **Propose** and **test** a hypothesis.

Setup
The temperature of the ice water should be about 5° C. Room-temperature water should be between 18°–25° C, and warm tap water should be between 45°–50° C.

Cooperative Grouping: threes—Assign roles as explained on page T24.

1 FOCUS

■ Have students identify the problem (how long it takes sugar to dissolve). Discuss other experiences of mixing things (drink mixes, paints, and so on) in water.

2 TEACH

■ Discuss step 4 with the class before they begin. You may want to introduce the term *hypothesis* as a guess that is able to be tested.
■ Have students use the Teacher Resource Master **Activity Worksheet,** pages 3 and 4, to record their data.

3 APPLY

■ Refer to the student hypothesis in step 4. Reinforce that it is not important that the hypothesis be correct, but that something was learned about the problem.

Close
■ Discuss the activity and questions.

PREPLAN

Lesson Objectives
3. **Define** *hypothesis.*
4. **List** the steps of the hypothesis.
5. **List** the steps of an experiment.
6. **Use** a control and a variable.

Science Background
■ A hypothesis is essentially an educated guess **that can be tested by experimentation.** In this way, hypotheses differ from mere predictions.

■ Only one variable at a time should be changed in an experiment, so that one can be sure what change caused what effect.

■ A control is used in most experiments for purposes of comparison.

Lesson Vocabulary
hypothesis
variables
control

1 FOCUS

⬚ Write the following question on the chalkboard or overhead: **Why is stating the problem the first step in the scientific method?** Have students **work cooperatively** in small groups to discuss possible answers. *If you want to solve a problem, you have to understand exactly what the problem is. Otherwise, you may waste a lot of time gathering unnecessary information.*

■ Use the goals on student page 10 to establish the purpose for studying this lesson.

Setting Up an Experiment

On his way home from school the next day, Tony saw Mrs. Ortiz, who owns a flower shop. Today she was stirring something in a pail with a long spoon. "What are you doing?" asked Tony.

Mrs. Ortiz explained that she was mixing some plant food into water for the plants in her greenhouse. Tony asked why she was stirring the mixture. "It helps dissolve the plant food in the water," said Mrs. Ortiz. "Most things will dissolve faster if you stir them."

10

TEACHER RESOURCE MASTERS

Tony thought about what Mrs. Ortiz said and asked, "Do you want to do an experiment?"

He explained that they were studying about scientific methods at school. First, they needed to state the problem they were trying to solve. Tony wrote the problem on a piece of paper.

Problem: How can we make plant food dissolve in water faster?

11

TEACHER RESOURCE MASTERS

Independent Practice   11

2   TEACH

■ Discuss the idea of a fair test, and ask students why it is important to have the same amount of water in each pail.
■ Ask students why Tony stirred only one pail. Point out that the pail not stirred is called the control.
■ Note that at each step throughout the experiment Tony is careful to write things down. Ask: **Why is it important to write things down as you go?** *A careful record of observations is important when it is time to think about results.*

Guided Practice
■ Check students' understanding of lesson concepts by discussing the Lesson Review questions on student page 15. If necessary, use the **reteaching strategy** in OPTIONS.

Independent Practice
■ Assign the Lesson 2 section of the Teacher Resource Master **Independent Practice,** page 11.

3   APPLY

■ Suggest these hypothetical experiments and have students identify the variables.
1. A man wants to find out how to make his homemade cookies crisper, so he tries baking them at different temperatures. (oven temperature, crispiness of cookies)
2. A girl wanted to see which paper towel would soak up the most water. She tested three brands. (amount of water absorbed, paper towel brands)

Close
■ Use Summary statements on student page 15 to review lesson concepts.

OPTIONS

Reteaching Strategy
■ Ask students to explain the difference between a hypothesis and a wild guess. Have them devise an experiment to test a wild guess.

OPTIONS

LANGUAGE CONNECTION

Reading: Instruct students to work in **cooperative groups** to write a brief paragraph in response to the following.

Think of a problem you would find interesting to study. State the problem clearly. Then write out the next step in the scientific method for solving your problem. Have groups exchange paragraphs, read the instructions, and write a hypothesis for the problem.

Travel all across the curriculum with our integrated Connections.

What is a hypothesis?

The second step in the scientific method is to guess a possible answer. It is important to set up an experiment to test if your guess is correct. A guess that can be tested with an experiment is called a **hypothesis** (hi PAHTH uh sus).

Mrs. Ortiz said, "We already have a hypothesis for our experiment." Tony wrote it down.

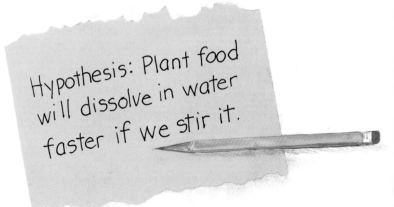

Hypothesis: Plant food will dissolve in water faster if we stir it.

Next, Tony and Mrs. Ortiz gathered their materials. They found two pails, a liter bottle, a thermometer, a tablespoon, the plant food, and the long spoon.

Tony poured exactly four liters of water into each pail. "It is important to have the same amount of water in each pail," said Mrs. Ortiz.

"Otherwise, it wouldn't be a fair test," said Tony.

12

TEACHER RESOURCE MASTERS

"We should also make sure the water temperatures are the same," said Mrs. Ortiz. She used the thermometer to take the temperature of the water in each pail. She showed Tony how to read the thermometer. The temperature of the water in each pail was 18°C. Then they carefully added exactly one level tablespoon of plant food to each pail. Tony stirred one of the pails while Mrs. Ortiz timed him for five minutes. Tony looked in the pail he was stirring and saw that the plant food had dissolved. The plant food in the other pail could still be seen on the bottom. [1]What did Tony and Mrs. Ortiz find out about their hypothesis?

1. It showed that their hypothesis had been correct. Stirring did make the plant food dissolve faster.

13

OPTIONS

♦ **Reinforcement:** Ask students to write hypotheses to solve these problems. **What makes your breath visible on a cold day? What makes car windows fog up on a cold day?**

TEACHER RESOURCE MASTERS

OPTIONS

● **Enrichment:** Ask students to write hypotheses to solve the problems they have wondered about concerning what causes rainbows, sunsets, or the color of the sky.

▲ **Challenge:** Have interested students make up hypotheses to solve the problems they listed during a twenty-four-hour period in Lesson 1.

Don't recognize these symbols? Remember that the key appears on the first page of the chapter.

1. It did not dissolve.

What is a control?

After you state a problem and suggest a hypothesis, you decide on an experiment. The experiment must test whether or not your guess is correct. Things that change in an experiment are **variables**. The variable that Tony and Mrs. Ortiz changed was the stirring. The variable that they tested was how to make the plant food dissolve faster. The pail that they didn't stir was the control. A **control** shows what happens if nothing is changed in an experiment. Without a control, Tony wouldn't know if stirring did any good. The plant food dissolved in the pail that Tony stirred. [1]What about the plant food in the control—the plant food that he didn't stir?

14

TEACHER RESOURCE MASTERS

There are other possible variables that Tony could test. It is important to test only one variable at a time. For example, the temperature of the water could be a variable. [1]What would have happened if Tony did not have water of the same temperature in each pail?

How many variables should you test at a time?

1. He wouldn't know if stirring or water temperature made the plant food dissolve.

Lesson Summary

- A guess that can be tested by an experiment is called a hypothesis.
- Something that changes in an experiment is called a variable.

Lesson Review

1. What is the second step in a scientific method?
2. What is the difference between a variable and a control?
3. What would happen if a scientist didn't use a control?

15

LESSON REVIEW ANSWERS

1. to state a hypothesis
2. A variable changes in an experiment; a control shows what happens if nothing is changed.
3. A scientist wouldn't know whether the variable that was changed had any effect on the results.

TEACHER RESOURCE MASTERS

PREPLAN

Lesson Objectives

7. Discuss the results from the experiment.

8. Compare the outcome with the hypothesis.

Science Background

■ The data of an experiment's results are more easily interpreted when organized and presented in tabular or graphic form.

Note: The activity on student page 22 may be used for guided discovery before you begin this lesson.

1 FOCUS

Write the following on the chalkboard or overhead: **The plant food that was stirred dissolved in five minutes. The plant food that was not stirred did not dissolve in five minutes.** Ask: **How could I write this in another way so that you could see the results at a glance?** *You could make a chart.* Have students **work cooperatively** in small groups to prepare a chart that records the results of the experiment accurately. For example:

Minutes	Stirred	Not stirred
5	dissolved	undissolved
20		dissolved

■ Use the goals on student page 16 to establish the purpose for studying this lesson.

LESSON 3 GOALS
You will learn
● that the results of an experiment can be compared to a control.
● that a chart can help you show the results of an experiment.

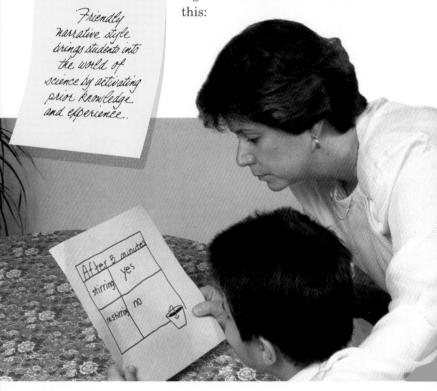

Friendly narrative style brings students into the world of science by activating prior knowledge and experience.

Recording and Discussing Data

Tony and Mrs. Ortiz talked about their experiment. Tony said, "In school I learned how to make a record of the results of an experiment. I'll write down the results tonight and show them to you tomorrow."

When Tony got home, he told his mother about the experiment. They worked together and made a chart that looked like this:

16

TEACHER RESOURCE MASTERS

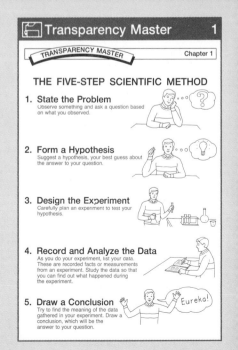

Transparency Master 1

TRANSPARENCY MASTER — Chapter 1

THE FIVE-STEP SCIENTIFIC METHOD

1. State the Problem
Observe something and ask a question based on what you observed.

2. Form a Hypothesis
Suggest a hypothesis, your best guess about the answer to your question.

3. Design the Experiment
Carefully plan an experiment to test your hypothesis.

4. Record and Analyze the Data
As you do your experiment, list your data. These are recorded facts or measurements from an experiment. Study the data so that you can find out what happened during the experiment.

5. Draw a Conclusion
Try to find the meaning of the data gathered in your experiment. Draw a conclusion, which will be the answer to your question.

Eureka!

ACTIVITY

You Can...

Make a Chart

Scientists must know how to organize their data. One way to organize data is to use a chart. This chart shows how the height of two plants changed. You can make your own chart. Talk to ten friends. Find out how many brothers and sisters each friend has. Put your data into a chart. Who has the most brothers? sisters?

Looking at his results, Tony could tell that his hypothesis seemed to be correct. He thought about other variables. He wondered how long it would take the plant food to dissolve in warm water. He decided to try another experiment with Mrs. Ortiz.

For one of the last steps of the scientific method, you must make a record of your results. It may also help if you discuss the results of your experiment with others. A chart can help you think about the results of an experiment. Finally, you need to decide whether or not the results support your hypothesis. If the results do not support your hypothesis, you may want to make another guess and design a new experiment to test your new guess.

Integrate science with Reading, Writing, and Math using these short margin features.

SCIENCE AND . . .
Reading

What do you think will happen when Tony and Mrs. Ortiz add plant food to warm water? The plant food will
A. dissolve slower.
B. dissolve faster.
C. not dissolve.

17

TEACH

■ Help students construct a bar graph using the same data Tony and Anne used in their chart. Be sure students realize that both show the same information.

■ Often, the results of one experiment lead to more questions. Ask: **What question did Tony think of after his experiment was completed?** *He wondered if plant food would dissolve even faster in warm water.*

Guided Practice

■ Check students' understanding of lesson concepts by discussing the Lesson Review questions on student page 21. If necessary, use the **reteaching strategy** in OPTIONS.

Independent Practice

■ Assign the Lesson 3 section of the Teacher Resource Master **Independent Practice,** page 12.

3 APPLY

■ Have students design an experiment to test their hypotheses on the sticking classroom door.

Close

■ Use Summary statements on student page 21 to review lesson concepts.

OPTIONS

Reteaching Strategy

■ Ask students to design a chart to record data for an experiment to find out how changing the temperature of the water in which a goldfish swims affects its breathing. Say: **The data you have is the temperature of water and fish's breathing rate when you started the experiment, after you added ice, and after you waited five minutes.**

■ Refer to page 18 for teaching strategies for **You Can . . . Make a Chart.**

TEACHER RESOURCE MASTERS

Family Science   2

| FAMILY SCIENCE | Chapter 1 |

Name _____

In science class, your child is studying about the scientific method. This method has five steps: stating a problem, forming a hypothesis, setting up an experiment, recording and discussing results of the experiment, and comparing the results with the hypothesis. In this home activity, your child will use the scientific method.

DOES WRAPPING ICE CHANGE MELTING TIME?

Materials
ice cubes   old newspapers
two bowls   pencil and paper

What to do
1. Wrap one ice cube in a sheet of newspaper. Place it in one of the bowls.
2. Place an unwrapped ice cube in the other bowl.
3. Set the bowls next to each other on a table.
4. Guess whether the wrapped ice cube or the unwrapped one will melt faster. Write down your guess on a sheet of paper.
5. Check the two bowls every 15 minutes for an hour to see which ice cube has melted more. Record your observations. Compare the results with your original guess. Were you correct?

What did you learn?
1. Which ice cube melted faster? _the one that was not wrapped_
2. What effect does wrapping an ice cube in newspaper have? _The newspaper keeps out the warm air._

Using what you learned
1. If you want to thaw a package of frozen vegetables quickly for dinner, should you remove the wrapping? _yes_
2. Is an ice cooler more effective with the lid on or off? _with its lid on_

Independent Practice   12

| INDEPENDENT PRACTICE Continued | Chapter 1 |

Name _____

_d_ 9. The number of variables that should be tested at one time is
obj 4, 5   **a.** two.   **b.** four.   **c.** three.   **d.** one.

_b_ 10. The third step in the scientific method is to
obj 4, 5   **a.** think about the problem.   **c.** suggest a hypothesis.
           b. decide on an experiment.   **d.** state the problem.

Lesson 3 Recording and Discussing Data   Pages 16 to 23
Complete the sentences using the words below.
chart   record and discuss
compare   supports
hypothesis
11. A good way to record the results of an experiment is to use a _chart_ . obj 4, 7
12. One of the last steps of the scientific method is to _record and discuss_ the results. obj 6
13. The last step of the scientific method is to decide if the experiment _supports_ your hypothesis. obj 7
14. "I think the soap I saw on TV will clean the spoon fastest" is an example of a _hypothesis_ . obj 7

OPTIONS

YOU CAN . . . MAKE A CHART

Process Skills: Communicating/Interpreting data

Objective: Use a chart to **record data** and **interpret** the information.

Setup/Teach:

■ examples of completed charts paper and pencil

■ Show several examples of completed charts to students. Discuss what types of data are being shown, and clarify relationships that can be discovered by using the chart.

■ Show how charts make data more organized and easily read by presenting the same information in both chart form and in written paragraph form.

LANGUAGE CONNECTION

Writing: Write the following assignment on the chalkboard or on an overhead transparency. Have students form **cooperative groups** to decide upon their response.

Imagine that you have a brother or sister one year younger than you who wants to do the same experiment that Tony and Anne did. Write out clear instructions for him or her to follow. Include each step of the scientific method. Be sure to explain why she or he should carefully measure the same amount of soap and have the same amount of water at the same temperature for each batch.

Many times when you think about the results of an experiment, you will think of other experiments to try. That is what happened to Tony when he looked at his results.

At dinner that night, Tony suggested that they try the scientific method to solve the problem of finding the best dish soap for greasy pots and pans. Tony's father said he would buy different kinds of dish soap at the grocery store. They talked about the variables, controls, and possible hypotheses.

18

TEACHER RESOURCE MASTERS

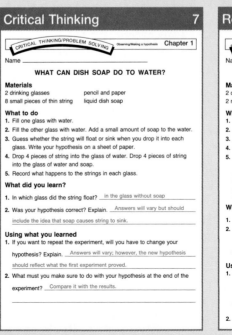

Critical Thinking　7

CRITICAL THINKING/PROBLEM SOLVING　Observing/Making a hypothesis　Chapter 1

Name _____

WHAT CAN DISH SOAP DO TO WATER?

Materials
2 drinking glasses　　　　pencil and paper
8 small pieces of thin string　liquid dish soap

What to do
1. Fill one glass with water.
2. Fill the other glass with water. Add a small amount of soap to the water.
3. Guess whether the string will float or sink when you drop it into each glass. Write your hypothesis on a sheet of paper.
4. Drop 4 pieces of string into the glass of water. Drop 4 pieces of string into the glass of water and soap.
5. Record what happens to the strings in each glass.

What did you learn?
1. In which glass did the string float? __in the glass without soap__
2. Was your hypothesis correct? Explain. __Answers will vary but should__ __include the idea that soap causes string to sink.__

Using what you learned
1. If you want to repeat the experiment, will you have to change your hypothesis? Explain. __Answers will vary; however, the new hypothesis__ __should reflect what the first experiment proved.__
2. What must you make sure to do with your hypothesis at the end of the experiment? __Compare it with the results.__

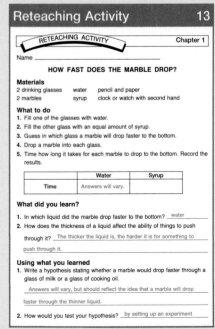

Reteaching Activity　13

RETEACHING ACTIVITY　Chapter 1

Name _____

HOW FAST DOES THE MARBLE DROP?

Materials
2 drinking glasses　water　pencil and paper
2 marbles　　　syrup　clock or watch with second hand

What to do
1. Fill one of the glasses with water.
2. Fill the other glass with an equal amount of syrup.
3. Guess in which glass a marble will drop faster to the bottom.
4. Drop a marble into each glass.
5. Time how long it takes for each marble to drop to the bottom. Record the results.

	Water	Syrup
Time	Answers will vary.	

What did you learn?
1. In which liquid did the marble drop faster to the bottom? __water__
2. How does the thickness of a liquid affect the ability of things to push through it? __The thicker the liquid is, the harder it is for something to__ __push through it.__

Using what you learned
1. Write a hypothesis stating whether a marble would drop faster through a glass of milk or a glass of cooking oil.
__Answers will vary, but should reflect the idea that a marble will drop__ __faster through the thinner liquid.__
2. How would you test your hypothesis? __by setting up an experiment__

The next night after dinner, it was time to experiment. Tony's father had bought two bottles of dish soap, the one Anne had seen on TV and a store-brand bottle. They also decided to test the one they already had at home.

It was hard to decide how to test the soap. They finally decided to rub a teaspoonful of grease on three spoons and stir the spoons in bowls filled with each type of soap and water. Anne's hypothesis was that the soap she saw on TV would clean the spoon fastest. Tony didn't think the kind of soap would make any difference. He thought all the soaps would clean the spoons with the same number of stirs.

Would You **Believe?**
People's tongue prints are as unique as their fingerprints.

19

OPTIONS

■ **Language Arts Skill:** Use "I WANT TO KNOW ABOUT . . . Taking Notes," student page 23, with this lesson.

♦ **Reinforcement:** Discuss how Tony and Anne tested their hypothesis. Ask students to identify the variables they explored.

TEACHER RESOURCE MASTERS

OPTIONS

● **Enrichment:** Ask students to use the scientific method to solve the following: What makes a glass of ice water wet on the outside?

▲ **Challenge:** Have interested students make up a problem to be solved by using the scientific method. After students have made up questions stating their problems, ask them to exchange questions with other interested students. Ask them to design an experiment to solve the problem which they received.

They measured the same amount of soap into each bowl. Then they mixed in the same amount of water. They checked the temperature of the water in each bowl to make sure it was the same. They noticed that the store-brand soap did not seem to make as many suds as the other two. Then they began to stir the greasy spoons. They checked the spoons after each stir. When all the grease was gone from each spoon, they wrote down the number of stirs that it had taken.

20

TEACHER RESOURCE MASTERS

After they collected their results, Tony and Anne made a chart like the one below. They found out that both of their hypotheses were wrong. Mother had been correct! Maybe they had been using the best dish soap all along!

	Number of stirs
Soap 1 – TV	11 stirs
Soap 2 – Storebrand	10 stirs
Soap 3 – Mother's	7 stirs

Lesson Summary

- The results of an experiment must be compared with the hypothesis.
- A chart can help you compare the results of an experiment.

Lesson Review

1. What is the last step of a scientific method?
★2. Why would you want to discuss the results of the experiment with someone?

21

OPTIONS

MATH CONNECTION

Have students try the following math problem.

Anne looked carefully at the chart that she and Tony had made. She decided to make a number sentence from the numbers of stirs they had made for each spoon. What number will make Anne's sentence true? $(11 + 10) + 7 = 11 + (10 + x)$
(The answer is 7.)

LESSON REVIEW ANSWERS

1. to decide whether or not the experiment supports your hypothesis
2. It helps you think about the experiment.

TEACHER RESOURCE MASTERS

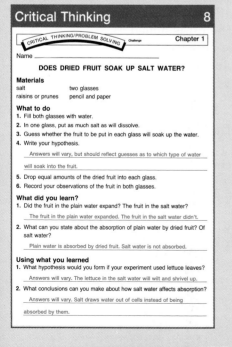

Critical Thinking   **8**

CRITICAL THINKING/PROBLEM SOLVING   Challenge   Chapter 1

Name _____

DOES DRIED FRUIT SOAK UP SALT WATER?

Materials
salt   two glasses
raisins or prunes   pencil and paper

What to do
1. Fill both glasses with water.
2. In one glass, put as much salt as will dissolve.
3. Guess whether the fruit to be put in each glass will soak up the water.
4. Write your hypothesis.

   Answers will vary, but should reflect guesses as to which type of water

   will soak into the fruit.

5. Drop equal amounts of the dried fruit into each glass.
6. Record your observations of the fruit in both glasses.

What did you learn?
1. Did the fruit in the plain water expand? The fruit in the salt water?

   The fruit in the plain water expanded. The fruit in the salt water didn't.

2. What can you state about the absorption of plain water by dried fruit? Of salt water?

   Plain water is absorbed by dried fruit. Salt water is not absorbed.

Using what you learned
1. What hypothesis would you form if your experiment used lettuce leaves?

   Answers will vary. The lettuce in the salt water will wilt and shrivel up.

2. What conclusions can you make about how salt water affects absorption?

   Answers will vary. Salt draws water out of cells instead of being

   absorbed by them.

PREPLAN

Time Allotment: 30 minutes

Process Skill: Hypothesizing/Observing

Objectives

1. **Use** a scientific method to solve an everyday problem.
2. **Make** and **record** observations.
3. **Draw inferences** and **make conclusions** based upon observations.

Setup

■ Use one "cut-rate" brand of dish soap.
■ Do not use glass containers, as they may become slippery.
 Cooperative Grouping: threes—Assign roles as explained on page T24.

1   FOCUS

■ Review the steps in this activity. Be sure students know that the oil stands for oil from greasy pots and pans.

2   TEACH

■ **Safety Considerations:** Use only warm tap water (40°–50°C).
■ While the five spoonfuls of oil may not totally remove all suds, the solutions will feel very greasy.
■ Have students use the Teacher Resource Master **Activity Worksheet,** pages 5 and 6, to record their data.

3   APPLY

■ Discuss how the scientific method could be useful in solving other everyday problems.

Close

■ Discuss the activity and questions.

ACTIVITY

How can you find the best soap?

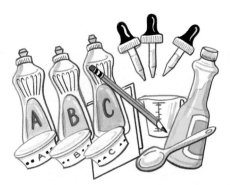

What you need

3 margarine tubs with lids
    (labeled A, B, and C)
3 brands liquid dish soap
    (labeled A, B, and C)
3 droppers
warm water
measuring cup
vegetable oil
small spoon
pencil and paper

What to do

1. Put 1 drop of soap A into tub A. Do the same with the other soaps and tubs.
2. Guess which soap would best clean greasy dishes.
3. Slowly add 125 mL of water to each tub.
4. Put the lids on the tubs and swirl them around.
5. Describe the suds in each tub.
6. Add 1 spoonful of oil to each tub. Repeat steps 4–5.

7. Repeat steps 4–6 until you have added 5 spoonfuls of oil to each tub. Record your observations after each spoonful.

What did you learn?

1. Which soap had the most suds after step 4?
2. What happened to the suds as you added more oil?

Using what you learned

1. Which soap would be best for washing greasy dishes?
2. If all soaps cost the same, which will probably be cheapest to use?

22

ACTIVITY RESPONSES

What did you learn?
1. Answers will vary. There should be observable differences in the amount of suds even before the oil is added.
2. The students should be able to observe less suds as oil is added. Also, the mixture should feel greasy after several spoonfuls of oil have been added. Globs of oil may also be visible.

Using what you learned
1. Answers will vary. The soap that kept the most suds as oil was added will be best.
2. Answers will vary. The soap that had the most suds will probably be the cheapest, because less of it will be needed to wash the same number of greasy dishes.

I WANT TO KNOW ABOUT...

Taking Notes

A detective is a person who searches for information that is not easy to find. A detective must investigate or find out information. He or she must closely study facts already known and ask questions to get all the information that is needed. A detective, while observing or asking questions, writes notes. These notes are important. They are the written record of what the detective has seen or heard.

A detective is like a doctor. A doctor observes or listens to a patient and records information. All information is then on hand when the doctor decides what is wrong with the patient.

As a student, you should work in the same way as a detective or doctor. You should observe, study, ask questions, and take notes. When you get ready to review, the notes can help you remember what you have already read or observed

Introduce students to careers, technology, or helpful language arts skills with I Want to Know About...

Language Arts

23

TEACHER RESOURCE MASTERS

Feature Background

■ Taking notes or recording data does not require writing down every word that is said or written. Key words or important ideas are enough.

■ Observing means that a person sees or senses especially through careful attention. Observing is not just looking with the eyes.

Feature Vocabulary

observe   record
investigate

Teaching Suggestions

■ Have students, for one minute, sit and observe in the classroom. After one minute, have students make notes about what they observed. When they are finished writing, start to talk about something completely different for a minute or two. Then go back and ask students what they observed without looking at their notes. Then ask them to look at their notes to see what they had forgotten.

■ Display a picture. Have students study the picture and take notes on what they see. Take the picture away and let students discuss their findings. Have one student record on the chalkboard the different data from the students.

■ Take students on a walk around or outside the school. Have students observe the different kinds of actions (a door being opened, a person mowing, a child playing). Bring students back into the classroom and have them record their data either on the chalkboard or on paper.

Summary

Chapter Closure: Have students work in **cooperative groups** to make up a commercial or a poster showing how problems are better solved using the scientific method than in other ways.

Science Words

Scramble the science words and have students unscramble and define each. (The scrambled words are as follows: breplom, syphotishe, rivabasel, cisciefint hetsmod, norloct.)

Student Responses

1. hypothesis
2. problem
3. variables
4. control
5. scientific methods

Recap chapter highlights with these summary statements and literal and critical thinking questions.

CHAPTER REVIEW

1

Summary

Lesson 1
- Scientific methods are used every day to solve problems.
- The first step in the scientific method is to state a problem.

Lesson 2
- An experiment is used to test a hypothesis.

- A variable is something in an experiment that changes.

Lesson 3
- The results of an experiment are compared to the hypothesis.
- A chart helps to compare the results of an experiment.

Science Words

Fill in the blank with the correct word or words from the list.

scientific methods

problem   **variables**

hypothesis   **control**

1. A guess that can be tested by an experiment is a(n) ___ .
2. The first step in a scientific method is to state a(n) ___ .
3. Things in an experiment that change are called ___ .
4. The pail that Tony didn't stir was the ___ .

5. Lists of steps scientists use to solve problems are ___ .

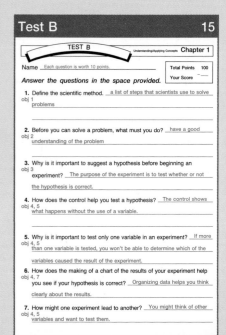

24

TEACHER RESOURCE MASTERS

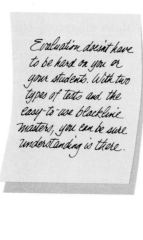

Evaluation doesn't have to be hard on you or your students. With two types of tests and the easy-to-use blackline masters, you can be sure understanding is there.

Test A   14

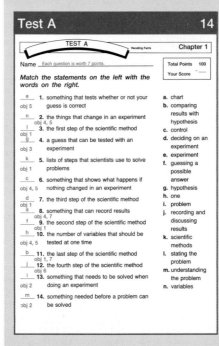

TEST A   Recalling Facts   **Chapter 1**

Name ___ Each question is worth 7 points.

Total Points 100
Your Score ___

Match the statements on the left with the words on the right.

e   1. something that tests whether or not your guess is correct
obj 5

n   2. the things that change in an experiment
obj 4, 5

l   3. the first step of the scientific method
obj 1

g   4. a guess that can be tested with an experiment
obj 3

k   5. lists of steps that scientists use to solve problems
obj 1

c   6. something that shows what happens if nothing changed in an experiment
obj 4, 5

d   7. the third step of the scientific method
obj 1

a   8. something that can record results
obj 4, 7

f   9. the second step of the scientific method
obj 1

h   10. the number of variables that should be tested at one time
obj 4, 5

b   11. the last step of the scientific method
obj 1, 7

j   12. the fourth step of the scientific method
obj 6

i   13. something that needs to be solved when doing an experiment
obj 2

m   14. something needed before a problem can be solved
obj 2

a. chart
b. comparing results with hypothesis
c. control
d. deciding on an experiment
e. experiment
f. guessing a possible answer
g. hypothesis
h. one
i. problem
j. recording and discussing results
k. scientific methods
l. stating the problem
m. understanding the problem
n. variables

Test B   15

TEST B   Understanding/Applying Concepts   **Chapter 1**

Name ___ Each question is worth 10 points.

Total Points 100
Your Score ___

Answer the questions in the space provided.

1. Define the scientific method. _a list of steps that scientists use to solve_
obj 1
problems

2. Before you can solve a problem, what must you do? _have a good_
obj 2
understanding of the problem

3. Why is it important to suggest a hypothesis before beginning an
obj 3
experiment? _The purpose of the experiment is to test whether or not_
the hypothesis is correct.

4. How does the control help you test a hypothesis? _The control shows_
obj 4, 5
what happens without the use of a variable.

5. Why is it important to test only one variable in an experiment? _If more_
obj 4, 5
than one variable is tested, you won't be able to determine which of the
variables caused the result of the experiment.

6. How does the making of a chart of the results of your experiment help
obj 4, 7
you see if your hypothesis is correct? _Organizing data helps you think_
clearly about the results.

7. How might one experiment lead to another? _You might think of other_
obj 4, 5
variables and want to test them.

Questions

Recalling Ideas
Correctly complete each of the following sentences.

1. The second step in a scientific method is to state a(n)
   - (a) problem.
   - (b) hypothe-sis.
   - (c) control.
   - (d) experiment.

2. After you state a problem and suggest a hypothesis, you then decide on a(n)
   - (a) observa-tion.
   - (b) control.
   - (c) experiment.
   - (d) variable.

3. How many variables should be tested at one time?
   - (a) one
   - (b) four
   - (c) three
   - (d) two

4. In the experiment with the two pails of water, the pail that was stirred was the
   - (a) control.
   - (b) variable.
   - (c) experiment.
   - (d) hypothesis.

Understanding Ideas
Answer the following questions using complete sentences.

1. Why should you state the problem before doing an experiment?

2. Why is it important to test only one variable at a time?

3. What might you do if your result doesn't support your hypothesis?

4. Why should you make a record of your results?

Thinking Critically
Think about what you have learned in this chapter. Answer the following questions using complete sentences.

1. Imagine that you are testing the effect of water on growing radish seeds. You plant 5 seeds in each of 10 different plots. The first plot gets only rain. Each remaining plot gets a little more water than the one before. After 5 days, count how many seeds have sprouted in each plot. What were the variables? What was the control?

2. Name an everyday problem you could study using scientific methods. Think of a hypothesis and a way to test it.

25

Questions

Recalling Ideas
1. b
2. c
3. a
4. b

Understanding Ideas
1. You should state the problem to be sure that you have a good understanding of what the problem is.
2. You test only one variable at a time so that the variable can be truly tested. If two variables were tested at the same time, you wouldn't know which one caused the change you observed.
3. Make another guess, and design a new experiment to test your new guess.
4. You should record your results to organize them and to help you think about them.

Thinking Critically
1. The variables were the amounts of water given to the plots. The control is the first plot, which received only rain.
2. Students should suggest an hypothesis that can be tested by the experiment they describe. In their experiment, only one variable at a time should be tested.

TEACHER RESOURCE MASTERS

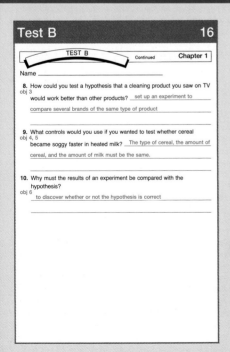

Test B   **16**

TEST B   Continued   Chapter 1

Name _____

8. How could you test a hypothesis that a cleaning product you saw on TV
obj 3
would work better than other products? __set up an experiment to__
__compare several brands of the same type of product__

9. What controls would you use if you wanted to test whether cereal
obj 4, 5
became soggy faster in heated milk? __The type of cereal, the amount of__
__cereal, and the amount of milk must be the same.__

10. Why must the results of an experiment be compared with the
hypothesis?
obj 6
__to discover whether or not the hypothesis is correct__

Matter

Planning Guide

Lessons	Objectives	Vocabulary
Chapter Introduction pp. 26, 27		
Lesson 1 Properties of Objects pp. 28–33	1. **Define** *property*. 2. **Define** *mass* and **recognize** that all objects have mass and take up space. 3. **Indicate** that the units of measuring mass are the gram and the kilogram.	property mass gram kilogram
Lesson 2 What is Matter? pp. 34–37	4. **Define** *matter* and **state** that matter is made of atoms. 5. **Define** *element*.	matter atom element
Lesson 3 States of Matter pp. 38–45	6. **List** and **compare** properties of matter in the solid, liquid, and gaseous states. 7. **Compare** the freedom of movement of particles within the three states.	solid liquid gas
Chapter Review pp. 46, 47		

Planning Guide

Text Activities		Teacher Resource Masters	Other Components
Title/Skill	**Materials per Group**		
Have You Ever . . . Experimented With the Space in a Cup? p. 27 Observing/Predicting Time Allotment: 30 minutes	plastic cup water marbles paper towels		**Activity Center:** "Who's Afraid of the Big Bad Wolf?"; "Ice Is Nice"; "Block Busters"; "Treasure Hunt"; "Playing with Play Dough"; "Water on Ice"
You Can . . . Sort the Shoes, p. 29 Classifying Time Allotment: 30 minutes	various types of shoes	Independent Practice, pp. 27, 28 Activity Worksheet, pp. 19, 20 Language Arts Connection, p. 25 ◆ Family Science, p. 18 Critical Thinking, p. 23 Math Connection, p. 26	Poster #1 Poster #2
How Do You Measure Mass? p. 23 Measuring/Predicting Time Allotment: 30 minutes	10 nickels 20 paper clips balance 4 small objects pencil and paper		
You Can . . . Find the Smallest Part, p. 36 Inferring Time Allotment 20 minutes	plastic knives, forks cooked carrots paper plates	Independent Practice, pp. 27, 28 ◆ Reteaching Activity, p. 29 ▲ Critical Thinking, p. 24	Mr. Wizard's World of Science Video Tape 16
Is It a Solid or a Liquid? p. 44 Classifying Time Allotment: 30 minutes	newspaper paper cup cornstarch paper towels pencil and paper water	Independent Practice, pp. 27, 28 Activity Worksheet, pp. 21, 22 Transparency Master p. 17	Color Tranparency #1 Mr. Wizard's World of Science Video Tape 17
		Test A, p. 30 Test B, pp. 31, 32	

◆ Basic / ▲ Advanced / All other masters are for use by all students.

For Exceptional Students

ESL/LEP

Chapter 2/Lesson 1, Page 29
Reading: Vocabulary Building

Build students' understanding of *property* by having the class brainstorm semantic maps for *size, shape, color,* and *texture.* Display the completed maps and write the words from the maps on index cards. Place the cards in a container. Then have students select a card, read the word aloud, identify its match on a semantic map, and find a common classroom object with that property.

Chapter 2/Lesson 1, Page 31
Language Arts: Sentence Structure

Focus students on the concept of measurement by showing them an object with a mass of about 1 gram, such as 2 paper clips, and an object with a mass of about 1 kilogram, such as a bag of fresh fruit. Have students hold both objects to compare. Then provide objects such as a pencil, a ruler, a scissors, a textbook, a potted plant, and a wastepaper basket. Hold up the pencil and model these sentence patterns: This is a *pencil.* I use *grams* to describe its mass. Have students select an object. Encourage them to compare the mass of their object to the mass of the paper clips and bag of fruit. Then have students repeat your model sentences replacing the key words with the name of *their* object and the unit of measure they would use to describe its mass.

Chapter 2/Lesson 3, Pages 39–42
Language Arts: Oral Speaking

Provide an example of a solid (book), a liquid (water), and a gas (air in a balloon). Give students an opportunity to handle the samples as you use the definitions from the text to describe them. For example, you might state that a book is a solid because it has a certain size and shape. Then ask students to find other examples of solid, liquid, and gas. Have students show their objects to the class and restate the definitions from the text to explain why their object is a solid, liquid, or gas.

Gifted

Chapter 2/Lesson 2, Page 37

Obtain a copy of the periodic table of the elements. Help students learn the names and symbols for some common elements. Distinguish between natural and synthetic elements. Ask students to pretend they are scientists who have discovered or made a new element. Have students answer the following questions: **What properties does your element have? How will you name your element? How will your element be useful?**

Mainstreamed

Chapter 2/Lesson 1, Page 31

Developmentally Handicapped: Place several objects, such as pen refills, chalk, blocks, buttons, and so on, in a sealed box. Cut out an opening. Direct students to reach into the box, touch one of the objects, and describe their observations about size, texture, shape, and function. Tape record their statements for later transcription and reading. Ask students to predict the mass of each object and how each object might be used for other purposes.

Compare predictions of mass with standard units such as grams.

Whole Class Science Project

Students can become familiar with the magnitude of common mass units by making a display of objects as reference masses. Have students find or bring from home two or three objects of various masses. Obtain a triple beam balance and show students how to determine the mass of their objects. Try to find objects that have masses very near 1, 5, 10, 20, 50, 100, 200, 500 grams and 1 kilogram. Have students make a creative display of these objects with labels indicating their masses. Then have each student present a "challenge" object whose mass other members of the class may estimate using the display as a guide.

Science Fair Projects

Individual students could do one of the following projects:

1. Devise a demonstration or experiment to show that no two objects can occupy the same space at the same time. One way of doing this is by water displacement. Sink objects in a container of water. Show that the water rises by an amount equal to the size of the object.

2. Solids and liquids are called the noncompressible states of matter because they cannot be pressed into a smaller space by ordinary amounts of force. Gases, though, are compressible because their particles are spread apart from each other. Devise ways of demonstrating the compressibility of gases and the noncompressibility of liquids and solids. A model hydraulic system consisting of two syringe bodies filled with water and connected by a length of plastic tubing will demonstrate the noncompressibility of liquids. Be sure there are no air bubbles in the syringes and tubes. Pressing the plunger of one syringe will cause the plunger of the other to move out.

Chapter Concepts

■ Matter is described by its properties. Mass and space are two properties common to all matter.

■ Matter is made of atoms and is found all around you.

■ The pattern and space between particles determine a matter's state—solid, liquid, or gas.

Chapter Background

■ Matter is identified by the properties of mass and volume. Every object that exists is matter.

■ Matter is made of atoms. Elements contain one kind of atom. Compounds contain two or more kinds of atoms.

■ Matter may be solid, liquid, or gaseous. Many substances can exist in all three states. Plasma, the fourth state of matter, is not discussed.

Look for These Symbols

- —Hands-on activity
- —Cooperative learning
- —Overhead transparency
- ♦ —Basic/Reinforcement
- ● —Average/Enrichment
- ▲ —Advanced/Challenge
- —Calculator Practice

SCIENCE
In Your World

26

CHAPTER 2

Matter

Everything around us takes up space. These children are trying to fit something into a space that is already filled. Papers and leaves use the space in the garbage can, so the bag will not fit.

Have You Ever...

Experimented With the Space in a Cup?

Fill the cup with water. Put it on a paper towel. What do you think will happen when you try to put something else into the space that is filled with water? Try it and see. Put a marble in the cup. What happens? What do you think will happen if you put another marble in the cup? Why do you think it will happen?

27

PREPLAN

Time Allotment: 30 minutes

Objectives
1. **Observe** that matter takes up space.
2. **Predict** what will happen when two "pieces" of matter try to occupy the same space.

Setup
If you wish to conduct this activity, you will need the following materials for each student or activity group:

plastic cup   water
marbles   paper towels

1   FOCUS

■ Ask a student to describe what is happening in the picture. Encourage students to talk about what they do when their trash cans are full.

2   TEACH

■ Have title and introductory paragraph read aloud.

Have You Ever . . .

▦ Use this activity as an introduction to characteristics of matter.

■ Have students place a paper towel under the cup, and caution them to hold marbles close to the top of the cup to avoid splashing.

■ **Student Responses**
1. Water spilled out of the cup.
2. The marble takes up the space that the water was in, so the water has to go somewhere else.

3   APPLY

■ Ask: **How we might solve the problem of what to do with our trash?**

Close
■ Tell students they will learn more about matter as they read Chapter 2.

pages 28–33

PREPLAN

Lesson Objectives

1. **Define** *property*.
2. **Define** *mass* and **recognize** that all objects have mass and take up space.
3. **Indicate** that the units of measuring mass are the gram and the kilogram.

Science Background

■ Weight is the measure of the force of gravity between two objects. Weight is calculated in newtons. If a person weighs 500 newtons (about 115 lb) on Earth, that same person will weigh about 80 newtons on the moon. The weight of an object changes with the force of gravity.

■ Mass is the amount (or quantity) of matter in an object. The mass of an object remains constant. It is not affected by gravity. Mass is measured in grams.

Lesson Vocabulary

property   mass
gram   kilogram

Note: The activity on student page 33 may be used for guided discovery before you begin this lesson.

1   FOCUS

■ Display several balls. Have students describe their properties. Based on those properties, have them predict which ball will bounce the highest. Have students suggest methods to test their predictions.

■ Use the goals on student page 28 to establish the purpose for studying this lesson.

> **LESSON 1 GOALS**
> You will learn
> ● that properties describe objects.
> ● the two properties that are common to all objects.
> ● two of the units used to measure mass.

1. Answers will vary. Students should describe properties that make a soccer ball unique.

Properties of Objects

Have you ever played soccer? A soccer ball is different from a basketball or a volleyball. Suppose you are sent to get a soccer ball. In the gym storage room, you will find many kinds of balls. Some are big and some are little. Some are made of plastic, some of leather, and some seem to be covered with soft fuzz. Some are white, some are brown, and some have more than one color. Some are soft and some are hard. Some are not even round! [1]How will you choose the right ball?

Objects have properties.

28

TEACHER RESOURCE MASTERS

We describe objects in many ways. Size and shape are used to describe objects. Color and smoothness or roughness can also be used to describe objects. Size, shape, color, smoothness, and roughness are some properties of objects. A **property** (PRAHP urt ee) is a characteristic of an object. What are some properties of the soccer ball you have been sent to get? How can you use properties to find the right kind of ball?

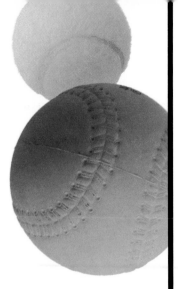

You Can...

Sort the Shoes

Work with a team of five other students. Each team member puts one shoe in a pile. Have a team member use one property to put the shoes into two groups. Take turns guessing that property. The first person to guess correctly then groups the shoes based on another property. Keep going until each team member has had a turn. What properties did members of your team use to group the shoes?

29

2   TEACH

■ Introduce the term *property*. Use the photographs and text to reinforce this definition. Discuss the game of kickball. Decide what properties a kickball has.

Have students **work cooperatively** to list items that have mass and take up space. This will lead into the definition of *matter*. Suggest things that don't have mass or take up space, such as thoughts, ideas, or feelings.

Guided Practice

■ Check students' understanding of lesson concepts by discussing the Lesson Review questions on student page 32. If necessary, use the **reteaching strategy** in OPTIONS.

Independent Practice

■ Assign the Lesson 1 section of the Teacher Resource Master **Independent Practice,** page 27.

3   APPLY

■ Discuss how objects vary in mass. Distribute some pieces of fruit: raisins, grapes, apricots, apples, oranges, bananas. Have students try to arrange them in order, from least mass to greatest.

Close

■ Use Summary statements on student page 32 to review lesson concepts.

OPTIONS

Reteaching Strategy

Distribute uncooked pasta to students. Have them list the properties of the pasta (color, hardness, sturdiness, shape). Have students soak the pasta in warm water for several minutes, then list any changes in its properties.

Resource Options

■ Use Poster #2, "Properties of Paint."
■ Refer to page 30 for teaching strategies for **You Can . . . Sort the Shoes.**

TEACHER RESOURCE MASTERS

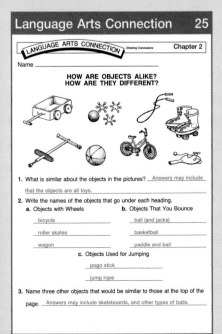

Language Arts Connection   25

LANGUAGE ARTS CONNECTION   Drawing Conclusions   Chapter 2

Name _____

HOW ARE OBJECTS ALIKE? HOW ARE THEY DIFFERENT?

1. What is similar about the objects in the pictures? _Answers may include_
   that the objects are all toys.
2. Write the names of the objects that go under each heading.
   a. Objects with Wheels   b. Objects That You Bounce
      bicycle   ball (and jacks)
      roller skates   basketball
      wagon   paddle and ball
   c. Objects Used for Jumping
      pogo stick
      jump rope
3. Name three other objects that would be similar to those at the top of the
   page. _Answers may include skateboards, and other types of balls._

Independent Practice   27

INDEPENDENT PRACTICE   Chapter 2

Name _Each question is worth 6 points._   Total Points 100   Your Score

**Lesson 1   Properties of Objects
             Pages 28 to 33**
Complete the sentences using the words below.
gram   mass   property
kilogram   space

1. A characteristic of an object is called a __property__. obj 1
2. How much there is of an object is its __mass__. obj 2
3. All objects have mass and take up __space__. obj 2
4. Two paper clips have a mass of about one __gram__. obj 3
5. A large mass would be measured with a unit of measure called a
   __kilogram__. obj 3

Lesson 2   What Is Matter?   Pages 34 to 37
Write the letter of the correct answer in the blank.
_b_ 6. Everything that takes up space and has mass is
obj 3   a. property.   b. matter.   c. liquid.   d. solid.
_a_ 7. All matter is made of tiny particles called
obj 3   a. atoms.   b. properties.   c. mass.   d. elements.
_d_ 8. Any matter made of only one kind of atom is an
obj 4   a. embryo.   b. animal.   c. organism.   d. element.
_a_ 9. The properties of elements are different because they are
obj 4   a. made of different kinds of atoms.
        b. made of different kinds of threads.
        c. too small to be seen.
        d. made of different amounts of gold.

OPTIONS

YOU CAN . . . SORT THE SHOES

Process Skill: Classifying

Objective: Classify objects based on their properties.

Setup/Teach

✋ Demonstrate some methods of classification with the entire class before having individual groups engage in the activity.

👥 Other objects may also be sorted (or substituted for shoes initially) in a similar manner. The best objects for this type of activity are those that have similar as well as dissimilar properties.

■ Student Responses

Color, size, shape, decorations, and so on.

LANGUAGE CONNECTION

👥 **Writing:** Have students work in **cooperative groups** to cut out pictures of solids and liquids from old magazines. Then have them write the properties of a liquid that make it like a solid and those that make it different.

Resource Options

■ Use Poster #1, "What in the World?"

You have to find a leather ball with black and white patches on it. Be sure to choose one that's hard so you know it's full of air. You use the properties of all the balls in the storage room to choose exactly the right one.

Now look at the pictures of balls. The balls are all different. All of them, however, are alike in two ways. First, all of them take up space. No two balls can be in the same place at the same time.

Second, all of the balls have mass. **Mass** is how much there is of an object. A bowling ball, for example, has more mass than a softball. The softball has more mass than a table tennis ball.

What is mass?

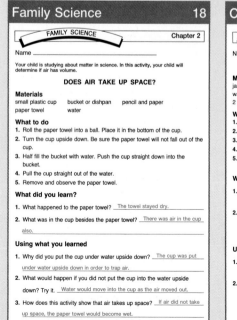
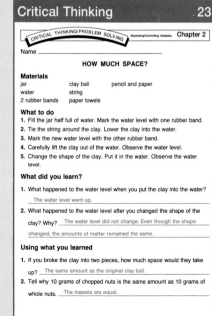

Objects have mass and take up space.

30

TEACHER RESOURCE MASTERS

Family Science   18

FAMILY SCIENCE   Chapter 2

Name _____

Your child is studying about matter in science. In this activity, your child will determine if air has volume.

DOES AIR TAKE UP SPACE?

Materials

small plastic cup   bucket or dishpan   pencil and paper
paper towel   water

What to do

1. Roll the paper towel into a ball. Place it in the bottom of the cup.
2. Turn the cup upside down. Be sure the paper towel will not fall out of the cup.
3. Half fill the bucket with water. Push the cup straight down into the bucket.
4. Pull the cup straight out of the water.
5. Remove and observe the paper towel.

What did you learn?

1. What happened to the paper towel? __The towel stayed dry.__
2. What was in the cup besides the paper towel? __There was air in the cup also.__

Using what you learned

1. Why did you put the cup under water upside down? __The cup was put under water upside down in order to trap air.__
2. What would happen if you did not put the cup into the water upside down? Try it. __Water would move into the cup as the air moved out.__
3. How does this activity show that air takes up space? __If air did not take up space, the paper towel would become wet.__

Critical Thinking   23

CRITICAL THINKING/PROBLEM SOLVING   Separating/Controlling Variables   Chapter 2

Name _____

HOW MUCH SPACE?

Materials

jar   clay ball   pencil and paper
water   string
2 rubber bands   paper towels

What to do

1. Fill the jar half full of water. Mark the water level with one rubber band.
2. Tie the string around the clay. Lower the clay into the water.
3. Mark the new water level with the other rubber band.
4. Carefully lift the clay out of the water. Observe the water level.
5. Change the shape of the clay. Put it in the water. Observe the water level.

What did you learn?

1. What happened to the water level when you put the clay into the water? __The water level went up.__
2. What happened to the water level after you changed the shape of the clay? Why? __The water level did not change. Even though the shape changed, the amounts of matter remained the same.__

Using what you learned

1. If you broke the clay into two pieces, how much space would they take up? __The same amount as the original clay ball.__
2. Tell why 10 grams of chopped nuts is the same amount as 10 grams of whole nuts. __The masses are equal.__

Small masses are measured in grams.

You can measure the mass of objects. One unit we use to measure mass is the gram. One **gram** is a very small amount of mass. Two paper clips have a mass of about one gram. A nickel has a mass of about five grams.

Sometimes you may want to measure a large mass. Large amounts of mass can be measured in kilograms (KEE luh grams). A **kilogram** is 1,000 grams. The mass of a large dump truck is about 10,000 kilograms. The mass of a baby is 4 kilograms. [1]What do you think your mass is?

SCIENCE AND . . .
Math

The mass of which of the following mid-size cars has a 4 in the hundreds place and a 7 in the ones place?
A. 1,534 kilograms
B. 1,724 kilograms
C. 1,437 kilograms
D. 1,374 kilograms

1. 8–9 year olds have masses of about 23–28 kilograms.

31

OPTIONS

SCIENCE AND . . . MATH
■ **Skill:** Use whole number place value.
■ **Student Response:** C

MATH CONNECTION
■ Refer students to "Science and . . . Math." Have them round each of the masses, included as four multiple choices, first to the nearest ten; then, to the nearest hundred. (1530, 1720, 1440, and 1370; 1500, 1700, 1400, and 1400)

◆ **Reinforcement:** A liter of water has a mass of 1 kilogram. Since a liter is very close in volume to a quart, you may wish to fill some quart milk cartons with water to give students a better understanding of the mass of a kilogram.

● **Enrichment:** Make a collection of items for students to compare. Include items with color, size, shape, and texture differences. Let the students classify and group these objects.

▲ **Challenge:** A gram can be subdivided into smaller units. One thousand milligrams (mg) make one gram. The milligram is commonly used to measure food additives and nutrients. Have students look at labels on food at home and report what they find that has been measured in milligrams.

TEACHER RESOURCE MASTERS

Math Connection   26

MATH CONNECTION   Measurement   Chapter 2

Name _Answers given are representative values only._

MAKE A MASS LINE

Below are two number lines that can be used for ordering the masses of objects. One line is used for grams and the other is used for kilograms. Find the mass of each object listed below the number lines. Write the name of each object on the mass line in the correct place. One example has been done for you. Answer the questions.

1. Use a balance to find the mass of each object.

	paper clips	nickel			pencil
grams	0 1 2 3 4 5 6 7 8 9 10
graham cracker	key	dime

nickel-5 g   key-_3_ g   graham cracker-_2_ g

6 paper clips-_3_ g   pencil-_10_ g   dime-_4_ g

a. Which object has the most mass? ____pencil____

b. Which object has the least mass? ___graham cracker___

c. Which two objects are closest in mass? _paper clips and key_

2. Use a metric bathroom scale to find the mass of each object.

	rock	apples	chair			boy
kilograms	0 2 4 6 8 10 12 14 16 18 20
wooden train	dog

boy-_20_ kg   wooden train-_3_ kg   rock-_2_ kg

small box of apples-_4_ kg   chair-_6_ kg   dog-_6_ kg

a. Which object has the most mass? ____boy____

b. Which object has the least mass? ____rock____

c. Which two objects are closest in mass? ___chair and dog___

OPTIONS

[icons] Gather objects of known mass for the students to estimate **working cooperatively.** If a balance is available, use standard masses or nickels (very close to 5 grams in mass) to compare various masses.

LESSON REVIEW ANSWERS

1. All objects take up space and have mass.

2. about five grams

3. No. It would take too many paper clips.

When choosing between two items, you can use the properties of objects to help you make decisions.

Lesson Summary

- A property is a characteristic of an object.
- All objects take up space and have mass.
- Two units used to measure mass are the gram and the kilogram.

Lesson Review

1. What are two properties of all objects?
2. What is the mass of one nickel?
★3. Would you use paper clips to measure the mass of a person? Why or why not?

32

TEACHER RESOURCE MASTERS

How do you measure mass?

What you need
10 nickels
20 paper clips
balance
4 small objects
pencil and paper

What to do
1. Predict the mass of each object in nickels and in paper clips.
2. Write your predictions on a chart. Start with the object you predict has the most mass.
3. Put 1 object on the left side of the balance. Place nickels and paper clips on the right side until both pans are balanced.
4. Record the number of nickels and paper clips used.
5. Repeat steps 3 and 4 for the other objects.

What did you learn?
1. How many of your predictions were correct?
2. Which object has the most mass?

Using what you learned
1. How can you find the mass for each object in grams? Try it.
2. When would it be hard to find the mass of objects using nickels and paper clips?

33

ACTIVITY RESPONSES

What did you learn?
1. Answers will vary.
2. Answers will vary. Students should discover that the size of an object does not necessarily have a direct relationship to its mass.

Using what you learned
1. A nickel has a mass of about 5 grams, and two paper clips have a mass of about 1 gram. Students can use these equivalents to estimate the mass of an object in grams.
2. Very small or very large objects would be difficult to measure. In addition, nickels and paper clips are not standard masses and, therefore, may vary.

PREPLAN

Time Allotment: 30 minutes
Process Skills: Measuring/Predicting

Objectives
1. **Predict** the masses of various objects.
2. **Classify** objects from least to most massive.
3. **Measure** the mass of various objects.
4. **Record** data using a table.

Setup
■ Calibrate the mass of your paper clips. Standard office paper clips should have a mass of about 1/2 gram each.
■ If pan balances aren't available, substitute a ruler suspended from a string. Hang paper cups from each end.
▓ **Cooperative Grouping:** fives—Assign roles as explained on page T24.

1 FOCUS

■ Have students predict the masses of some known objects.

2 TEACH

■ Students may need help computing the mass of each object in grams.
■ Help students understand that an object's size is not directly related to the number of objects used to balance it.
■ Have students use the Teacher Resource Master **Activity Worksheet,** pages 19 and 20, to record their data and answers.

3 APPLY

■ Emphasize that the mass of an object does not necessarily relate directly to the space it occupies. A sack of feathers has less mass than a bucket of water.

Close
■ Discuss the activity and questions with the class.

PREPLAN

Lesson Objectives

4. Define *matter* and **state** that matter is made of atoms.

5. Define *element*.

Science Background

▪ All matter is made of elements. There are 109 different elements.

▪ The smallest part of an element that has all the properties of that element is an atom. Thus, the smallest piece of gold is an atom of gold. The atom of gold cannot be broken down into smaller pieces without losing the properties of gold.

Lesson Vocabulary

matter   atom   element

1 FOCUS

Have students **work cooperatively** to make two lists. On one, have students record five examples of matter; on the second, have students record two examples that are not matter. Combine the lists into two large class lists. Discuss whether each entry is on the correct list.

▪ Use the goals on student page 34 to establish the purpose for studying this lesson.

LESSON 2 GOALS
You will learn
● that matter is found everywhere around you.
● that all matter is made of atoms.
● that some matter is made of one kind of atom.

What Is Matter?

Take just one minute to list as many things around you as possible. How many things did you list?

All of the things you listed are the same in one way. They all are matter.

Everything that takes up space and has mass is called **matter.** Rocks, clocks, bees, and trees are matter. Everything around you is made of matter. You are made of matter, too.

Matter can be a solid, a liquid, or a gas. The pictures on this page show matter that is solid, liquid, and gas.

34

TEACHER RESOURCE MASTERS

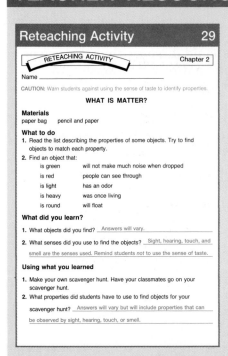

Reteaching Activity   29

RETEACHING ACTIVITY   Chapter 2

Name _____

CAUTION: Warn students against using the sense of taste to identify properties.

WHAT IS MATTER?

Materials
paper bag   pencil and paper

What to do
1. Read the list describing the properties of some objects. Try to find objects to match each property.
2. Find an object that:

is green	will not make much noise when dropped
is red	people can see through
is light	has an odor
is heavy	was once living
is round	will float

What did you learn?

1. What objects did you find? ___Answers will vary.___

2. What senses did you use to find the objects? ___Sight, hearing, touch, and smell are the senses used. Remind students *not* to use the sense of taste.___

Using what you learned

1. Make your own scavenger hunt. Have your classmates go on your scavenger hunt.
2. What properties did students have to use to find objects for your scavenger hunt? ___Answers will vary but will include properties that can be observed by sight, hearing, touch, or smell.___

Matter is made of smaller parts.

From far away, the blanket in the picture looks as if it is all one piece. As you get closer, however, you see that the blanket is made of many small threads woven together. [1]How might you get a good view of each separate thread?

Each thread in the blanket is made of even smaller parts. The small parts are called atoms. An **atom** is the smallest part of any kind of matter. Remember that all matter is the same in some ways. All matter has mass and takes up space. This is also true of atoms. Atoms have mass and take up space.

1. Look at the blanket with a hand lens.

What is an atom?

35

2 TEACH

■ Introduce the term *atoms* to the students. Point to various types of matter, and ask the students to tell what makes up each type. The students should realize that atoms are common to all matter.
■ Different types of matter have different properties. Explain to students that these differences arise because of the different atoms that make up the matter and the different ways these atoms are joined together.

Guided Practice

■ Check students' understanding of lesson concepts by discussing the Lesson Review questions on student page 37. If necessary, use the **reteaching strategy** in OPTIONS.

Independent Practice

■ Assign the Lesson 2 section of the Teacher Resource Master **Independent Practice,** page 27.

3 APPLY

■ Ask: *What form of matter fills balloons?* (gas) To demonstrate that gas has mass and takes up space, distribute uninflated balloons. Have students blow them up as an example of gas as matter.

Close

■ Use Summary statements on student page 37 to review lesson concepts.

OPTIONS

Reteaching Strategy

Distribute small objects, clear plastic wrap, and containers in assorted shapes and sizes. Have students use the objects for atoms, wrap groups of atoms for elements, and arrange the elements in containers as different kinds of matter.

TEACHER RESOURCE MASTERS

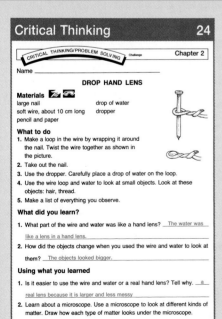

Critical Thinking   24

CRITICAL THINKING/PROBLEM SOLVING   Challenge   Chapter 2

Name _____

DROP HAND LENS

Materials
large nail   drop of water
soft wire, about 10 cm long   dropper
pencil and paper

What to do
1. Make a loop in the wire by wrapping it around the nail. Twist the wire together as shown in the picture.
2. Take out the nail.
3. Use the dropper. Carefully place a drop of water on the loop.
4. Use the wire loop and water to look at small objects. Look at these objects: hair, thread.
5. Make a list of everything you observe.

What did you learn?

1. What part of the wire and water was like a hand lens? The water was
   like a lens in a hand lens.
2. How did the objects change when you used the wire and water to look at them? The objects looked bigger.

Using what you learned

1. Is it easier to use the wire and water or a real hand lens? Tell why. a
   real lens because it is larger and less messy
2. Learn about a microscope. Use a microscope to look at different kinds of matter. Draw how each type of matter looks under the microscope.

Independent Practice   27

INDEPENDENT PRACTICE   Chapter 2

Name Each question is worth 6 points.   Total Points 100
                                          Your Score ___

**Lesson 1 Properties of Objects
       Pages 28 to 33**
Complete the sentences using the words below.
gram   mass   property
kilogram   space

1. A characteristic of an object is called a __property__. obj 1
2. How much there is of an object is its __mass__. obj 2
3. All objects have mass and take up __space__. obj 2
4. Two paper clips have a mass of about one __gram__. obj 3
5. A large mass would be measured with a unit of measure called a __kilogram__. obj 3

Lesson 2 What Is Matter?   Pages 34 to 37
Write the letter of the correct answer in the blank.
__b__ 6. Everything that takes up space and has mass is
obj 3   a. property. b. matter. c. liquid. d. solid.
__a__ 7. All matter is made of tiny particles called
obj 3   a. atoms. b. properties. c. mass. d. elements.
__d__ 8. Any matter made of only one kind of atom is an
obj 4   a. embryo. b. animal. c. organism. d. element.
__a__ 9. The properties of elements are different because they are
obj 4   a. made of different kinds of atoms.
         b. made of different kinds of threads.
         c. too small to be seen.
         d. made of different amounts of gold.

OPTIONS

YOU CAN . . . FIND THE SMALLEST PART

Process Skill: Inferring

Objective: Infer that changing the physical appearance of the carrot does not change the nature of the particles in the carrot.

Setup/Teach

Safety Consideration: Make sure that the students use plastic knives for cutting the cooked carrots. Do not allow students to try to cut fresh, uncooked carrots.

■ **Student Response**

Accept all reasonable responses. Emphasize that no matter how small students cut or mash the carrot, they still have part of a carrot.

Resource Options

■ Show selections from "Change of State," *Mr. Wizard's World of Science Video Library*, Merrill Publishing Company.

ACTIVITY

You Can...

Find the Smallest Part

When is a carrot no longer a carrot? See if you can keep cutting a cooked carrot into smaller and smaller pieces. When you think the carrot can't be cut anymore, use a fork to mash what is left. Stop when you think the carrot is no longer a carrot. What is your reason for thinking the carrot has changed?

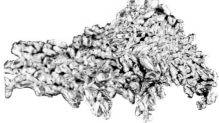

Matter made of only one kind of atom is called an **element.** You probably already know of some elements. For example, gold is an element. Gold is made of gold atoms. No other element contains gold atoms. The properties of elements are different because they are made of different kinds of atoms.

Gold is an element.

36

TEACHER RESOURCE MASTERS

Lesson Summary

- Everything that takes up space and has mass is called matter.
- An atom is the smallest part of any kind of matter.
- An element is made of only one kind of atom.

Lesson Review

1. What is an element?
★2. Is a shadow matter? Why or why not?

CHAPTER 2/LESSON 2

pages 34–37

Would You Believe?

Unlike most other metals, gold doesn't rust or lose its shine.

OPTIONS

◆ **Reinforcement:** If you have colored beads, you may want to join several together into models of matter. In some cases, have the models exactly the same; in some cases, make them different. Ask the students to pick out which models represent the same type of matter and tell why.

● **Enrichment:** If you have hand magnifying lenses available, let students use them to look at many different objects.

▲ **Challenge:** Some students may be interested in looking a a periodic table of the elements. See **SCIENCE In Your World,** Level 6.

LESSON REVIEW ANSWERS

1. matter that is made of one kind of atom
2. No. It has no mass and does not take up any space.

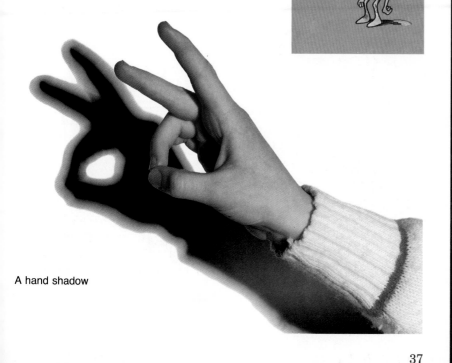

A hand shadow

37

TEACHER RESOURCE MASTERS

pages 38–45

PREPLAN

Lesson Objectives

6. List and **compare** properties of matter in the solid, liquid, and gaseous states.

7. Compare the freedom of movement of particles within the three states.

Science Background

■ Solid, liquid, and gaseous states of the same matter differ in physical properties such as shape and volume. These differences are due to the motion and spacing of particles. Though the particles of a solid are in constant motion, they vibrate within a geometric pattern. Thus, solids have a definite size (volume) and shape. Particles in liquids vibrate rapidly enough to overcome some of their mutual attraction so that they tumble over one another. Thus, liquids take the shapes of their containers. Gaseous particles travel rapidly enough to overcome mutual attraction. They have no definite volume or shape.

Lesson Vocabulary

solid   liquid   gas

Note: The activity on student page 44 may be used for guided discovery before you begin this lesson.

1   FOCUS

■ Have students list some properties of wood, milk, and air. Have students focus on how the properties of each differ. Lead students to the concept of states of matter.

■ Use the goals on student page 38 to establish the purpose for studying this lesson.

LESSON 3 GOALS
You will learn
- the properties of solids.
- the properties of liquids.
- that some matter has properties of both solids and liquids.
- the properties of gases.

What are the groupings of matter as solids, liquids, and gases called?

States of Matter

You remember from Lesson 1 that some properties of objects are size, shape, color, smoothness, and roughness. Now you'll see how the properties of an object can show the object's state of matter.

Wood, milk, and air have different properties. They are put in different groups because of their different properties. Wood is a solid, milk is a liquid, and air is a gas. Matter can be grouped by whether it is a solid, a liquid, or a gas. Solids, liquids, and gases are states of matter.

38

TEACHER RESOURCE MASTERS

Wood is a solid. A **solid** is matter that has a certain size and shape. Most of the objects you see are in the solid state. Your desk is a solid. It does not change its shape or size.

Atoms are particles of matter. Solids, liquids, and gases are all made up of particles of matter. Particles of matter are always moving. How much the particles are moving tells the state of the matter—solid, liquid, or gas.

In a solid, the particles are packed closely together in a definite pattern. The particles can only shake. They can't move out of their pattern. Solids don't change shape because of the pattern of the particles in them.

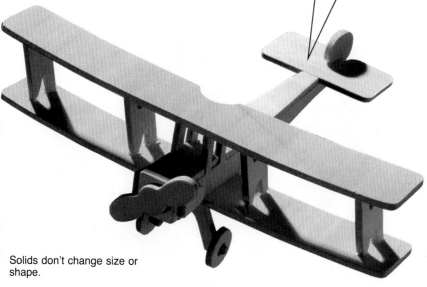

Solids don't change size or shape.

39

TEACHER RESOURCE MASTERS

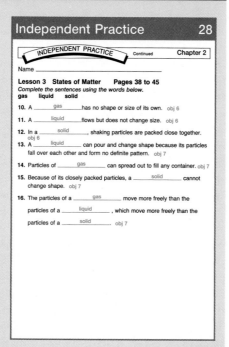

Independent Practice 28

INDEPENDENT PRACTICE Continued Chapter 2

Name _____

Lesson 3 States of Matter Pages 38 to 45
Complete the sentences using the words below.
gas   liquid   solid

10. A ____gas____ has no shape or size of its own. obj 6

11. A ____liquid____ flows but does not change size. obj 6

12. In a ____solid____, shaking particles are packed close together. obj 6

13. A ____liquid____ can pour and change shape because its particles fall over each other and form no definite pattern. obj 7

14. Particles of ____gas____ can spread out to fill any container. obj 7

15. Because of its closely packed particles, a ____solid____ cannot change shape. obj 7

16. The particles of a ____gas____ move more freely than the particles of a ____liquid____, which move more freely than the particles of a ____solid____. obj 7

2   TEACH

■ Display a piece of yarn, a glass of water and ice, an inflated balloon, and a jar of paint. Have students observe the properties of each to establish the idea of the solid state.

Have clear containers of various shapes available. Allow students to pour colored water into each container and notice how the liquid changes shape. Keep the volume of water constant.

Guided Practice

■ Check students' understanding of lesson concepts by discussing the Lesson Review questions on student page 43. If necessary, use the **reteaching strategy** in OPTIONS.

Independent Practice

■ Assign the Lesson 3 section of the Teacher Resource Master **Independent Practice,** page 28.

3   APPLY

■ Ask students to list three properties of solids and three properties of liquids.

Close

■ Use Summary statements on student page 43 to review lesson concepts.

OPTIONS

Reteaching Strategy

Have students construct models of matter in the solid and liquid states. Beads and wooden dowels or gumdrops and toothpicks could be used. Have students do more than one layer of the model so that they see the three-dimensional arrangement of particles.

Resource Options

■ Show selections from "Chemistry in the Kitchen," *Mr. Wizard's World of Science Video Library,* Merrill Publishing Company.

OPTIONS

LANGUAGE CONNECTION

■ **Writing:** Have students write a composition describing to a young child what it would be like to be a particle of wood, a particle of milk, a particle of butter, and a particle of air. Instruct students to write the definitions of the following: property, mass, matter, atom, element, solid, liquid, and gas. Then ask them to use each definition in describing life as each of the particles.

Resource Options

Use Color Transparency #1, "Matter May Be Solid, Liquid, or Gaseous."

1. The milk is the shape of the pitcher.
2. The milk is the shape of the glass.

What can change in a liquid? What can't change?

Milk is a liquid (LIHK wud). A **liquid** is matter that has a certain size or volume but does not have a shape of its own. A liquid takes the shape of its container. Look at the picture of the milk. [1]What shape is the milk in the pitcher? [2]What shape is the same milk in the glass?

Liquids flow. They can be poured. You can pour milk from a pitcher into a glass. Liquids also have a certain volume. When you pour milk from a small carton into a tall glass, the shape of the milk changes, but the amount of milk is still the same.

Liquids are also made of particles. The particles in liquids move more freely than those in solids. Particles in liquids fall over each other and don't form a definite pattern. Liquids pour and change shape because of the way their particles move.

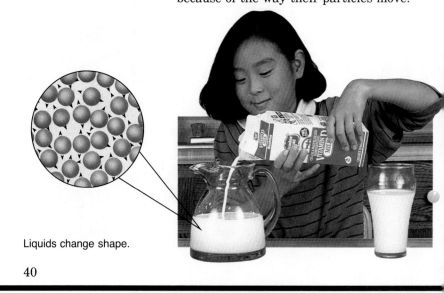

Liquids change shape.

40

TEACHER RESOURCE MASTERS

Some matter has properties of both liquids and solids. This kind of matter seems to have a definite shape as solids do. However, its particles don't form a definite pattern. This kind of matter may even change shape slowly over time.

Look at the picture of butter. Cold butter has a definite shape and volume. Now think about spreading butter on warm toast. As the butter warms, it gets softer and softer. Soon it flows like a liquid, doesn't it? So butter has some properties of both solids and liquids.

A gelatin dessert is also like a solid and a liquid. It has a definite mass. It keeps its shape, but its particles are not in a pattern. That explains why its shape can easily be changed. [1]What other matter can you think of that has some properties of both solids and liquids?

1. Students may suggest candle wax, Silly Putty, taffy, gum, and clay.

OPTIONS

◆ **Reinforcement:** Display an assortment of various foods, both solid and non-solid. Have students describe the properties of each and put the solids in one group.

● **Enrichment:** Some students may have noted that some solids (salt, sugar, sand, and so on) can be poured. Have students **work cooperatively** to research this question and draw some inferences about the "pouring" of powdered solids.

▲ **Challenge:** You may wish to introduce the term *crystal* to able students. The regular pattern in solid matter is known as a crystalline structure. Ask students to research crystal shapes.

41

TEACHER RESOURCE MASTERS

OPTIONS

Career: Use "I WANT TO KNOW ABOUT . . . a Hot-Air Balloonist," student page 45, with this lesson.

Distribute large plastic food bags to students. Have them fill the bags with air and then seal the bags. Ask students to put their filled bags into a small container. This vividly demonstrates that air takes up space.

Gas has no size or shape.

What state of matter is air?

1. The amount of space between the particles would get smaller.

A **gas** is matter that has no shape or size of its own. Air is a gas. Air takes the shape of any container it is in. It also spreads out to fill any size container. Air particles can spread out to fill a large container such as a barrel. The same amount of air can also be put into a smaller container such as a jar.[1] What would happen to the space between particles when air is moved from a large to a small container?

Gas particles move very freely. They are also farther apart from each other than the particles of a liquid or a solid. The particles of a gas spread out to fill any container. The same amount of gas can fill a small jar or a large room.

42

TEACHER RESOURCE MASTERS

States of matter

OPTIONS

Demonstrate that a gas fills its container. Spray a small amount of room freshener in one corner of the room. Have students indicate when they smell the odor.

LESSON REVIEW ANSWERS
1. solid, liquid, and gas
2. solid
3. gas
4. Both take up space and have mass. Both have a definite volume. Solids have a definite shape; liquids take the shape of their container.

Lesson Summary

- Solid matter has a certain size and shape.
- Liquid matter has a certain size but doesn't have a shape of its own.
- Some matter has properties of both solids and liquids.
- Matter that is a gas doesn't have a size or shape of its own.

Lesson Review

1. What are three states of matter?
2. Matter in which state does not easily change its shape?
3. Which state of matter can spread to fill any size container?
4. How are the properties of solids and liquids alike? How are they different?

43

TEACHER RESOURCE MASTERS

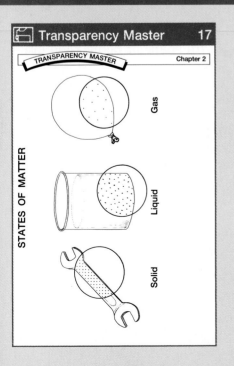

Transparency Master 17

TRANSPARENCY MASTER   Chapter 2

STATES OF MATTER

Gas

Liquid

Solid

PREPLAN

Time Allotment: 30 minutes

Process Skill: Classifying

Objectives

1. **Examine** unknown matter to see how it is like a solid.
2. **Examine** unknown matter to see how it is like a liquid.

Setup

■ The "mystery matter" is made by mixing cornstarch and water. Add water to the cornstarch until a consistency similar to toothpaste is reached, approximately 5 parts cornstarch to 3 parts water. Place several spoonfuls in a paper cup for each student. Stir in food coloring if you wish.

■ **Cooperative Grouping:** twos—Assign roles as explained on page T24.

1   FOCUS

■ Discuss the properties of solids and liquids. Make two lists on the chalkboard.

2   TEACH

■ **Safety Consideration:** Caution students not to taste the unknown matter.
■ Ask: **How is the mystery matter like a solid? A liquid?**
■ Have students use the Teacher Resource Master **Activity Worksheet,** pages 21 and 22, to record their data and answers.

3   APPLY

■ Encourage students to think of everyday examples of matter that has properties of both solids and liquids.

Close

■ Discuss the activity and the questions with the class.

ACTIVITY

Is it a solid or a liquid?

What you need 🚫 ✋

newspaper
paper cup
"mystery matter"
paper towels
pencil and paper

What to do

1. Cover your desk with newspaper.
2. Get a cup of "mystery matter" from your teacher.
3. Carefully test the "mystery matter." Try the following things:
   (a) Try to pour it.
   (b) Poke it with your fingers.

Test	Observations
Pouring "mystery matter"	
Poking "mystery matter"	
Rolling "mystery matter"	
Other	

   (c) Roll it into a ball and try to bounce it on the desk.
4. Make a chart like the one above and record your observations.

What did you learn?

1. How was the "mystery matter" like a solid?
2. How was it like a liquid?

Using what you learned

1. What properties of butter make it like the "mystery matter"?
2. Gelatin, glass, and peanut butter are also like the "mystery matter." How does temperature make them more like a liquid or a solid?

44

ACTIVITY RESPONSES

What did you learn?
1. It was like a solid when rolled into a ball. All answers that refer to the substance having a certain shape or being rigid are correct.
2. It flowed and changed shape.

Using what you learned
1. Both butter and the mystery matter sometimes have a certain shape. Both also will sometimes flow.
2. As the temperature gets higher, the substances act more like liquids. They act more like solids as the temperature gets lower.

I WANT TO KNOW ABOUT...

A Hot-Air Balloonist

George McCall is a hot-air balloonist. He and a friend are preparing a hot-air balloon for takeoff. Before this can happen, George must inflate the balloon. He turns on a burner to heat the air in the balloon. Heated air is lighter than the same amount of cooler air.

The inflated balloon is about seven stories high. The balloon is made of light, strong nylon covered with a thin plastic coating. The nylon holds the heated air in the balloon. A basket called a gondola hangs under the balloon. This is where George and his friend will ride. Heavy bags of sand, tied to the gondola, help keep the balloon on the ground.

Everything is now ready. George and his friend climb into the gondola. They untie the sand bags and leave them on the ground. The inflated balloon and gondola rise into the air.

George and his friend don't feel as if they are moving. But they see that the trees and houses are getting farther and farther away. The balloon drifts with the wind. After a while the air in the balloon cools. George turns on the burner to heat the air and keep the balloon up. When George wants to land, he releases some of the heated air. Slowly they drift to Earth, and the ride is over for the day.

Career

Feature Background

■ Heated air is less dense than cold air. A propane burner is used to heat the air inside the balloon.

■ The balloonist must make intermittent blasts of the burner to enable the balloon to stay at a constant height because the air inside the balloon gradually cools.

■ To obtain more information about ballooning clubs and activities, write the Balloon Federation of America, Suite 430, 821 15th Street, N.W., Washington, DC 20005.

Feature Vocabulary

gondola   nylon

Teaching Suggestions

■ Discuss student experiences with balloons.

■ Blow up a round balloon. Use a piece of string to measure its circumference. Place the balloon in the sun for an hour. Measure the circumference. Place the balloon in a freezer and measure it again. Compare the measurements and discuss reasons for the differences.

■ Invite a balloonist to talk with the class about ballooning.

Summary

Chapter Closure: Have the students **work cooperatively** to locate in the text the page number and paragraph that refers to each of the summary statements. Discuss answers in class and help students who have difficulty with this task to locate the needed information.

Science Words

Have the students **work cooperatively** to devise a "mystery" numerical code in which they can write the science words. Students should exchange papers and attempt to solve each other's codes. Pictures drawn by the code maker or short word clues can be included to help make decoding the words easier.

■ **Student Responses**

1. gas
2. matter
3. element
4. liquid
5. solid
6. atom
7. mass

CHAPTER REVIEW

2

═ Summary ═

Lesson 1
- A property is a characteristic of an object.
- All objects take up space and have mass.
- The gram and kilogram are used to measure mass.

Lesson 2
- Matter is anything around you that takes up space and has mass.
- All matter is made of atoms.

- An element is made of only one kind of atom.

Lesson 3
- Solid matter has a certain size and shape.
- Liquid matter has a certain size but not a certain shape.
- Some matter has properties of both solids and liquids.
- Matter that is a gas has no size or shape of its own.

═ Science Words ═

Fill in the blank with the correct word or words from the list.

mass	atom	kilograms	liquid	property
matter	element	solid	gas	gram

1. Matter that has no shape or size of its own is called a(n) ____.
2. All objects that have mass and take up space are ____.
3. A(n) ____ is made of only one kind of atom.
4. A(n) ____ has a certain size but no shape of its own.
5. Matter that has a certain size and shape is called a(n) ____.
6. The smallest part of matter is called a(n) ____.
7. How much there is of an object is called ____.

46

TEACHER RESOURCE MASTERS

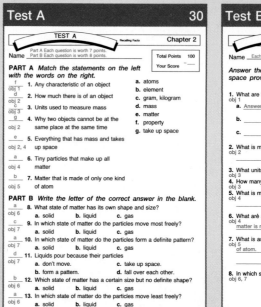

Test A   30

TEST A   Recalling Facts   Chapter 2

Name ___ Part A Each question is worth 7 points.
Part B Each question is worth 8 points.

Total Points 100
Your Score ___

PART A *Match the statements on the left with the words on the right.*

f   **1.** Any characteristic of an object
obj 1
d   **2.** How much there is of an object
obj 2
c   **3.** Units used to measure mass
obj 3
g   **4.** Why two objects cannot be at the same place at the same time
obj 2
e   **5.** Everything that has mass and takes up space
obj 2, 4
a   **6.** Tiny particles that make up all matter
obj 4
b   **7.** Matter that is made of only one kind of atom
obj 5

a. atoms
b. element
c. gram, kilogram
d. mass
e. matter
f. property
g. take up space

PART B *Write the letter of the correct answer in the blank.*

a   **8.** What state of matter has its own shape and size?
obj 6   a. solid   b. liquid   c. gas
c   **9.** In which state of matter do the particles move most freely?
obj 7   a. solid   b. liquid   c. gas
a   **10.** In which state of matter do the particles form a definite pattern?
obj 7   a. solid   b. liquid   c. gas
d   **11.** Liquids pour because their particles
obj 7   a. don't move.   c. take up space.
   b. form a pattern.   d. fall over each other.
b   **12.** Which state of matter has a certain size but no definite shape?
obj 6   a. solid   b. liquid   c. gas
a   **13.** In which state of matter do the particles move least freely?
obj 6   a. solid   b. liquid   c. gas

Test B   31

TEST B   Understanding/Applying Concepts   Chapter 2

Name ___ Each question is worth 7 points.

Total Points 100
Your Score ___

Answer the questions in the space provided.

1. What are three properties of an apple?
obj 1
  a. Answers may include color, texture, and other properties.
  b. ___
  c. ___

2. What is mass? ___ Mass is how much there is of an object.
obj 2

3. What units are used to measure mass? ___ grams and kilograms
obj 3
4. How many grams are in two kilograms? ___ 2,000 grams
obj 3
5. What is matter? ___ Matter is anything that has mass and takes up space.
obj 4

6. What are atoms? ___ Atoms are the smallest part of any kind of matter. All
obj 4
matter is made of atoms.

7. What is an element? ___ An element is matter that is made of only one kind
obj 5
of atom.

8. In which state of matter are particles packed closest together? ___ solid
obj 6, 7

Questions

Recalling Ideas

*Correctly complete each of the
following sentences.*

1. Particles move least freely in
   (a) grams.   (c) liquids.
   (b) solids.   (d) gases.

2. A person's mass is best
   measured in
   (a) atoms.   (c) kilograms.
   (b) Celsius.   (d) properties.

3. A characteristic of an object
   is a(n)
   (a) atom.   (c) property.
   (b) element.   (d) matter.

4. Matter is made of
   (a) grams.   (c) patterns.
   (b) liquids.   (d) atoms.

5. A softball has less mass than
   a
   (a) bowling   (c) feather.
   ball.
   (b) tennis   (d) pin.
   ball.

6. The unit used to measure the
   masses of very small objects
   is the
   (a) element.   (c) atom.
   (b) gram.   (d) kilogram.

Understanding Ideas

*Answer the following questions
using complete sentences.*

1. What are two properties that
   all matter has?

2. Why are there so many kinds
   of matter?

Thinking Critically

*Think about what you have
learned in this chapter. Answer
the following questions using
complete sentences.*

1. Most gases cannot be seen.
   How do we know they are
   there?

2. How is a crayon like both a
   solid and a liquid?

47

Questions

Recalling Ideas

1. b	**4.** d
2. c	**5.** a
3. c	**6.** b

Understanding Ideas

1. All matter has mass and takes up space.

2. There are many kinds of matter because atoms can be joined together in many ways.

Thinking Critically

1. Gases take up space. When gases are enclosed, such as in a balloon, evidence that gases take up space can be seen when the balloon gets bigger as it is inflated.

2. A crayon feels hard like a solid. However, its particles don't form a definite pattern and its shape can change over a period of time.

TEACHER RESOURCE MASTERS

Test B	32

TEST B   Continued   Chapter 2

Name _____

9. In which state of matter are particles farthest apart? __gas__
obj 6, 7
10. In which state of matter do particles move least freely? __solid__
obj 6, 7
11. What makes each state of matter different from the other states? __The__
obj 6, 7   arrangement of particles and freedom of particle movement make the

   states different.

12. Tell one way a liquid is different from a solid. __Answers may vary. A__
obj 6, 7   liquid will flow, a solid will not.

13. Tell one way a gas is different from both a solid and a liquid. __Answers__
obj 6, 7   may vary. A gas can expand to fill any container.

14. Explain why states of matter have different properties. __The amount of__
obj 6   space between particles and the movement of particles of matter

   determine the properties.

Changes in Matter

Planning Guide

Lessons	Objectives	Vocabulary
Chapter Introduction pp. 48–49		
Lesson 1 Changing Matter pp. 50–55	1. **Identify** some ways the physical properties of matter can be changed. 2. **Compare** what happens when matter expands and contracts.	physical change
Lesson 2 Changing States of Matter pp. 56–61	3. **Explain** the role of heat in the change of state from solid to liquid and from liquid to solid. 4. **Describe** what happens to liquid matter when it evaporates and to gas matter when it condenses.	evaporation condensation
Lesson 3 Combining Matter pp. 62–65	5. **Describe** mixtures and **identify** common mixtures. 6. **Describe** compounds. 7. **Understand** that a chemical change takes place when a compound forms.	mixture compound chemical change
Chapter Review pp. 66, 67		

Planning Guide

Text Activities		Teacher Resource Masters	Other Components
Title/Skill	**Materials per Group**		
Have You Ever . . . Seen Matter Changing? p. 49 Observing/Hypothesizing Time Allotment: 30 minutes	2 small, widemouth jars water soil salt		**Activity Center** "Wings of Wax"; "Mixing It Up"; "Ice Is Nice"; "Fire"; "Playing With Play Dough"; "Water On Ice"
How Can You Make a Dime Dance?, p. 55 Inferring Time Allotment: 45 minutes	soft-drink bottle freezer safety goggles dropper dime pencil and paper	Independent Practice, pp. 43, 44 Activity Worksheet, pp. 35, 36 ◆ Family Science, p. 34 ◆ Reteaching Activity, p. 45	Poster #2 Mr. Wizard's World of Science Video Tape 16
You Can . . . Win the Ice Cube Race, p. 57 Hypothesizing/Experimenting Time Allotment: 30 minutes	ice cubes	Independent Practice, pp. 43, 44 Activity Worksheet, pp. 37, 38 ▲ Critical Thinking, p. 40 Critical Thinking, p. 39 Transparency Master, p. 33	Color Transparency #2 Mr. Wizard's World of Science Video Tape 20 Activity Book, pp. 13, 14
How Does Water Change? p. 61 Observing Time Allotment: 15 minutes on two different days	baking dish water tape plastic wrap paper cup pencil and paper		
Who Will Stop the Rust? p. 345 Controlling Variables/ Predicting Time Allotment: 40 minutes; 5 minutes each day for 5 days and then 15 minutes to compare results	objects that will rust including washer or paper clips made from iron or steel materials such as paint, oil, masking tape, and plastic wrap, plant mister	Independent Practice, pp. 43, 44 Language Arts Connection, p. 41 Math Connection, p. 42	Mr. Wizard's World of Science Tape 19 Activity Book, pp. 15, 16 Activity Book, pp. 35, 36
		Test A, p. 46 Test B, pp. 47, 48	

◆ Basic / ▲ Advanced / All other masters are for use by all students.

Changes in Matter

For Exceptional Students

ESL/LEP

Chapter 3/Lesson 1, Page 50

Ask students to divide a paper into six columns. Tell them to write the following as column headings: **Object, Color, Size, Shape, Smoothness,** and **Roughness.** Then have students list objects in the room with the physical properties of these objects in the appropriate columns.

Play a guessing game with students, using physical properties of objects as the clues. Assist them by writing on the chalkboard, **I am thinking of an object that is (color), is (size), has a   shape, and looks and feels (smooth or rough) .** Students can use the pattern as the basis of their riddle if they wish.

Chapter 3/Lesson 2, Page 60

Write these words on the chalkboard: **melting, freezing, evaporation, condensation.** Ask students to write each word and draw a picture that depicts an occasion in which they were personally involved when one of these changes of state occurred. Have students make up a sentence about each of their drawings.

Chapter 3/Lesson 3, Page 62

Ask students to list mixtures that they often make. Have them discuss how they make these mixtures. Let them give a recipe for their favorite salad or fruit drink.

Gifted

Chapter 3/Lesson 2, Page 57

Have students carefully record the results of each student's ice cube melting time in minutes and seconds. Help them make a data table and a simple bar graph of the results. Ask questions about the graph to help them interpret the data.

Challenge the students to see how long they can preserve an ice cube from completely melting. They may use scrap materials to make a container for the ice cube. Following this activity, discuss commercial insulating containers and materials, which ones seem to be the most efficient, and how they might be improved.

Mainstreamed

Chapter 3/Lesson 3, Page 64

Learning Disabled: Prepare a two-column matrix. Label one column "Matter Combined" (A), the other "Result" (B). Under column A list the following items: various coins, various fruit pieces, salt and water, chocolate and milk, iron and oxygen, wood and oxygen, and so on. Under column B write the words "Mixture" and "Compound" next to each item in Column A. Direct students to match the appropriate result for each combination by circling one of the words.

Whole Class Science Project

Ask students to observe happenings in their surroundings, both at home and at school, for two or three days. They should look carefully for examples of changes in matter. Some changes will be caused by manipulation of matter by humans such as in cooking or the cutting of wood. Other changes will appear to take place on their own such as in the evaporation of water or the spoilage of fruit. Have students keep a log and record the changes they observe. Students should speculate on the causes of apparently "natural" changes. At the end of the time, collect examples of changes in matter on the chalkboard. Have students characterize the changes as chemical or physical and give reasons for their choices.

Science Fair Projects

Individual students could do one of the following projects:

1. Devise a way to demonstrate the expansion and contraction of solid matter. One way is to clamp a metal bar at one end to a long board. Attach the opposite end to a pivoted pointer made from a soda straw and a pin. Insert the pin through the straw and into the board so that one end of the pivoting straw is very long and the other end very short. Attach the short end to the end of the metal bar with a bit of clay or a drop of glue. When the bar expands or contracts a small distance, the long end of the straw should move a large distance. Heat the rod with a hair dryer and cool it with a towel wrapped around ice cubes. Try to avoid heating or cooling the board. Be prepared to explain why the bar changes length.

2. Changes in state from a solid to a liquid to a gas may be demonstrated by placing a loose solid material, such as puffed cereal, plastic foam spheres, dry ice, and dry beans in a clear, unbreakable container. The container should be no more than one-third full. Devise a way of causing the container to vibrate varying amounts. One possibility is an adjustable household electric massager. By experimenting with containers and materials, it may be possible to get a good demonstration by shaking the container in the hands. As "particle" motion increases, the container will demonstrate a solid, a liquid, and finally a gas. Be able to explain how particle motion explains the properties of the three states.

Chapter Concepts

■ A change in the physical properties of matter is a physical change.
■ Matter may change state when it gains or loses heat.
■ Matter can be combined in mixtures, where each type of matter keeps its physical properties, or in compounds, where elements combine during a chemical change.

Chapter Background

■ The most common type of physical change is a change of state. The composition of the substance undergoing change remains the same.
■ Chemical changes are often called chemical reactions. A compound is formed from the chemical reaction of two or more elements.
■ Both compounds and mixtures are combinations of matter. Mixtures result from physical change, and the components keep their identifying characteristics.

Looking Ahead

■ Contact a chemist or physicist to discuss the makeup of matter and the changes that occur in the states of matter.

Look for These Symbols

   —Hands-on activity

   —Cooperative learning

   —Overhead transparency

◆ —Basic/Reinforcement

● —Average/Enrichment

▲ —Advanced/Challenge

   —Calculator Practice

SCIENCE
In Your World

48

CHAPTER 3

Changes in Matter

When you walk in the rain, raindrops on your raincoat look clearer than water in puddles. How does water change when it falls on the ground? How does the ground change when it gets wet?

ACTIVITY
Have You Ever...

Seen Matter Changing?

You will need two jars about half filled with water. You should also have about 50 g of dirt and 50 g of salt. Observe the water, the dirt, and the salt. Record your observations. Then pour the dirt into one jar and the salt into another. Stir the mixtures. How has each kind of matter changed? Record your observations. Do you think you could separate the dirt or the salt from the water? How?

49

PREPLAN

Time Allotment: 30 minutes

Objectives
1. **Observe** the differences between dirt-and-water and salt-and-water mixtures.
2. **Hypothesize** methods for separating mixtures.

Setup
If you wish to conduct the activity, you will need the following materials for each student or activity group:

2 small, widemouth jars	water
50 g soil	50 g salt

1 FOCUS

■ Ask several students to describe what they see in the picture on page 48. Direct students' attention to the muddiness of the water in the puddle.

2 TEACH

■ Have the title and introductory paragraph read aloud.

Have You Ever . . .
Have students **work cooperatively** in groups of four.
■ Stir the mixtures well before observing.
■ **Student Responses**
1. The water is dirty; the dirt is mud.
2. The water looks cloudy; the salt has dissolved.
3. You could strain out the dirt or let the water evaporate.

3 APPLY

■ Ask: **In what ways is cake batter like the mixtures you made?** *Ingredients are mixed together with liquid.*

Close
■ Ask: **What else might mix with rainwater?** *fertilizers, chemicals, etc.*

PREPLAN

Lesson Objectives

1. Identify some ways the physical properties of matter can be changed.

2. Compare what happens when matter expands and contracts.

Science Background

■ Physical changes are common in our environment. Changes of state are physical changes. Altering the physical appearance or shape of matter by bending, breaking, or tearing doesn't change the nature of the particles in matter. When these particles don't change, the changes are physical changes.

■ Heat can cause matter to change state. Heat also causes matter to expand and contract. Matter tends to expand as it is heated since the particles gain energy and therefore move faster and farther apart from each other. The opposite occurs when matter loses heat. In that case, the particles move more slowly and closer together. The matter contracts.

Note: The activity on student page 55 may be used for guided discovery before you begin this lesson.

Lesson Vocabulary

physical change

1 FOCUS

■ Display a torn piece of paper, a raw and a cooked egg, a burning match, and a ball of modeling clay. Using these objects and the photographs, discuss the wide variety of daily changes taking place in matter.

■ **Safety Consideration:** Do not let students handle the burning match.

■ Use the goals on student page 50 to establish the purpose for studying this lesson.

Changing Matter

┌─ **LESSON 1 GOALS** ─┐
You will learn
● that the properties of matter can change.
● that matter can expand and contract.
● why heat causes matter to expand.
└────────────────────┘

Have you ever helped build a doghouse? Maybe you helped with sanding the wood smooth, or perhaps you helped with the painting. If you worked carefully, the changes you made helped the doghouse to look its best.

In working with wood, you caused some of the properties of the wood to change. Color, size, shape, smoothness, and roughness are some physical properties of matter. Physical properties of matter can be used to tell how matter looks or feels. A change in a physical property is called a **physical change**. What physical change are the people in the picture with the doghouse causing?

1. They are changing the color.

50

TEACHER RESOURCE MASTERS

Family Science   34

┌──── FAMILY SCIENCE ────┐   Chapter 3
Name _____

Your child is learning about properties of matter in science. The purpose of this home activity is to observe bubbles and to find ways to change their properties.

ALL ABOUT BUBBLES

Materials
one straw   liquid soap   water   paper cup   pencil and paper

What to do
1. Fill the paper cup almost full of water.
2. Put in five drops of soap and mix.
3. Use the straw to blow bubbles.
4. Write what you observe in the chart below.
5. Add five more drops of soap and repeat steps 3 and 4.
6. Add ten more drops and repeat steps 3 and 4.

Number of Drops	Color of Bubbles	Shape of Bubbles	Size
5 drops	clear, some blue, purple, or pink	round, oval	small
10 drops	colors tend to reflect surrounding colors	round, oval	large, if blown slowly
20 drops	same as above	round, oval, may stick to each other	same as above

What did you learn?

1. How did the amount of soap change the bubbles? ___The more soap that___ ___was added, the larger the bubbles; the number of bubbles increased.___

2. What other ways can you change bubbles? ___Answers will vary.___

Using what you learned

1. Try the ways you listed in question 2 above. Tell how the bubbles changed. ___The colors and shapes of the bubbles changed.___

Physical changes

You can break, bend, tear, or stretch some solids. When a solid is broken, bent, torn, or stretched, its shape is changed.

The physical properties of a liquid or a gas can also be changed. Look at the picture of the paint on this page. [1]How have the properties of the matter—that is, the paint—changed?

How can you change the shape of a solid?

1. The color and shape have changed.

51

TEACHER RESOURCE MASTERS

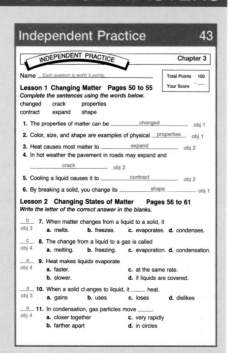

Independent Practice 43

INDEPENDENT PRACTICE Chapter 3

Name ___Each question is worth 5 points.___ Total Points 100
  Your Score

Lesson 1 Changing Matter Pages 50 to 55
Complete the sentences using the words below.
changed   crack   properties
contract   expand   shape

1. The properties of matter can be ____changed____. obj 1
2. Color, size, and shape are examples of physical ___properties___. obj 1
3. Heat causes most matter to ____expand____. obj 2
4. In hot weather the pavement in roads may expand and ____crack____. obj 2
5. Cooling a liquid causes it to ____contract____. obj 2
6. By breaking a solid, you change its ____shape____. obj 1

Lesson 2 Changing States of Matter   Pages 56 to 61
Write the letter of the correct answer in the blanks.

__b__ 7. When matter changes from a liquid to a solid, it
obj 3   **a.** melts.   **b.** freezes.   **c.** evaporates. **d.** condenses.

__c__ 8. The change from a liquid to a gas is called
obj 4   **a.** melting.   **b.** freezing.   **c.** evaporation. **d.** condensation.

__a__ 9. Heat makes liquids evaporate
obj 4   **a.** faster.   **c.** at the same rate.
  b. slower.   **d.** if liquids are covered.

__a__ 10. When a solid changes to liquid, it ____ heat.
obj 3   **a.** gains   **b.** uses   **c.** loses   **d.** dislikes

__a__ 11. In condensation, gas particles move ____.
obj 4   **a.** closer together   **c.** very rapidly
  b. farther apart   **d.** in circles

2 TEACH

■ Introduce the concept of physical properties. Point out that physical changes involve the physical properties of matter.
■ Review and compare the arrangement of the particles of matter in solids, liquids, and gases.
■ Discuss the use of tar strips (expansion joints) in streets and buildings.

Guided Practice

■ Check students' understanding of lesson concepts by discussing the Lesson Review questions on student page 54. If necessary, use the **reteaching strategy** in OPTIONS.

Independent Practice

■ Assign the Lesson 1 section of the Teacher Resource Master **Independent Practice,** page 43.

3 APPLY

■ Have students compare the amount of space they require when sitting in the classroom to the amount required when running and playing on the playground. This is analogous to the amount of space between particles of matter in different states.

Close

■ Use Summary statements on student page 54 to review lesson concepts.

OPTIONS

Reteaching Strategy

The following demonstration may make these concepts more concrete. Inflate a balloon and measure its circumference. Heat the balloon in warm water. After removing the balloon from the water, have students quickly measure its circumference again.

Resource Options

■ Use Poster #2, "Properties of Paint."

OPTIONS

LANGUAGE CONNECTION

Reading: Write the following question on the chalkboard or an overhead. **What is the main idea of this lesson?** *Heat causes matter to expand.* Have students work in **cooperative groups** to find the answer.

◆ **Reinforcement:** Arrange for each student to have a small scrap piece of pine or other soft wood and fine sandpaper. Take the students outdoors (to minimize dust). Have them alter the texture of the wood with the sandpaper.

■ **Safety Consideration:** Have students wear safety goggles for this activity.

● **Enrichment:** Give several items (clay, string, chalk, pencil, eraser, or wire) to a group of students. Ask them to change the items in some way to make them look different. Ask the other students to report what changes were made. Discuss if the properties of each type of matter changed.

Resource Options

■ Show selections from "Change of State," *Mr. Wizard's World of Science Video Library,* Merrill Publishing Company.

---

1. It would mean that the water was cooling down.

Heat can cause a physical change of matter. Think of how a thermometer works. When a thermometer is in a warm area, the liquid in the tube rises. It rises because the liquid expands when it is heated. Matter that expands gets bigger. It takes up more space. Most matter expands when it is heated. Most matter also contracts when it cools. Matter that contracts gets smaller. It takes up less space. Look at the thermometer on this page. [1]If the liquid in the tube contracts, what would it mean?

Liquid expands

52

TEACHER RESOURCE MASTERS

Air expands

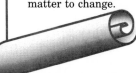

SCIENCE AND . . .
Reading

What is the main idea of this lesson?
A. Students like to run on playgrounds.
B. People do not like cracks in the roads.
C. Heat causes matter to expand.
D. Thermometers cause matter to change.

Matter expands because heat makes the particles of matter move faster. As they move faster, the particles move farther apart. This movement makes the matter expand. When a car is driven for a long time, the tires get hot. [1]What do you think happens to the air in those tires?

Sometimes problems take place when matter expands. Concrete in roads may expand and crack in hot weather. Naturally, people want to stop the roads from cracking. To solve the problem of concrete cracking, some roads are built with tar strips between the sections of concrete. The soft tar moves out of the way to allow the concrete to expand. That means there is less chance that the concrete will crack.

1. The air expands.

Why is tar placed between sections of concrete?

53

OPTIONS

SCIENCE AND . . . READING
- **Skill:** Identify the main idea of a selection.
- **Student Response:** C.

● **Enrichment:** Have students **work cooperatively** to research the history of thermometers.

▲ **Challenge:** You may wish to demonstrate the properties of a bimetallic strip (made of two different metals that expand at different rates) to your class. Have students investigate how they are used in thermostats.
- Ask students to infer how a thermometer works.

TEACHER RESOURCE MASTERS

LESSON REVIEW ANSWERS

1. Shape, size, color, and smoothness can be changed.
2. It contracts.
3. Heat makes the particles of matter move faster and farther apart.

1. They are changing the colors, shapes, and surfaces.

There are many ways to cause physical changes of matter. [1]How are the boys in the picture making physical changes to matter?

Changing physical properties

Lesson Summary

- Size, shape, color, and smoothness of matter can be changed.
- Heat causes matter to expand.
- Matter contracts when it cools.

Lesson Review

1. What are some physical properties that can be changed?
2. What happens to most matter when it is cooled?
★3. How does heat cause matter to expand?

54

TEACHER RESOURCE MASTERS

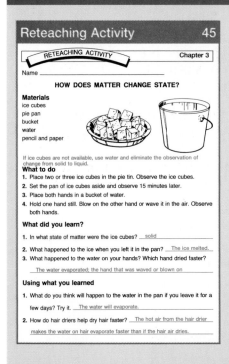

Reteaching Activity   45

RETEACHING ACTIVITY   Chapter 3

Name _____

HOW DOES MATTER CHANGE STATE?

Materials
ice cubes
pie pan
bucket
water
pencil and paper

If ice cubes are not available, use water and eliminate the observation of change from solid to liquid.
What to do
1. Place two or three ice cubes in the pie tin. Observe the ice cubes.
2. Set the pan of ice cubes aside and observe 15 minutes later.
3. Place both hands in a bucket of water.
4. Hold one hand still. Blow on the other hand or wave it in the air. Observe both hands.

What did you learn?

1. In what state of matter were the ice cubes? __solid__

2. What happened to the ice when you left it in the pan? __The ice melted.__
3. What happened to the water on your hands? Which hand dried faster?

__The water evaporated; the hand that was waved or blown on__

Using what you learned

1. What do you think will happen to the water in the pan if you leave it for a few days? Try it. __The water will evaporate.__

2. How do hair driers help dry hair faster? __The hot air from the hair drier__
__makes the water on hair evaporate faster than if the hair air dries.__

How can you make a dime dance?

What you need

soft-drink bottle
freezer
safety goggles
dropper
dime
pencil and paper

What to do

1. Place the empty bottle in the freezer for 30 minutes.
2. Put on the safety goggles.
3. Put the cold bottle on a table. Using the dropper, place a few drops of water on the rim of the bottle.
4. Cover the mouth of the bottle with a dime.
5. Watch the dime and the bottle for a few minutes and record your observations.

Test	Observations
1 minute	
3 minutes	
5 minutes	
7 minutes	

What did you learn?

1. What happened to the dime?
2. What happened to the air in the bottle?

Using what you learned

1. From the results of this activity, how do you know that air is matter?
2. How is what happened to the air in the bottle similar to how a thermometer works?

55

ACTIVITY RESPONSES

What did you learn?
1. The dime kept being pushed up (it danced on the rim of the bottle).
2. As it warmed, the air inside the bottle expanded.

Using what you learned
1. The expanding air pushed up the dime, showing that air has volume. The dime and the air can't occupy the same space at the same time.
2. Just as the air in the bottle expands when it warms, the liquid in a thermometer expands when it warms. The liquid then rises in the tube.

PREPLAN

Time Allotment: 45 minutes
Process Skill: Inferring

Objectives
1. **Infer** that air expands as it warms.
2. **Recognize** that cold air takes up less space than warm air.

Setup
■ If a freezer isn't available, cool the bottle in a regular refrigerator or, if the weather is cold, outside.

Cooperative Grouping: fives—Assign roles as explained on page T24.

1 FOCUS

■ Review through discussion the concepts of expansion and contraction of matter before beginning the activity.

2 TEACH

■ Steps 3 and 4 should be done promptly, before air in the chilled bottle warms.
■ Be sure the entire surface of the rim has been moistened to insure a proper seal.
■ The dime should begin "dancing" in a minute or so. Depending on the size and temperature of the bottle, the dime may continue to move for several minutes.
■ Have students use the Teacher Resource Master **Activity Worksheet,** pages 35 and 36, to record their data and answers.

3 APPLY

■ You may wish to have interested students investigate which variables determine how long the dime will continue to dance. They may suggest the size of the bottle, length of time in freezer, and so on.

Close
■ Discuss the activity and questions with the class.

PREPLAN

Lesson Objectives

3. **Explain** the role of heat in the change of state from solid to liquid and from liquid to solid.
4. **Describe** what happens to liquid matter when it evaporates and to gas matter when it condenses.

Science Background

■ All changes of state involve energy changes. Heat is absorbed or given off. Melting and evaporation absorb heat. Condensation and freezing emit heat.
■ Attractive forces hold particles close together in the solid state. As heat is absorbed, the particles move faster and partially overcome these attractive forces. Thus, the solid melts. A similar process occurs in a liquid as it changes to a gas.
■ Conversely, as matter is cooled and heat is given off, the particles move more slowly. As the particles of a gas, for example, slow down, the attraction between the particles pulls them closer together. Thus, the gas liquefies, or condenses.
■ This explanation of changing states is called the kinetic theory.

Lesson Vocabulary

evaporation   condensation

Note: The activity on student page 61 may be used for guided discovery before you begin this lesson.

1   FOCUS

■ About half an hour before beginning the lesson, place a glass of ice cubes in the room so that it is visible to students. When you begin, ask students what is happening to the ice cubes, and why. Lead students to the realization that heat from the room causes the ice to liquefy.
■ Use the goals on student page 56 to establish the purpose for studying this lesson.

Changing States of Matter

LESSON 2 GOALS
You will learn
● that heat may cause matter to change state.
● the difference between melting and freezing.
● the difference between evaporation and condensation.

1. The juice changed from the solid state to the liquid state.

2. The heat came from the air around the can.

What if you want juice for breakfast? You open a can of frozen juice, but the juice does not pour. Disappointed, you leave the can on the counter for a while. Later you try to pour the juice again. This time the juice pours easily. [1]Why could you pour the juice the second time you tried?

You already learned that adding or losing heat causes matter to expand or contract. Now you will see that heat may also cause matter to change its state. [2]Where did the heat come from that melted the frozen juice? When things get hotter or colder, they can melt or freeze. Things melt when they change from solids to liquids. Things freeze when they change from liquids to solids.

Heat changes matter

56

TEACHER RESOURCE MASTERS

ACTIVITY

You Can...

Win the Ice Cube Race

Think of different ways to melt an ice cube. Choose the way that you predict will be the fastest. Gather any materials you need and try the method you chose. Remember to record how long it takes for your ice cube to melt. Compare your results with those of your classmates. Which method worked best? What was the shortest time?

When matter gains or loses heat, the matter can change state. When solids melt, they change to the liquid state. The solid frozen orange juice gained heat when it melted. On the other hand, liquids freeze when they change to the solid state. Liquids lose heat when they freeze.

Remember from Lesson 3 in Chapter 2 what the particles in solids look like. They are arranged into a definite pattern. Even though all particles move, the particles in solids move the least. They can only shake back and forth or up and down in their places. They stay in their patterns, and they don't change shape.

What word describes the change of matter from the solid state to the liquid state?

57

2 TEACH

■ Introduce the term *melt*, and relate it to heat.

■ Initiate a discussion of the loss of heat when matter freezes. Point out the difference in the way particles are free to move in the solid and liquid states.

Guided Practice

■ Check students' understanding of lesson concepts by discussing the Lesson Review questions on student page 60. If necessary, use the **reteaching strategy** in OPTIONS.

Independent Practice

■ Assign the Lesson 2 section of the Teacher Resource Master **Independent Practice,** page 43.

3 APPLY

■ Challenge students to think of ways to keep an ice cube solid for the longest time.

Close

■ Use Summary statements on student page 60 to review lesson concepts.

OPTIONS

Reteaching Strategy

Have students sketch the arrangements of particles in the solid, liquid, and gaseous states.

Resource Options

Use Color Transparency #2, "Changing States of Matter."

■ Refer to page 58 for teaching strategies for **You Can . . . Win the Ice Cube Race.**

TEACHER RESOURCE MASTERS

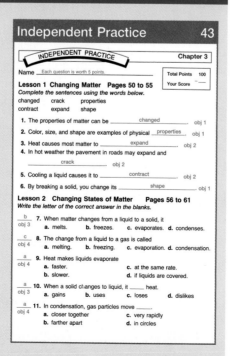

Independent Practice   43

| INDEPENDENT PRACTICE | Chapter 3 |

Name ___Each question is worth 5 points.___   Total Points 100   Your Score ___

Lesson 1 Changing Matter   Pages 50 to 55
Complete the sentences using the words below.

changed   crack   properties
contract   expand   shape

1. The properties of matter can be ___changed___ .   obj 1
2. Color, size, and shape are examples of physical ___properties___ .   obj 1
3. Heat causes most matter to ___expand___ .   obj 2
4. In hot weather the pavement in roads may expand and ___crack___ .   obj 2
5. Cooling a liquid causes it to ___contract___ .   obj 2
6. By breaking a solid, you change its ___shape___ .   obj 1

Lesson 2   Changing States of Matter   Pages 56 to 61
Write the letter of the correct answer in the blanks.

___b___ 7. When matter changes from a liquid to a solid, it
obj 3   a. melts.   b. freezes.   c. evaporates.   d. condenses.

___c___ 8. The change from a liquid to a gas is called
obj 4   a. melting.   b. freezing.   c. evaporation.   d. condensation.

___a___ 9. Heat makes liquids evaporate
obj 4   a. faster.   c. at the same rate.
    b. slower.   d. if liquids are covered.

___a___ 10. When a solid changes to liquid, it ___ heat.
obj 3   a. gains   b. uses   c. loses   d. dislikes

___a___ 11. In condensation, gas particles move ___ .
obj 4   a. closer together   c. very rapidly
    b. farther apart   d. in circles

OPTIONS

YOU CAN . . . WIN THE ICE CUBE RACE

Process Skills: Forming Hypotheses/ Experimenting

Objective: Hypothesize and **experiment** to find a fast method for melting ice cubes.

Setup/Teach

■ **Safety Considerations:** Remind students not to put the ice cubes in their mouths. Use only warm tap water, and do not allow students to break their own ice.

■ A class chart can be made listing the various methods and resulting times.

LANGUAGE CONNECTION

Writing: Present the following writing task. Imagine you and your little sister made a big snowperson (a solid). The next day was warmer and it melted. Your sister cried. Write a letter to your sister explaining why the snowperson melted. Use correct grammar.

◆ **Reinforcement:** Initiate a discussion comparing melting and freezing temperatures of common materials. Students should realize that the melting and freezing points are the same (that is, water melts and freezes at 0°C). Emphasize the relationship between melting and freezing.

● **Enrichment:** If possible, freeze several liquids either in a freezer or outdoors, if the weather permits. Observe which liquid freezes first.

Resource Options

■ Use Activity Book, "Measuring," pages 13 and 14.

■ Show selections from "Combustion," *Mr. Wizard's World of Science Video Library,* Merrill Publishing Company.

Would You Believe?

In eastern Siberia, temperatures can be so low that the moisture from a person's breath can freeze and fall to the ground.

Now ask yourself, "When a solid melts into a liquid, what are the particles doing?" Remember that solids gain heat to melt. The added heat makes the particles in the solids move faster. Heat also makes the particles move apart. The pattern that the particles had been in breaks down. The particles begin moving past each other. As the pattern breaks down, the solids change to liquids. You may have seen ice change to liquid water. Most solids melt if enough heat is added.

When liquids freeze, they change to the solid state. Liquids freeze when enough heat is removed from them. As heat is lost, the particles of liquid matter move more slowly. They move closer together. When the particles form a definite pattern, the liquid has become a solid.

Solids melt

58

TEACHER RESOURCE MASTERS

Liquids can also change to gases. Remember that particles of liquids move from place to place. They bump into each other. The particles on the top layer of a liquid may be bumped away from the rest of the liquid. These particles become a gas. This change from a liquid to a gas is called **evaporation** (ih vap uh RAY shun).

What is the change from a liquid to a gas called?

Water evaporates

After people wash their clothes, they use dryers or hang the clothes outside to dry. In the dryer or outdoors, warm temperatures speed evaporation. Although liquids can evaporate at any temperature, adding heat makes them evaporate faster. [1]Why do you think this is true?

1. Particles move faster at higher temperatures. Therefore, they are more likely to get bumped away from the surface of the liquid.

59

OPTIONS

▲**Challenge:** Have students (with adult assistance) determine the temperature of their refrigerators (including the freezers) at home. Compare results.

■ Have students describe what a bathroom looks and feels like after someone has taken a hot shower. They will probably state that it is hot, steamy, wet, and damp. Most will be familiar with a steamy mirror. Relate these experiences to condensation.

TEACHER RESOURCE MASTERS

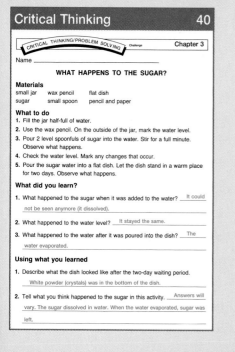

Critical Thinking   40

CRITICAL THINKING/PROBLEM SOLVING   Challenge   Chapter 3

Name _____

WHAT HAPPENS TO THE SUGAR?

Materials
small jar   wax pencil   flat dish
sugar   small spoon   pencil and paper

What to do
1. Fill the jar half-full of water.
2. Use the wax pencil. On the outside of the jar, mark the water level.
3. Pour 2 level spoonfuls of sugar into the water. Stir for a full minute. Observe what happens.
4. Check the water level. Mark any changes that occur.
5. Pour the sugar water into a flat dish. Let the dish stand in a warm place for two days. Observe what happens.

What did you learn?

1. What happened to the sugar when it was added to the water? __It could not be seen anymore (it dissolved).__

2. What happened to the water level? __It stayed the same.__

3. What happened to the water after it was poured into the dish? __The water evaporated.__

Using what you learned

1. Describe what the dish looked like after the two-day waiting period. __White powder (crystals) was in the bottom of the dish.__

2. Tell what you think happened to the sugar in this activity. __Answers will vary. The sugar dissolved in water. When the water evaporated, sugar was left.__

OPTIONS

▲ **Challenge:** Initiate a discussion of why dew usually forms early in the morning. Have the students make inferences as to what is meant by the terms *relatively cool* and *relatively warm*.

LESSON REVIEW ANSWERS

1. The particles move faster, and the pattern breaks down. The particles move faster and are bumped away from the rest of the liquid.

2. The liquid may freeze. The gas may become liquid.

3. Its particles slow down, move closer together, and change to a liquid.

1. Possible answers include condensation on grass, windows, and mirrors.

Sometimes a gas may lose heat. As the gas cools, its particles slow down and move closer together. The gas can change to a liquid. The change from a gas to a liquid is called **condensation** (kahn den SAY shun). Water will form on a glass of iced tea on a warm day. The cold glass causes some of the water that is a gas in the air to condense on the glass. [1]Where have you seen other examples of a gas condensing?

Gases condense

Lesson Summary

- Adding heat may change matter from the solid state to the liquid state. Removing heat may change matter from the liquid state to the solid state.
- Evaporation is the change of matter from a liquid to a gas. Condensation is the change of matter from a gas to a liquid.

Lesson Review

1. What happens to the speed and pattern of particles of matter when heat is added to a solid? to a liquid?
2. What may happen when heat is removed from a liquid? from a gas?
★3. What happens to particles of gas during condensation?

60

TEACHER RESOURCE MASTERS

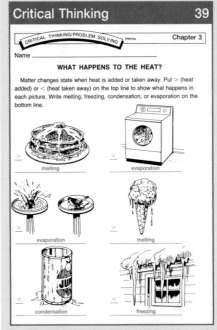

Critical Thinking 39

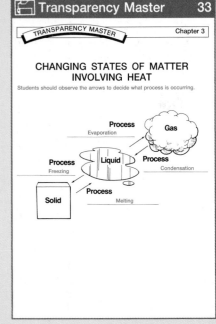

Transparency Master 33

ACTIVITY

How does water change?

What you need
baking dish
water
tape
plastic wrap
paper cup
pencil and paper

What to do
1. Place the dish by a window.
2. Fill the dish half full of water.
3. Cover the dish tightly with plastic wrap.
4. Tape the plastic wrap to the dish. Predict what will happen.
5. Observe the dish each day for 2 days.
6. Record your observations.

2. What happened to the plastic wrap?
3. What changes did you observe between the first and second day?

Using what you learned
1. What caused the changes?
2. What do you think would happen if you took the plastic wrap off the dish? Try it and find out.
3. How does this activity show why bathroom mirrors sometimes become foggy?

What did you learn?
1. What happened to the total amount of water in the covered dish?

61

ACTIVITY RESPONSES

What did you learn?
1. It was unchanged.
2. Water drops formed on the plastic wrap.
3. Water from the dish formed in droplets on the plastic wrap. It evaporated and then condensed.

Using what you learned
1. Heat from the sun made the water in the dish evaporate. It condensed on the cooler plastic wrap.
2. The water in the dish would evaporate. After a few days all the water would be gone from the dish.
3. The water from the bath or shower is warm. Some of it changes state to water vapor (evaporates) which then condenses on the cool surfaces of the mirrors.

PREPLAN

Time Allotment: 15 minutes on two different days

Process Skill: Observing

Objectives
1. **Build** a working model of evaporation and condensation.
2. **Explain** how the model works.

Setup
Cooperative Grouping: fives—Assign roles as explained on page T24.

1 FOCUS

■ Have students use their experiences to speculate about what will happen in the covered dish.

2 TEACH

■ Use the first period to distribute the materials and set up the activity. You might also use this time to record the student predictions about what will happen during the two-day waiting period.
■ Try not to move the dish at the end of the waiting period. Too much movement will make the water on the plastic wrap fall back into the pan.
■ You may wish to have students investigate other variables that may affect the rate of evaporation.
■ Have students use the Teacher Resource Master **Activity Worksheet,** pages 37 and 38, to record their data and answers.

3 APPLY

■ Ask: **What does this activity tell you about caring for a closed terrarium?**
A closed terrarium does not have to be watered as often as plants in the open air.

Close
■ Discuss the activity and questions with the class.

PREPLAN

Lesson Objectives

5. Describe mixtures and **identify** common mixtures.

6. Describe compounds.

7. Understand that a chemical change takes place when a compound forms.

Science Background

■ Mixtures can be made up of combinations of any amounts of solids, liquids, or gaseous substances.

■ A mixture is formed when two or more substances are physically combined. In compounds the elements are chemically combined.

■ The components of mixtures retain their properties and can, therefore, be separated by physical means. Compounds can be broken down only through chemical changes.

■ Chemical changes occur through chemical reactions and always result in the formation of one or more new substances.

■ Technological applications of chemical changes produce most of our consumer goods. These goods range from soda cans to food additives, from polyester fabrics to paints and plastics.

Lesson Vocabulary

mixture   compound
chemical change

1 FOCUS

■ Begin the lesson by displaying a common mixture, such as a jar of mixed beans or coins, to the class. Ask students if they could separate the mixture and how.

■ Use the goals on student page 62 to establish the purpose for studying this lesson.

LESSON 3 GOALS
You will learn
● the properties of a mixture.
● the properties of a compound.
● that a chemical change takes place when a compound is formed.

Combining Matter

In the picture on this page, the boy is counting money. There are different kinds of coins mixed in the pile. As he counts the coins, the boy separates them. The pile of coins is a mixture of different types of matter. The coins are not changed by mixing them together. They can be separated after they are mixed. Matter that is mixed together without changing the properties of each type of matter is called a **mixture.**

There are many mixtures. A fruit salad is a mixture. Different amounts of each fruit can be added to a salad. The properties of each fruit, however, do not change. The pieces of fruit can be separated after they are mixed.

Separating mixtures

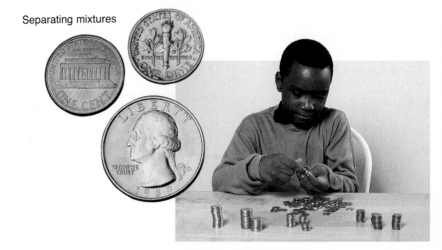

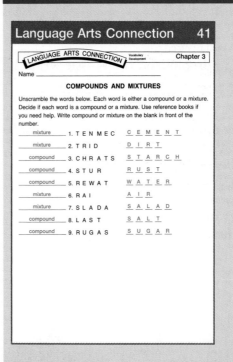

62

TEACHER RESOURCE MASTERS

Language Arts Connection   41

LANGUAGE ARTS CONNECTION   Vocabulary Development   Chapter 3

Name _____

COMPOUNDS AND MIXTURES

Unscramble the words below. Each word is either a compound or a mixture. Decide if each word is a compound or a mixture. Use reference books if you need help. Write compound or mixture on the blank in front of the number.

mixture	1. T E N M E C	C E M E N T
mixture	2. T R I D	D I R T
compound	3. C H R A T S	S T A R C H
compound	4. S T U R	R U S T
compound	5. R E W A T	W A T E R
mixture	6. R A I	A I R
mixture	7. S L A D A	S A L A D
compound	8. L A S T	S A L T
compound	9. R U G A S	S U G A R

However, not all mixtures can be taken apart as easily as a pile of coins or a fruit salad. For example, you can make a mixture called salt water if you mix table salt with water. Salt water doesn't look like a mixture. But it is a mixture, and it can be separated. You simply evaporate the water, and the salt is left behind.

Iron rusts

Different elements can be combined in such a way that they can't be easily separated later. Instead of mixtures we call them compounds. A **compound** is a kind of matter formed from two or more elements. The properties of a compound are different from the properties of the elements that make it up. A **chemical change** takes place when a compound forms.

Rust is a compound. A chemical change takes place when the elements iron and oxygen combine to form rust. The properties of rust are not the same as the properties of either iron or oxygen.

What kind of change takes place when a compound is formed?

Use Application Activity on pages 345, 346.

63

---

2   TEACH

■ Ask students to tell what properties the boy is using to separate the mixture on page 62.
■ Encourage students to brainstorm a list of common mixtures.
■ Point out that chemical changes cause the formation of new types of matter.

Guided Practice

■ Check students' understanding of lesson concepts by discussing the Lesson Review questions on student page 64. If necessary, use the **reteaching strategy** in OPTIONS.

Independent Practice

■ Assign the Lesson 3 section of the Teacher Resource Master **Independent Practice,** page 44.

3   APPLY

■ Use Application Activity, "Who Will Stop the Rust?" on student pages 345 and 346.

Close

■ Use Summary statements on student page 64 to review lesson concepts.

OPTIONS

Reteaching Strategy

Select a simple cake or cookie recipe. As each ingredient is added, ask the students if a mixture or compound is being made. Stirring the dry ingredients together creates a mixture. Adding baking soda, baking powder, and heat results in a chemical change forming new compounds. They can discuss how the end product differs from the original ingredients.

Resource Options

■ Show selections from "Chemical Reactions," *Mr. Wizard's World of Science Video Library,* Merrill Publishing Company.

TEACHER RESOURCE MASTERS

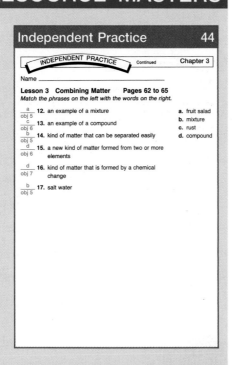

Independent Practice   44

INDEPENDENT PRACTICE   Continued   Chapter 3

Name _____

Lesson 3   Combining Matter   Pages 62 to 65
Match the phrases on the left with the words on the right.

  a   **12.** an example of a mixture
obj 5

  c   **13.** an example of a compound
obj 6

  b   **14.** kind of matter that can be separated easily
obj 5

  d   **15.** a new kind of matter formed from two or more
obj 6   elements

  d   **16.** kind of matter that is formed by a chemical
obj 7   change

  b   **17.** salt water
obj 5

a. fruit salad
b. mixture
c. rust
d. compound

OPTIONS

MATH CONNECTION

■ Give students the following math problem. Linc unloaded boxes of fruit from his brother's truck. Labels on the boxes read as follows: 36 honeydew melons, 17 pineapples, 21 coconuts, 46 grapefruits, 9 watermelons, 24 baskets of strawberries, and 2 boxes of grapes. Name the fruit with even-numbered labels and those with odd-numbered labels.

Science and Technology: Use "I WANT TO KNOW ABOUT . . . Making Diamonds," student page 65, with this lesson.

● **Enrichment:** Make a mixture of salt or sugar and water. Place in a shallow pan or dish and allow the water to evaporate so students can observe the salt (or sugar) left behind. You could cover one such pan with a piece of plastic wrap. The water that condenses on the inside of the plastic wrap will not taste salty.

▲ **Challenge:** Have able students **work cooperatively** to research and report to the class on mixtures used in food, building materials, or other consumer products.

Resource Options
■ Use Activity Book, "Who Will Stop the Rust?" pages 35 and 36.
■ Use Activity Book "Hypothesizing," pages 15 and 16.

LESSON REVIEW ANSWERS

1. The parts of the salad have their same properties.
2. Answers may include rust, smoke, ashes.
3. chemical

1. Ashes, smoke, and gases form when wood burns.

New compounds form when something burns. When wood burns, most of the elements in the wood combine with oxygen in the air. [1]What new compounds are formed when wood burns?

Lesson Summary

- A mixture is different kinds of matter mixed together. In a mixture, each type of matter keeps its own properties.
- A compound is a combination of elements that is not a mixture. A compound has different properties than those of the elements from which it is made.
- A chemical change takes place when a compound is formed.

Lesson Review

1. Why is a salad a mixture?
2. Give an example of a compound.
★3. What kind of change takes place when a piece of wood is burned?

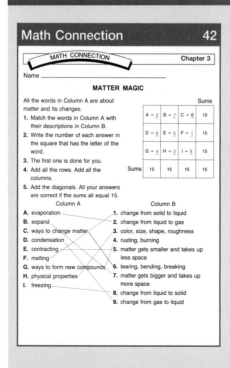

New compounds form

64

TEACHER RESOURCE MASTERS

Math Connection   42

MATH CONNECTION   Chapter 3

Name _____

MATTER MAGIC

All the words in Column A are about matter and its changes.

1. Match the words in Column A with their descriptions in Column B.
2. Write the number of each answer in the square that has the letter of the word.
3. The first one is done for you.
4. Add all the rows. Add all the columns.
5. Add the diagonals. All your answers are correct if the sums all equal 15.

			Sums
A = 2	B = 7	C = 6	15
D = 9	E = 5	F = 1	15
G = 4	H = 3	I = 8	15
Sums 15	15	15	15

Column A
A. evaporation
B. expand
C. ways to change matter
D. condensation
E. contracting
F. melting
G. ways to form new compounds
H. physical properties
I. freezing

Column B
1. change from solid to liquid
2. change from liquid to gas
3. color, size, shape, roughness
4. rusting, burning
5. matter gets smaller and takes up less space
6. tearing, bending, breaking
7. matter gets bigger and takes up more space
8. change from liquid to solid
9. change from gas to liquid

I WANT TO KNOW ABOUT...

Making Diamonds

Carol Lee makes diamonds. The diamonds are not used for jewelry, but they are used in industries. Diamonds are made from carbon. It normally takes Mother Nature millions of years to form a diamond. Carol, however, makes diamonds every day in her lab.

In the first step, Carol mixes carbon with some metals. She heats the mixture to a temperature of about 1,300°C. The mixture is put under great pressure. The mixture melts, and the carbon becomes diamond. When it cools, each diamond is cleaned.

Artificial diamonds are used in many ways. Large, high-quality diamonds are used on saws for cutting rocks and on drill bits for oil wells.

Small, imperfect artificial diamonds are combined with other materials to polish the edges of people's glasses and car windows. Carol says that in many cases her diamonds are better than natural diamonds.

Science and Technology

65

Feature Background

■ The process described here is a high-pressure process. This process is used commonly in industry. A low-pressure process is being developed in which methane is bombarded with microwaves. It decomposes and diamonds are produced.

■ Because peanut butter and diamonds are both essentially carbon, some companies that produce industrial diamonds demonstrate that diamonds can be made from peanut butter.

Feature Vocabulary

diamonds   carbon   pressure

Teaching Suggestions

■ Explain that, although one thinks of the diamond as primarily a gemstone, about 12 million carats of industrial diamonds are imported into the United States annually.

■ Inform students that industrial diamonds are also produced in the United States. The first synthetic diamonds were made in 1955 by General Electric.

■ Inform students that diamonds are the hardest known minerals.

TEACHER RESOURCE MASTERS

Summary

Chapter Closure: Ask the students to rewrite each summary statement changing a word or phrase to make the statements false. Have the students exchange papers. Without using their books, the students should correct and rewrite each statement to make it true again. Answers can be checked by the students by referring to their texts.

Science Words

Play "Hangman" using the science words. The person who supplies the last letter to solve the word must use the word in a sentence correctly or the "Hangman" wins.

Student Responses

1. chemical change
2. mixture
3. condensation
4. compound

CHAPTER REVIEW

3

Summary

Lesson 1
- Properties of matter can be changed.
- Adding or removing heat can cause matter to expand or contract.

Lesson 2
- Matter may change state when heat is added or taken away.
- Solids melt when they change to liquids, and liquids freeze when they change to solids.

- The change from a liquid to a gas is evaporation, and the change from a gas to a liquid is condensation.

Lesson 3
- Matter that is mixed together but keeps its own properties is called a mixture.
- A compound has properties different from the elements that make it up.
- A chemical change takes place when a compound is formed.

Science Words

Fill in the blank with the correct word or words from the list.

evaporation   compound   mixture
condensation   physical change   chemical change

1. To form a compound, a ____ takes place.
2. The change from a liquid to a gas is called ____.
3. The change from a gas to a liquid is called ____.
4. Matter that is formed from two or more elements is a(n) ____.

66

TEACHER RESOURCE MASTERS

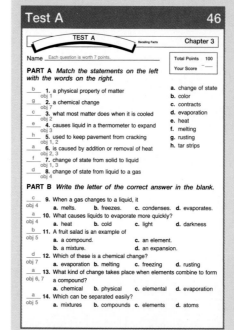

Test A   46

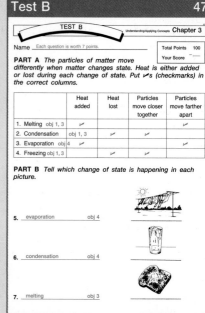

Test B   47

Questions

Recalling Ideas
Correctly complete each of the following sentences.

1. When rust forms, the kind of change that takes place is
   (a) state. (c) chemical.
   (b) physical. (d) evaporation.
2. An example of a common mixture is
   (a) oxygen. (c) rust.
   (b) fruit salad. (d) salt.
3. Evaporation speeds up when liquids are exposed to
   (a) heat. (c) condensation.
   (b) expansion. (d) cold.

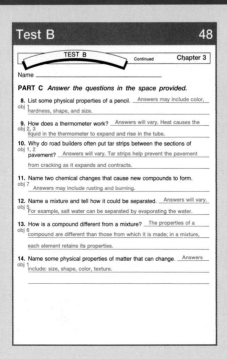

Understanding Ideas
Answer the following questions using complete sentences.

1. Name two ways that heat changes matter.
2. Name a solid, liquid, and gas and tell how the physical properties of each can be changed.
3. What may happen to pavement in hot weather?
4. What happens to liquid when it freezes?
5. Describe the process of evaporation.
6. What happens to gas when it condenses?

Thinking Critically
Think about what you have learned in this chapter. Answer the following questions using complete sentences.

1. Why would people pour hot water on tight jar lids?
2. You are cooking stew. There is too much liquid in the pan. Why do you take the cover off the pan?

67

Questions

Recalling Ideas
1. c
2. b
3. a

Understanding Ideas
1. Heat changes matter by causing it to expand and to change its state.
2. A block of wood can be carved to change its shape, or painted to change its color; water vapor in the air can condense into dew on a cool morning; dye can be added to water to change its color. Accept all reasonable answers.
3. Heat may cause the pavement to expand and break.
4. It loses heat and changes to the solid state.
5. Liquid may evaporate if particles on the top layer of the liquid are bumped away from the liquid and become a gas.
6. The gas particles lose heat, slow down, and move closer together.

Thinking Critically
1. People pour hot water on tight jar lids so the metal of the lid expands and the lid can be removed from the jar.
2. You take the cover off the pan so the liquid will evaporate more quickly.

TEACHER RESOURCE MASTERS

Test B   48

TEST B — Continued — Chapter 3

Name _____

PART C *Answer the questions in the space provided.*

8. List some physical properties of a pencil. Answers may include color, hardness, shape, and size.
obj 1

9. How does a thermometer work? Answers will vary. Heat causes the liquid in the thermometer to expand and rise in the tube.
obj 2, 3

10. Why do road builders often put tar strips between the sections of pavement? Answers will vary. Tar strips help prevent the pavement from cracking as it expands and contracts.
obj 1, 2

11. Name two chemical changes that cause new compounds to form. Answers may include rusting and burning.
obj 7

12. Name a mixture and tell how it could be separated. Answers will vary. For example, salt water can be separated by evaporating the water.
obj 5

13. How is a compound different from a mixture? The properties of a compound are different than those from which it is made; in a mixture, each element retains its properties.
obj 6

14. Name some physical properties of matter that can change. Answers include: size, shape, color, texture.
obj 1

Forces and Work

Planning Guide

Lessons	Objectives	Vocabulary
Chapter Introduction pp. 68, 69		
Lesson 1 Force pp. 70–73	1. **Define** *force*. 2. **Explain** that the force needed to move an object depends on the object's mass. 3. **Estimate** the relative amounts of force required to move various objects.	force
Lesson 2 Gravity and Friction pp. 74–77	4. **Define** *gravity*. 5. **Give examples** of effects of gravity. 6. **Define** *friction* and **give examples** of properties affecting friction.	gravity friction
Lesson 3 Work and Energy pp. 78–83	7. **Operationally define** *work*. 8. **Determine** when work is done. 9. **Define** *energy*.	work energy
Chapter Review pp. 84, 85		

Planning Guide

Text Activities		Teacher Resource Masters	Other Components
Title/Skill	**Materials per Group**		
Have You Ever . . . Compared How Objects Move? p. 69 Experimenting/Forming Hypotheses Time Allotment: 30 minutes	marble pencil paper (crumpled into a ball) wooden block		**Activity Center:** "Toyland"; "Floating Through Space"; "Fancy Footwear"
How Do You Measure Force? p. 73 Observing/Inferring/ Predicting Time Allotment: 45 minutes	cardboard strip long, thin rubber band masking tape 30 cm string 3 paper clips 5 small objects pencil and paper	Independent Practice, pp. 59, 60 Transparency Master, p. 49 Activity Worksheet, pp. 51, 52 Critical Thinking, p. 55 ▲ Critical Thinking, p. 56	Poster #3 Mr. Wizard's World of Science Video Tape 2
You Can . . . Reduce Friction, p. 76 Experimenting Time Allotment: 10 minutes	marbles liquid soap paper towels	Independent Practice, pp. 59, 60 Activity Worksheet, pp. 53, 54 ▲ Reteaching Activity, p. 61 ◆ Family Science, p. 50	Mr. Wizard's World of Science Video Tape 3 Mr. Wizard's World of Science Video Tape 4 Activity Book, p. 17, 18
How Can You Change Friction? p. 77 Observing/Separating and Controlling Variables Time Allotment: 30 minutes	Puller Pal chalkboard eraser string smooth table sandpaper dish towel pencil and paper		
		Independent Practice, pp. 59, 60 Language Arts Connection, p. 57 Health Connection, p. 58	Mr. Wizard's World of Science Video Tape 6
		Test A, p. 62 Test B, pp. 63, 64	Science Words Software

◆ Basic / ▲ Advanced / All other masters are for use by all students.

Forces and Work

For Exceptional Students

ESL/LEP

Chapter 4/Lesson 1, Page 70

To help students with the concept of mass, ask them to compare the masses of several objects in the room. Write an example on the chalkboard: **The pencil has a larger mass than the paper.** Students can use the sentence to fill in other objects or change the pattern if they wish. After they have each offered several comparisons, write another pattern on the chalkboard: **I need more force to lift a _____ than to lift a _____.** Ask students to complete the pattern with objects of their choice.

Chapter 4/Lesson 2, Page 74

Write the following sentence on the chalkboard: **There is much friction when I pull a box over the rough floor.** Students should provide other examples changing "much" to "little" or "less" if appropriate. They may change the objects pulled and the surfaces over which the objects are pulled. This will enforce students' understanding of friction, while at the same time they practice their English conversation.

Chapter 4/Lesson 3, Page 78

Ask students to list five examples of a force being used and work being done. They may also give five examples of a force being used and no work being done. They should mention whether work was done or not. It may help to write a pattern on the chalkboard: **Work done: I pushed the shopping cart around the supermarket. No work done: I pushed against the big box but could not move it.**

Gifted

Chapter 4/Lesson 2, Page 76

Challenge gifted students to create a "downhill course" from scrap materials so that a small rubber ball takes exactly one minute to complete the course. Allow students some brainstorming time to suggest friction-causing surfaces they might use. After the downhill courses are completed, have students suggest modifications for their course if a metal ball or golf ball were to replace the rubber ball.

Mainstreamed

Chapter 4/Lesson 2, Page 76

Visually Impaired: Give students materials having a variety of surfaces, such as ice, silk, satin, sandpaper (all grades), rug pieces (shag/pile), tiles, or cloth. Ask the students to arrange the surfaces according to the force of friction. After the students have touched or visually inspected the surfaces, have them describe the texture of the surface. Reinforce verbal diversity in the descriptions.

Whole Class Science Project

Have the class investigate the relationship between mass and force. Divide the class into groups. Give each group a cardboard box (one side open, all boxes of same size). Have each group use objects made of one material (cloth, wood, iron, and so on) to fill the box. When boxes have been filled, use a scale to determine the force required to lift each box and its contents. Have the class create a display that shows the results of the investigation, perhaps organizing the list from materials that require greatest force to lift to those that require least force.

As an extension of this project, reinforce the concept that the mass of an object is not determined by size. Have a group of students fill a large box with cloth. A different group should fill a smaller box with wood. Observe the forces required to lift each box. What box sizes are required so that forces needed to lift each box (of cloth, of wood) are equivalent?

Be sure students realize that differences in force were caused by differences in mass, even though the boxes might be the same size.

Science Fair Projects

Individual students could do one of the following projects:

1. Compare the resources used and methods of energy production in three of the following energy types: fossil fuel, geothermal, solar, hydroelectric, nuclear.
2. Investigate the effects of mass and surface area on the time objects take to fall a certain distance. Compare objects of the same area but different masses and the same masses but different areas.
3. Research the nature of materials used to construct gymnasium floors. A suitable material must allow balls to bounce, be easy to run on, and help reduce injuries when a person falls. Find out whether newer materials are better than wood.

CHAPTER 4

pages 68–85

Chapter Concepts
■ The force needed to move an object depends on the object's mass.
■ The forces of gravity and friction affect the amount of force needed to move an object.
■ Energy is the ability to do work by exerting a force to move an object through a distance.

Chapter Background
■ The force with which Earth attracts an object depends on the object's mass. Therefore, the force needed to lift an object depends on its mass. The greater the mass, the greater the force of attraction, and therefore the greater the force needed to overcome that attraction.
■ Whenever a force is applied to move an object across the surface of another object, a force of friction opposes the applied force. In order for motion to occur, the applied force must be large enough to overcome the force of friction. Lubricants and smooth surfaces are used to reduce friction.
■ Energy is the ability to do work. Therefore, energy is the ability to exert a force to move an object. We obtain energy from food. Cars burn fuel to obtain energy to move.

Look for These Symbols

—Hands-on activity

—Cooperative learning

—Overhead transparency

◆ —Basic/Reinforcement

● —Average/Enrichment

▲ —Advanced/Challenge

—Calculator Practice

SCIENCE
In Your World

68

CHAPTER 4

Forces and Work

On a windy day, you may notice that walking is more difficult when the wind blows against you. Can you think of other times when the wind makes you work harder? Are there times when the wind makes your work easier?

Have You Ever...

Compared How Objects Move?

Some things move more easily than others. If you think like a scientist, you can discover more about the wind and moving objects. Collect a wooden block, a marble, a crumpled ball of paper, and a pencil. Try to blow each one across the floor. Which are easier to move? Try testing other objects. What properties do you think make an object easy or difficult to move by wind?

69

PREPLAN

Time Allotment: 30 minutes

Objectives
1. **Discuss** the effects of wind on objects.
2. **Hypothesize** the properties of an object that make it easily moved by wind.

Setup
■ If you wish to conduct the activity, you will need the following materials for each student or activity group:

marble   paper (crumpled into a ball)
pencil   wooden block

1   FOCUS

■ Ask a student to describe what is happening in the picture on page 68.

2   TEACH

■ Have the title and introductory paragraph read aloud.
■ Ask: **How can the wind make you work harder?** *Answers will vary; when it blows against you; when it blows things away from you.*

Have you Ever . . .
Use this activity as an introduction to force needed to move an object.
Have students **work cooperatively** in groups of four to complete this activity.
■ **Student Responses**
1. An object's weight and size can affect the ease with which it can be moved.
2. Objects that are rounded can be moved more easily than those that have corners.

3   APPLY

■ Brainstorm ways in which other forces are like the wind and ways in which they are different.

Close
■ Students will learn more about forces and work in Chapter 4.

PREPLAN

Lesson Objectives

1. **Define** *force*.
2. **Explain** that the force needed to move an object depends on the object's mass.
3. **Estimate** the relative amounts of force required to move various objects.

Science Background

■ Any push or pull is a force. Only an unbalanced force on an object produces motion. An unbalanced force is one that is greater than the force that opposes motion. When a small child pushes on a large refrigerator, the force from the child never exceeds the force of friction from the floor on the refrigerator. Consequently, the refrigerator doesn't move.

Lesson Vocabulary

force

Note: The activity on student page 73 may be used for guided discovery before you begin this lesson.

1 FOCUS

Explain and demonstrate the definition of force as any push or pull. Have students lift both heavy and light objects. Ask them to characterize the objects as being light or heavy and to compare the force needed to move the objects. Be sure each person uses the word "force" correctly in the comparison.

■ Use the goals on student page 70 to establish the purpose for studying this lesson.

LESSON 1 GOALS

You will learn
● what is needed to move objects.
● that the amount of force needed to move an object depends on the object's mass.

1. You use a pull.

Using pushes and pulls

Force

We can move objects in different ways. Many objects will move if you push them. Other objects move when you pull them. A push or a pull is a **force.** The children at the playground swings are using forces. They are using pushes and pulls.

An object moves when you lift it. Lifting is a force. [1]Do you use a push or a pull to lift a chair off the floor? Some objects can be lifted by using a small force. Other objects need greater force to be lifted. The amount of force needed to lift or move an object depends on how much matter the object has. Another way to say it is that the force needed depends on the object's mass.

70

TEACHER RESOURCE MASTERS

Transparency Master   49

TRANSPARENCY MASTER   Chapter 4

Each picture shows a push or a pull. Have students tell what force is being used.

PUSH OR PULL?

Pull

Push

Push

Pull

Imagine you and a friend are helping to clear away the trash from an empty lot. It will make a good playground when the bricks and branches are cleared away. You fill two wheelbarrows with trash. One wheelbarrow has mostly bricks. The other has mostly branches. Both wheelbarrows are the same size. But the wheelbarrow full of bricks takes more force to push. That is because the wheelbarrow of bricks has more mass than the wheelbarrow of branches.

71

2 TEACH

Point out that mass doesn't mean "size." Take two large cartons of equal size. Fill one with light objects such as packing material or pillows. Fill the other with books. Have students attempt to slide each across the floor and make inferences about their relative masses.

Guided Practice
■ Check students' understanding of lesson concepts by discussing the Lesson Review questions on student page 72. If necessary, use the **reteaching strategy** in OPTIONS.

Independent Practice
■ Assign the Lesson 1 section of the Teacher Resource Master **Independent Practice,** page 59.

3 APPLY

Show students a wheelbarrow or wagon. Then show students one pile of light objects such as pillows, one pile of medium objects such as paper, and one pile of heavy objects such as books. Ask students to guess which pile needs the most force and the least force to move it. Have students fill the wheelbarrow or wagon with each pile and push or pull it across the floor.

Close
■ Use summary statements on student page 72 to review lesson concepts.

OPTIONS

Reteaching Strategy
Organize a game of tug-of-war in a grassy area. Ask students how they will know which side has used more force.

Resource Options
■ Show selections from "Inertia," *Mr. Wizard's World of Science Video Library,* Merrill Publishing Company.

TEACHER RESOURCE MASTERS

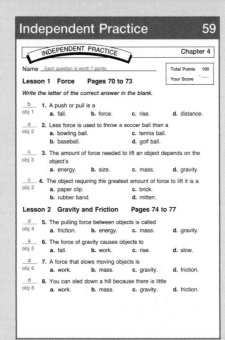

Independent Practice   59

INDEPENDENT PRACTICE   Chapter 4

Name ___Each question is worth 7 points.___   Total Points 100
                                                  Your Score ___

Lesson 1   Force   Pages 70 to 73

Write the letter of the correct answer in the blank.

b   **1.** A push or pull is a
obj 1   **a.** fall.   **b.** force.   **c.** rise.   **d.** distance.

a   **2.** Less force is used to throw a soccer ball than a
obj 2   **a.** bowling ball.   **c.** tennis ball.
        b. baseball.   **d.** golf ball.

c   **3.** The amount of force needed to lift an object depends on the
obj 3   object's
        a. energy.   **b.** size.   **c.** mass.   **d.** gravity.

c   **4.** The object requiring the greatest amount of force to lift it is a
obj 2   **a.** paper clip.   **c.** brick.
        b. rubber band.   **d.** mitten.

Lesson 2   Gravity and Friction   Pages 74 to 77

d   **5.** The pulling force between objects is called
obj 4   **a.** friction.   **b.** energy.   **c.** mass.   **d.** gravity.

a   **6.** The force of gravity causes objects to
obj 5   **a.** fall.   **b.** work.   **c.** rise.   **d.** slow.

d   **7.** A force that slows moving objects is
obj 6   **a.** work.   **b.** mass.   **c.** gravity.   **d.** friction.

d   **8.** You can sled down a hill because there is little
obj 6   **a.** work.   **b.** mass.   **c.** gravity.   **d.** friction.

OPTIONS

 SCIENCE AND . . . MATH

Skill: Add whole numbers.

Student Response: A. 112 kg

MATH CONNECTION

Have students work in **cooperative groups** to solve this problem: Willie and his three sisters each carry 10-k backpacks. What is the total mass of the backpacks? (40 kg)

♦ **Reinforcement:** Ask: **What kind of forces do you use to move objects in the classroom?**

● **Enrichment:** Discuss the safe way to move or lift objects. Students may want to make safety posters, showing the correct methods of lifting.

▲ **Challenge:** Arrange three pennies on a smooth surface as shown:

Challenge students to move penny C to a position between A and B *without* moving penny B or touching penny A. Solution: Press down on penny B. Slide penny C toward B, releasing it just before it hits the edge of B. The force of the blow will be transmitted through B to A, which will scoot to the left. C can then be placed between A and B.

Resource Options

■ Use Poster #3, "Forces, Simple Machines, and Family Fun."

LESSON REVIEW ANSWERS

1. a push or a pull
2. More force is needed to push the teacher because of the larger mass.

More force is needed to lift an object with a large mass. Look at the picture below. It would take more force to lift the bowling ball than the soccer ball. Which ball has more mass?

More force is needed to lift a larger mass.

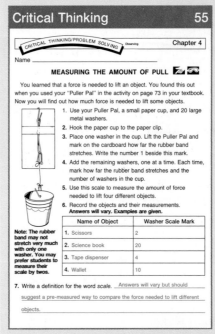

SCIENCE AND . . .
Math

Lance and Maria carried boxes of supplies. Lance's box had a mass of 73 kg. Maria's had a mass of 39 kg. What was the mass of both boxes?
A. 112 kg.
B. 34 kg.
C. 102 kg.
D. 44 kg.

Lesson Summary

● Force is needed to move objects.
● The greater an object's mass, the more force is needed to move the object.

Lesson Review

1. What is force?
★2. Will more force be needed to push you or your teacher on a swing? Why?

72

TEACHER RESOURCE MASTERS

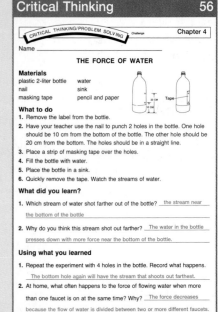

Critical Thinking	55

CRITICAL THINKING/PROBLEM SOLVING   Observing   Chapter 4

Name _____

MEASURING THE AMOUNT OF PULL

You learned that a force is needed to lift an object. You found this out when you used your "Puller Pal" in the activity on page 73 in your textbook. Now you will find out how much force is needed to lift some objects.

1. Use your Puller Pal, a small paper cup, and 20 large metal washers.
2. Hook the paper cup to the paper clip.
3. Place one washer in the cup. Lift the Puller Pal and mark on the cardboard how far the rubber band stretches. Write the number 1 beside this mark.
4. Add the remaining washers, one at a time. Each time, mark how far the rubber band stretches and the number of washers in the cup.
5. Use this scale to measure the amount of force needed to lift four different objects.
6. Record the objects and their measurements. **Answers will vary. Examples are given.**

Note: The rubber band may not stretch very much with only one washer. You may prefer students to measure their scale by twos.

Name of Object	Washer Scale Mark
1. Scissors	2
2. Science book	20
3. Tape dispenser	4
4. Wallet	10

7. Write a definition for the word *scale*. __Answers will vary but should__ suggest a pre-measured way to compare the force needed to lift different objects.

Critical Thinking	56

CRITICAL THINKING/PROBLEM SOLVING   Challenge   Chapter 4

Name _____

THE FORCE OF WATER

Materials
plastic 2-liter bottle   water
nail   sink
masking tape   pencil and paper

What to do
1. Remove the label from the bottle.
2. Have your teacher use the nail to punch 2 holes in the bottle. One hole should be 10 cm from the bottom of the bottle. The other hole should be 20 cm from the bottom. The holes should be in a straight line.
3. Place a strip of masking tape over the holes.
4. Fill the bottle with water.
5. Place the bottle in a sink.
6. Quickly remove the tape. Watch the streams of water.

What did you learn?
1. Which stream of water shot farther out of the bottle? __the stream near__ the bottom of the bottle
2. Why do you think this stream shot out farther? __The water in the bottle__ presses down with more force near the bottom of the bottle.

Using what you learned
1. Repeat the experiment with 4 holes in the bottle. Record what happens. __The bottom hole again will have the stream that shoots out farthest.__
2. At home, what often happens to the force of flowing water when more than one faucet is on at the same time? Why? __The force decreases__ because the flow of water is divided between two or more different faucets.

How do you measure force?

What you need

cardboard strip
long rubber band
masking tape
30 cm string
3 paper clips
5 small objects
pencil and paper

What to do

1. Make a "Puller Pal" like the one shown.
2. Make a pencil mark on the cardboard to show where the rubber band ends.
3. Hook an object to your Puller Pal. Lift the object.
4. Make a pencil mark on the cardboard to show how far the rubber band stretches. Write the name of the object by the mark.
5. Repeat steps 3 and 4 with all of the objects.

What did you learn?

1. Which object took the most force to lift? How do you know?
2. Which object took the least force?

Using what you learned

1. Suppose you had to lift two of the same kind of pens at once. Predict how much force you would need. Test your prediction.
2. Do you think more force is needed to pull a small book across a table or lift it? Use the Puller Pal to find out.

73

ACTIVITY RESPONSES

What did you learn?

1. Answers will depend on objects used. The one that stretched the rubber band the most took the most force.
2. Answers will depend on objects used. The one that stretched the rubber band the least took the least force.

Using what you learned

1. Students should say it will take twice as much force. Due to the elastic properties of rubber bands however, doubling the weight may not double the distance the rubber band stretches.
2. It usually takes more force to lift an object than to pull it across the table. However, the types of surfaces on the table and the object affect the force needed.

PREPLAN

Time Allotment: 45 minutes

Process Skills: Observing/Inferring/Predicting

Objectives

1. **Estimate** relative amounts of force required to move various objects.
2. **Recognize** that a scale may be used to compare and measure force.

Setup

■ Use poster board strips that are 6 cm by 30 cm. Rubber bands should be long, thin, and as much alike as possible.
■ Slip one end of the rubber band into one paper clip. Attach the paper clip to one end of the cardboard strip and secure with masking tape. Slip the free end of the rubber band into a second paper clip.
Cooperative Grouping: fives—Assign roles as explained on page T24.

1   FOCUS

■ Review the discussion of force. Have students estimate which objects will take the least or most amount of force to lift. Record estimates on the chalkboard.

2   TEACH

■ **Safety Considerations:** Remind students to handle the Puller Pal carefully. Warn them not to lift heavy objects.
■ Have students use the Teacher Resource master **Activity Worksheets,** pages 51 and 52, to record their data and answers.

3   APPLY

■ Discuss and compare findings with estimates made in the Focus section.

Close

■ Discuss the activity and questions with the class.

PREPLAN

Lesson Objectives

4. Define *gravity*.
5. Give examples of effects of gravity.
6. Define *friction* and **give examples** of properties affecting friction.

Science Background

■ Gravity is a property of all matter that causes it to attract all other matter. The amount of attraction between two objects depends on the masses of both objects and the distance between them. A person exerts a force on Earth equal to the force Earth exerts on the person. However, because Earth is much more massive, we don't see the effects of this force on Earth. For example, Earth is not "pushed away" when we jump from its surface.

■ Friction is the force that resists motion between two objects in contact. Friction depends on the nature of the surfaces. Friction causes objects in motion to slow down and eventually stop. Friction also causes heat and the wearing away of the surfaces in contact.

Lesson Vocabulary

gravity   friction

Note: The activity on student page 77 may be used for guided discovery before you begin this lesson.

1 FOCUS

[icon] Have one student throw a ball straight up in the air. Release a roller skate at the top of a ramp made from a board and some books. Pour some water from a pitcher into a glass. Tell students that the same force acted on the objects. Have students suggest what that force might be.

■ Use the goals on student page 74 to establish the purpose for studying this lesson.

LESSON 2 GOALS
You will learn
● that there is a pulling force between objects.
● that friction slows moving objects.
● that physical properties affect friction.

What is gravity?

Have you ever noticed that, no matter how high you jump, you always come back down? Or have you noticed that, no matter how high in the air you throw a ball, that ball always comes back down? There's a reason for that. Earth pulls on objects. This pull brings you back to Earth when you jump into the air. The attraction or pulling force between objects is called **gravity** (GRAV ut ee). Gravity is a property of all matter. The pull of gravity is greatest when two objects are close together. As the two objects get farther apart, the pulling force on each object becomes less.

Would You Believe?

At Earth's center, a person would be weightless because an equal amount of mass would pull him from all directions.

74

TEACHER RESOURCE MASTERS

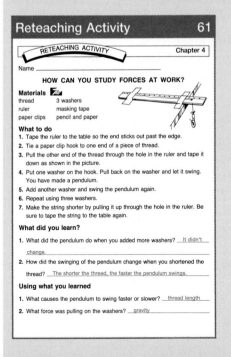

Reteaching Activity 61

RETEACHING ACTIVITY   Chapter 4

Name _____

HOW CAN YOU STUDY FORCES AT WORK?

Materials [icon]
thread   3 washers
ruler   masking tape
paper clips   pencil and paper

What to do
1. Tape the ruler to the table so the end sticks out past the edge.
2. Tie a paper clip hook to one end of a piece of thread.
3. Pull the other end of the thread through the hole in the ruler and tape it down as shown in the picture.
4. Put one washer on the hook. Pull back on the washer and let it swing. You have made a pendulum.
5. Add another washer and swing the pendulum again.
6. Repeat using three washers.
7. Make the string shorter by pulling it up through the hole in the ruler. Be sure to tape the string to the table again.

What did you learn?
1. What did the pendulum do when you added more washers? ___It didn't change.___
2. How did the swinging of the pendulum change when you shortened the thread? ___The shorter the thread, the faster the pendulum swings.___

Using what you learned
1. What causes the pendulum to swing faster or slower? ___thread length___
2. What force was pulling on the washers? ___gravity___

Friction

Friction (FRIHK shun) is the force that slows down or stops objects in motion. Imagine that you are riding a bike on level ground. If you stop pedaling, think about what happens. Friction between your bike tires and the ground slows you. Now imagine the same bike ride, but this time use the brakes. Think about what happens now. The friction that slows you this time is friction between your bike tires and the brake pads.

Friction happens whenever one object moves over another. The amount of friction depends on the kind of surfaces that touch each other. There is more friction when an object moves over a rough surface than when it moves over a smooth surface. For example, you are able to ride a sled very fast down a hill covered with snow. You could not ride a sled as easily on a grassy hill. Because the grass is not as smooth as snow, there is more friction.

What is friction?

SCIENCE AND . . .
Reading
Why is it safer to wear shoes with rough rubber soles than smooth leather soles on a wet, slippery day?
A. Rubber doesn't get wet.
B. Rubber has more friction.
C. Rubber costs more.

Friction is less on a smooth surface.

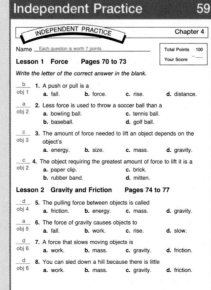

75

2 TEACH

Introduce the concept of friction by having students roll a ball across the floor and observe what happens. Students should notice that it slows down.

Problem Solving: Have students give examples in which they think friction is helpful or harmful. List these in two columns on the chalkboard.

Guided Practice
- Check students' understanding of lesson concepts by discussing the Lesson Review questions on student page 76. If necessary, use the **reteaching strategy** in OPTIONS.

Independent Practice
- Assign the Lesson 2 section of the Teacher Resource Master **Independent Practice,** page 59.

3 APPLY

Have students roll a ball across a tile floor, a long foam mat spread on a floor, and a carpeted floor, and observe what happens. Ask students to describe the three kinds of surfaces. Have students compare the amount of friction needed to slow down the ball on each surface.

Close
- Use summary statements on student page 76 to review lesson concepts.

OPTIONS

Reteaching Strategy
- Have students demonstrate examples of helpful friction and harmful friction.

Resource Options
- Show selections from "Gravity," *Mr. Wizard's World of Science Video Library,* Merrill Publishing Company.
- Refer to page 76 for teaching strategies for **SCIENCE AND . . . READING.**

TEACHER RESOURCE MASTERS

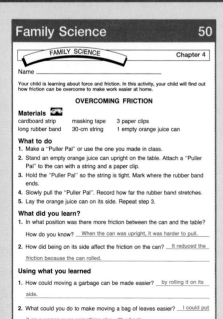

Family Science 50

FAMILY SCIENCE Chapter 4

Name _____

Your child is learning about force and friction. In this activity, your child will find out how friction can be overcome to make work easier at home.

OVERCOMING FRICTION

Materials
cardboard strip   masking tape   3 paper clips
long rubber band   30-cm string   1 empty orange juice can

What to do
1. Make a "Puller Pal" or use the one you made in class.
2. Stand an empty orange juice can upright on the table. Attach a "Puller Pal" to the can with a string and a paper clip.
3. Hold the "Puller Pal" so the string is tight. Mark where the rubber band ends.
4. Slowly pull the "Puller Pal". Record how far the rubber band stretches.
5. Lay the orange juice can on its side. Repeat step 3.

What did you learn?
1. In what position was there more friction between the can and the table? _When the can was upright, it was harder to pull._
2. How did being on its side affect the friction on the can? _It reduced the friction because the can rolled._

Using what you learned
1. How could moving a garbage can be made easier? _by rolling it on its side._
2. What could you do to make moving a bag of leaves easier? _I could put it on a wagon or on something else with wheels._

Independent Practice 59

INDEPENDENT PRACTICE Chapter 4

Name _Each question is worth 7 points._   Total Points 100
                                            Your Score ___

Lesson 1   Force   Pages 70 to 73
Write the letter of the correct answer in the blank.

_b_ 1. A push or pull is a
obj 1   a. fall.   b. force.   c. rise.   d. distance.

_a_ 2. Less force is used to throw a soccer ball than a
obj 2   a. bowling ball.   c. tennis ball.
         b. baseball.   d. golf ball.

_c_ 3. The amount of force needed to lift an object depends on the
obj 3   object's
         a. energy.   b. size.   c. mass.   d. gravity.

_c_ 4. The object requiring the greatest amount of force to lift it is a
obj 2   a. paper clip.   c. brick.
         b. rubber band.   d. mitten.

Lesson 2   Gravity and Friction   Pages 74 to 77

_d_ 5. The pulling force between objects is called
obj 4   a. friction.   b. energy.   c. mass.   d. gravity.

_a_ 6. The force of gravity causes objects to
obj 5   a. fall.   b. work.   c. rise.   d. slow.

_d_ 7. A force that slows moving objects is
obj 6   a. work.   b. mass.   c. gravity.   d. friction.

_d_ 8. You can sled down a hill because there is little
obj 6   a. work.   b. mass.   c. gravity.   d. friction.

OPTIONS

YOU CAN . . . REDUCE FRICTION

Process Skill: Experimenting

Objective: Demonstrate two ways to reduce friction between sliding surfaces.

Setup/Teach

- Tell students to use uniform pressure and speed each time.

SCIENCE AND . . . READING

- **Skill:** Draw logical conclusions.
- **Student Response:** B

LANGUAGE CONNECTION

Writing: Have half the students write about a school without gravity. Have the rest write about one where gravity is ten times the Earth's gravity.

Science and Technology: Use "I WANT TO KNOW ABOUT . . . Choosing Good Wheels," student page 83, with this lesson.

♦ **Reinforcement:** Have students drop a sheet of paper held horizontally. Crumple the paper into a tight ball and drop it again. Record observations.

▲ **Challenge:** Have students investigate a pendulum. Using a stopwatch, time ten free swings; divide by ten to find the time used for one. Study the effect of changing the mass of the object while keeping the length the same.

Resource Options

- Show selections from "Action and Reaction," *Mr. Wizard's World of Science Video Library*, Merrill Publishing Co.
- Use Activity Book, "Hypothesizing," pages 17 and 18.

LESSON REVIEW ANSWERS

1. because of the pull of gravity
2. water or oil would reduce friction

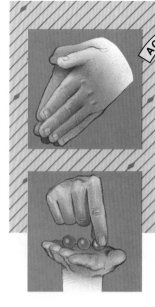

You Can...

Reduce Friction

Quickly rub your hands together about 20 times. How do they feel? Put several marbles in your hands and rub them together again. Do they feel as warm? Try it again, but first put a little liquid soap on your hands. How warm do they feel now? How else might you reduce friction?

Lesson Summary

- The attraction or pulling force between two objects is called gravity.
- Friction causes moving objects to slow down or stop.
- Contact between rough objects causes more friction than contact between smooth objects.

Lesson Review

1. Why do raindrops fall toward Earth?
★2. How would getting water or oil on your bike tires affect the brakes?

76

TEACHER RESOURCE MASTERS

ACTIVITY

How can you change friction?

What you need

Puller Pal
chalkboard eraser
string
smooth table
sandpaper
dish towel
pencil and paper

What to do

1. Attach the Puller Pal to the eraser with a string.
2. Put the eraser on the table and hold the Puller Pal so the string is tight. Mark where the rubber band ends.
3. Slowly pull the eraser on the table top. Mark how far the rubber band stretches. Record this on a chart.
4. Repeat step 3, use a piece of sandpaper on the table.
5. Repeat step 3 again, putting a towel on the table.

What did you learn?

1. Which surface made the most friction? How do you know?
2. How did the sandpaper affect friction?

Using what you learned

1. What kind of surface would be the best to use with a skateboard?
2. Why can't you get rid of all friction?
3. How could you make more friction? Why would more friction be useful?

77

ACTIVITY RESPONSES

What did you learn?
1. The towel had the most friction. The table the least. The amount of stretch of the rubber band was greatest for the towel and least for the table.
2. The sandpaper had less friction than the towel but more than the table.

Using what you learned
1. The skateboard would work best on a smooth surface.
2. Friction occurs whenever two objects roll or slide over each other.
3. You can increase friction by using rough or sticky surfaces in contact or by increasing the force pressing two surfaces together. We increase the friction in order to prevent objects from slipping or to stop or slow moving objects. Specific examples will vary.

PREPLAN

Time Allotment: 30 minutes

Process Skills: Observing/Separating and Controlling Variables

Objectives
1. **Measure** the amount of friction on different surfaces.
2. **Infer** how surfaces affect friction.

Setup
■ Try the activity ahead of time to make sure there is enough friction between the eraser and the surface you plan to use to give a reading on the Puller Pal.

Cooperative Grouping: threes—Assign roles as explained on page T24.

1 FOCUS

■ Review what students already know about friction. Ask them to think of surfaces that might have different amounts of friction, such as wet floors, bumpy sidewalks, icy sidewalks, and so on. Have students predict which surface they think will have the most and least friction.

2 TEACH

Have one student hold down the sandpaper or towel while another student pulls the eraser over it.
■ Students should pull the eraser at the same, steady rate in all trials.
■ Have students use the Teacher Resource Master **Activity Worksheet,** pages 53 and 54, to record their data and answers.

3 APPLY

■ Ask students to make lists of situations in which it is advantageous to reduce or increase friction.

Close
■ Discuss the activity and questions.

PREPLAN

Lesson Objectives
7. **Operationally define** *work*.
8. **Determine** when work is done.
9. **Define** *energy*.

Science Background
■ In a scientific sense, work is done only when a force causes an object to move. A person pulling on a rope tied to a tree does no work on the tree unless the tree is moved.

■ The amount of work done is determined by both the force exerted and the distance the object is moved in the direction of the force. If you carry a stack of books across a room, you may exert a large upward force to support the books. However, besides the distance moved, the work done depends only upon the small horizontal force needed to push the books forward through the air as you carry them. When you raise the books, the work done then depends on the upward force needed to lift the books.

Lesson Vocabulary
work   energy

1   FOCUS

Assign groups to **work cooperatively** playing tug-of-war in a grassy or carpeted area. Allow students to wear gloves or socks to protect their hands. Stop the game after a few minutes and ask students to tell which side used more force. Then ask students to show the distance and direction the losing side moved. Work is done when the force of one side causes the other side to move in the direction of the force.

■ Use the goals on student page 78 to establish the purpose for studying this lesson.

LESSON 3 GOALS
You will learn
● that work is done when a force moves an object.
● that energy is used when work is done.
● that there are different sources of energy.

Work and Energy

Did you know you are doing work even when you're playing a game? Scientists say that **work** is done when a force moves an object. Is work being done in the picture on this page? How do you know?

To find the amount of work done on an object, you need to know two things. You must know how much force is needed to move the object. You must also know how far the object is moved. That is, the amount of work done depends on both force and distance. More work was done when the wheelbarrow full of bricks was pushed than when the wheelbarrow full of branches was pushed. More work is also done if you push the wheelbarrow five meters instead of three meters.

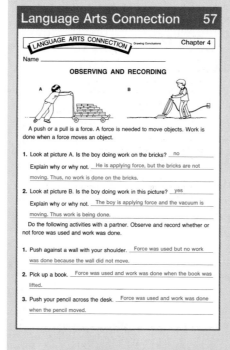

78

TEACHER RESOURCE MASTERS

Language Arts Connection   57

LANGUAGE ARTS CONNECTION   Drawing Conclusions   Chapter 4

Name _____

OBSERVING AND RECORDING

A push or a pull is a force. A force is needed to move objects. Work is done when a force moves an object.

1. Look at picture A. Is the boy doing work on the bricks? __no__
   Explain why or why not. __He is applying force, but the bricks are not moving. Thus, no work is done on the bricks.__

2. Look at picture B. Is the boy doing work in this picture? __yes__
   Explain why or why not. __The boy is applying force and the vacuum is moving. Thus work is being done.__

Do the following activities with a partner. Observe and record whether or not force was used and work was done.

1. Push against a wall with your shoulder. __Force was used but no work was done because the wall did not move.__

2. Pick up a book. __Force was used and work was done when the book was lifted.__

3. Push your pencil across the desk. __Force was used and work was done when the pencil moved.__

Remember that an object must be moved for work to be done on the object. You may push with all your might on a stalled car. However, if you don't move the car, you haven't done work on the car.

Look at the picture below of the children playing a game of tug-of-war. As long as one team is able to pull the other team, you know that work is being done. However, if the teams are even in strength and neither team could move the other, no work is done. [1]Why?

1. Neither team is being moved.

79

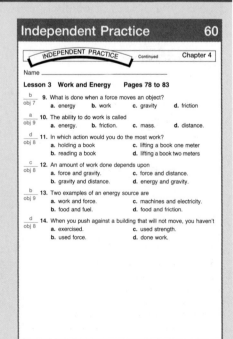

TEACHER RESOURCE MASTERS

Independent Practice   **60**

INDEPENDENT PRACTICE *Continued*   **Chapter 4**

Name _____

Lesson 3   Work and Energy   Pages 78 to 83

__b__   **9.** What is done when a force moves an object?
obj 7   **a.** energy   **b.** work   **c.** gravity   **d.** friction

__a__   **10.** The ability to do work is called
obj 9   **a.** energy.   **b.** friction.   **c.** mass.   **d.** distance.

__d__   **11.** In which action would you do the most work?
obj 8   **a.** holding a book   **c.** lifting a book one meter
       b. reading a book   **d.** lifting a book two meters

__c__   **12.** An amount of work done depends upon
obj 8   **a.** force and gravity.   **c.** force and distance.
       b. gravity and distance.   **d.** energy and gravity.

__b__   **13.** Two examples of an energy source are
obj 9   **a.** work and force.   **c.** machines and electricity.
       b. food and fuel.   **d.** food and friction.

__d__   **14.** When you push against a building that will not move, you haven't
obj 8   **a.** exercised.   **c.** used strength.
       b. used force.   **d.** done work.

2   TEACH

■ If energy is the ability to do work, it is also the ability to move something by using a force. Have students look at each of the illustrations in this chapter and try to find examples that illustrate energy. Ask them to explain their choices. In each case they should show how an object is being moved using a force.

Guided Practice

■ Check students' understanding of lesson concepts by discussing the Lesson Review questions on student page 82. If necessary, use the **reteaching strategy** in OPTIONS.

Independent Practice

■ Assign the Lesson 3 section of the Teacher Resource Master **Independent Practice,** page 60.

3   APPLY

Have four students **working cooperatively** stack equal size books or boxes to four different heights. Ask the class to tell which student is doing more work and to explain why. Guide students to use the words *force, work, move,* and *distance* in their explanations.

Close

■ Use the summary statements on student page 82 to review the lesson concepts.

OPTIONS

Reteaching Strategy

Have students working in **cooperative groups** conduct a survey of work done at home and the force needed to do the work. Students should also note the motion caused by the force.

Resource Options

■ Show selections from "Fluid Flow," *Mr. Wizard's World of Science Video Library,* Merrill Publishing Company.

OPTIONS

LANGUAGE CONNECTION

Writing: Have students **work in cooperative groups** to explain in writing why they can slide down a playground slide. Is gravity necessary? Is friction necessary? Is any work done?

◆ **Reinforcement:** Review and reinforce the relationship among force, work, and movement. Have students push against an object they can't move and then lift a small object. Ask in which case more work was done. Have them lift an object a distance and then lift it a greater distance. Again ask them to compare the work done. Last, have students lift a light object and a heavy object the same distance and compare the work done.

● **Enrichment:** Have students, **working in cooperative groups,** attach one small object to their Puller Pal. Lift the object ten centimeters off the table and measure the amount of force used. Attach a second object and lift it ten centimeters off the table. Record the force used. Ask the groups which time more work was done. Students should answer that since both objects moved the same distance, more work was done when more force was used.

▲ **Challenge:** Have interested students investigate various forms and sources of energy used by people to do work.

People need fuel.

What is energy?

Each time a force moves an object, such as the wheelbarrow or the teams, work is done. When work is done, energy (EN ur jee) is used. **Energy** is the ability to do work. The more work you do, the more energy you use.

To do work, people need a source of energy. People get energy from the food they eat.

80

TEACHER RESOURCE MASTERS

Health Connection   58

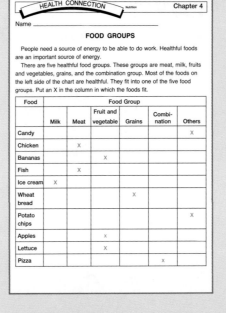

HEALTH CONNECTION   Nutrition   Chapter 4

Name _____

FOOD GROUPS

People need a source of energy to be able to do work. Healthful foods are an important source of energy.

There are five healthful food groups. These groups are meat, milk, fruits and vegetables, grains, and the combination group. Most of the foods on the left side of the chart are healthful. They fit into one of the five food groups. Put an X in the column in which the foods fit.

Food	Food Group					
	Milk	Meat	Fruit and vegetable	Grains	Combination	Others
Candy						X
Chicken		X				
Bananas			X			
Fish		X				
Ice cream	X					
Wheat bread				X		
Potato chips						X
Apples			X			
Lettuce			X			
Pizza					X	

Machines also need a source of energy. But machines can't eat food. What do machines use for energy? Sometimes forces in nature supply this energy. Falling water in a stream, for example, may turn a paddlewheel that turns a stone that grinds grain into flour.

Machines need fuel.

81

OPTIONS

■ List some examples of motion and have students determine the energy source. Some examples may be a car being moved when fuel is burned in an engine, a toy train that is powered by a battery, a kite being blown by the wind, and a rocking chair being moved by a person who gets energy from food.

TEACHER RESOURCE MASTERS

LESSON REVIEW ANSWERS

1. when a force is used to move the object

2. the ability to do work (use a force to move an object)

3. no, because the door didn't move

Most of the energy that runs machines is supplied by fuel or electricity. Gasoline supplies the energy needed to run the engines of cars. Electricity runs machines such as computers.

Whenever work is done by a machine or by a person, energy is needed. The more work you do, the more energy you use.

Lesson Summary

- The amount of work done depends on both force and distance.
- The more work you do, the more energy you use.
- Food and fuel are two sources of energy.

Lesson Review

1. When is work done on an object?
2. What is energy?
★3. Is work being done when you push on a door that won't open? Why or why not?

82

TEACHER RESOURCE MASTERS

I WANT TO KNOW ABOUT...

Choosing Good Wheels

Most skateboard wheels are made of polyurethane (pahlee YUR uh thayne). Polyurethane is a special plastic that has gas bubbled into it. Some wheels are better than others. How can you choose good wheels?

Some skateboard wheels are made quickly by machines. Hundreds can be made in an hour, so these wheels don't cost too much. A needle on a machine squirts polyurethane into molds. These wheels are not very hard, and there is too much friction to roll fast. You can tell when wheels are made this way by looking for a small hole on the surface where the needle was taken out.

The best wheels are made in polished steel or glass molds. Hot polyurethane is poured into the mold. The polyurethane is then baked in an oven to make it harder. Making these wheels takes about two weeks. That's why these wheels cost more.

Which wheels are best? Look for hard, smooth wheels that are colored evenly and don't have air bubbles.

Science and Technology

83

TEACHER RESOURCE MASTERS

Feature Background

■ Professional skateboarders use wheels made by pouring hot polyurethane into molds and baking it. The process is constantly monitored to make sure all gas bubbles are removed and shape and color are uniform.

■ The hardness of wheels is measured on a machine called a durometer. The durometer measures the resistance of the wheels to denting.

■ Generally, fast wheels are hard, and slow wheels are softer.

■ Large-diameter wheels are faster than small-diameter wheels, because they roll over obstructions and the bearings move more slowly.

Feature Vocabulary

mold
polyurethane

Teaching Suggestions

Ask students who have skateboards to show them and explain their features.

■ Explain that as skateboarding has become more popular, technology has improved the wheels and bearings.

■ Invite an owner of a skateboarding shop to demonstrate the parts of a skateboard, explain how skateboards have changed, and show safety equipment.

■ Obtain skateboarding books from the library and place them in a reading corner.

Summary

Chapter Closure: As a homework assignment, have students locate the specific page and paragraph that mentions each of the summary statements. As a class, reread the appropriate paragraphs and discuss the information they contain.

Science Words

Have students **work cooperatively** in groups to draw pictures that illustrate the meanings of each of the science words. For example, gravity may be shown by a picture of a falling object. Friction can be shown by sandpaper being used, a pencil being used, or by a drawing of a stopped car.

Student Responses

1. work
2. gravity
3. Energy
4. friction
5. force

CHAPTER REVIEW

4

Summary

Lesson 1
- Force is needed to move objects.
- The amount of force needed to move an object depends on the object's mass.

Lesson 2
- Gravity is the pulling force between objects.
- Friction causes moving objects to slow down or stop.

- Rough surfaces cause more friction than smooth surfaces.

Lesson 3
- Work is done when a force moves an object.
- Energy is the ability to do work.
- Energy comes from many different sources.

Science Words

Fill in the blank with the correct word or words from the list.

**force   friction   energy
gravity   work**

1. When a force moves an object you have done ___ .
2. The pulling force between objects is called ___ .
3. ___ is the ability to do work.
4. A force that slows down moving objects is called ___ .
5. A push or a pull is a(n) ___ .

84

TEACHER RESOURCE MASTERS

Test A   62

TEST A   Recalling Facts   Chapter 4

Name _Each question is worth 9 points._   Total Points 100
                                              Your Score ___

Match the statements on the left with the words on the right.

c   **1.** Any push or pull
obj 1
g   **2.** Affects force needed to move
obj 3   something
f   **3.** Causes a thrown ball to fall to Earth
obj 5
h   **4.** Gravity is a pulling force between all of
obj 4   these
e   **5.** A force that slows moving objects
obj 6
i   **6.** Type of surface with *least* friction
obj 6
j   **7.** Done when a wagon is pulled a
obj 8   distance
d   **8.** Work depends on these two
obj 7
a   **9.** The ability to do work
obj 9
b   **10.** Source of energy for people
obj 9
k   **11.** An object requiring more force to move
obj 2   than a piece of paper does

a. energy
b. food
c. force
d. force and distance
e. friction
f. gravity
g. mass
h. objects
i. smooth
j. work
k. book

Test B   63

TEST B   Understanding/Applying Concepts Chapter 4

Name _Each question is worth 10 points._   Total Points 100
Answer the questions in the space provided. Your Score ___

1. What is a force? _A force is any push or pull._
obj 1

2. What is friction? _Friction is a force that slows moving objects._
obj 6

3. Tell what work is and give an example. _Work is done when a force_
obj 7 _moves an object. An example might be lifting a book._

4. What is gravity? _Gravity is a pulling force between objects._
obj 4

5. What is energy? _Energy is the ability to do work._
obj 9

6. Look at the pictures below. Tell which object would take the greatest
obj 2, 3 force to move and why. _The wagon with two children in it will take more_
force to move because it has more mass.

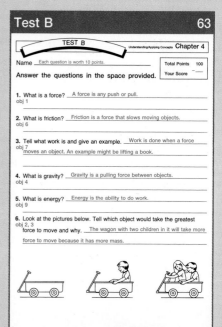

Questions

Recalling Ideas

Correctly complete each of the following sentences.

1. A ball falls when it is thrown because of
   (a) pressure. (c) friction.
   (b) gravity.   (d) air.
2. You may move an object when you use
   (a) air.   (c) mass.
   (b) friction. (d) force.
3. The force needed to lift an object depends on the object's
   (a) mass.   (c) friction.
   (b) energy.   (d) shape.
4. Work is being done when you are
   (a) reading. (c) holding a chair.
   (b) sitting.   (d) lifting a pencil.
5. If you push on an object but don't move it, you have
   (a) a large mass.
   (b) felt gravity.
   (c) not done work.
   (d) done work.
6. The amount of work done on an object depends on
   (a) force and distance.
   (b) distance and gravity.
   (c) force and friction.
   (d) mass and force.

Understanding Ideas

Answer the following questions using complete sentences.

1. Which will take more force to lift, (a) a wooden block the size of a chalkboard eraser or (b) a wooden block the size of a shoe box? Why?
2. Why are different amounts of force needed to move different objects?
3. Why is it hard for a car to stop on ice?

Thinking Critically

Think about what you have learned in this chapter. Answer the following questions using complete sentences.

1. You and a friend each pull a wagon up a hill. Both wagons are the same except yours is filled with books. Who does more work? Why?
2. Why are most playground slides made with smooth surfaces?

85

Questions

Recalling Ideas

1. b
2. d
3. a
4. d
5. c
6. a

Understanding Ideas

1. The wooden block the size of a shoe box will require more force to lift because it has more wood (mass) than the block of the same type of wood the size of a chalkboard eraser.
2. The more matter there is in an object, the greater the force necessary to move it.
3. It is difficult because there is little friction between the car tires and the ice.

Thinking Critically

1. You do more work than your friend. You both caused the wagons to move the same distance, but you exerted a greater force because your wagon was full of books and therefore had more mass.
2. Smooth surfaces cause less friction, so the slide will be slippery.

TEACHER RESOURCE MASTERS

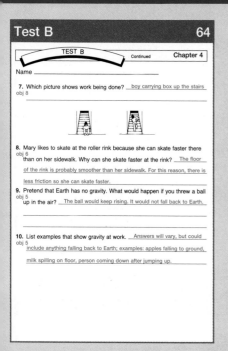

Test B   **64**

TEST B   Continued   Chapter 4

Name _____

7. Which picture shows work being done? __boy carrying box up the stairs__
obj 8

8. Mary likes to skate at the roller rink because she can skate faster there
obj 6
than on her sidewalk. Why can she skate faster at the rink? __The floor__
of the rink is probably smoother than her sidewalk. For this reason, there is
less friction so she can skate faster.

9. Pretend that Earth has no gravity. What would happen if you threw a ball
obj 5
up in the air? __The ball would keep rising. It would not fall back to Earth.__

10. List examples that show gravity at work. __Answers will vary, but could__
obj 5
include anything falling back to Earth; examples: apples falling to ground,
milk spilling on floor, person coming down after jumping up.

Machines

Planning Guide

Lessons	Objectives	Vocabulary
Chapter Introduction pp. 86, 87		
Lesson 1 Simple Machines, Lever pp. 88–93	1. **Recognize** the need for and purpose of simple machines. 2. **Define** *simple machine*.	simple machine lever
Lesson 2 Inclined Plane, Wedge, and Screw pp. 94–97	3. **Define** *inclined plane*. 4. **Compare** the similarities and differences among inclined planes, wedges, and screws.	inclined plane wedge screw
Lesson 3 Wheel and Axle, Pulley pp. 98–101	5. **Define** *wheel and axle*. 6. **Define** *pulley*. 7. **Give examples** of how pulleys are used.	wheel and axle pulley
Lesson 4 Compound Machines pp. 102–105	8. **Distinguish** between simple and compound machines. 9. **Identify** different simple machines making up compound machines and **give examples** of some compound machines.	compound machine
Chapter Review pp. 106–107		
Unit Review pp. 108–109		

Planning Guide

Text Activities		Teacher Resource Masters	Other Components
Title/Skill	**Materials per Group**		
Have You Ever . . . Moved a Load of Books? p. 87 Predicting/Experimenting Time Allotment: 30 minutes	small box or lunchbox 4–8 hardback books thread toy truck or wagon		**Activity Center:** "Toyland"; "New and Improved"; "As the Wheel Turns"
How Do Levers Work? p. 93 Observing/Measuring Time Allotment: 30 minutes	3 pencils, 2 small paper cups, masking tape, metric ruler, clay, 8 metal washers, pencil and paper	Independent Practice, pp. 75, 76 ▲ Critical Thinking, p. 72 Activity Worksheet, pp. 67, 68	Mr. Wizard's World of Science Video Tape 1 Color Transparency #3 Color Transparency #4 Activity Book, pp. 19, 20
How Do Inclined Planes Make Work Easier? p. 97 Observing/Measuring Time Allotment: 20 minutes	4 books, Puller Pal, metric ruler, milk carton, 8 marbles, ramp (board)	Independent Practice, pp. 75, 76 Activity Worksheet, pp. 69, 70	Poster #3 Mr. Wizard's World of Science Video Tape 1
		Independent Practice, pp. 75, 76 ◆ Reteaching Activity, p. 77 Transparency Master, p. 65	Mr. Wizard's World of Science Video Tape 1
You Can . . . Invent A Machine, p. 103 Formulating Models Time Allotment: 45 minutes **A Balancing Act,** p. 347 Measuring/Observing/ Classifying Time Allotment: 40 minutes	materials to build a machine model gram masses objects to measure mass pans or cups paper clips drinking straws string pan balance	Independent Practice, pp. 75, 76 Language Arts Connection, p. 73 ◆ Family Science, p. 66 Critical Thinking, p. 71 Social Studies Connection, p. 74	Activity Book, p. 37, 38
		Test A, p. 78 Test B, pp. 79, 80	Software: "What Will Happen?"
			Unit Test

◆ Basic / ▲ Advanced / All other masters are for use by all students.

Machines

For Exceptional Students

ESL/LEP

Chapter 5/Lesson 1, Page 92
Ask students to write sentences that show how a seesaw works. Provide a pattern: **If the fulcrum of the seesaw is in the middle, I can lift someone as heavy as I am.** After they have practiced their sentences, ask students where they would move the fulcrum to lift someone heavier than they are and lighter than they are.

Ask students to draw examples of other levers, for example, hammer, crowbar, scissors, and pliers. Ask them to label the levers in their own language and in English.

Chapter 5/Lesson 2, Page 94
Ask students to draw an example of how an inclined plane is used. Tell them to write a sentence about how an inclined plane helps people to do work. Provide a model on the chalkboard. **My uncle carried the chair up the inclined plane. I pushed the cart up the inclined plane.**

Chapter 5/Lesson 3, Page 98
Ask students to list some objects that have a wheel and axle. Have them make up sentences from their list. Write pattern sentences on the chalkboard: **Wheels and axles make a car easier to move. A pencil sharpener has a wheel and axle.**

Gifted

Chapter 5/Lesson 1, Page 88
Use diagrams and verbal explanation to show students the makeup of three classes of levers. A first-class lever has its fulcrum positioned between the force and load, as when a carpenter's hammer is used to pull a nail from lumber. A second-class lever has the fulcrum at one end of the lever and load between the fulcrum and force, as in the use of a nutcracker to crack a nut. A third-class lever has the fulcrum at one end and the force positioned between fulcrum and load, as in a baseball bat being swung by a batter.

Have students design machines containing levers that would help do the following tasks. Have them explain the class of lever used.
1. Transport a large boulder 31 meters.
2. Use miniature players to play a box game version of hockey or soccer in the classroom.
3. Open a bottle of soft drink that is sealed with a crown cap.
4. Raise a heavy barrel 30 cm from the ground to a cement patio.

Mainstreamed

Chapter 5/Lesson 1, Page 88

Mild Behavior Disorders: Bring in examples of the six simple machines. Have students physically examine each machine. Ask students to describe the type of work each simple machine does. Then show students examples of compound machines. Have them identify the simple machines that make up the compound machine. Prepare a follow-up worksheet in which students can match compound machines with their simple machine components.

Projects to Do

Whole Class Science Project

Divide the class into six groups. Give each group the name of one of the simple machines. Have the groups do research to find a compound machine that utilizes that simple machine as one of its components. Have each group report to the class.

Discuss the safety risks involved in the operation of various compound machines because of excessive noise, danger of injury, and so on. Make a list in class of problems caused by some machinery. Have student groups choose one of the problems and do research to find out how factories have solved these problems to maintain a safe work place for employees.

Science Fair Projects

Individual students could do one of the following projects:

1. Make a display with models of the three classes of levers. Describe each type of lever and how each type is important in daily life.
2. Design a mobile or other object of aesthetic appeal that makes use of each of the six simple machines in its construction.
3. Make a display that explains the use of pulleys for decreasing the force needed to lift objects or change direction of a force used to move an object. Show the advantages involved in using pulleys for each purpose, such as lifting a heavy load with a multiple pulley system.
4. Demonstrate how wheels and axles are used in gears on machines. Design a machine with gears that change direction of motion in order to do a task, such as in an eggbeater.

CHAPTER 5

pages 86–107

Chapter Concepts

■ Simple machines make work seem easier by changing the direction or amount of force needed to do work.
■ Wedges and screws are made up of inclined planes and are used to move objects.
■ Using a wheel and axle reduces the force needed to turn the axle. A pulley reduces or changes the direction of a force.
■ Compound machines are made of and combine the work of two or more simple machines.

Chapter Background

■ Machines make work easier but never decrease the amount of work that must be done. Some machines make work easier by reducing the amount of force that must be applied in order to move a load.
■ In any machine, there is a trade-off between force and distance. Machines that increase the applied force require that the force move a greater distance than the load moves.

Look for These Symbols

    —Hands-on activity
    —Cooperative learning
    —Overhead transparency
◆ —Basic/Reinforcement
● —Average/Enrichment
▲ —Advanced/Challenge
    —Calculator Practice

CHAPTER 5

Machines

It is not easy to push a full grocery cart through the store. But think how much more difficult it would be to move those groceries without a cart to help you.

Have You Ever...

Moved a Load of Books?

Find a small box about the size of a lunchbox. Predict how many books you could put in the box and pull with a thread. Record your prediction, then experiment. How many books can you pull before the thread breaks? Now put the box into a toy truck or wagon. Predict the number of books you can pull. Will the number be the same, more, or less than your first prediction? Try it and see.

87

PREPLAN

Time Allotment: 30 minutes

Objectives
1. Discuss the difficulty of moving groceries without a cart.
2. Observe the difference in the amount of force needed to pull a load with and without wheels.

Setup
■ If you wish to conduct this activity, you will need the following materials for each student or activity group:
small box/lunchbox   thread
4–8 hardback books   toy truck/wagon

1   FOCUS

■ Ask students to look at the picture on page 86. Ask: **Is the grocery cart hard to push? Why?**

2   TEACH

■ After the title and introductory paragraph have been read aloud, ask if there are other ways to move heavy loads.
■ Record the responses on the chalkboard. Write all suggestions that use wheels in one group. Then ask students if there is one thing that is the same.

Have You Ever . . .
Use this activity as an introduction to how machines make work seem easier.
Have students **work cooperatively** in groups of four to complete the activity.
■ **Student Responses**
When the box is on the truck, wheels make pulling easier.

3   APPLY

■ Discuss other places where wheels aid in moving objects.

Close
■ Tell students that they will learn more about how machines work in Chapter 5.

PREPLAN

Lesson Objectives

1. **Recognize** the need for and purpose of simple machines.
2. **Define** *simple machine*.

Science Background

■ A machine is any device that helps us do work. Some machines increase the applied force. Sometimes machines are used only to change the direction of the applied force. Another use of a machine is to increase the speed or range of movement.

■ Machines never decrease the amount of work that must be done, but rather make it easier by spreading it out over a longer distance or time, or by making it more convenient in some way.

■ The fulcrum, load, and applied force of levers may be in any arrangement. If the distance from the fulcrum to the force is greater than the distance from the fulcrum to the load, the lever increases applied force.

Lesson Vocabulary

simple machine   lever

Note: The activity on student page 93 may be used for guided discovery before you begin this lesson.

1   FOCUS

■ Have students brainstorm as many different machines as they can. List the machines on the chalkboard and have students tell what work is done by each machine. Point out to students that objects do not have to be complex to be classified as a machine. Many simple tools and other objects are also machines.

■ Use the goals on student page 88 to establish the purpose for studying this lesson.

Simple Machines, Lever

LESSON 1 GOALS
You will learn
● why simple machines are important.
● why a lever is a simple machine.
● that not all levers are the same.

Jenny found a big rock in the middle of the bike path around the lake. "That could be dangerous," she said to her friend Erich. "Someone could have an accident. Let's move the rock off the path." But the rock was too heavy for Jenny and Erich to lift. They could barely push it.

Then Erich saw a long board and had an idea. "Here, Jenny," he said, "help me lift just one edge of the rock so we can slide the end of this board under it. There. Now we must push this log under the board close to the rock. Now I'll just push down hard on the other end of the board and see what happens!"

88

TEACHER RESOURCE MASTERS

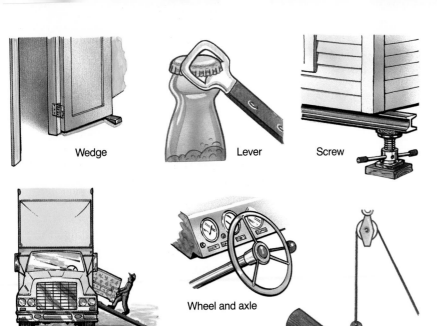

Wedge

Lever

Screw

Inclined plane

Wheel and axle

Pulley

Sure enough, the heavy rock rolled away when Erich pushed down on the board. The board and the log made a simple machine. People can use many kinds of machines to do work. A machine with only a few or even no moving parts is called a **simple machine.** Simple machines can be used to make work seem easier to do. They can change the amount of force needed to do work. They can also change the direction of the force. However, machines do not decrease the amount of work that is done. The pictures on this page show the six kinds of simple machines.

TEACHER RESOURCE MASTERS

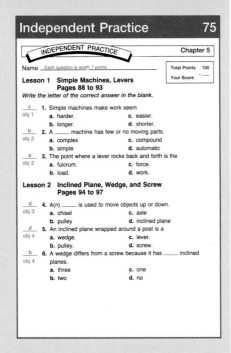

Independent Practice   75

INDEPENDENT PRACTICE   Chapter 5

Name _Each question is worth 7 points._   Total Points 100   Your Score __

Lesson 1   Simple Machines, Levers
           Pages 88 to 93
Write the letter of the correct answer in the blank.

_c_   1. Simple machines make work seem
obj 1   **a.** harder.   **c.** easier.
         b. longer.   **d.** shorter.
_b_   2. A ____ machine has few or no moving parts.
obj 2   **a.** complex   **c.** compound
         b. simple   **d.** automatic
_a_   3. The point where a lever rocks back and forth is the
obj 2   **a.** fulcrum.   **c.** force.
         b. load.   **d.** work.

Lesson 2   Inclined Plane, Wedge, and Screw
           Pages 94 to 97

_d_   4. A(n) ____ is used to move objects up or down.
obj 3   **a.** chisel   **c.** axle
         b. pulley   **d.** inclined plane
_d_   5. An inclined plane wrapped around a post is a
obj 4   **a.** wedge.   **c.** lever.
         b. pulley.   **d.** screw.
_b_   6. A wedge differs from a screw because it has ____ inclined
obj 4   planes.
         a. three   **c.** one
         b. two   **d.** no

---

2   TEACH

■ Emphasize that machines do not reduce the amount of work.

Point out that using a machine to change the direction of a force can make work seem easier. In the illustration on page 88, the child can use some of the downward force of weight to provide an upward force to help lift the log. Have students form **cooperative groups** to think of other examples in which changing the direction of a force makes work seem easier.

Guided Practice
■ Check students' understanding of lesson concepts by discussing the Lesson Review questions on student page 92. If necessary, use the **reteaching strategy** in OPTIONS.

Independent Practice
■ Assign the Lesson 1 section of the Teacher Resource Master **Independent Practice,** page 75.

3   APPLY

■ Construct a simple lever as in the activity on page 93. Demonstrate its use in lifting an object. Point to each part of the lever and have students write its name as well as the name of the machine.

Close
■ Use Summary statements on student page 92 to review lesson concepts.

OPTIONS

Reteaching Strategy
Discuss with students any situation in which they have used a lever. Display a bottle opener and a screwdriver. Ask students to use these tools to open a bottle and a can of paint. Have them find the load, fulcrum, and force each time.

OPTIONS

LANGUAGE CONNECTION

Reading: Draw the four lever situations shown below on an overhead transparency.

Ron		Jim
Ron	▲	Jim
Ron	▲	Jim
Ron	▲	Jim

Have students work in **cooperative groups** to answer the following question. Ron weighs twice as much as Jim. On which seesaw is the fulcrum placed so the two boys can ride? (3)

HEALTH CONNECTION

■ Have students research and report on how and why the arm and leg of a human are considered to be levers.

◆ **Reinforcement:** Refer to the illustrations on page 89. Ask students how they could use each simple machine in the drawing. The wheel and axle could be used to steer a truck or automobile. The wedge acts as a doorstop by exerting an upward force on the door. The pulley set could be used to pull or lift heavy objects. The lever might be used to lift the rock. The ramp is used to move objects to a higher or lower level. The screw is used as a jack to lift the corner of a house.

Resource Options

Use Color Transparency #3, "Simple Machines."

Use Color Transparency #4, "Help These Children Seesaw."

■ Use Activity Book, "Predicting," pages 19 and 20.

Lever

Jenny and Erich made a lever. A **lever** is a simple machine that is used to move objects. It is important to remember three things about levers. The object to be moved by a lever is called the load. The point where a lever rocks back and forth is called a fulcrum (FUL krum). The push or pull that moves a lever is the force. Find the load, fulcrum, and force on the lever that Jenny and Erich made.

Levers can also be used to change the direction of the force needed to lift an object. Think about a seesaw. When you push down on one end, the person on the other end goes up.

What should you remember about levers?

A hammer as a lever

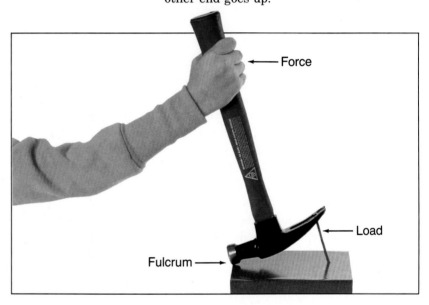

90

TEACHER RESOURCE MASTERS

Levers can also be used to change the amount of force. Think about the seesaw again. Elena, the little girl in the top picture, wants to play on the seesaw with her older sister. She is too little to lift her older sister when the fulcrum is in the middle. When the fulcrum is moved closer to her older sister, as in the picture on the left, then Elena is able to lift her sister.

Look at the bottom picture. Elena's younger brother wants to ride on the seesaw. Elena is now the heavier one. Therefore, she must move the fulcrum closer to herself. Elena has discovered that the amount of force needed to lift a load depends on where the fulcrum is.

91

OPTIONS

▲ **Challenge:** Have interested students investigate how the distance the lever must be moved varies with the force required to move a given load.

■ If most students are familiar with wheelbarrows and how they are used, ask them to draw a wheelbarrow and label the load, force, and fulcrum.

▨ Another kind of lever has the fulcrum at one end and the load at the other. The effort force is exerted between the two. An ordinary household broom is an example of this type of lever. You may want to demonstrate a broom and challenge students to identify the fulcrum, force, and load and to tell what is gained by using this type of lever. A short, slow movement of the force (the hand) produces a long, faster motion of the load (the friction of the broom against the floor).

Resource Options
■ Show selections from "Simple Machines," *Mr. Wizard's World of Science Video Library,* Merrill Publishing Company.

TEACHER RESOURCE MASTERS

OPTIONS

Problem Solving: Construct a simple lever like those used in the Activity on page 93 (or larger if possible). Arrange it so that a Puller Pal may be hooked to one end to provide a downward force. The Puller Pal will be used upside down. Use a load large enough to cause the Puller Pal to stretch when the fulcrum is in the center of the lever. Tape the load in place. Display this setup to students and ask them to predict, on the basis of what they have learned, how the reading on the Puller Pal will change as the fulcrum is moved toward and away from the load. Proceed to vary the fulcrum's position so students can see if their predictions were correct. If possible, set up a station where students can try this experiment for themselves. An advantage of this approach is that students can actually feel the force increase and decrease as the fulcrum is moved back and forth.

LESSON REVIEW ANSWERS

1. a machine with few or no moving parts
2. force, load, and fulcrum
3. When the fulcrum is closer to the load, less force is needed to lift the load.

Would You Believe?

Bryan Allen pedaled an aircraft called the *Gossamer Albatross* across the English Channel.

Jenny and Erich pushed the log close to the rock. With the fulcrum closer to the load, less force was needed to lift the load. [1] What would have happened if they had not pushed it close to the rock?

Lesson Summary

- Simple machines can be used to change the amount of force needed to do work or to change the direction of a force.
- A simple machine has few or no moving parts and makes work seem easier to do.
- The position of the fulcrum is not the same on all levers.

Lesson Review

1. What is a simple machine?
2. What are the three parts of a lever?
★3. How does changing the position of the fulcrum on a lever change the amount of force needed?

1. They would have needed to use more force.

Using a lever

TEACHER RESOURCE MASTERS

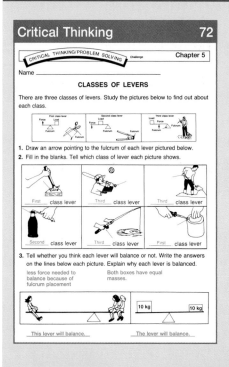

Critical Thinking 72

CRITICAL THINKING/PROBLEM SOLVING Challenge Chapter 5

Name _____

CLASSES OF LEVERS

There are three classes of levers. Study the pictures below to find out about each class.

1. Draw an arrow pointing to the fulcrum of each lever pictured below.
2. Fill in the blanks. Tell which class of lever each picture shows.

First class lever | Third class lever | Third class lever
Second class lever | Third class lever | First class lever

3. Tell whether you think each lever will balance or not. Write the answers on the lines below each picture. Explain why each lever is balanced.

less force needed to balance because of fulcrum placement | Both boxes have equal masses.

This lever will balance. | The lever will balance.

How do levers work?

What you need

3 pencils
2 small paper cups
masking tape
metric ruler
clay
8 metal washers
pencil and paper

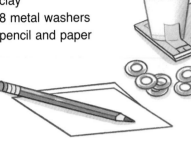

What to do

1. Tape a paper cup to each end of the ruler. Tape the pencils together as shown. Put them under the middle of the ruler.
2. Put a small clay ball in one of the cups.
3. Add washers one at a time to the other cup until the clay ball is lifted.
4. Record how many washers it took to lift the ball of clay.
5. Move the fulcrum and try again.

What did you learn?

1. What simple machine did you make?
2. What was the force?
3. What was the load?
4. How many washers lifted the load?

Using what you learned

1. You want to balance a 20-g box and a 10-g box on your ruler. Where should you put the pencils?
2. Why is it easier to pry open a can of paint using a long screwdriver rather than a short one?

93

ACTIVITY RESPONSES

What did you learn?

1. a lever
2. The weight of the washers was the force.
3. The ball of clay was the load.
4. Answers will vary according to the mass of the clay and the washers.

Using what you learned

1. closer to the 20 g box
2. The long screwdriver has a longer effort arm, thus less force is needed to move the lid.

PREPLAN

Time Allotment: 30 minutes
Process Skills: Observing, Measuring

Objectives

1. **Construct** and **demonstrate** a simple lever.
2. **Predict** where the fulcrum should be placed in order to balance a load.

Setup

■ Thick, wooden rulers work well as levers. Plastic or metal rulers tend to bend too much to be effective. Alternatively, use wooden lattice trim purchased at local lumber stores. Large metal washers may be purchased in bulk at some hardware stores.

Cooperative Grouping: threes—Assign roles as explained on page T24.

1 FOCUS

■ Display the completed apparatus for student reference. Compare the activity to a playground seesaw.

2 TEACH

■ Have different-sized balls of clay. Allow students to repeat the activity using a different clay ball and compare their results. They may also wish to try two identical clay balls to see if twice the number of washers are needed.
■ Have students use the Teacher Resource Master **Activity Worksheet,** pages 67 and 68, to record their data and answers.

3 APPLY

■ Relate the activity to everyday levers seesaws, bottle openers, shovels, and so on.

Close

■ Discuss the activity and questions.

PREPLAN

Lesson Objectives

3. **Define** *inclined plane.*
4. **Compare** the similarities and differences among inclined planes, wedges, and screws.

Science Background

■ An inclined plane is any slanted surface used to move objects from one level to another. In using an inclined plane to raise an object, the work accomplished is moving the object vertically to a higher level. The inclined plane makes this work easier by raising the object gradually over a long horizontal distance.

■ The wedge is a type of inclined plane. Usually it is used to produce a great sideways force to spread or split a material as the wedge is forced into it.

■ A screw is an inclined plane that is wrapped around an object. A spiral mountain road is usually thought of as an inclined plane. However, when the spiral plane itself is turned in order to move an object along it or to exert a force on an object, it is thought of as a screw.

Lesson Vocabulary

inclined plane   wedge   screw

Note: The activity on student page 97 may be used for guided discovery before you begin this lesson.

1 FOCUS

Display various examples of inclined planes, wedges, and screws. Have the students choose two examples and draw pictures showing how each can be used.

■ Use the goals on student page 94 to establish the purpose for studying this lesson.

LESSON 2 GOALS
You will learn
● that an inclined plane is a simple machine used to move objects.
● that a wedge has two important uses.
● that a screw is a type of inclined plane.

What is an inclined plane?

Inclined Plane, Wedge, and Screw

When you are riding your bike to the top of a hill, do you like to take the steepest path? Probably not, unless you are in a big hurry. You know that it means hard riding to take the steepest path. If you want to use less force, you take a longer path that isn't so steep.

A path going to the top of a hill is an example of an inclined plane. An **inclined plane** is a simple machine used to move objects to a higher or lower place. In the picture, both inclined planes reach the same high point. But one inclined plane is longer than the other. Because this inclined plane is not as steep, less force is needed to get to the top.

94

TEACHER RESOURCE MASTERS

A **wedge** (WEJ) is a simple machine made of two inclined planes. Knife blades, chisels, pins, and the blade of a hatchet or ax are all examples of wedges. Work is done when the wedge presses against two objects. A wedge can be used to push objects apart. Logs are split by using axes and hatchets. The blade of the hatchet or ax is forced into the log. It pushes the pieces of log apart.

A **screw** is an inclined plane wrapped around a post. Screws, drill bits, and other objects commonly found in your home make use of the inclined plane. Have you ever used a screw to push two objects together? Have you ever seen a drill bit push some material out of the way?

Try making a screw by cutting an inclined plane out of paper. Wrap this paper around a cardboard tube. The edges of the paper are like the ridges of a screw.

How is a wedge useful?

Inclined plane around a post

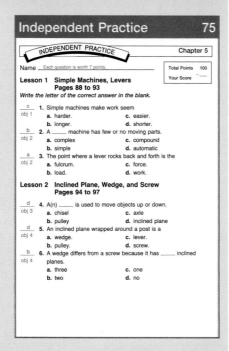

Wedge

95

2 TEACH

■ Avoid using stairs as an example of an inclined plane. They are an inclined plane only when being used as a ramp, such as when a large piece of furniture is being moved. A wheelchair ramp is a better example of an inclined plane.

Have students wrap a string along the threads of a large screw or bolt, then unwind the string to see how far the load must travel in order to move the length of the bolt or screw.

Guided Practice

■ Check students' understanding of lesson concepts by discussing the Lesson Review questions on student page 96. If necessary, use the **reteaching strategy** in OPTIONS.

Independent Practice

■ Assign the Lesson 2 section of the Teacher Resource Master **Independent Practice,** page 75.

3 APPLY

■ Have students list where they have seen or used inclined planes. Discuss how each inclined plane makes work easier.

Close

■ Use Summary statements on student page 96 to review lesson concepts.

OPTIONS

Reteaching Strategy

Review the meaning of inclined plane, wedge, and screw. Have students find and list examples of inclined planes, wedges, and screws in your classroom. Have students discuss or show how each simple machine is used to make work easier.

Resource Options

■ Use Poster #3, "Forces, Simple Machines, and Family Fun."

TEACHER RESOURCE MASTERS

Independent Practice 75

INDEPENDENT PRACTICE Chapter 5

Name _____ Each question is worth 7 points.

| Total Points | 100 |
| Your Score | |

Lesson 1 Simple Machines, Levers
Pages 88 to 93
Write the letter of the correct answer in the blank.

c obj 1 1. Simple machines make work seem
  a. harder. c. easier.
  b. longer. d. shorter.

b obj 2 2. A _____ machine has few or no moving parts.
  a. complex c. compound
  b. simple d. automatic

a obj 2 3. The point where a lever rocks back and forth is the
  a. fulcrum. c. force.
  b. load. d. work.

Lesson 2 Inclined Plane, Wedge, and Screw
Pages 94 to 97

d obj 3 4. A(n) _____ is used to move objects up or down.
  a. chisel c. axle
  b. pulley d. inclined plane

d obj 4 5. An inclined plane wrapped around a post is a
  a. wedge. c. lever.
  b. pulley. d. screw.

b obj 4 6. A wedge differs from a screw because it has _____ inclined planes.
  a. three c. one
  b. two d. no

OPTIONS

LANGUAGE CONNECTION

Reading: Have students **work in pairs** to discuss the following problem.

Imagine that you have a pile of firewood to split. You have a choice of two axes; one with a short, thick axe head, the other with a long, slim axe head. Explain which one you would choose, and why. (slim requires less force)

♦ **Reinforcement:** Have students cut a triangular piece of paper and wrap it around a pencil to form a screw.

● **Enrichment:** Ask students to discover which holds better, a nail or a screw. They can do this with a heavy piece of corrugated cardboard, a nail, and a screw. *Turn* the screw and *push* the nail through the cardboard. Allow the head of each to extend about 5 mm. Leave a small gap between two desks. Have a student try to pull out the screw and the nail, and compare the amount of force needed to remove them.

▲ **Challenge:** Have students explain why less force is needed to peel an apple or potato with a sharp knife than with a dull one.

Resource Options

■ Show selections from "Simple Machines," *Mr. Wizard's World of Science Video Library,* Merrill Publishing Co.

LESSON REVIEW ANSWERS

1. ramps, paths on hills
2. screw-inclined plane wrapped around a post, wedge-two inclined planes
3. screw

---

1. You would want to take the path that goes around the hill.
2. You would use less force, but you would not do less work.

Suppose you had to pull a heavy load to the top of a hill. One path is very steep and goes straight up. The other path goes around and around the hill before reaching the top. [1]Which path would you take with your heavy load? [2]Why?

Lesson Summary

- An inclined plane is a simple machine used to move objects to higher or lower places.
- A wedge is a simple machine used to raise objects or to push them apart.
- A screw is an inclined plane wrapped around a post.

Lesson Review

1. Name two examples of inclined planes.
2. Tell how a screw and a wedge are like inclined planes.
★3. What simple machine is used to attach a hose to a faucet?

96

TEACHER RESOURCE MASTERS

How do inclined planes make work easier?

What you need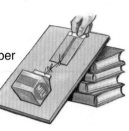

4 books
Puller Pal
metric ruler
milk carton
8 marbles
ramp (board)
pencil and paper

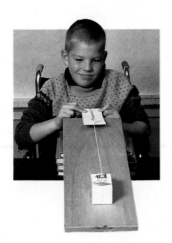

What to do

1. Pile 4 books on top of each other.
2. Put 8 marbles into the milk carton.
3. Lift the milk carton with the Puller Pal until the bottom of the carton is even with the top book.
4. Measure how far the rubber band stretches.
5. Set up the ramp, milk carton, and Puller Pal as shown.
6. Pull the carton up the ramp. Mark how far the rubber band stretches.

What did you learn?

1. Which way took more force to move the carton?
2. Which way took a longer distance?

Using what you learned

1. Find out what happens to the force needed if the ramp is made steeper.
2. Why are roads built around mountains instead of straight up the sides?

97

ACTIVITY RESPONSES

What did you learn?

1. lifting it straight up
2. using the inclined plane

Using what you learned

1. The steeper the ramp, the more force needed to lift the milk carton. Students could use more books to make the ramp steeper and try the activity again.
2. It takes less force to wind gradually up the slope of the mountain than to drive straight to the top. Students should infer that the greater the distance traveled in reaching the top, the less force is needed.

PREPLAN

Time Allotment: 20 minutes
Process Skills: Observing, Measuring

Objectives

1. **Demonstrate** the use of an inclined plane to move an object.
2. **Recognize** how inclined planes make work seem easier.

Setup

■ Try the activity ahead of time using students' Puller Pals. If the rubber band stretches too far or not far enough, experiment to see how many marbles students should use.

■ **Cooperative Grouping:** fives—Assign roles as explained on page T24.

1 FOCUS

■ Review the application of the inclined plane. Ask students to predict how much force will be needed to lift the carton using the inclined plane.

2 TEACH

■ A removable bookshelf works well as an inclined plane.
■ Spring scales may be substituted for Puller Pals.
■ Have students use the Teacher Resource Master **Activity Worksheet,** pages 69 and 70, to record their data and answers.

3 APPLY

■ Use two or more boards of different lengths and have students compare the force needed to pull the cartons on these boards. Discuss other practical applications of inclined planes.

Close

■ Discuss the activity and questions with the class.

pages 98–101

PREPLAN

Lesson Objectives

5. **Define** *wheel and axle*.
6. **Define** *pulley*.
7. **Give examples** of how pulleys are used.

Science Background

■ The wheel and axle is actually a lever that can turn continuously. Normally, the applied force acts along the edge of the wheel and the load is at the edge of the axle. Thus, the force is applied at a greater distance from the fulcrum than the load. Therefore, the force applied to the wheel results in a larger force at the axle.

■ Pulleys are also variations of the lever but are not wheels and axles. A single fixed pulley serves as an excellent example of how changing the direction of a force can make work easier.

Lesson Vocabulary

wheel and axle   pulley

1   FOCUS

■ Sailing vessels commonly use many pulleys for ropes that control sails. Obtain pictures from old magazines showing pulleys in use, either on boats or in other places, and display them on a poster or bulletin board.

■ Use the goals on student page 98 to establish the purpose for studying this lesson.

> **LESSON 3 GOALS**
> You will learn
> ● that a wheel and axle is a simple machine.
> ● that a pulley is a simple machine with two different uses.

Wheel and axle

Wheel and Axle, Pulley

Wheels make loads easier to move. A **wheel and axle** is a simple machine with a wheel that turns a post. The post is called an axle. Wheels and axles are seen on cars, trains, trucks, and bicycles. Look at the picture of the doorknob and axle. The doorknob is the wheel that turns the axle. The distance around the doorknob is greater than the distance around the axle. Therefore, less force is needed to turn the wheel than to turn the axle.

98

TEACHER RESOURCE MASTERS

Reteaching Activity   77

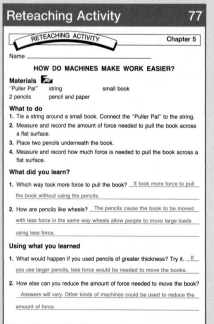

RETEACHING ACTIVITY   Chapter 5

Name

HOW DO MACHINES MAKE WORK EASIER?

Materials
"Puller Pal"   string   small book
2 pencils   pencil and paper

What to do
1. Tie a string around a small book. Connect the "Puller Pal" to the string.
2. Measure and record the amount of force needed to pull the book across a flat surface.
3. Place two pencils underneath the book.
4. Measure and record how much force is needed to pull the book across a flat surface.

What did you learn?

1. Which way took more force to pull the book? _It took more force to pull the book without using the pencils._

2. How are pencils like wheels? _The pencils cause the book to be moved with less force in the same way wheels allow people to move large loads using less force._

Using what you learned

1. What would happen if you used pencils of greater thickness? Try it. _If you use larger pencils, less force would be needed to move the books._

2. How else can you reduce the amount of force needed to move the book? _Answers will vary. Other kinds of machines could be used to reduce the amount of force._

Transparency Master   65

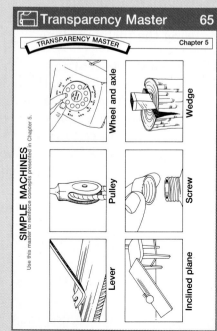

TRANSPARENCY MASTER   Chapter 5

SIMPLE MACHINES
Use this master to reinforce concepts presented in Chapter 5.

Wheel and axle   Wedge
Pulley   Screw
Lever   Inclined plane

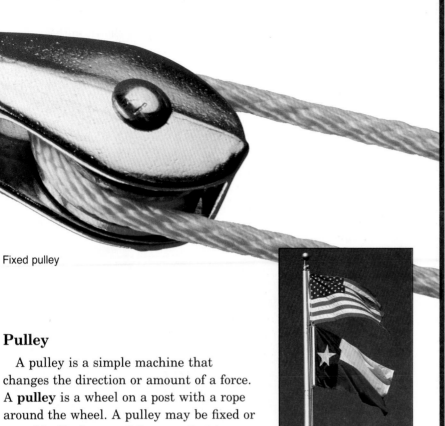

Fixed pulley

Pulley

A pulley is a simple machine that changes the direction or amount of a force. A **pulley** is a wheel on a post with a rope around the wheel. A pulley may be fixed or movable. Each part of the rope that is wrapped around the pulley supports a part of the load. One fixed pulley is shown in the top drawing. A fixed pulley can make work seem easier to do by changing the direction of the force. This type of pulley is used to raise a flag on a flagpole. You pull down on the rope. As you pull down, the flag that is attached to the other side of the rope moves up the pole.

99

TEACHER RESOURCE MASTERS

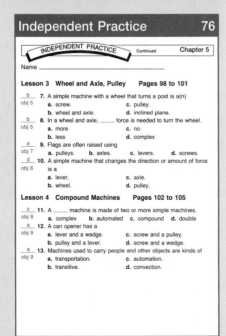

Independent Practice   76

INDEPENDENT PRACTICE   Continued   Chapter 5

Name _____

Lesson 3   Wheel and Axle, Pulley   Pages 98 to 101

_b_   **7.** A simple machine with a wheel that turns a post is a(n)
obj 5
    a. screw.   **c.** pulley.
    b. wheel and axle.   **d.** inclined plane.

_b_   **8.** In a wheel and axle, _____ force is needed to turn the wheel.
obj 5
    a. more   **c.** no
    b. less   **d.** complex

_a_   **9.** Flags are often raised using
obj 7
    a. pulleys.   **b.** axles.   **c.** levers.   **d.** screws.

_d_   **10.** A simple machine that changes the direction or amount of force
obj 6   is a
    a. lever.   **c.** axle.
    b. wheel.   **d.** pulley.

Lesson 4   Compound Machines   Pages 102 to 105

_c_   **11.** A _____ machine is made of two or more simple machines.
obj 8
    a. complex   **b.** automated   **c.** compound   **d.** double

_a_   **12.** A can opener has a
obj 9
    a. lever and a wedge.   **c.** screw and a pulley.
    b. pulley and a lever.   **d.** screw and a wedge.

_a_   **13.** Machines used to carry people and other objects are kinds of
obj 9
    a. transportation.   **c.** automation.
    b. transitive.   **d.** convection.

2   TEACH

■ Not all wheels are examples of a wheel and axle. They qualify only if a force is applied to the wheel in order to turn the axle or vice versa.

■ Many students may not know that a doorknob is a wheel and axle. Turning the latch with the knob requires less force than turning only the smaller axle.

Guided Practice

■ Check students' understanding of lesson concepts by discussing the Lesson Review questions on student page 101. If necessary, use the **reteaching strategy** in OPTIONS.

Independent Practice

■ Assign the Lesson 3 section of the Teacher Resource Master **Independent Practice,** page 76.

3   APPLY

Have students study the school grounds to find examples of simple machines such as a seesaw (lever), flagpole (pulley), wheelchair ramp (inclined plane), and so on.

Close

■ Use Summary statements on student page 101 to review lesson concepts.

OPTIONS

Reteaching Strategy

■ To review the meaning of wheel and axle, bring a bicycle, a tricycle, a roller skate, a skateboard, or a scooter to class. Have students point to examples of wheels and axles. Guide students to explain how a force applied to the wheel turns the axle or vice versa.

Resource Options

■ Show selections from "Simple Machines," *Mr. Wizard's World of Science Video Library*, Merrill Publishing Company.

OPTIONS

LANGUAGE CONNECTION

■ **Writing:** Have students rewrite the following passage. Instruct them to fill in the blanks with the correct pronouns by choosing from the words in parentheses.

Dad and _____ (I, me) were standing in the open doorway of the loft of _____ (ours, our) barn. _____ (We, Us) were pulling hay bales up into the loft with a rope. _____ (Him, He) hooked up a single fixed pulley above the doorway. That made it much easier for Dad and _____ (my, me) to pull down on _____ (ours, our) end of the rope and bring up each bale on the other end. (Answers in order are *I, our, We, He, me, our.*)

♦ **Reinforcement:** Have students make a list of as many devices as they can that use wheels and axles. Compare the size of the wheels of each.

● **Enrichment:** Some students may be interested to learn how cranks qualify as wheel and axles. Have students investigate gears and how they are used to do work.

▲ **Challenge:** If possible, bring a bicycle into your classroom. Have students identify as many examples of wheels and axles as possible. Encourage them to infer the reason for the size and location of each.

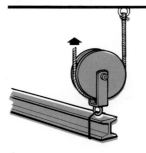

A movable pulley is shown in the drawing on this page. It is helpful in a different way. Using a movable pulley can decrease the force needed to lift a load. The force can be cut in half if one movable pulley is used to lift the load.

Using less force to lift a load makes the job seem easier. Pulleys and wheels and axles, like the other simple machines you have learned about in this chapter, make our jobs seem easier.

100

TEACHER RESOURCE MASTERS

Lesson Summary

- A wheel and axle is a simple machine with a wheel that turns a post.
- A pulley is a simple machine that changes the direction or amount of force.

Lesson Review

1. Why is it easier to pull a cart with wheels than a cart with no wheels?
★2. Give examples of how a pulley can change the direction of a force.

101

OPTIONS

SOCIAL STUDIES CONNECTION

■ Have students investigate the way of life of Amish people and their attitudes toward machines.

LESSON REVIEW ANSWERS

1. Wheels make loads easier to move.
2. Each part of the rope that is wrapped around a pulley supports part of the load. That means as you pull down, the load moves up.

TEACHER RESOURCE MASTERS

PREPLAN

Lesson Objectives
8. Distinguish between simple and compound machines.
9. Identify different simple machines making up compound machines and **give examples** of some compound machines.

Science Background
■ In modern society, most of the machines people use are compound machines.
■ Compound machines may have many moving parts. They also may have no moving parts (example: axe).
■ Industries may use presses, molding machines, pumps, mixers, valves, automated welding machines, and complex, computer-controlled assembly and conveyer systems.
■ Transportation is another common use of compound machines.

Lesson Vocabulary
compound machine

1 FOCUS

■ Exhibit a pencil sharpener, a bicycle, and kitchen or workshop tools that are compound machines. Have students identify the simple machines present.
■ Use the goals on student page 102 to establish the purpose for studying this lesson.

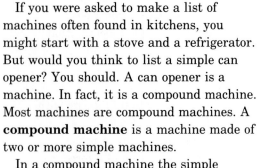

LESSON 4 GOALS
You will learn
● the difference between simple and compound machines.
● that most machines are compound machines.
● that people use compound machines for many reasons.

Compound machine

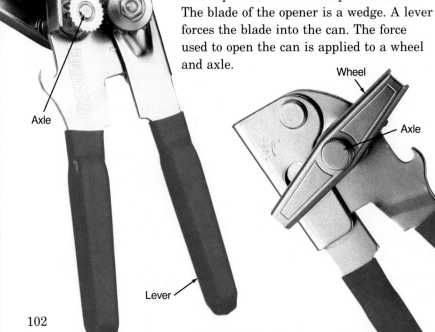

Compound Machines

If you were asked to make a list of machines often found in kitchens, you might start with a stove and a refrigerator. But would you think to list a simple can opener? You should. A can opener is a machine. In fact, it is a compound machine. Most machines are compound machines. A **compound machine** is a machine made of two or more simple machines.

In a compound machine the simple machines are connected. The work each simple machine does is combined to do the job of the compound machine. For example, a can opener has three simple machines. The blade of the opener is a wedge. A lever forces the blade into the can. The force used to open the can is applied to a wheel and axle.

102

TEACHER RESOURCE MASTERS

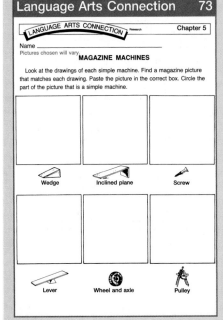

Language Arts Connection 73

LANGUAGE ARTS CONNECTION Research   Chapter 5
Name _____
Pictures chosen will vary. **MAGAZINE MACHINES**

Look at the drawings of each simple machine. Find a magazine picture that matches each drawing. Paste the picture in the correct box. Circle the part of the picture that is a simple machine.

Wedge   Inclined plane   Screw

Lever   Wheel and axle   Pulley

Family Science 66

FAMILY SCIENCE   Chapter 5
Name _____
Your child is learning about machines in science. This home activity will give your child an opportunity to see how the many kinds of machines are important.

MACHINES AROUND THE HOME

What to do
1. Look around the house and make a list of machines you use to do work. Some examples of machines found at home are: brooms, bottle openers, and washing machines.

rake	dishwasher
shovel	can opener
lawn mower	screwdriver
car	hammer
bicycle	sewing machine

2. Draw a circle around each compound machine on your list.

What did you learn?

1. How do you know if a machine is a compound or simple machine? A simple machine has few or no moving parts. Compound machines are made of two or more simple machines put together.

2. List three different ways that you could group the machines. Answers will vary.
   a. by use   c. number of moving parts
   b. simple or compound

Using what you learned

1. What safety rules should be followed with two of the machines in your home? Answers will vary depending on machines chosen.

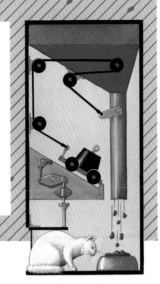

ACTIVITY

You Can...
Invent a Machine

Think about the simple machines you have learned about. Now, invent a machine using two or more simple machines. First, draw a picture of your machine. Label the simple machines in your drawing. Then, build a model of your machine. Display it in class. Tell your classmates how it works and what it does.

People Use Machines

How did you get to school today? If you rode in a bus or car or on your bicycle, you used a compound machine. People can use compound machines to move themselves or objects from place to place. Machines that carry people and objects are kinds of transportation. Bicycles, trucks, trains, boats, and planes are compound machines that are kinds of transportation.

People use machines for other reasons, too. Machines are useful in factories. People also use machines in growing food. Machines can do some work more quickly than people can. Machines also do work that is dangerous or harmful to people.

SCIENCE AND . . .
Writing

Choose the word or group of words that belongs in the space. You ___ a compound machine when you rode your bicycle last weekend.
A. use
B. uses
C. are using
D. were using

103

TEACHER RESOURCE MASTERS

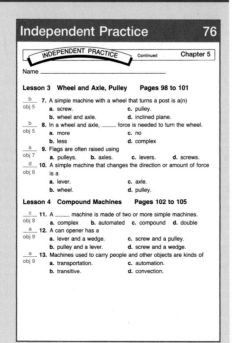

Independent Practice   76

INDEPENDENT PRACTICE   Continued   Chapter 5

Name _____

Lesson 3   Wheel and Axle, Pulley   Pages 98 to 101

_b_ **7.** A simple machine with a wheel that turns a post is a(n)
obj 5
   a. screw.   c. pulley.
   b. wheel and axle.   d. inclined plane.

_b_ **8.** In a wheel and axle, ___ force is needed to turn the wheel.
obj 5
   a. more   c. no
   b. less   d. complex

_a_ **9.** Flags are often raised using
obj 7
   a. pulleys.   b. axles.   c. levers.   d. screws.

_d_ **10.** A simple machine that changes the direction or amount of force
obj 6   is a
   a. lever.   c. axle.
   b. wheel.   d. pulley.

Lesson 4   Compound Machines   Pages 102 to 105

_c_ **11.** A ___ machine is made of two or more simple machines.
obj 8
   a. complex   b. automated   c. compound   d. double

_a_ **12.** A can opener has a
obj 9
   a. lever and a wedge.   c. screw and a pulley.
   b. pulley and a lever.   d. screw and a wedge.

_a_ **13.** Machines used to carry people and other objects are kinds of
obj 9
   a. transportation.   c. automation.
   b. transitive.   d. convection.

OPTIONS

YOU CAN . . . INVENT A MACHINE

Process Skill: Formulating Models

Objective: Design and **build** a compound machine.

Setup/Teach

■ Have students research how specific inventions may have changed society. Some examples include the telephone, xerography machine, and automobile.

SCIENCE AND . . . WRITING

■ **Skill:** Recognize correct verb tense.

■ **Student Response:** D

♦ **Reinforcement:** Choose one object in the classroom. Discuss all the different machines used to manufacture and transport that object from the time it was a raw material until it arrived in the classroom.

● **Enrichment:** Ask students to identify the simple machines used in these compound machines:
1. scissors
2. a brace and bit used to drill holes
3. a punch-style can opener

▲ **Challenge:** Write to a large car or airplane manufacturing company and find out how their engineers use computers to design cars or planes.

LESSON REVIEW ANSWERS

1. A compound machine is made of two or more simple machines.
2. Answers may include a can opener, egg beater, tape recorder, and refrigerator.
3. The work of the simple machines in a compound machine is combined to do a job so that work can be done more quickly and/or more safely.

How would you try to open a can of soup if you didn't have a can opener? It would be very difficult and dangerous. A can opener is just one example of how machines can make our lives easier.

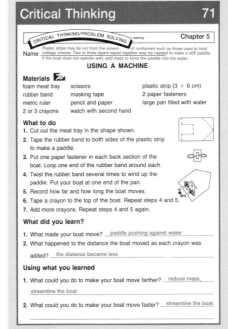

Compound machines

Lesson Summary

• A compound machine is made of two or more simple machines.
• People may use compound machines to move from place to place, to do work quickly, or to do work that is dangerous.
• People use many compound machines in their homes.

Lesson Review

1. What is the difference between a simple and a compound machine?
2. Name two compound machines found in the home.
★3. Why would a compound machine sometimes be more useful than a simple machine?

104   Use Application Activity on pages 347, 348.

TEACHER RESOURCE MASTERS

Critical Thinking 71

CRITICAL THINKING/PROBLEM SOLVING Inferring   Chapter 5

Name _____ Plastic strips may be cut from the covers of containers such as those used to hold cottage cheese. Two or three layers taped together may be needed to make a stiff paddle. If the boat does not operate well, add mass to force the paddle into the water.

USING A MACHINE

Materials
foam meat tray   scissors   plastic strip (3 × 6 cm)
rubber band   masking tape   2 paper fasteners
metric ruler   pencil and paper   large pan filled with water
2 or 3 crayons   watch with second hand

What to do
1. Cut out the meat tray in the shape shown.
2. Tape the rubber band to both sides of the plastic strip to make a paddle.
3. Put one paper fastener in each back section of the boat. Loop one end of the rubber band around each.
4. Twist the rubber band several times to wind up the paddle. Put your boat at one end of the pan.
5. Record how far and how long the boat moves.
6. Tape a crayon to the top of the boat. Repeat steps 4 and 5.
7. Add more crayons. Repeat steps 4 and 5 again.

What did you learn?
1. What made your boat move? __paddle pushing against water__
2. What happened to the distance the boat moved as each crayon was added? __the distance became less__

Using what you learned
1. What could you do to make your boat move farther? __reduce mass, streamline the boat__
2. What could you do to make your boat move faster? __streamline the boat__

Social Studies Connection 74

SOCIAL STUDIES CONNECTION Seeing Relationships   Chapter 5

Name _____

INVENT A MACHINE

1. Collect various objects such as spools, rubber bands, hangers, wooden toys, and empty boxes.
2. Use the objects to build your own machine. For example, have one lever put another lever into motion, or have one wheel turn another wheel.
3. Draw your machine in the space below.

1. List the objects you used to make your machine. __Answers will vary.__

2. How did your machine work? __Answers will vary.__

3. Was your machine simple or compound? __Most will be compound machines.__

I WANT TO KNOW ABOUT...

A Bicycle Tester

Joseph Pérex is a bicycle racer who also test-rides bicycles. Some tests require that Joseph lie on his back to pedal the bikes. These bikes are designed for speed. Another bike that Joseph has been testing is an enclosed bike. A canopy, or cover, is placed over the frame and the rider. Scientists hope to discover a canopy that will lower wind resistance without adding much weight.

Joseph enjoys testing bicycles, but he also wants to compete in the Olympics some day. After the Olympics, Joseph hopes to test pedal-powered aircraft and boats.

Improvements from testing cars, aircraft, and other experimental products often find their way to the general public. The same is true with bicycle improvements. In a few years, your new bike may look like one Joseph has been testing.

Career

105

TEACHER RESOURCE MASTERS

Feature Background

■ Refer to *Smithsonian* magazine, January, 1985, for a description of modern human-powered vehicles (HPV).

■ How fast can a bike travel? In 1980, a two-person pedal-powered vehicle traveled 101.24 kph on a California speedway.

■ A group interested in promoting pedal power is the International Human-Powered Vehicle Association, P.O. Box 2068, Seal Beach, CA 90740.

Teaching Suggestions

■ Explain that pedal-powered machines use human energy very efficiently.

■ Discuss why it is important to save energy. Remind students that cars use fossil fuels.

■ Discuss how the use of bicycles can keep us healthy and keep the environment cleaner.

■ Invite a member of a bike racing club to talk to the class about bike racing.

Summary

Chapter Closure: As a homework assignment, have students write questions that can be answered by each summary statement. Use the student-prepared questions orally to review the concepts learned in this unit.

Science Words

Have students work in **cooperative groups** to prepare a booklet about machines. Allow one or two pages for each science word. Students should draw or cut pictures from magazines, catalogs, or other sources to illustrate each word. The science word and its meaning should be included with each group of pictures.

Student Responses

1. compound machine
2. wheel and axle
3. screw
4. inclined plane
5. wedge
6. simple machine
7. pulley
8. lever

CHAPTER REVIEW 5

Summary

Lesson 1
- Simple machines change the amount or direction of force.
- Simple machines have few or no moving parts.

Lesson 2
- Inclined planes are used to move objects.
- Inclined planes, wedges, and screws are similar.

Lesson 3
- A wheel and axle is a wheel that turns a post.
- A pulley changes the direction or amount of a force.

Lesson 4
- Compound machines contain two or more simple machines.
- Most machines are compound machines.

Science Words

Fill in the blank with the correct word or words from the list.

simple machine	**screw**
wheel and axle	**lever**
inclined plane	**pulley**
compound machine	**wedge**

1. A machine made of two or more simple machines is called a(n) ____.
2. A doorknob is an example of a(n) ____.
3. An inclined plane wrapped around a post is a(n) ____.
4. A ramp is a(n) ____.
5. A knife blade is an example of a(n) ____.
6. A machine with few or no moving parts is a(n) ____.
7. A simple machine with a rope and a wheel is a(n) ____.
8. A seesaw is an example of a(n) ____.

106

TEACHER RESOURCE MASTERS

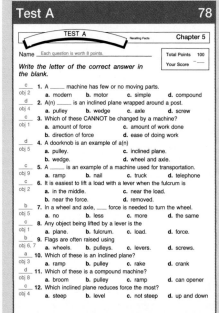

Test A   78

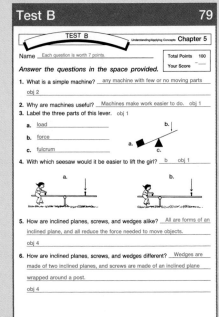

Test B   79

Questions

Recalling Ideas

Correctly complete each of the following sentences.

1. The simple machine formed from two inclined planes is a
   (a) wedge. (c) lever.
   (b) screw. (d) wheel and axle.
2. A can opener is a compound machine that contains a wedge, lever, and
   (a) fixed pulley.
   (b) inclined plane.
   (c) movable pulley.
   (d) wheel and axle.
3. A doorknob is a
   (a) wedge. (c) wheel and axle.
   (b) screw. (d) pulley.
4. Simple machines can change the direction or the amount of
   (a) work.   (c) energy.
   (b) force. (d) mass.

Understanding Ideas

Answer the following questions using complete sentences.

1. Give two reasons why a pulley is used to lift an object.

2. How does work seem easier to do when an inclined plane is used?

Thinking Critically

Think about what you have learned in this chapter. Answer the following questions using complete sentences.

1. Why are machines often used to paint cars in factories?
2. How do you change the position of the fulcrum on a lever in order to move a heavier load?

107

Questions

Recalling Ideas

1. a
2. d
3. c
4. b

Understanding Ideas

1. A pulley changes the direction of a force or decreases the amount of force needed to lift a load.
2. An inclined plane reduces the force needed to do work. A longer distance is traveled on an inclined plane. Therefore, less force is needed.

Thinking Critically

1. Machines are often used to paint cars in factories, because it is not healthy for people to inhale paint fumes for a long period of time. Painter robots can also paint faster and more neatly than people.
2. To move a heavier load, you move the fulcrum toward the load.

TEACHER RESOURCE MASTERS

Test B   80

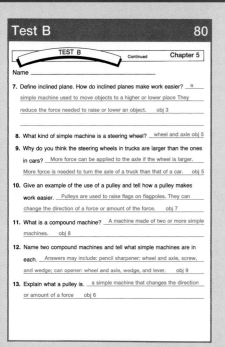

TEST B   Continued   Chapter 5

Name _____

7. Define inclined plane. How do inclined planes make work easier? __a__ simple machine used to move objects to a higher or lower place They reduce the force needed to raise or lower an object.   obj 3

8. What kind of simple machine is a steering wheel? __wheel and axle obj 5__

9. Why do you think the steering wheels in trucks are larger than the ones in cars? __More force can be applied to the axle if the wheel is larger.__ More force is needed to turn the axle of a truck than that of a car.   obj 5

10. Give an example of the use of a pulley and tell how a pulley makes work easier. __Pulleys are used to raise flags on flagpoles. They can__ change the direction of a force or amount of the force.   obj 7

11. What is a compound machine? __A machine made of two or more simple__ machines.   obj 8

12. Name two compound machines and tell what simple machines are in each. __Answers may include: pencil sharpener: wheel and axle, screw,__ and wedge; can opener: wheel and axle, wedge, and lever.   obj 9

13. Explain what a pulley is. __a simple machine that changes the direction__ or amount of a force   obj 6

Checking for Understanding

1. Scientific methods are lists of steps used to solve problems. They can help find answers to everyday problems.

2. Accept all reasonable answers. Answers may include size, shape, color, roughness, smoothness.

3. The bowling ball has more mass.

4. Simple machines have few or no moving parts. Compound machines may have many moving parts. Compound machines are made of two or more simple machines.

5. Mass is measured in grams and kilograms.

6. Both solids and liquids have a definite size or volume.

7. Evaporation is the change of matter from a liquid to a gas. Condensation is the change of matter from a gas to a liquid.

8. A mixture is matter that can be mixed together in any amount with each type of matter keeping its own properties. A compound has properties that are different from those of its elements. A chemical change takes place when a compound forms.

9. No work was done because the box didn't move.

10. Work is what is done when a force moves an object. Energy is the ability to do work. Energy is used when work is done.

11. Both the wedge and the screw are made from inclined planes. A wedge is made of two inclined planes. A screw is an inclined plane wrapped around a post.

12. Accept all reasonable answers. Wheels and axles are used in doorknobs, cars, trains, trucks, and bicycles.

13. Accept all reasonable answers. Compound machines are used in transportation, in factories, and on farms.

Recalling Activities

1. Using scientific methods, it is discovered that sugar dissolves faster in warm

Checking for Understanding

Write a short answer for each question or statement.

1. What are scientific methods, and how can they be used to help you?
2. Name five properties that describe objects.
3. Why is more force used to lift a bowling ball than a soccer ball?
4. Compare compound machines and simple machines.
5. What units are used to measure the mass of an object?
6. In what way are solids and liquids the same?
7. What is the difference between evaporation and condensation?
8. What is the difference between a mixture and a compound?
9. If you push on a big box but it doesn't move, why haven't you done any work?
10. Describe the difference between work and energy.
11. How are a wedge and a screw alike? different?
12. Name several uses for a wheel and axle.
13. How are compound machines used outside the home?

Recalling Activities

Write a short paragraph for each question or statement.

1. How fast will sugar dissolve?
2. How can you find the best soap?
3. How do you measure mass?
4. Is it a solid or a liquid?
5. How can you make a dime dance?
6. How does water change?
7. How do you measure force?
8. How can you change friction?
9. How do levers work?
10. How do inclined planes make work easier?

TEACHER RESOURCE MASTERS

Project Ideas

1. Use flat ice cream sticks and other materials to build a model of a bridge used for a highway. Design the bridge so that it will keep the pavement from cracking due to expansion during hot weather. Show your model to the class.

2. Invent a machine that performs a household task. Draw a picture of the machine and show how it helps people.

Books to Read

How Things Work edited by Donald J. Crump, National Geographic Society: Washington, DC, 1983.

Simple Machines by Rae Bains, Troll Associates: Mahwah, NJ, 1985.

This book will introduce you to all kinds of simple machines.

Bet You Can! Science Possibilities to Fool You by Vicky Cobb and Kathy Darling, Avon Books: New York, 1983.

TEACHER RESOURCE MASTERS

water than in cold water. As the temperature of the water rises, sugar dissolves more easily.

2. Use a scientific method to test the amount of suds left in different soaps after adding equal amounts of oil to each.

3. Mass is measured using a balance. Objects to be measured are placed on one side of the balance. Objects with a known mass are added to the other side of the balance until both sides are at an equal height.

4. An object can be identified as a solid or a liquid by observing its properties. The substance tested has characteristics of both solids and liquids depending on its temperature.

5. The dime can be made to move when air in the bottle warms. Warm air in the bottle expands, pushing on the dime.

6. Heat can cause water to evaporate, turning into water vapor. If the water vapor cools, it turns back into liquid.

7. Force can be measured using a Puller Pal. Objects lifted by rubber bands that stretched the most took more force to lift.

8. You can change friction by making a surface of contact smoother or rougher.

9. Levers can move objects using a fulcrum and force. The closer the fulcrum is to the object, the less force is needed to move the object.

10. Inclined planes make work easier because as the steepness of the plane is reduced, the force needed to move something up the plane is also reduced.

Project Ideas

Have students work individually or in **cooperative groups** to complete one of the projects listed.

Books to Read

♦ *Simple Machines*
● *Bet You Can! Science Possibilities to Fool You*
▲ *How Things Work*

Earth Science

Bulletin Board

Goals: This bulletin board will illustrate three rock types: igneous, sedimentary, and metamorphic. Students will be able to classify the processes and information presented in this unit.

Materials: small envelopes
large envelopes
pictures of igneous, sedimentary, and
metamorphic rocks
yarn or ribbon
poster board for labels

Procedure: Begin by dividing the board into three equal sections with the yarn or ribbon. Label the sections Igneous, Sedimentary, and Metamorphic. Place the appropriate pictures in the correct section. Have several envelopes placed under each heading. Provide, or have students prepare, several cards on which appear words or phrases associated with each rock type. For example, *mud, layer, sediment, magma,* and *pressure* are some possible choices. Place the cards in a large envelope. Allow students to **work cooperatively** at the bulletin board to place the cards in the envelopes under the correct heading.

Science Center

Goals: This science center is designed to enable students to match changes that occur in nature with the appropriate stage of the water cycle.

Materials: index cards
envelope
picture of water cycle, rain clouds,
mountains with snow, and river
push pins/tape

Procedure: Have students write a term like *rain, sleet, hail, glacier, dew, fog, clouds, reservoir, puddle,* and others on one side of an index card and write the answer on the back using the appropriate stage of the water cycle (evaporation, condensation, precipitation, and storage). Students should continue to add terms of processes of nature that occur to blank cards and place them in the envelope throughout the unit. Have students go to the science center individually, remove a card from the envelope, and pin or tape it to the appropriate stage of the water cycle. After placing all cards, students should remove cards one at a time and check their answers by looking on the back. Place cards in the envelope for other students.

Places to Go, People to See

Field Trip Ideas

Find an eroded area, such as near a river or stream. Take the class there to collect rock samples and to observe the effects of erosion.

Arrange a trip to a reservoir or to a facility that studies and records climate.

Speakers and Visitors

Hold a "Rock Day" during which students act as speakers. They may show their own rock collections or pictures of rocks.

You may wish to contact a geologist or a rock-collecting club to visit the class.

Audiovisuals for the Students

Films and Filmstrips

A Drop of Water, 16 mm, 14 min., color, Barr Films.
The Ways of Water, 16 mm, 13 min., color, EBEC.
What We Get From the Earth, 1 filmstrip, 1 sound cassette, 15 min., color, National Geographic Society.

Videotapes

Rivers: The Work of Running Water, 22 min., color, Encyclopaedia Britannica Educational Corp.
Rocks That Form on the Earth's Surface, 17 min., color, EBEC.
Rocks That Originate Underground, 23 min., color, EBEC.
The Ways of Water, 13 min., color, EBEC.
What Makes Clouds? 19 min., color, EBEC.
Mr. Wizard's World of Science Video Library, Merrill Publishing Company: Tape 16, "Change of State."

Computer Software

Earth Science Covers effects of nature on the environment. Two disks include The Changing Face of the Earth, Rocks and Mountains, Questions and Answers about the Earth, and Energy from the Sun.
Type: Tutorial, Games
Hardware: Apple II$^+$, IIe, IIc, Commodore 64, IBM PC, PCjr.
Supplier: Orange Cherry Media
Learning About Science Series: Learning About Water Students learn about the vital role of water on Earth, the water cycle, potential and kinetic energy, condensation, and evaporation. Includes a videocassette.
Type: Tutorial, Quiz
Hardware: Apple II +, IIe, IIc, IBM PC, PCjr.
Supplier: AIMS Media

Resources for the Teacher

Materials at Little/No Cost

Soil Conservation Service
South Building, Room 0054, Box 2890
Washington, DC 20013
Send a long, self-addressed stamped envelope and ask for "Conservation and the Water Cycle."

Resource Books

Cattermole, Peter and Patrick Moore. *The Story of the Earth.* New York: Cambridge University Press, 1985.
Dietrich, R. V. and Reed Wicander. *Minerals, Rocks and Fossils.* New York: John Wiley and Sons, 1983.
Eicher, Don L., et al. *The History of the Earth's Crust.* Englewood Cliffs, NJ: Prentice-Hall, 1984.

UNIT 2

Earth Science

UNIT CONCEPTS

Chapter 6

■ Rocks are composed of minerals and are formed by processes occurring in the crust and mantle of Earth.

■ Rocks are always changing as part of the rock cycle and can be classified according to their mode of formation into three groups: igneous, sedimentary, and metamorphic.

Chapter 7

■ Water, wind, ice, and living things weather rocks.

■ Wind, water, and ice cause erosion.

Chapter 8

■ The weather is affected by the evaporation and condensation of Earth's water.

■ Cirrus, stratus, and cumulus clouds are indicative of certain kinds of weather.

■ Climate is the usual type of weather that occurs at a given place over time. The Earth is divided into three climatic zones.

Chapter 9

■ Evaporation, condensation, and precipitation are all parts of the water cycle that provide water for living things.

■ Precipitation results in groundwater and runoff.

■ There are both natural and people-made places for water storage.

Earth Science

110

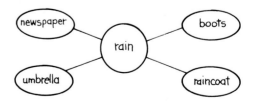

T he rain to the wind said,
"You push and I'll pelt."
They so smote the garden bed
That the flowers actually knelt,
And lay lodged—though not dead.
I know how the flowers felt.

"Lodged"
Robert Frost

111

ACTIVITY CENTER

For fun, hands-on, independent activities that integrate reading, writing, math, and technology with the chapters in this unit, have students complete some or all of the Activity Center Activities below. Look for specific chapter references in the Lesson Planning Guides.

Reading: 5 Rock On!
6 Weathering the Storm,
7 Let Your Fingers Do the Drilling
Writing: 5 A Rocky Story,
6 Words of Weather,
7 The Days of the Drop
Math: 5 When You're Hot, You're Hot! **6** Down the Drain, **7** Mack and Bill
Technology: 5 Bubbling Rocks, **6** How Warm Is It?
7 How Can You Clean It?

CONNECTING LITERATURE TO SCIENCE

Understanding the Selection

■ Lead students in a discussion about rainstorms, encouraging them to focus on the effects of heavy rain. Tell students that you are going to read a poem about a storm.

■ Read the poem aloud. Then have students read the poem aloud with you.

■ Ask: **What did the rain say that it would do? What did the rain tell the wind to do?** *The rain would pelt and the wind would push.* Ask: **How do you know that the rain was not a gentle rain?** *The flowers were beaten down.*

■ Ask: **Did the poet know how the flowers felt?** *yes* Ask students to describe how they think the flowers felt. Possible answers include *drenched, beaten down, lifeless.*

Relating the Selection to Unit Concepts

■ Ask students other ways water can fall from the clouds besides in the form of rain. Possible answers include *snow, hail, sleet.*

■ Discuss the effect that temperature has on precipitation. Ask: **During what time of the year would you expect to see snow and sleet? Why?** *the winter, because the temperatures are colder.*

Relating the Selection to the Student's World

■ Have students look at the photograph and tell what they see. *an umbrella.*

■ Ask: **In what kinds of weather do you usually see people using umbrellas? Why?** *People use umbrellas when it rains to keep from getting wet.*

■ Draw a cluster diagram on the board and ask students to name some things that people wear or use to protect themselves in the rain. See the example below.

Rocks

Planning Guide

Lessons	Objectives	Vocabulary
Chapter Introduction pp. 112, 113		
Lesson 1 Rocks and Earth's Layers pp. 114–119	1. Operationally define *mineral.* 2. Operationally define *rock.* 3. Identify Earth's layers. 4. Compare Earth's crust, mantle, and core.	mineral crust mantle core
Lesson 2 How Rocks Form pp. 120–129	5. Operationally define *magma, lava, igneous rock, sediments, sedimentary rock, metamorphic rock.* 6. **Explain** how igneous, sedimentary, and metamorphic rocks form. 7. Operationally define *rock cycle.* 8. **Explain** the processes in the rock cycle.	magma lava igneous rock sediments sedimentary rock metamorphic rock rock cycle
Chapter Review pp. 130, 131		

Planning Guide

Text Activities		Teacher Resource Masters	Other Components
Title/Skill	**Materials per Group**		
Have You Ever . . . Made Layers? p. 113 Observing Time Allotment: 30 minutes	red, yellow, and green gelatin loaf pan bananas table knife refrigerator		**Activity Center:** "Rock On"; "A Rocky Story"; "Bubbling Rocks"
How Can Sediments Make Layers? p. 119 Observing/Inferring Time Allotment: 30–45 minutes **An Age-old Problem,** p. 349 Interpreting Data /Controlling Variables Time Allotment: 40 minutes; 15 minutes for conclusion	plastic jar and lid sand, gravel, humus water hand lens newspaper crayons pencil and paper 4 aluminum pie pans 2 kg each of sand, silt, clay, gravel, clay, saw dust, and fine leaf mulch water 2 large leaves	Independent Practice, pp. 91, 92 Activity Worksheet, pp. 83, 84 ▲ Critical Thinking, p. 88 Math Connection, p. 90 ◆ Reteaching Activity, p. 93 Transparency Master, p. 81	Color Transparency #5 Activity Book, pp. 41, 42
You Can . . . Study Rocks Made by People, p. 125 Observing/Communicating Time Allotment: 10 minutes **How Does Sedimentary Rock Form?** p. 128 Formulating Models/ Observing Time Allotment: 30 minutes plus 48–72 hrs. for drying **Build a Shelter,** p. 351 Observing/Interpreting Data Time Allotment: 40 minutes to complete projects; 1 week to test; 20 minutes to conclude	piece of concrete piece of asphalt hand lens pencil and paper paper cup Epsom salts, water sand hand lens newspaper pencil and paper variety of rocks, sand, and clay water student materials	Independent Practice, pp. 91, 92 Activity Worksheet, pp. 85, 86 Language Arts Connection, p. 89 Critical Thinking, p. 87 ◆ Family Science, p. 82	Color Transparency #6 Activity Book, pp. 39, 40
		Test A, p. 94 Test B, pp. 95, 96	

◆ Basic / ▲ Advanced / All other masters are for use by all students.

CHAPTER 6

Machines

For Exceptional Students

ESL/LEP

Chapter 6/Lesson 1, Page 114
Give each student a rock. Ask students to list as many properties of their rock as possible. Ask them to draw their rock and to write sentences about it using the following properties: color, size, shape, and texture.

Chapter 6/Lesson 1, Page 116
Ask students to draw a picture of Earth's layers. Discuss how the layers differ. Write on the chalkboard: **The center section of Earth is the _____. The outer layer of Earth is the _____. Layers of rock beneath the crust make up the _____.** Have students fill in the blanks. Let them use the pattern sentences to describe their drawings.

Chapter 6/Lesson 2, Page 120
Write the following terms and phrases on the chalkboard in two columns: **igneous rock, sedimentary rock,** and **metamorphic rock;** and **changed by heat and pressure, made of sediments pressed together,** and **made from cooled magma or lava.** Ask students to produce the terms and to match them with the phrases. Have students write sentences using the terms.

Gifted

Chapter 6/Lesson 2, Page 127
Have gifted students organize a class rock collection. Using information from the text, allow these students to analyze rocks brought in by the entire class, speculate upon the kinds of minerals each contains, and attempt to classify each rock. Let the students use reference books to check their predictions. They may wish to share the class collection with a group of younger students or display it.

Mainstreamed

Chapter 6/Lesson 2, Page 127
Developmentally Handicapped: Prepare a series of response cards. On one side of each card, tape a magnified picture of a rock. On the reverse side, write the type of rock it is (igneous, sedimentary, metamorphic). Have exceptional students work in 1:1 tutoring pairs, each "tutor" showing the cards, prompting correct responses where necessary, and praising accurate identification based on properties. Partners may switch roles.

Whole Class Science Project

Have students collect rocks in different locations and place them in the classroom in a mineral and/or rock identification center. Provide information and supplies students will need to properly identify the rocks and minerals. Students should separate and label the rocks *igneous, metamorphic,* or *sedimentary* and discuss where the rocks were obtained in the community. Have students research to determine if there has been any historical event to cause the rocks in your area to be different. Provide supplies for the students such as the Mohs' hardness scale, streak or porcelain plate for streak test, hammer for breaking to check for cleavage, and information on how to test for the minerals. If possible, obtain a set of minerals purchased from a scientific supply house containing representative examples of siliceous, nonmetallic and metallic ores, and gem minerals so students can compare the minerals in their rocks to this sample. Divide students into four groups and have them perform tests to classify minerals. Students should test minerals for hardness, cleavage, luster, and crystal structure. Have each group report about the minerals found in each of the three groups of rocks and tell the use for the minerals.

Science Fair Projects

Individual students could do one of the following projects:

1. Display different samples of sedimentary rocks (such as conglomerate, sandstone, limestone, shale, and rock salt) and look for grains of sand, silt, or clay. Using a magnifying glass, students should draw what they see and find out how each of these rocks is formed.

2. Display a model of Earth and its layers. Use a styrofoam ball at least 15 cm (6 in.) in diameter. Cut a good-sized wedge out of the ball so the inside can be seen to the center. Draw lines and color the areas to show the relative thickness of Earth's layers. On poster board, draw pictures and report about the composition of the different layers and tell about the thicknesses.

3. Using broken rocks and a magnifying glass, look for the mineral crystals that will be different in color, shape, and size. Draw different shapes of minerals on a poster board and report what minerals are used for, where they are found, and why they are important.

CHAPTER 6

pages 112–131

Chapter Concepts

■ Rocks are composed of minerals and are formed by processes occurring in the crust and mantle of Earth.

■ Rocks are always changing as part of the rock cycle and can be classified according to their mode of formation into three groups: igneous, sedimentary, and metamorphic.

Chapter Background

■ Sedimentary rocks form at or very near Earth's surface by processes of weathering, erosion, deposition, and cementation. Igneous and metamorphic rocks are the result of internal processes deep within the lower crust and upper mantle.

Looking Ahead

■ Hold a "Rock Day" during which students acts as speakers. They may show their own rock collections or pictures of rocks.

■ You may wish to contact a geologist or a rock-collecting club to visit the class.

Look for These Symbols

   —Hands-on activity

   —Cooperative learning

   —Overhead transparency

◆ —Basic/Reinforcement

● —Average/Enrichment

▲ —Advanced/Challenge

SC —Science Center

   —Calculator Practice

SCIENCE
In Your World

112

CHAPTER 6

Rocks

Along the highway, you may have seen places where the rock has been cut so a road can go through. Sometimes you can see patterns in the rock. Patterns like the one in the picture show how many layers of sand, shells, or plants helped form the rock.

Have You Ever...

Made Layers?

Pour 236 mL of red gelatin into a loaf pan. Cool in the refrigerator until firm. Add 236 mL of yellow gelatin and cool until firm. Slice bananas and cover the yellow gelatin. Pour on 236 mL of green gelatin and cool until firm. Cut a slice of gelatin. How is your dessert like the picture on page 112?

113

PREPLAN

Time Allotment: 30 minutes

Objectives
1. **Observe** layers in sedimentary rock.
2. **Create and compare** layers of gelatin to layers in sedimentary rock.

Setup
■ If you wish to conduct the activity, you will need the following materials for each student or activity group:
236 mL each of red, yellow, and green
   gelatin mixture   table knife
1 banana   loaf pan   refrigerator

1 FOCUS

■ Direct students' attention to the picture on page 112. Ask why there are road cuts like the one in the picture.

2 TEACH

■ After having the introductory paragraph read aloud, ask for volunteers to point out the patterns in the rock. Ask what the lines could represent.

Have You Ever . . .
Use this activity as an introduction to sedimentary rock.
Have students **work cooperatively** in groups of four.
■ **Safety Consideration:** Caution students to work with an adult at home.
■ **Student Response**
1. The layers of gelatin and bananas are like the layers in the rock.

3 APPLY

■ Ask students what other things come in layers. Record their responses.

Close
■ Students will study about rocks and Earth structures.

PREPLAN

Lesson Objectives

1. **Operationally define** *mineral.*
2. **Operationally define** *rock.*
3. **Identify** Earth's layers.
4. **Compare** Earth's crust, mantle, and core.

Science Background

■ Mineralogists define a mineral as a naturally occurring, inorganic solid with a definite chemical composition.

■ It is not possible to take rock samples from the deeper parts of the crust, let alone the mantle or core. The deepest mines and oil wells do not penetrate very far into the crust. Density, temperature, and composition of the mantle and core are inferred from indirect evidence.

■ Scientists have studied earthquake shock waves as they pass through Earth. The behavior of these seismic waves gives indirect evidence of Earth's interior. Scientists know the crust is as thin as 5 km in the ocean basins and as thick as 60 km under mountain ranges such as the Himalayas. The rigid crust sits suspended on a plastic-like upper mantle.

Lesson Vocabulary

mineral   crust   mantle   core

Note: The activity on student page 119 may be used for guided discovery before you begin this lesson.

1   FOCUS

■ Show students a collection of photos or magazine pictures that have rocks in them. Some of the pictures might show buildings, fences, or monuments made of rock. Ask what all of the pictures have in common.

■ Use the goals on student page 114 to establish the purpose for studying this lesson.

Rocks and Earth's Layers

LESSON 1 GOALS
You will learn
● that rocks are made of minerals.
● that rocks have different properties.
● that Earth has layers.

Carla likes to collect rocks. She often wonders how the rocks formed. Her favorite rocks are shown in the picture on this page. Each rock has different properties. How would you describe each rock?

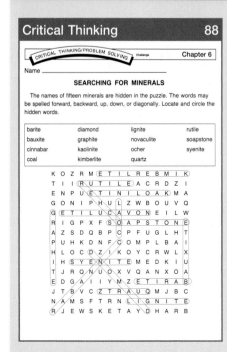

Carla's favorite rocks

What Are Rocks?

A gelatin salad is somewhat like a rock. The salad is a mixture of gelatin and different fruit. In the picture of gelatin salad on this page, you can see the different parts mixed together. You might see pieces of peach, pear, or grape. The pieces are different colors, sizes, and shapes. How many different parts of the salad mixture do you see?

114

TEACHER RESOURCE MASTERS

Critical Thinking   88

CRITICAL THINKING/PROBLEM SOLVING   Challenge   Chapter 6

Name _____

SEARCHING FOR MINERALS

The names of fifteen minerals are hidden in the puzzle. The words may be spelled forward, backward, up, down, or diagonally. Locate and circle the hidden words.

barite	diamond	lignite	rutile
bauxite	graphite	novaculite	soapstone
cinnabar	kaolinite	ocher	syenite
coal	kimberlite	quartz	

```
K O Z R M E T I L R E B M I K
T I I R U T I L E A C R D Z I
E N P U E T I N I L O A K M A
G O N I P H U L Z W B O U V Q
G E T I L U C A V O N E I L W
R I G P X F S O A P S T O N E
A Z S D Q B P C P F U G L H T
P U H K D N F C O M P L B A I
H L O C D Z I K O Y C R W L X
I H S Y E N I T E M E D K I U
T J R Q N U O X V Q A N X O A
E D G A I I Y M Z E T I R A B
J T B V C Z T R A U Q M J B C
N A M S F T R N L I G N I T E
R J E W S K E T A Y D H A R B
```

Math Connection   90

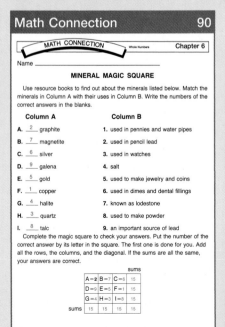

MATH CONNECTION   Whole Numbers   Chapter 6

Name _____

MINERAL MAGIC SQUARE

Use resource books to find out about the minerals listed below. Match the minerals in Column A with their uses in Column B. Write the numbers of the correct answers in the blanks.

Column A

A. __2__ graphite
B. __7__ magnetite
C. __6__ silver
D. __9__ galena
E. __5__ gold
F. __1__ copper
G. __4__ halite
H. __3__ quartz
I. __8__ talc

Column B

1. used in pennies and water pipes
2. used in pencil lead
3. used in watches
4. salt
5. used to make jewelry and coins
6. used in dimes and dental fillings
7. known as lodestone
8. used to make powder
9. an important source of lead

Complete the magic square to check your answers. Put the number of the correct answer by its letter in the square. The first one is done for you. Add all the rows, the columns, and the diagonal. If the sums are all the same, your answers are correct.

			sums
A=2	B=7	C=6	15
D=9	E=5	F=1	15
G=4	H=3	I=8	15
sums 15	15	15	15

Rocks are also mixtures of different things. You can often see parts of the mixture. Look at the rock pictured on this page. What different colors do you see? Each different color is a different part of the rock.

The different parts that make a rock are called minerals (MIHN uh rulz). A **mineral** is a solid found in nature. Minerals are made of chemicals. They are not living, and their inside structures are crystals.

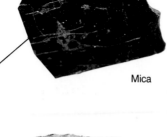
Mica

Granite

Quartz

Feldspar

It is fun to look at some rocks that are mixtures of different minerals. Just as minerals have different properties, rocks also have different properties. Some rocks are made of many different minerals and are colorful. Other rocks are made of just one mineral and are plain. Some rocks are smooth, and others are rough. Some rocks are very hard, and others are soft.

115

2 TEACH

■ Discuss how you can tell minerals apart. Color, shine, crystal shape, and hardness are properties used to identify minerals.

■ Discuss the relationship between rocks and minerals. Explain that a rock is a mixture of minerals. Use mixture analogies: peanuts and popcorn (Cracker Jacks), bridge mix candy, and chocolate chip cookies. Explain minerals are the components of the "rock" mixture.

■ Identify places in your neighborhood where rocks are being used in fences, buildings, roads, monuments, and so on.

Guided Practice

■ Check students' understanding of lesson concepts by discuss the Lesson Review questions on student page 118. If necessary, use the **reteaching strategy** in OPTIONS.

Independent Practice

■ Assign the Lesson 1 section of the Teacher Resource Master **Independent Practice,** page 91.

3 APPLY

■ Use Application Activity, "Build a Shelter," on student pages 351 and 352.

Close

■ Use Summary statements on student page 118 to review lesson concepts.

OPTIONS

Reteaching Strategy

Make a chart on the chalkboard with the headings "Crust," "Mantle," and "Core." Have students list the various properties of each under the correct heading as the chapter is discussed.

Resource Options

Use Color Transparency #5, "Earth's Layers."

TEACHER RESOURCE MASTERS

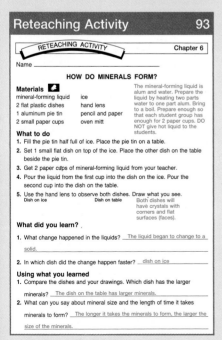

Reteaching Activity 93

RETEACHING ACTIVITY — Chapter 6

Name _____

HOW DO MINERALS FORM?

Materials
mineral-forming liquid   ice
2 flat plastic dishes   hand lens
1 aluminum pie tin   pencil and paper
2 small paper cups   oven mitt

The mineral-forming liquid is alum and water. Prepare the liquid by heating two parts water to one part alum. Bring to a boil. Prepare enough so that each student group has enough for 2 paper cups. DO NOT give hot liquid to the students.

What to do
1. Fill the pie tin half full of ice. Place the pie tin on a table.
2. Set 1 small flat dish on top of the ice. Place the other dish on the table beside the pie tin.
3. Get 2 paper cups of mineral-forming liquid from your teacher.
4. Pour the liquid from the first cup into the dish on the ice. Pour the second cup into the dish on the table.
5. Use the hand lens to observe both dishes. Draw what you see.
Dish on ice   Dish on table   Both dishes will have crystals with corners and flat surfaces (faces).

What did you learn?
1. What change happened in the liquids? _The liquid began to change to a solid._
2. In which dish did the change happen faster? _dish on ice_

Using what you learned
1. Compare the dishes and your drawings. Which dish has the larger minerals? _The dish on the table has larger minerals._
2. What can you say about mineral size and the length of time it takes minerals to form? _The longer it takes the minerals to form, the larger the size of the minerals._

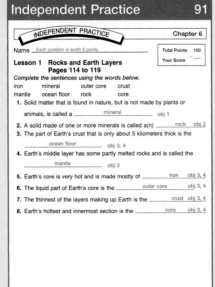

Independent Practice 91

INDEPENDENT PRACTICE — Chapter 6

Name _Each question is worth 6 points._   Total Points 100   Your Score ___

Lesson 1 Rocks and Earth Layers
Pages 114 to 119
Complete the sentences using the words below.

iron   mineral   outer core   crust
mantle   ocean floor   rock   core

1. Solid matter that is found in nature, but is not made by plants or animals, is called a ___mineral___ obj 1
2. A solid made of one or more minerals is called a(n) ___rock___ obj 2
3. The part of Earth's crust that is only about 5 kilometers thick is the ___ocean floor___ obj 3, 4
4. Earth's middle layer has some partly melted rocks and is called the ___mantle___ obj 3
5. Earth's core is very hot and is made mostly of ___iron___ obj 3, 4
6. The liquid part of Earth's core is the ___outer core___ obj 3, 4
7. The thinnest of the layers making up Earth is the ___crust___ obj 3, 4
8. Earth's hottest and innermost section is the ___core___ obj 3, 4

OPTIONS

LANGUAGE CONNECTION

Writing: Organize students into **cooperative groups.** Tell each group to explain in writing why Earth can be compared to a peach. Then select another object, and describe Earth by comparing Earth's parts to the parts of the object your group selected.

◆ **Reinforcement:** Have students make models of Earth's layers using different size circles of different color construction paper. Have them glue the circles onto a sheet of construction paper of contrasting color. Have them label the parts of their diagram. Display the work on a bulletin board.

● **Enrichment:** Obtain samples of granite and have the students examine them with a hand lens. Help students determine how many different minerals make up the rock. Have them describe the properties of each kind of mineral.

▲ **Challenge:** Have students build their own rock and mineral collection using reference books from the library to identify their rocks.

Resource Options
■ Use Activity Book, "Build a Shelter," pages 41 and 42.

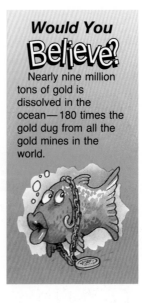

Would You Believe?
Nearly nine million tons of gold is dissolved in the ocean—180 times the gold dug from all the gold mines in the world.

Where Are Rocks Found?

Earth has layers like a peach. When you slice a peach, you can see its layers. A thin skin is all around the outside. A thick layer is in the middle. A seed is in the center. Scientists cannot slice Earth, of course. But scientists know that Earth has layers, too. Look at the peach and Earth in the picture on this page. Compare them.

The outside layer of Earth is called the **crust.** Mountains, valleys, and ocean floors are all part of Earth's crust. Most of the crust is solid rock. The small rocks you find on the ground come from larger rocks of the crust. Some areas of the crust are covered with soil.

How are a peach and Earth similar?

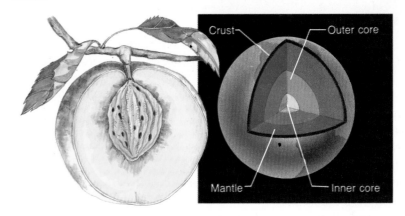

The layers of a peach are like Earth's.

116

TEACHER RESOURCE MASTERS

The crust is thin like the skin of a peach. Earth's crust, however, is not even in thickness. It is thin in some places and thick in others. Ocean-floor crust is thinner than the crust under land areas. The crust of the ocean floor is about 5 kilometers thick. The crust is about 35 kilometers thick under most land areas. It is even thicker under mountains.

Earth's crust is not even in thickness.

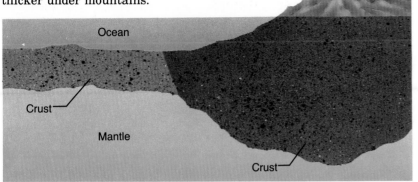

Other rock beneath the crust make up the **mantle** (MANT ul). The mantle is Earth's middle layer. It can be compared to the middle part of the peach, the part that you eat. Mantle rocks are different from rocks in the crust. Mantle rocks are more tightly packed. Some are partly melted.

Like a peach, Earth also has a center section. The **core** is the hottest and innermost part of Earth. It has two parts. The outer core is liquid. The inner core is solid. Both parts of the core are very hot and made mostly of iron.

How are mantle rocks different from rocks in Earth's crust?

117

OPTIONS

■ Explain that you can directly observe the inside of a peach. No one can cut Earth in half. You cannot directly observe its layers. The picture of Earth's interior is a model.

■ Have students make a list of different parts of Earth's crust. Answers might include rocks, mountains, oceans, hills, plains, plateaus, soil, glaciers, and so on.

■ If possible, arrange a field trip to a local outcrop of rocks. These are common in mountainous areas, along ridges, and along road cuts, among other places.

■ Explain that crust is thicker under mountains because of their size. Mountains have deep "roots" of rock to support their weight.

SOCIAL STUDIES CONNECTION

■ Study maps showing mineral deposits around the world. Talk about how different minerals are used by people.

TEACHER RESOURCE MASTERS

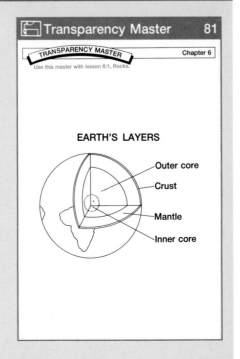

Transparency Master 81

TRANSPARENCY MASTER Chapter 6
Use this master with lesson 6:1, Rocks.

EARTH'S LAYERS

- Outer core
- Crust
- Mantle
- Inner core

LESSON REVIEW ANSWERS

1. solid matter that is found in nature but is not made by plants or animals
2. The Earth's crust is represented by the skin of the peach, the mantle is like its middle layer, and the core is represented by the seed.

Carla wondered if any of the rocks in her collection had come from Earth's mantle. She decided to read some more about rocks.

Lesson Summary

- Rocks are made of one or more minerals.
- Rocks may be smooth or rough, colorful or plain.
- The crust, mantle, and core are layers of Earth.

Lesson Review

1. What is a mineral?
★2. How are Earth's layers like a peach?

118   Use Application Activity on pages 351, 352.

TEACHER RESOURCE MASTERS

How can sediments make layers?

What you need

clear plastic jar with lid
soil mixture
newspaper
hand lens
water
crayons
pencil and paper

What to do

1. Use the hand lens to observe the soil mixture, and write your observations on a chart. Fill 1/3 of the jar with this soil.
2. Add water until the jar is almost full. Tightly screw on the lid.
3. Shake the jar up and down 10 times.
4. Put the jar on a table and wait 10 minutes. Use the hand lens to observe what happens. Draw what you see and fill in your chart.

What did you learn?

1. How did the soil mixture look at first?
2. What happened after you shook the jar?
3. In what order did the particles settle?

Using what you learned

1. What are the layers of particles called?
2. Where can you find layers like this outside?
3. How might these layers be changed into rock?

119

PREPLAN

Time Allotment: 30–45 minutes

Process Skills: Formulating Models/Observing

Objectives

1. **Observe** sediments being deposited in layers.
2. **Compare** properties of the layers.
3. **Infer** how sediments are changed to rock.

Setup

To prepare soil mixture mix soil, sand, and gravel.

Cooperative Grouping: twos—Assign roles as explained on page T24.

1 FOCUS

■ Ask: **Where have you been where there was lots of sand or gravel?** *beaches, rivers, deserts, and so on* **How do you think the sand or gravel got there?** *wind or running water*

2 TEACH

 Cover work areas with newspapers for easier cleanup.
■ Check each jar lid to see that it is properly tightened.
■ Have students use the Teacher Resource Master **Activity Worksheet,** pages 83 and 84, to record their data and answers.

3 APPLY

■ Use the experiences in this activity as an introduction to the second activity.

Close

■ Discuss the activity and questions.

ACTIVITY RESPONSES

What did you learn?

1. There were pieces of soil, sand, and gravel all mixed togther.
2. The soil particles settle out in layers.
3. The largest particles are in the bottom layer. Each layer going up from the bottom has smaller particles than the last.

Using what you learned

1. The settled particles are called sediments.
2. Sediments can be found in places where water runs. Examples are along the edges of sidewalks, in gutters, at the end of driveways, and at the bottoms of hills, creeks, and rivers.
3. Sediments might be changed to rock if they become buried, squeezed, and cemented together.

PREPLAN

Lesson Objectives

5. Operationally define *magma, lava, igneous rock, sediments, sedimentary rock, metamorphic rock.*

6. Explain how igneous, sedimentary, and metamorphic rocks form.

7. Operationally define *rock cycle.*

8. Explain the processes in the rock cycle.

Science Background

■ Intrusive igneous rocks are those that form when magma lithifies. Common intrusive rocks are granite, andesite, and diorite. Extrusive igneous rocks form when lava cools on Earth's surface. These include obsidian, basalt, and lava flows.

■ Sedimentary rocks can be classified as detrital or chemical. Detrital rocks are those that are composed of fragments of preexisting rocks. Sandstone, siltstone, conglomerate, and mudstone are detrital rocks. Chemical rocks include limestone, dolomite, and chalk.

■ Metamorphic rocks are classified as banded and nonbanded. Schist and gneiss are examples of banded metamorphic rocks. Marble and quartzite are examples of nonbanded metamorphic rocks.

Lesson Vocabulary

magma	lava
igneous rock	sediments
metamorphic rock	sedimentary rock
rock cycle	

Note: The activity on student page 128 may be used for guided discovery before you begin this lesson.

1   FOCUS

Have students **work cooperatively** in groups to examine a piece of concrete. Point out that concrete is an artificial rock. It is made by people.

■ Use the goals on student page 120 to establish the purpose for studying this lesson.

LESSON 2 GOALS
You will learn
● that there are three types of rocks.
● how some kinds of rock form.
● that changes take place in rocks as part of the rock cycle.

How Rocks Form

Carla looked closely at one of the rocks from her rock collection. It was entirely black and seemed very light for its size. It seemed to be made of millions of tiny bubbles. How had it been formed?

Some rocks form from melted Earth material. Hot liquid material that forms inside Earth is called **magma** (MAG muh). Magma moves around inside Earth, and in some places it comes near the surface.

Sometimes magma flows onto Earth's surface. A magma flow often takes place at a volcano. When magma reaches Earth's surface, it is called **lava** (LAHV uh).

Lava

Magma

Inside a Volcano

120

TEACHER RESOURCE MASTERS

A rock that forms from cooled magma or lava is called an **igneous** (IHG nee us) **rock.** Igneous rocks don't all look the same. Magma cools much more slowly than lava because it is still underground. The igneous rocks that form when magma cools slowly have large minerals. You can see the minerals without a hand lens.

Lava cools quickly because it is above the ground. Large minerals don't have time to form. Rocks formed from cooled lava have small mineral pieces. The mineral pieces may be so small you can't see them.

121

TEACHER RESOURCE MASTERS

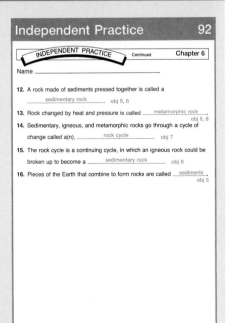

Language Arts Connection 89

LANGUAGE ARTS CONNECTION Composition   Chapter 6

Name _____

VOLCANO

Mount St. Helens is a volcano in the state of Washington. In the past few years it has erupted several times. Much damage has been done to the area around the volcano. This has caused people to relocate and has changed the habitats of much of the wildlife. Mount St. Helens is one volcano in a chain that extends from California to Washington.

- Mount Rainier
- Mount St. Helens
- Mount Hood
- Mount Shasta
- Mount Lassen

Look at the map. Choose one of the volcanoes. Make up a story about it. Pretend that you live near the volcano. Tell what would happen if your volcano would erupt. Use these words in your story: magma, lava, erupt, igneous rocks. Draw a picture on the back of this paper to go with your story.

Answers will vary.

Independent Practice 92

INDEPENDENT PRACTICE   Continued   Chapter 6

Name _____

12. A rock made of sediments pressed together is called a

_____sedimentary rock_____ obj 5, 6

13. Rock changed by heat and pressure is called ___metamorphic rock___ obj 5, 6

14. Sedimentary, igneous, and metamorphic rocks go through a cycle of

change called a(n), ___rock cycle___ obj 7

15. The rock cycle is a continuing cycle, in which an igneous rock could be

broken up to become a ___sedimentary rock___ obj 8

16. Pieces of the Earth that combine to form rocks are called ___sediments___ obj 5

2   TEACH

■ Ask: **How can you change liquid water to solid water?** *When the temperature of water becomes low enough, water freezes.* Liquid rock material, magma, is like water. Magma solidifies when it cools.

■ Ask for volunteers to explain what the word *cycle* means. Elicit the idea of a repeating process. List examples of cycles. Answers may include the phases of the moon; the wheels of a bicycle, which go round and round; and so on.

Guided Practice

■ Check students' understanding of lesson concepts by discussing the Lesson Review questions on student page 127. If necessary, use the **reteaching strategy** in OPTIONS.

Independent Practice

■ Assign the Lesson 2 section of the Teacher Resource Master **Independent Practice,** page 92.

3   APPLY

■ Use Application Activity, "An Age-old Problem," on student pages 349 and 350.

Close

■ Use Summary statements on student page 127 to review lesson concepts.

OPTIONS

Reteaching Strategy

Have students construct a chart with the headings "Igneous Rocks," "Sedimentary Rocks," and "Metamorphic Rocks" and record the properties and mode of formation of each type of rock on the chart.

Resource Options

Use Color Transparency #6, "The Rock Cycle."

OPTIONS

LANGUAGE CONNECTION

Reading: Organize students into **cooperative groups.** Assign each group the following analysis. At the end of the lesson, how does Carla feel about what she has learned about her collection? Find out who in your group has a collection. Have him/her share some interesting facts with the group about the collection. Then have the group report to the class about how what they learned compares with what Carla learned about rocks.

ART CONNECTION

Obtain some potter's clay. Have students design an object. Dry the objects for several days. Have students paint their creations. If a kiln is available, you could have the objects fired and glazed.

Resource Options

■ Use Activity Book, "An Age-old Problem, pages 39 and 40.

Carla looked again at her rock. She couldn't see any mineral pieces in it, so she decided it had been formed from cooled lava.

Rocks Formed From Sediments

Water, wind, and ice are constantly breaking large rocks into smaller rocks. Small rocks are breaking into even smaller pieces. These pieces are called sediments (SED uh munts). **Sediments** are pieces of Earth material. They are carried by wind, ice, and water. When the wind or water slows down or the ice melts, the sediments are dropped. After a period of time, the sediments become pressed together to form rock. A **sedimentary** (sed uh MENT uh ree) **rock** is a rock made of sediments that are pressed together.

What are sedimentary rocks made of ?

122

TEACHER RESOURCE MASTERS

Some sedimentary rocks are made when sediments pile up in a lake or ocean. Limestone is a sedimentary rock formed in this way. Some small sea animals use the mineral calcite in the water to make their shells. When they die, they fall to the ocean floor where they pile up. Over a very long time, these shells form layers and harden into rock. Sometimes the shells are big enough to see, and sometimes they are very tiny.

Sandstone

Limestone

123

OPTIONS

■ Use "I WANT TO KNOW ABOUT . . . a Rock Scientist," student page 129, with this lesson.

♦ **Reinforcement:** Draw a diagram of the rock cycle on poster board. Find small pieces of sedimentary, igneous, and metamorphic rocks. Glue them to the appropriate places on the diagram.

● **Enrichment:** Have interested students find out how concrete is made. Explain that concrete is an artificial conglomerate. Show a piece of natural conglomerate. Have students compare the natural rock to the artificial one.

TEACHER RESOURCE MASTERS

OPTIONS

▲ **Challenge:** Have students research the production of bricks. Have them compare adobe and fired bricks to sedimentary and metamorphic rocks.

📷 Have students use an instamatic camera to take photos of weathering and erosion. Suggest a local park where they can observe stream, wind, and humanmade erosion and weathering. Make a bulletin board display with the photographs.

■ Take a quick walk around the school yard and look for sediments. Check along sidewalks, driveways, gutters, around playground equipment, and so on.

■ Obtain samples of quartz and feldspar-rich sandstone, a granite, and a gneiss. Display the specimens as you discuss the rock cycle. Explain that weathering and erosion of a granite produce sediments that can form a sandstone. If the granite is subjected to heat and pressure deep within Earth, the metamorphic rock gneiss is formed.

Rocks Formed From Other Rocks

Deep inside Earth it is very hot, and the pressure is great. Rock that is buried deep inside Earth becomes hot and is under great pressure. Temperature and pressure can change rocks. A rock that has been changed by heat and pressure is a **metamorphic** (met uh MOR fihk) **rock.** Igneous and sedimentary rocks can become metamorphic rocks. Heat and pressure can also change one type of metamorphic rock into another type of metamorphic rock.

Metamorphic rocks can be grouped by the way they look. Some of them have stripes caused by great pressures within Earth. Other metamorphic rocks are not striped. Which metamorphic rock in the picture on this page is striped?

Carla looked at her rock collection. She found that she had several striped rocks. Proudly she added the word *metamorphic* to their labels.

124

TEACHER RESOURCE MASTERS

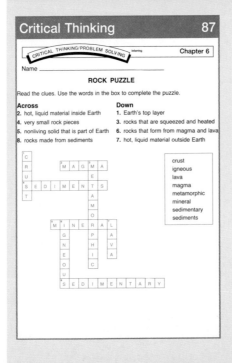

ACTIVITY

You Can...

Study Rocks Made by People

Observe a piece of concrete with a hand lens. Draw what you see. Now observe a piece of asphalt and make a second drawing. Use resource materials to find out how concrete and asphalt are made. What kinds of natural rocks are these two most like? Why do you think this is so?

OPTIONS

YOU CAN . . . STUDY ROCKS MADE BY PEOPLE

Process Skills: Observing/Communicating

Objective: Compare asphalt and concrete with natural rocks.

Setup/Teach

■ Obtain pieces of concrete from broken sidewalks or driveways. City or county road departments are good sources for pieces of asphalt.

■ Provide resource materials to help students find out how these products are produced. Concrete is made in a manner similar to sedimentary rocks—specifically conglomerates. Asphalt might be compared to an igneous rock as it cooled and hardened from melted material.

The Rock Cycle

A cycle is a set of changes that happen over and over again. Day and night make a cycle. Spring, summer, fall, and winter make a cycle, too. [1]Can you think of other cycles?

Rocks go through a cycle, too. You have just learned the three different kinds of rocks and how they form. These rocks are all closely related. Over very long periods of time, rocks change. The cycle of change that sedimentary, igneous, and metamorphic rocks go through is called the **rock cycle.**

1. Answers may include days in a week, the phases of the moon, and the growth cycles of living things.

What is the rock cycle?

125

TEACHER RESOURCE MASTERS

OPTIONS

Have students examine samples of sand and gravel. Let them compare the samples to larger rocks. Review weathering processes that break rocks into pieces. Also review how sediments are hardened into rock.

■ Show pictures of lava flows, and review how igneous rock forms.

Examine samples of metamorphic rocks like gneiss or schist. Review how heat and pressure change rocks.

■ Explain that coal forms from the compaction of altered plant remains over millions of years.

Obtain some samples of bituminous coal and anthracite. Have students examine the rocks with hand lenses.

■ Inform students that bituminous coal is a sedimentary rock whereas anthracite is a metamorphic rock.

■ Emphasize that changes caused by heat and pressure take place very slowly.

Look at the drawing of the rock cycle on this page. There is no beginning or end to the rock cycle. An igneous rock could be broken up by water, wind, and ice to form a sedimentary rock. It could also be heated and put under great pressure to become a metamorphic rock. A sedimentary rock can be melted to form an igneous rock, or it can be heated and put under great pressure to form a metamorphic rock. A metamorphic rock can be broken up by water, wind, and ice to form a sedimentary rock. It can also be melted to form an igneous rock.

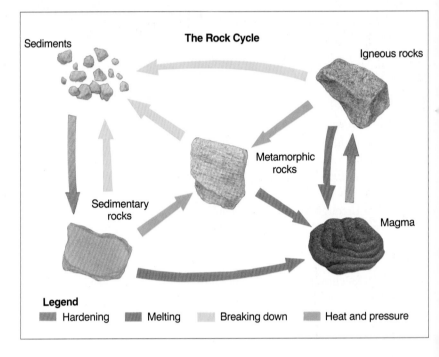

The Rock Cycle

Sediments

Igneous rocks

Metamorphic rocks

Sedimentary rocks

Magma

Legend
Hardening   Melting   Breaking down   Heat and pressure

126

TEACHER RESOURCE MASTERS

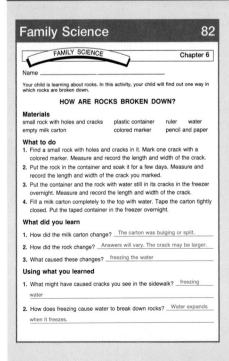

Family Science 82

FAMILY SCIENCE   Chapter 6

Name _____

Your child is learning about rocks. In this activity, your child will find out one way in which rocks are broken down.

HOW ARE ROCKS BROKEN DOWN?

Materials
small rock with holes and cracks   plastic container   ruler   water
empty milk carton   colored marker   pencil and paper

What to do
1. Find a small rock with holes and cracks in it. Mark one crack with a colored marker. Measure and record the length and width of the crack.
2. Put the rock in the container and soak it for a few days. Measure and record the length and width of the crack you marked.
3. Put the container and the rock with water still in its cracks in the freezer overnight. Measure and record the length and width of the crack.
4. Fill a milk carton completely to the top with water. Tape the carton tightly closed. Put the taped container in the freezer overnight.

What did you learn
1. How did the milk carton change? _The carton was bulging or split._
2. How did the rock change? _Answers will vary. The crack may be larger._
3. What caused these changes? _freezing the water_

Using what you learned
1. What might have caused cracks you see in the sidewalk? _freezing water_
2. How does freezing cause water to break down rocks? _Water expands when it freezes._

Carla said to herself, "That's really interesting. I've always thought of a rock as something that doesn't change. And that's true, when you compare the rock cycle with one that changes really fast, like day and night or the seasons. But now I'm finding out that everything changes. Some things change fast, and rocks change very, very slowly."

Lesson Summary

- Igneous, sedimentary, and metamorphic are the three types of rocks found on Earth.
- Igneous, sedimentary, and metamorphic rocks are formed in different ways.
- Each type of rock is changed to a different type of rock as part of the rock cycle.

Lesson Review

1. Give two examples of a cycle.
2. What is lava?
3. Describe how an igneous rock might be changed to a sedimentary rock.

Use Application Activity on pages 349, 350.

127

SCIENCE AND . . .
Math

At school, Mariko showed her rock collection in 7 rows of 8 rocks each. Alonzo showed his rocks in 9 rows of 6 rocks each. Who had more rocks? How many more?
A. Alonzo, 7 more
B. Mariko, 7 more
C. Alonzo, 2 more
D. Mariko, 2 more

OPTIONS

SCIENCE AND . . . MATH
- **Skill:** Multiply whole numbers.
- **Student Response:** D

LESSON REVIEW ANSWERS

1. Answers may include day and night, days of the week, seasons, or phases of the moon.
2. magma that reaches Earth's surface
3. Water, wind, and ice can break igneous rock into sediments that can become cemented together to form sedimentary rocks.

TEACHER RESOURCE MASTERS

PREPLAN

Time Allotment: 30 minutes plus an additional 48- to 72-hours drying time

Process Skills: Formulating Models/Observing

Objectives

1. **Demonstrate** the process of forming a sedimentary rock.
2. **Construct** artificial sandstone.

Setup

■ Combine two parts water with one part Epsom salts for cementing solution.

■ **Cooperative Grouping:** twos—Assign roles as explained on page T24.

1   FOCUS

■ Have several different sandstones on hand for students to examine with hand lenses. Ask: **Where is sandstone forming?** *beaches, rivers, arid regions, etc.*

2   TEACH

■ Make sure the sand dries completely and ask students to remove the cup carefully.

■ Have students use the Teacher Resource Master **Activity Worksheet,** pages 85 and 86, to record their data and answers.

3   APPLY

■ Have samples of limestone, chert, sandstone, shale, chalk, coal, and conglomerate available for students to examine. Have them choose the specimens that formed in a similar way to the "sandstone" made in the activity.

Close

■ Discuss the activity and questions.

ACTIVITY

How does sedimentary rock form?

What you need 🚫

paper cup
cementing solution
sand
hand lens
newspaper
pencil and paper

What to do

1. Fill the cup half full of sand. Pack the sand with your hand. Tell what the sand is like using a chart.
2. Slowly add cementing solution until all of the sand is wet.
3. Put the cup in a warm place until the sand dries completely.
4. Carefully tear away the paper cup.
5. Observe the "sandstone" with the hand lens. Write about what you see on your chart.

What did you learn?

1. How did the sand change?
2. How is your "rock" like sedimentary rock?

Using what you learned

1. If you found clam shells in sedimentary rock, what could you say about the place where the rock formed?
2. Why is your "sandstone" not a rock?

128

ACTIVITY RESPONSES

What did you learn?

1. It is hard and cemented together.
2. It is made of many sediments that have been "glued" together.

Using what you have learned

1. It may have formed in the ocean or in another body of water.
2. It was not formed by natural processes.

I WANT TO KNOW ABOUT...

A Rock Scientist

Peter Schwans is a scientist who studies and describes rocks. Peter studies sedimentary rock in Utah, a state that has plenty of rocks!

Peter spends every summer collecting rock samples. To begin a day's work, he drives a van over rough country high into the mountains. He uses a rock hammer to break off rock pieces and takes them back to the lab to study.

Peter also takes notes. He marks each day's work on a map that shows Earth's surface. He marks the kinds of rocks that are above and below the ones he has broken off. Peter uses his map to find out what this part of Utah was like long ago.

Peter has learned that Utah used to be much different. Millions of years ago, Utah was covered by a large sea that washed away the mountain ranges. This Earth material later formed the sedimentary rocks that Peter studies today.

Career

129

TEACHER RESOURCE MASTERS

Feature Background

■ While many sedimentologists work in laboratories, others do field work. Such scientists are called field geologists. They observe the structures and positions of Earth's rocks. Field geologists study sequences of rocks called outcrops.

■ Arrange a field trip to a local quarry or highway road cut to allow students to examine crops.

Teaching Suggestions

Obtain a sample of a sedimentary rock. Allow students to examine it with a hand lens. Have them sketch what they see.

■ Obtain a topographic map of the United States or your local region. Discuss what natural features are featured. Students could sketch the region's surface features.

■ Discuss what scientists are predicting Earth will be like a few thousand years from now.

Summary

Chapter Closure: Write the summary statements on the board leaving out one or two key words. Have students supply the missing words. Help students summarize the material covered in the chapter by discussing the summary statements.

Science Words

■ Scramble the science words. Have students reassemble the letters in the proper order. After writing the word have students provide the definition for the word.

Student Responses

1. igneous rock
2. crust
3. sedimentary rock
4. mantle
5. core
6. metamorphic rock
7. mineral

CHAPTER REVIEW 6

▰ Summary ▰

Lesson 1
- Rocks are made of one or more minerals.
- Rocks may be smooth or rough, colorful or plain, made of minerals or just one mineral.
- Earth's layers are the crust, mantle, and core.

Lesson 2
- Three types of rocks are igneous, sedimentary, and metamorphic.
- Igneous, sedimentary, and metamorphic rocks are formed in different ways.
- Rocks change through a process called the rock cycle.

▰ Science Words ▰

Fill in the blank with the correct word or words from the list.

mineral	lava
crust	igneous
mantle	sediments
core	sedimentary
magma	metamorphic
	rock cycle

1. Cooled magma forms ___.
2. Earth's top layer is the ___.
3. Sediments that are pressed together form ___.
4. Earth's middle layer is the ___.
5. The innermost part of Earth is the ___.
6. A rock changed by heat and pressure is called ___.
7. Solid matter found in nature that is not made by plants or animals is a(n) ___.

130

TEACHER RESOURCE MASTERS

Test A   94

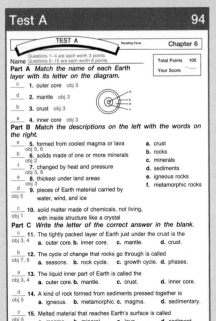

Test B   95

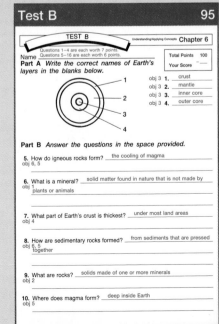

Questions

Recalling Ideas
Correctly complete each of the following sentences.
1. Magma forms rocks with
    (a) large minerals.
    (b) small minerals.
    (c) no minerals.
    (d) only one mineral.
2. Rocks are mixtures of
    (a) magma. (c) minerals.
    (b) gelatin. (d) lava.
3. Most of Earth's crust is
    (a) very hot. (c) liquid.
    (b) solid rock. (d) partly melted.
4. Rocks formed from lava have
    (a) large minerals.
    (b) small minerals.
    (c) medium minerals.
    (d) large and small minerals.

Understanding Ideas
Answer the following questions using complete sentences.
1. How do sedimentary rocks form?
2. Tell about Earth's layers and the rocks in these layers.
3. Describe a metamorphic rock as it changes in the rock cycle.

Thinking Critically
Think about what you have learned in this chapter. Answer the following questions using complete sentences.
1. What could you do in order to decide whether a certain igneous rock formed near the surface of Earth or deeper inside Earth's crust?
2. If you found a rock that appeared to be made of smaller rocks and shells, what kind would it be and how would it have formed?

131

TEACHER RESOURCE MASTERS

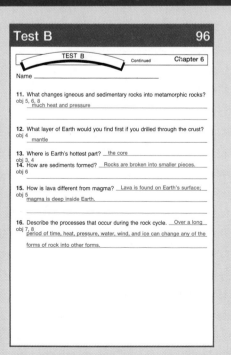

Test B   96

TEST B   Continued   Chapter 6

Name _____

11. What changes igneous and sedimentary rocks into metamorphic rocks?
obj 5, 6, 8   much heat and pressure

12. What layer of Earth would you find first if you drilled through the crust?
obj 4   mantle

13. Where is Earth's hottest part? the core
obj 3, 4
14. How are sediments formed? Rocks are broken into smaller pieces.
obj 6

15. How is lava different from magma? Lava is found on Earth's surface;
obj 5   magma is deep inside Earth.

16. Describe the processes that occur during the rock cycle. Over a long
obj 7, 8   period of time, heat, pressure, water, wind, and ice can change any of the
    forms of rock into other forms.

Questions

Recalling Ideas
1. a
2. c
3. b
4. b

Understanding Ideas
1. Sedimentary rocks are formed from sediments that are pressed together.
2. The top layer is called the crust. Most of it is solid rock. The crust is not of even thickness. It is thinner under the ocean floor than under land areas. The mantle is the middle layer. Mantle rocks are tightly packed, and some are partly melted. The core is the inner layer made of two parts. The outer core is liquid, and the inner core is solid. The core is the hottest part of Earth.
3. A metamorphic rock could be broken up to form a sedimentary rock or melted to form an igneous rock. An igneous rock could be broken up to form a sedimentary rock or heated and put under pressure to form a metamorphic rock. A sedimentary rock could be heated and put under pressure to form a metamorphic rock, or it could be melted to form an igneous rock.

Thinking Critically
1. The igneous rock could be studied to determine the size of its minerals. Igneous rocks with very small minerals form near or at the surface of Earth. Igneous rocks with larger minerals form more slowly, deep inside Earth.
2. It would be a sedimentary rock, which would have been formed when the small rocks and shells were pressed together to form rock.

Nature Changes Rocks

Planning Guide

Lessons	Objectives	Vocabulary
Chapter Introduction pp. 132, 133		
Lesson 1 Weathering pp. 134–139	1. **Operationally define** *weathering*. 2. **Identify** four different processes which change rock.	weathering glacier
Lesson 2 Soil and Erosion pp. 140–143	3. **Explain** how soil forms. 4. **Define** *erosion*.	erosion
Chapter Review pp. 144, 145		

Planning Guide

Text Activities		Teacher Resource Masters	Other Components
Title/Skill	Materials per Group		
Have You Ever . . . Made Changes in Rocks? p. 133 Observing/Inferring Time Allotment: 30 minutes	2 rocks piece of paper		**Activity Center:** "Rock On"; "A Rocky Story"
How Can Water Break Rocks? p. 139 Formulating Models/ Observing Time Allotment: 30 minutes, plus a freezing period of 24 hours	plastic film container with lid water masking tape freezer pencil and paper	Independent Practice, pp. 107, 108 Activity Worksheet, pp. 99, 100 ◆ Family Science, p. 98 Critical Thinking, p. 103 ◆ Reteaching Activity, p. 109	Activity Book, pp. 21
You Can . . . Study Soil Erosion, p. 141 Formulating Models/ Observing Time Allotment: 30 minutes	stream table watering can or sprinkling bottle mixture of mud, sand, gravel, and pebbles water	Independent Practice, pp. 107, 108 Activity Worksheet, pp. 101, 102 Language Arts Connection, p. 105 Transparency Master, p. 97 ▲ Critical Thinking, p. 104 Social Studies Connection, p. 106	Activity Book, pp. 43, 44
How Do Different Soils Compare? p. 143 Observing Time Allotment: 30 minutes	3 soil samples hand lens 3 paper cups 6 bean seeds water metric ruler 3 labels pencil and paper		
Soil Savers! p. 353 Predicting/Measuring Time Allotment: 40 minutes to build; 15 minutes to conclude	aluminum pan soil water pan balance books paper cups gram masses natural materials		
		Test A, p. 110 Test B, pp. 111, 112	

◆ **Basic** / ▲ **Advanced** / All other masters are for use by all students.

Nature Changes Rocks

For Exceptional Students

ESL/LEP

Chapter 7/Lesson 1, Page 135
Ask students to pronounce the following words on the chalkboard: **weathering, glacier.** Discuss with them the meaning of the words. Help students to prepare a newscast about the changes in rocks caused by these forces in nature. Although students know that weathering takes place over a long time, the newscasts will tell the story with a sense of urgency.

Have students play a guessing game. Each student should make up a riddle asking What am I? Write an example on the chalkboard: **I carry rocks downstream, causing the rocks to bump and break. What am I?** *Water*

Chapter 7/Lesson 2, Page 140
Write this haiku about erosion on the chalkboard.

> **Erosion**
> **Water, wind, and ice**
> **Carry rocks to new places—**
> **Robbed from here; dropped there.**

Ask students to write another haiku or other type of poem about erosion or weathering. Have them illustrate their poems.

Gifted

Chapter 7/Lesson 1, Page 139
Permit gifted students to look for examples of various signs of weathering on the schoolgrounds or in the community. Ask them to classify each example they find. Suggest that the students take the rest of the class on a guided tour or produce a photo essay or slide show to illustrate examples of weathering. Ask the students to predict what some of the examples they cited will look like in three, five, or ten years.

Mainstreamed

Chapter 7/Lesson 1, Page 139
Physically Disabled: Give students three response cards. Label the first card "Changed by Animals"; the second card "Changed by Wind or Water"; and the third card "Changed by Plants." Then, verbally describe situations (e.g., digging tunnels, cracks in pavement). Have students hold up the correct response card. (NOTE: Allow for more than one answer; reinforce verbal participation.)

Whole Class Science Project

Have students survey a community building to determine the material used in the construction of the outer walls. Have them list the name of the building, the year it was built, the type of stone used, and any weathering that has occurred. The weathering report should include what students think the main agents of weathering might be (rain, wind, ice, or other) and to what extent the weathering has affected the stones. Information should be compiled and reported to the class.

Science Fair Projects

Individual students could do one of the following projects:

1. Compare a sample of topsoil from a flower or vegetable bed with a sample of subsoil (collected from 50 cm into the earth) for quantities of humus and pebbles or stones. Keeping all conditions the same, plant a seed in each sample to see which kind of soil produces a sturdier plant.

2. After soaking sandstone, limestone, or brick in water overnight and then placing it in a freezer, students will remove and discover the effects of freezing water on the rock. They will present a display of weathered rock and discuss the effects that freezing water can have on rocks in nature.

3. Using two pans of collected topsoil, making long vertical furrows in one and contour furrows in the other, sprinkle water on each to discover why land management uses contour furrows. Research to find out how erosion affects farmers, and display pictures and reports on how growers deal with erosion.

4. Pour water over limestone. Collect this water in a pan, and let it evaporate to discover that a coating of limestone is left. Use this illustration to demonstrate how caves are formed from running water.

CHAPTER

7

pages 132–145

Chapter Concepts
■ Water, wind, ice, and living things weather rocks.
■ Wind, water, and ice cause erosion.

Chapter Background
■ Earth is always changing. Rocks at the surface change by erosion and weathering. Other changes occur below Earth's surface.
■ Weathering and erosion include various chemical and physical processes.
■ Subsurface changes are due to heat and pressure from overlying rocks and from the heat given off by radioactive elements in some rocks.

Looking Ahead
■ Find an eroded area, such as those near a river or stream. Take the class there to collect rock samples and to observe the effects of erosion.

Look for These Symbols

—Hands-on activity
—Cooperative learning
—Overhead transparency
♦ —Basic/Reinforcement
● —Average/Enrichment
▲ —Advanced/Challenge
—Calculator Practice

SCIENCE
In Your World.

132

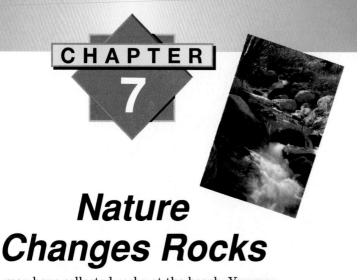

CHAPTER 7

Nature Changes Rocks

You may have collected rocks at the beach. You may have looked for rocks in a river. Rocks you find near the water often feel smooth to the touch. How do you think moving water might change a rock's surface from rough to smooth?

ACTIVITY
Have You Ever...

Made Changes in Rocks?

Gather together two rocks and a piece of paper. Rub the rocks together over the paper for three minutes. Observe the paper. What do you see? What would eventually happen to the rocks if you continued to rub them together?

133

PREPLAN

Time Allotment: 30 minutes

Objectives
1. **Hypothesize** how water makes a rock smooth.
2. **Observe** sediment and recognize that the surface of a rock has been changed.

Setup
■ If you wish to conduct the activity, you will need the following materials for each student or activity group:
2 rocks (sandstone works best)   paper

1   FOCUS

■ Ask students to describe what is happening in the picture.
■ Elicit ideas from students about where they go to find rocks. Record student responses, putting those that are in or around water in one column.

2   TEACH

■ After the title and introductory paragraph have been read aloud, ask students to suggest different methods for making surfaces smooth. Record responses.

Have You Ever . . .
Use this activity as an introduction to weathering.
Have students **work cooperatively** in groups of four.
■ **Student Responses**
1. The surfaces of the rocks have been worn away, and sediment is on the paper.
2. Rocks get smaller and smoother.

3   APPLY

■ Ask students to think of other ways that nature might change rocks.

Close
Earth processes that change rocks will be studied in Chapter 7.

PREPLAN

Lesson Objectives

1. **Operationally define** *weathering*.
2. **Identify** four different processes which change rock.

Science Background

■ Water, ice, wind, gravity, and organisms are agents of change that sculpt Earth's landscape.

■ Weathering can be mechanical or chemical. Mechanical weathering is the physical breaking of rocks into smaller and smaller pieces without changing the composition of the rock. On the other hand, chemical weathering involves a chemical transformation of a rock into one or more new compounds.

■ Water is the most common agent of change. Water changes Earth's landscape by erosion, weathering, deposition, solution, and frost wedging.

Lesson Vocabulary

weathering   glacier

Note: The activity on student page 139 may be used for guided discovery before you begin this lesson.

1   FOCUS

[※] Have students examine some well-rounded river rocks. Ask: **How did these rocks become rounded?** *Some students may realize that water and abrasion by other rocks and sediments produced the smooth surfaces.*

■ Use the goals on student page 134 to establish the purpose for studying this lesson.

Weathering

LESSON 1 GOALS
You will learn
● that weathering is always taking place.
● that four forces in nature change rocks.

In the picture on this page, Leon is hunting for certain kinds of stones. He wants to throw the stones across the water and make them skip. He looks for stones that are flat and smooth with rounded edges. Leon wonders, "How do they get that way? Most rocks are rough. They have sharp edges. Where do the smooth stones come from?"

Water, wind, ice, and living things change rocks. The change often happens slowly. Over a long period of time, rocks are broken into smaller parts. The breaking down or wearing away of rock is called **weathering**. Weathering is always taking place.

What is weathering?

134

TEACHER RESOURCE MASTERS

Water and Wind Change Rocks

Water changes rocks in different ways. Fast-moving water moves rocks downstream. As they move, the rocks bump into each other. Over a long time, the rocks wear down and become smooth and rounded. Leon's skipping stones have been worn down by moving water. Look at the picture of the rocks on this page. [1]How has the river changed these rocks?

1. The river has smoothed them.

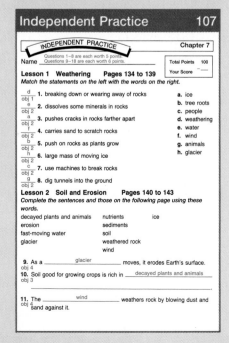

Water also changes rocks when the water freezes and thaws. During warm weather, water flows into cracks and spaces in rocks. When the temperature gets cold enough, water freezes. When water freezes, it expands. The ice in the cracks of rocks pushes the cracks farther apart. Over many years, water in the cracks may melt and freeze many times. The cracks get bigger with time. When the cracks are big enough, the rocks break.

135

TEACHER RESOURCE MASTERS

Independent Practice 107

INDEPENDENT PRACTICE   Chapter 7

Questions 1–8 are each worth 5 points.
Name   Questions 9–18 are each worth 6 points.   Total Points 100   Your Score ___

Lesson 1   Weathering   Pages 134 to 139
Match the statements on the left with the words on the right.

__d__ **1.** breaking down or wearing away of rocks   **a.** ice
obj 1
__e__ **2.** dissolves some minerals in rocks   **b.** tree roots
obj 2   **c.** people
__a__ **3.** pushes cracks in rocks farther apart   **d.** weathering
obj 2   **e.** water
__f__ **4.** carries sand to scratch rocks   **f.** wind
obj 2
__b__ **5.** push on rocks as plants grow   **g.** animals
obj 2   **h.** glacier
__h__ **6.** large mass of moving ice
obj 2
__c__ **7.** use machines to break rocks
obj 2
__g__ **8.** dig tunnels into the ground
obj 2

Lesson 2   Soil and Erosion   Pages 140 to 143
Complete the sentences and those on the following page using these words.

decayed plants and animals	nutrients	ice
erosion	sediments	
fast-moving water	soil	
glacier	weathered rock	
	wind	

9. As a ____glacier____ moves, it erodes Earth's surface.
obj 4
10. Soil good for growing crops is rich in ____decayed plants and animals____
obj 3

11. The ____wind____ weathers rock by blowing dust and
obj 4   sand against it.

2   TEACH

■ Compare the sandblasting of a building with erosion and weathering by wind-blown sediments.

Problem Solving: Ask: **How does water dissolve minerals?** Give student groups a spoonful of rock salt, a piece of colored construction paper, and a hand lens. Have them pour the salt on the paper and observe it with the hand lens. Have students sketch several salt crystals. Now give each group a small, clear container with a top that is about half full of water. Have them place the rock salt in the jar and observe it carefully. Ask students to describe what they see and to explain why it happened.

Guided Practice

■ Check students' understanding of lesson concepts by discussing the Lesson Review questions on student page 138. If necessary, use the **reteaching strategy** in OPTIONS.

Independent Practice

■ Assign the Lesson 1 section of the Teacher Resource Master **Independent Practice,** page 107.

3   APPLY

■ Have students discuss three different ways water can weather rocks.

Close

■ Use Summary statements on student page 138 to review lesson concepts.

OPTIONS

Reteaching Strategy

■ Have students compare the weathering of rocks in streams and rivers with how an eraser gets rounded after use.

Resource Options

■ Use Activity Book, "Hypothesizing," pages 21 and 22.

OPTIONS

LANGUAGE CONNECTION

■ **Writing:** Have students rewrite the following passage using correct subject-verb agreement.

John and I (go,went) riding on our bicycles yesterday to find examples of weathering. We (saw,seen) lots of cracks in sidewalks where roots had broken through. Smooth rocks and others with holes in them (was,were) down by the stream. On the way home, John and I (rode,ridden) by a truck dumping crushed rocks for a driveway. *(went,saw,were,rode)*

ART CONNECTION

■ Have students bring in tiny rocks of varying colors. Have them glue their rocks to a sheet of heavy paper to make a picture. Students can share rocks to have a wider variety in their pictures.

◆ **Reinforcement:** Obtain some rocks that have been rounded by weathering. Break some of the rocks into pieces. Have students examine the broken pieces and compare the freshly broken pieces to the weathered, worn rock. Discuss differences and how the broken pieces might become rounded.

Water can change rocks in yet another way. Rain and groundwater can soak into rocks. Some minerals in rocks dissolve in the water. The water carries away the minerals from the rocks. Holes are left where the minerals used to be.

There is another way ice can weather rocks. A **glacier** (GLAY shur) is a large mass of ice that moves. Frozen in the glacier are large rocks, sand, and soil. The rocks scratch the surfaces over which the glaciers move. The picture of the rock with long scratches shows a rock weathered by a glacier.

What is a glacier?

Glaciers weather rock.

136

TEACHER RESOURCE MASTERS

Wind also weathers rocks. Strong winds pick up and carry dust and sand. These small particles scratch rocks, and the rocks slowly wear away. Sometimes windblown sediments weather rocks into strange shapes.

Wind weathers rock.

Plants break rocks.

Plants and Animals Change Rocks

Plants, too, can change rocks. Some plants grow in soil that has collected in the cracks of rocks. The plant roots push on the rocks as the plants grow. The rocks may break if the plants grow large enough. Strong tree roots can even break sidewalks and curbs. Look around your neighborhood. See if you can find places where plants are breaking sidewalks.

Some animals change rocks. Animals make places for weathering to happen. Some animals dig tunnels in the ground and loosen rocks and soil. Air and water can then move deeper into the ground.

137

OPTIONS

SOCIAL STUDIES CONNECTION

■ Have students research naturally occurring rock formations that are caused by weathering. Have them locate some of them on maps. Examples might be natural bridges, caves, sea caves, glacial grooves, and canyons.

● **Enrichment:** Have interested students research how limestone caves and caverns form.

TEACHER RESOURCE MASTERS

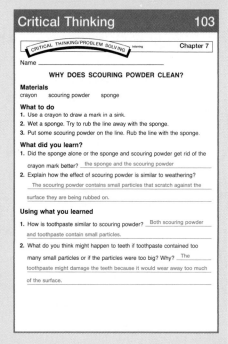

Critical Thinking   103

CRITICAL THINKING/PROBLEM SOLVING Inferring   Chapter 7

Name _____

WHY DOES SCOURING POWDER CLEAN?

Materials
crayon   scouring powder   sponge

What to do
1. Use a crayon to draw a mark in a sink.
2. Wet a sponge. Try to rub the line away with the sponge.
3. Put some scouring powder on the line. Rub the line with the sponge.

What did you learn?
1. Did the sponge alone or the sponge and scouring powder get rid of the crayon mark better? _the sponge and the scouring powder_
2. Explain how the effect of scouring powder is similar to weathering? _The scouring powder contains small particles that scratch against the surface they are being rubbed on._

Using what you learned
1. How is toothpaste similar to scouring powder? _Both scouring powder and toothpaste contain small particles._
2. What do you think might happen to teeth if toothpaste contained too many small particles or if the particles were too big? Why? _The toothpaste might damage the teeth because it would wear away too much of the surface._

OPTIONS

▲ **Challenge:** Have students compare pieces of limestone and quartz to see which weathers faster. Have them examine both closely with a hand lens and soak several pieces of each in water for a day. Place the limestone pieces in a plastic jar of water. Screw the lid on tightly. Shake the jar vigorously for at least 5 minutes. Then have students examine both the water and the limestone carefully and describe any changes they see. Repeat the same activity with the pieces of quartz. Compare the results. Ask: **Which was weathered more?** *limestone* Ask: **Why do you think so?** *Limestone is made of calcite, which is less resistant to weathering than quartz.*

LESSON REVIEW ANSWERS

1. the breaking or wearing away of rock
2. Plant roots push on rocks as plants grow. In time, the rocks may break.
3. Water can wear down and smooth rocks; it can flow into cracks, freeze, and make the cracks larger; it can dissolve minerals in rocks.

People change rocks, too. People use machines to break rocks. People dig tunnels and build roads through rocks. People build houses or statues out of rocks. To get enough small rocks to use for buildings, workers break the rocks into small pieces. The pieces are then put together to make walls or to cover roofs. The people in the pictures on this page are changing rocks. [1] How can you change rocks?

Lesson Summary

- Rocks are constantly worn away or broken down by weathering.
- Water, wind, ice, and living things change rocks.

Lesson Review

1. What is weathering?
2. Describe how plants can change rock.
★3. How can water change rock?

1. Answers will vary. Students may say they can break, chip, rub, sand, scratch, glue, and polish rocks.

People change rocks.

138

TEACHER RESOURCE MASTERS

Family Science 98

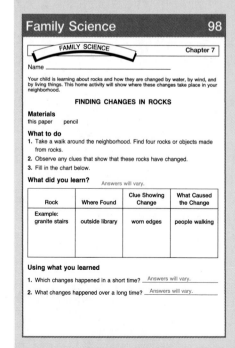

FAMILY SCIENCE   Chapter 7

Name _____

Your child is learning about rocks and how they are changed by water, by wind, and by living things. This home activity will show where these changes take place in your neighborhood.

FINDING CHANGES IN ROCKS

Materials
this paper   pencil

What to do
1. Take a walk around the neighborhood. Find four rocks or objects made from rocks.
2. Observe any clues that show that these rocks have changed.
3. Fill in the chart below.

What did you learn? Answers will vary.

Rock	Where Found	Clue Showing Change	What Caused the Change
Example: granite stairs	outside library	worn edges	people walking

Using what you learned
1. Which changes happened in a short time? Answers will vary.
2. What changes happened over a long time? Answers will vary.

Reteaching Activity 109

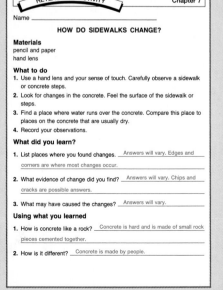

RETEACHING ACTIVITY   Chapter 7

Name _____

HOW DO SIDEWALKS CHANGE?

Materials
pencil and paper
hand lens

What to do
1. Use a hand lens and your sense of touch. Carefully observe a sidewalk or concrete steps.
2. Look for changes in the concrete. Feel the surface of the sidewalk or steps.
3. Find a place where water runs over the concrete. Compare this place to places on the concrete that are usually dry.
4. Record your observations.

What did you learn?
1. List places where you found changes. Answers will vary. Edges and corners are where most changes occur.
2. What evidence of change did you find? Answers will vary. Chips and cracks are possible answers.
3. What may have caused the changes? Answers will vary.

Using what you learned
1. How is concrete like a rock? Concrete is hard and is made of small rock pieces cemented together.
2. How is it different? Concrete is made by people.

How can water break rocks?

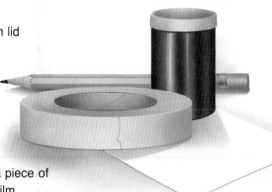

What you need
plastic film container with lid
water
masking tape
freezer
pencil and paper

What to do
1. Write your name on a piece of tape. Place it on the film container.
2. Fill the container with water and snap the lid on tightly. Draw a picture of the container on your chart.
3. Place the container in a freezer for one day.
4. Remove the container and observe it. Draw the picture on your chart.

What did you learn?
1. How has the water changed?
2. What happened to the container?
3. What caused the change?

Container before freezing	Container after freezing

Using what you learned
1. Why isn't it safe to put glass bottles filled with liquid in a freezer?
2. Suppose water freezes in empty spaces in a rock. What might happen to the rock?

139

ACTIVITY RESPONSES

What did you learn?
1. It froze.
2. The top was pushed off, and the sides bulged out.
3. Water expands when it freezes and takes up more space, causing an outward force.

Using what you learned
1. They can break.
2. The rock might crack or break.

PREPLAN

Time Allotment: 30 minutes, plus a freezing period of 24 hours

Process Skill: Observing

Objectives
1. **Recognize** that when water freezes it expands.
2. **Identify** the ice as the cause of the broken film canister.

Setup
■ Make sure that freezer space is available in the faculty lounge or cafeteria.

Cooperative Grouping: threes—Assign roles as explained on page T24.

1   FOCUS

■ Explain that one process by which water weathers rocks is called frost wedging. Water enters rocks and soil and will expand upon freezing. Water expands about 9 percent when it freezes and exerts a tremendous outward force. If sufficient volume is present, the rock will shatter.

2   TEACH

■ Ask students where they have seen examples of frost wedging in nature. Answers may include streets, highways, and sidewalks. Many potholes are the result of alternate freezing and thawing.
■ Have students use the Teacher Resource Master **Activity Worksheet** pages 99 and 100, to record their data and answers.

3   APPLY

■ Obtain photographs in which plant roots have grown into fractures and wedged rocks apart.

Close
■ Discuss the activity and questions.

PREPLAN

Lesson Objectives
1. **Explain** how soil forms.
2. **Define** *erosion*.

Science Background
■ Soil is our most important natural resource. It is necessary to all life on land. Topsoil is the layer which contains plant food. The next layer is subsoil which has little or no plant food. The substratum has materials like gravel, clay, or bedrock.

Lesson Vocabulary
erosion

Note: The activity on student page 143 may be used for guided discovery before you begin this lesson.

1 FOCUS

■ Examine different samples of soil. Decide what kind of soil it is according to its weathering process.

■ Use the goals on student page 140 to establish the purpose for studying this lesson.

LESSON 2 GOALS
You will learn
● that soil is made of Earth materials.
● that water, wind, and ice cause erosion.

Soil and Erosion

When you pick up a handful of soil, you have weathered rock in your hand. Water, wind, ice, and living things break rocks into small pieces. Over time, weathering makes the pieces even smaller. The weathered rock becomes soil when it mixes with decayed plants and animals.

The kind of soil formed depends on the kind of weathered rock and the amount of decayed plants and animals. Clay-rich rocks will weather to form clay-rich soils. Soils rich in decayed plants and animals are good for growing crops. Spaces between small pieces of soil hold water, air, and nutrients needed by plants.

Would You **Believe?** It takes 100 pounds of water to produce a single pound of food.

Top soil

Subsoil

Rock layer

140

TEACHER RESOURCE MASTERS

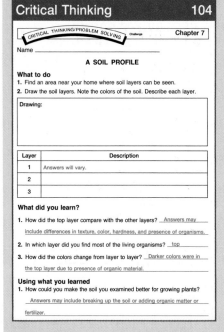

Critical Thinking 104

CRITICAL THINKING/PROBLEM SOLVING Challenge — Chapter 7

Name _____

A SOIL PROFILE

What to do
1. Find an area near your home where soil layers can be seen.
2. Draw the soil layers. Note the colors of the soil. Describe each layer.

Drawing:

Layer	Description
1	Answers will vary.
2	
3	

What did you learn?
1. How did the top layer compare with the other layers? __Answers may include differences in texture, color, hardness, and presence of organisms.__
2. In which layer did you find most of the living organisms? __top__
3. How did the colors change from layer to layer? __Darker colors were in the top layer due to presence of organic material.__

Using what you learned
1. How could you make the soil you examined better for growing plants?
__Answers may include breaking up the soil or adding organic matter or fertilizer.__

Language Arts Connection 105

LANGUAGE ARTS CONNECTION Composition — Chapter 7

Name _____

PICTURING WEATHERING AND EROSION

Describe how weathering and erosion might change this picture.

_____
_____
_____
_____
_____
_____
_____
_____

You Can...

Study Soil Erosion

Place a mixture of damp mud, sand, gravel, and pebbles at the top of a stream table. Use 3 books to raise the top. Use a sprinkling bottle or watering can to make it rain on the mixture. Which particles move fastest and farthest down the slope? What size of soil particles on hills and in fields is most easily eroded by water?

Erosion

Water, wind, and ice weather rocks and also cause erosion (ih ROH zhun). **Erosion** is the movement of soil and rocks to new places. Hillsides erode when water from heavy rains carries away soil and loose rocks. When the water slows down, soil and rocks are dropped in other places.

Fast-moving water in rivers and streams also causes erosion. Rocks and soil from upstream are carried downstream.

Wind causes erosion in dry areas. Strong winds can pick up and carry away loose dirt and sand.

141

2 TEACH

■ Have students compare the size of sediments carried by wind with those carried by running water.

Guided Practice

■ Check students' understanding of lesson concepts by discussing the Lesson Review questions on student page 142. If necessary, use the **reteaching strategy** in OPTIONS.

Independent Practice

■ Assign the Lesson 2 section of the Teacher Resource Master **Independent Practice,** page 107.

3 APPLY

■ Use Application Activity, "Soil Savers!" on student pages 353 and 354.
■ Have students differentiate between erosion and weathering.

Close

■ Use the summary statements on student page 142 to review the lesson concepts.

OPTIONS

Reteaching Strategy

■ Have students collect pictures from old magazines and newspapers that depict erosion and weathering. Have them bring the photos to class. Make two headings on the bulletin board. Have students classify each photo as either erosion or weathering.
■ Refer to page 142 for teaching strategies for **You Can . . . Study Soil Erosion.**

Resource Options

■ Use Activity Book, "Soil Savers!" pages 43 and 44.

TEACHER RESOURCE MASTERS

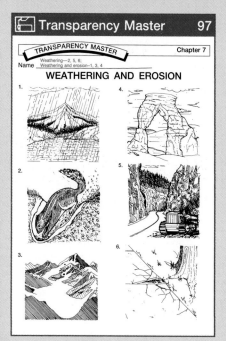

Transparency Master	97

TRANSPARENCY MASTER   Chapter 7

Name   Weathering—2, 5, 6;
Weathering and erosion—1, 3, 4

WEATHERING AND EROSION

Independent Practice	107

INDEPENDENT PRACTICE   Chapter 7

Name   Questions 1–8 are each worth 5 points.
Questions 9–18 are each worth 6 points.

Total Points	100
Your Score	

Lesson 1 Weathering   Pages 134 to 139
Match the statements on the left with the words on the right.

d **1.** breaking down or wearing away of rocks
obj 1
e **2.** dissolves some minerals in rocks
obj 2
a **3.** pushes cracks in rocks farther apart
obj 2
f **4.** carries sand to scratch rocks
obj 2
b **5.** push on rocks as plants grow
obj 2
h **6.** large mass of moving ice
obj 2
c **7.** use machines to break rocks
obj 2
g **8.** dig tunnels into the ground
obj 2

a. ice
b. tree roots
c. people
d. weathering
e. water
f. wind
g. animals
h. glacier

Lesson 2 Soil and Erosion   Pages 140 to 143
Complete the sentences and those on the following page using these words.

decayed plants and animals   nutrients   ice
erosion   sediments
fast-moving water   soil
glacier   weathered rock
wind

9. As a _____glacier_____ moves, it erodes Earth's surface.
obj 4
10. Soil good for growing crops is rich in _decayed plants and animals_
obj 3

11. The _____wind_____ weathers rock by blowing dust and
obj 4 sand against it.

OPTIONS

YOU CAN . . . STUDY SOIL EROSION

Process Skill: Formulating a Model

Objective: Construct a model of a stream table to **demonstrate** soil erosion.

Setup/Teach

■ stream table; watering can or sprinkling bottle; mixture of mud, sand, gravel, and pebbles; water

Student Responses

Finer grains traveled faster and farther, followed by sand, gravel, and pebbles.

SCIENCE AND . . . READING

■ **Skill:** Identify the best summary of a selection.

■ **Student Response:** C

 ◆ **Reinforcement:** Divide students into **cooperative groups.** Each group will have a similar plant but a different type of soil and will compare progress of the plants over time.

● **Enrichment:** Discuss how sandblasting makes older stone buildings look new and clean.

▲ **Challenge:** Interested students can research methods used by farmers to control soil erosion.

LESSON REVIEW ANSWERS

1. soil rich in plant and animal matter
2. the movement of soil and rocks
3. Heavy rains carry away soil and loose rocks; fast-moving water in rivers and streams carries rocks and soil downstream.

Erosion changes rocks.

SCIENCE AND . . . Reading

Choose the best summary of the **entire** chapter.
A. People use machines to change rocks.
B. Rocks can be changed into strange shapes.
C. Wind, water, and ice change rocks and cause erosion.

Glaciers erode Earth's surface. As glaciers move, rocks and sediments become frozen in the ice and move along with the glacier. When the ice melts, rocks and sediments drop off along the edges of the glacier.

Glaciers, wind, rain, or rivers may have moved soil and rocks to your area. Over time, erosion moves soil from one place to another. Erosion and weathering are always taking place.

Lesson Summary

● Soil is made of pieces of rocks and plant and animal parts.
● Water, wind, and ice move soil and rocks to new places.

Lesson Review

1. Which soils are good for growing crops?
2. What is erosion?
★3. How does water cause erosion?

142   Use with Application Activity on pages 353, 354.

TEACHER RESOURCE MASTERS

Social Studies Connection   106

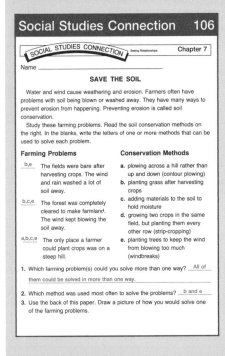

SOCIAL STUDIES CONNECTION Seeing Relationships   Chapter 7

Name _____

SAVE THE SOIL

Water and wind cause weathering and erosion. Farmers often have problems with soil being blown or washed away. They have many ways to prevent erosion from happening. Preventing erosion is called soil conservation.

Study these farming problems. Read the soil conservation methods on the right. In the blanks, write the letters of one or more methods that can be used to solve each problem.

Farming Problems

b,e The fields were bare after harvesting crops. The wind and rain washed a lot of soil away.

b,c,e The forest was completely cleared to make farmland. The wind kept blowing the soil away.

a,b,c,e The only place a farmer could plant crops was on a steep hill.

Conservation Methods

a. plowing across a hill rather than up and down (contour plowing)
b. planting grass after harvesting crops
c. adding materials to the soil to hold moisture
d. growing two crops in the same field, but planting them every other row (strip-cropping)
e. planting trees to keep the wind from blowing too much (windbreaks)

1. Which farming problem(s) could you solve more than one way? All of them could be solved in more than one way.

2. Which method was used most often to solve the problems? b and e
3. Use the back of this paper. Draw a picture of how you would solve one of the farming problems.

How do different soils compare?

What you need
3 soil samples
hand lens
3 paper cups
6 bean seeds
water
metric ruler
3 labels
pencil and paper

What to do
1. Use the hand lens to observe soils A, B, and C. Record how the soils look and feel.
2. Fill each paper cup with a different soil sample. Pack down the soils.
3. Label each cup A, B, or C to go with the soil samples.
4. Plant 2 seeds in each cup and place them by a window.
5. Add equal amounts of water to moisten the soil. Repeat this step as needed.
6. Measure and record plant growth on a chart after the first and second weeks.

What did you learn?
1. How do the soil colors and textures compare?
2. In which soil did the plants grow best?

Using what you learned
1. Which soil is best in a garden? Why?
2. Why should each cup of soil get equal amounts of water and light?

143

ACTIVITY RESPONSES

What did you learn?
1. Soil C is the darkest in color. Soils A and C will compact easily. Soil B is light in color and will fall through the fingers when squeezed.
2. soil C

Using what you learned
1. Soil C, because it allows drainage and is rich in nutrients
2. Water and light must be the same because the only variable the activity is testing is how soil type affects plant growth.

PREPLAN

Time Allotment: 30 minutes
Process Skill: Observing

Objectives
1. **Observe** and **describe** different soil samples.
2. **Determine** which soil promotes the best plant growth.

Setup
■ Obtain three different types of soil: rich in clay, sandy, rich in humus.
■ Soak beans 24 hours before planting.
▧ **Cooperative Grouping:** fives—Assign roles as explained on page T24.

1 FOCUS

■ Go through each step of the activity with students. Encourage them to make detailed observations.

2 TEACH

▧ Ideally, students should have cups ⅔ full of soil after the soils are packed.
■ Plant the beans 1–2 cm deep. The deeper they are planted, the longer they will take to grow above the soil.
■ Remind students to pay attention to bean plant health as well as growth (height).
■ Have students use the Teacher Resource Master **Activity Worksheet,** pages 101 and 102, to record their data and answers.

3 APPLY

■ Explain that cacti are common in deserts. Ask: **What kind of soil is best for cacti?** *sandy soils*

Close
■ Discuss the activity and questions.

Summary

Chapter Closure: Divide the class into **cooperative groups** of four. Assign each group two of the summary statements. Have them write a question for each of their statements. Collect the questions, reassemble the group, and ask the questions. Help students summarize the material covered in the chapter by discussing the summary statements.

Science Words

Give students sheets of 1-cm square graph paper. Have them make word search puzzles using the science words. Allow them to trade puzzles with classmates.

Student Responses

1. erosion
2. weathering

CHAPTER REVIEW
7

Summary

Lesson 1
- Rocks are constantly worn away or broken down.
- Water, wind, ice, and living things weather rocks.

Lesson 2
- Soil is pieces of rocks and decayed plants and animals.
- Water, wind, and ice move soil and rocks, causing erosion.

Science Words

Fill in the blank with the correct word or words from the list.

weathering
erosion   **glacier**

1. The movement of soil and rocks to new places is ____ .
2. The breaking down of rocks is called ____ .

144

TEACHER RESOURCE MASTERS

Test A   110

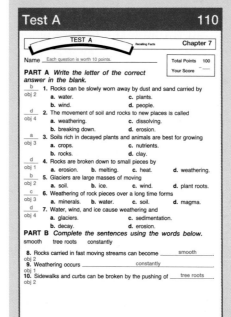

TEST A   Recalling Facts   Chapter 7

Name __Each question is worth 10 points.__   Total Points 100
                                               Your Score ___

PART A *Write the letter of the correct answer in the blank.*

_b_ obj 2 **1.** Rocks can be slowly worn away by dust and sand carried by
    a. water.   **c.** plants.
    b. wind.   **d.** people.

_d_ obj 4 **2.** The movement of soil and rocks to new places is called
    a. weathering.   **c.** dissolving.
    b. breaking down.   **d.** erosion.

_a_ obj 3 **3.** Soils rich in decayed plants and animals are best for growing
    a. crops.   **c.** nutrients.
    b. rocks.   **d.** clay.

_d_ obj 1 **4.** Rocks are broken down to small pieces by
    a. erosion.   **b.** melting.   **c.** heat.   **d.** weathering.

_b_ obj 2 **5.** Glaciers are large masses of moving
    a. soil.   **b.** ice.   **c.** wind.   **d.** plant roots.

_c_ obj 3 **6.** Weathering of rock pieces over a long time forms
    a. minerals.   **b.** water.   **c.** soil.   **d.** magma.

_d_ obj 4 **7.** Water, wind, and ice cause weathering and
    a. glaciers.   **c.** sedimentation.
    b. decay.   **d.** erosion.

PART B *Complete the sentences using the words below.*
smooth   tree roots   constantly

8. Rocks carried in fast moving streams can become ____ smooth
obj 2
9. Weathering occurs ____ constantly
obj 1
10. Sidewalks and curbs can be broken by the pushing of ____ tree roots
obj 2

Test B   111

TEST B   Understanding/Applying Concepts   Chapter 7

Name __Each question is worth 10 points.__   Total Points 100
                                               Your Score ___

Geologists have a special interest in how nature changes rocks. Imagine that you are a geologist studying how rocks change.

1. How could you tell if a rock were being weathered? __It would be__
obj 1 breaking down into smaller pieces or being worn away.

2. How does fast moving water cause rocks to change as they tumble
obj 2 downstream? __Corners and edges break off and the rocks become__
smooth.

3. How can water in cracks change rocks during winter? __Water freezes,__
obj 3 expands, and makes cracks larger. Sometimes this process breaks rocks.

4. How can wind change rocks? __Dust and sand carried by strong winds__
obj 2 can scratch and slowly wear away rock.

5. How do tree roots change sidewalks and curbs? __They push on them__
obj 2 and break them.

Questions

Recalling Ideas

Correctly complete each of the following sentences.

1. Animals affect the weathering of Earth when
   (a) they sleep.
   (b) they drink water.
   (c) they dig tunnels.
   (d) they eat food.
2. Earth's rocks are
   (a) never changing.
   (b) always changing.
   (c) always large.
   (d) never broken.
3. Rocks may break when plants
   (a) decay.   (c) dig tunnels.
   (b) grow.   (d) dissolve.
4. Soils that are good for growing crops are rich in
   (a) clay.
   (b) sand.
   (c) clay and sand.
   (d) decayed plants and animals.
5. Wind causes erosion in
   (a) cold areas.   (c) dry areas.
   (b) warm areas.   (d) wet areas.
6. Rocks with rounded edges were worn down by
   (a) being thrown.
   (b) moving water.
   (c) snow.
   (d) freezing water.
7. Ice in the cracks of rocks
   (a) smooths rocks.
   (b) melts rocks.
   (c) makes cracks larger.
   (d) makes cracks smaller.

Understanding Ideas

Answer the following questions using complete sentences.

1. How is soil formed?
2. How does water change rocks?
3. How can glaciers cause weathering and erosion?

Thinking Critically

Think about what you have learned in this chapter. Answer the following questions using complete sentences.

1. Why do you never really see the "same" rocks from one year to the next even though you live in the same area?
2. How do weathering and erosion affect the life of a farmer who grows crops?

145

TEACHER RESOURCE MASTERS

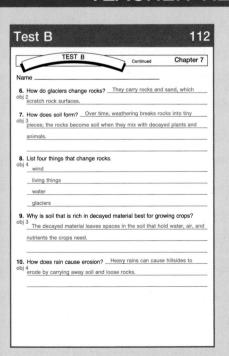

Test B   **112**

TEST B   Continued   Chapter 7

Name _____

6. How do glaciers change rocks? <u>They carry rocks and sand, which</u>
obj 2 <u>scratch rock surfaces.</u>

7. How does soil form? <u>Over time, weathering breaks rocks into tiny</u>
obj 3 <u>pieces; the rocks become soil when they mix with decayed plants and</u>
<u>animals.</u>

8. List four things that change rocks.
obj 4 <u>wind</u>
<u>living things</u>
<u>water</u>
<u>glaciers</u>

9. Why is soil that is rich in decayed material best for growing crops?
obj 3 <u>The decayed material leaves spaces in the soil that hold water, air, and</u>
<u>nutrients the crops need.</u>

10. How does rain cause erosion? <u>Heavy rains can cause hillsides to</u>
obj 4 <u>erode by carrying away soil and loose rocks.</u>

Questions

Recalling Ideas

1. c
2. b
3. b
4. d
5. c
6. b
7. c

Understanding Ideas

1. Weathering over a long period of time breaks rocks into very small pieces. Spaces between these small pieces hold water, air, and nutrients. All of these ingredients (bits of rock, water, air, nutrients) are combined as soil.
2. Water changes rock by weathering and erosion. Fast-moving water moves rocks downstream. As they bump into each other, small pieces of the rocks and sediments break off. Water itself also smoothes rocks and sediments. When water freezes, it expands. It can break rocks by getting into the cracks and freezing. Holes can be left in rocks when minerals are removed.
3. As glaciers move, they carry large rocks, sand, and sediments. These objects scratch the surface over which the glaciers move. Glaciers cause erosion when they move rocks and sediments and then deposit them elsewhere.

Thinking Critically

1. We never really see the "same" rocks year after year because they are always changing. Forces in nature such as water, ice, wind, and plants and animals are constantly changing rocks.
2. Weathering and erosion affect the life of a farmer who grows crops because weathering (which is the breaking down or wearing away of rocks) constantly creates new soil over a period of many years. The weathering of different rocks creates different types of soils (e.g., sandy, clay-rich). Erosion affects the life of such a farmer in that erosion is the movement of sediments and rocks to new places. If sediments rich in decayed plant and animal parts are moved, the quality of the farmer's soil will be affected.

Weather and Climate

Planning Guide

Lessons	Objectives	Vocabulary
Chapter Introduction pp. 146, 147		
Lesson 1 Evaporation and Condensation pp. 148–153	1. **Define** *water vapor.* 2. **Identify** factors that affect evaporation. 3. **Give examples** of where condensation forms.	atmosphere water vapor dew frost
Lesson 2 Clouds and Precipitation pp. 154–157	4. **Operationally define** *dew, frost, clouds, fog,* and *precipitation.* 5. **List** the forms of precipitation and **tell** how they are different.	clouds cirrus cumulus stratus precipitation
Lesson 3 Climate pp. 158–163	6. **Define** *climate.* 7. **Identify** the climate zones in the world. 8. **Explain** how large bodies of water, mountains, and cities can affect weather.	climate polar zones tropics temperate zones
Chapter Review pp. 164, 165		

Planning Guide

Text Activities		Teacher Resource Masters	Other Components
Title/Skill	**Materials per Group**		
Have You Ever . . . Made Dew Drops? p. 147 Observing Time Allotment: 30 minutes	pitcher water ice stirrer thermometer		Activity Center: "Weathering the Storm"; "Words of Weather"; "When You're Hot You're Hot"; "How Warm Is It?"
When Does Water Evaporate Fastest? p. 153 Observing/Inferring Time Allotment: 20 minutes set up; 5 minutes observing for several hours	water 3 paper towels small paper cup watch pencil and paper	Independent Practice, pp. 123, 124 Activity Worksheet, pp. 115, 116 ♦ Family Science, p. 114 Critical Thinking, p. 119	Activity Book, pp. 23, 24 Mr. Wizard's World of Science Video Tape 16
How Do Amounts of Precipitation Compare? p. 157 Interpreting Data Time Allotment: 30 minutes	paper and pencil	Independent Practice, pp. 123, 124 Activity Worksheet, pp. 117, 118 ♦ Reteaching Activity, p. 125 Math Connection, p. 122 Language Arts Connection, p. 121	Activity Book, pp. 25, 26
You Can . . . Make a Temperature Graph, p. 161 Communicating Time Allotment: 45 minutes **Who Will Stop the Rain?** p. 355 Observing/Inferring/Controlling Variables/Interpreting Data Time Allotment: 40 minutes	local telephone directory envelope first-class postage stamp paper and pencil pieces of cotton cloth water pan spray bottles materials to choose for weatherproofing	Independent Practice, pp. 123, 124 ▲ Critical Thinking, p. 120 Transparency Master, p. 113	Activity Book, pp. 45, 46
		Test A, p. 126 Test B, pp. 127, 128	

♦ Basic / ▲ Advanced / All other masters are for use by all students.

Weather and Climate

For Exceptional Students

ESL/LEP

Chapter 8/Lesson 1, page 152
Write these word pairs on the chalkboard: **water vapor and evaporation, water vapor and condensation, condensation and dew, water vapor and frost.** Ask students to make up sentences in which both words in a pair are used. For example, **When evaporation occurs, water vapor is formed.** Have students make up riddles that are answered by one member of the preceding word pairs. For example, write on the chalkboard **My name is water vapor. When it turns cold, what happens to me? Answers: Condensation occurs.**

Chapter 8/Lesson 2, page 155
Ask students to write the following across the top of a sheet of paper: **Cirrus Cloud, Cumulus Cloud, Stratus Cloud.** Tell them to draw each kind of cloud beneath its name. Discuss the kind of weather related to each cloud. Ask students to write a sentence beneath each cloud drawing describing the kind of weather the cloud brings. (Cirrus—nice weather; puffy, white cumulus—nice weather; low, dark gray cumulus—rain; low, thick stratus—rain or snow)

Chapter 8/Lesson 3, page 158
Have students use the picture of Earth on page 158 to locate where they live now. Ask them what climate zone they live in. Tell them to list adjectives to describe the climate where they live. Ask them to tell in what climate zone the country of their origin is. Let them list adjectives to describe what the climate in the country of their origin is like. Have them make up sentences in which they compare the climates of where they live now and where they came from. Write a sample sentence appropriate to your group of students. Samples: **It is (colder, warmer) in (Tokyo) than it is in San Francisco. It rains (more, less) there than it does here.** Students at different levels of English proficiency may provide more or less descriptive sentences.

Gifted

Chapter 8/Lesson 3, Page 162
Have gifted students record weather predictions from three different sources and the actual weather each day for a period of time. Allow students to decide what data they will collect about the weather and how they will collect it. Have the students judge which source was most accurate.

Mainstreamed

Chapter 8/Lesson 2, Page 156
Mild Behavior Disorders: Pair exceptional student(s) with a partner. The partner has stimulus cards representing the various types of cloud formations (such as cirrus, cumulus, stratus). Face-up in front of the exceptional students are response cards showing associated weather conditions and/or cloud characteristics (such as thin/white, ice crystals, nice weather). The back of the card indicates the correct cloud type. A student encourages his or her partner to select all cards associated with the "stimulus" card. Feedback is provided by the partner when he or she turns over the response cards. Partners are to switch roles.

Whole Class Science Project

Have students plan and organize their own weather station. They can read in reference books how to build some of the instruments they will use, such as a barometer, thermometer, weather vane, hygrometer, rain gauge, device to measure snow-fall, or any other instruments needed. They should record information on a weather chart for a month. Make seven columns on a sheet of paper, putting the date and time the weather observations are made each day. The weather should be observed about the same time each day. In the other col-umns, ask students to put down the following infor-mation: temperature outdoors, air pressure, humid-ity, direction and speed of the wind, condition of the sky, and kind and amount of precipitation, if any. In order to depict how much of the sky is covered with clouds, fill in all, part, or none of a circle in the "condition of the sky" column. Students should collect the weather forecast from the newspaper each day of the month and display these on a chart. Have them compare the actual weather for each day with the weather predicted for that day, and see how often the forecaster was correct. Students should compile information from the weather chart for the month and the predictions from the newspa-per and write a report on the weather conditions for the month. They could research to compare this month to the same month for the last five years to see if the trend is similar.

Science Fair Projects

Individual students could do one of the following projects:
1. Using a balance, lamp, fan, plastic sheets, food coloring, and hot and cold water, students should investigate evaporation observing one variable at a time. Students will relate this investigation to the effects that air, moisture, wind, and sun have on evaporation in our environment.
2. Conduct an investigation to determine if weather has an effect on human emotions. Have students select at least 10 or more family members or friends they can speak with daily for a period of time. On a chart, record humidity, barometric pressure, temperature, cloud formations, and feelings of these people daily. Compare the weather data with the people's state of mind and conclude whether or not fluctuations of feelings seem to have any connection with the weather.

Chapter Concepts

■ The weather is affected by the evaporation and condensation of Earth's water.
■ Cirrus, stratus, and cumulus clouds are indicative of certain kinds of weather.
■ Climate is the usual type of weather that occurs at a given place over time. The Earth is divided into three climatic zones.

Chapter Background

■ Earth's atmosphere serves several functions: it provides the air necessary for life; it plays an important role in distributing energy over the planet; it insulates Earth; and it shields Earth's surface from large amounts of ultraviolet radiation.
■ Nitrogen and oxygen are the most abundant gases in the atmosphere. Water vapor is present between 0 and 4 percent by volume.
■ The hydrologic cycle is powered by solar energy

Look for These Symbols

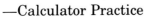 —Hands-on activity

—Cooperative learning

—Overhead transparency

◆ —Basic/Reinforcement

● —Average/Enrichment

▲ —Advanced/Challenge

—Calculator Practice

SCIENCE
In Your World

146

CHAPTER 8

Weather and Climate

Weather is a result of the condition of Earth's air. The air may be warm or cold, wet or dry. As the air condition changes, so does the weather.

Have You Ever...

Made Dew Drops?

One condition that changes our weather is the changing state of water in the air. Put some water into a pitcher. Record the temperature. Now add ice and stir the water. Keep adding ice and keep stirring the water until drops of water form on the outside of the pitcher. Then measure the temperature again. What is the temperature when the drops form? What caused the water drops to form? How does this help explain how dew is formed?

147

PREPLAN

Time Allotment: 30 minutes

Objectives
1. **Understand** that weather is affected by air conditions.
2. **Observe** the conditions in which water drops form on the outside of a pitcher.

Setup
■ If you wish to perform this activity, you will need the following materials for each student or activity group:
pitcher
water   ice   stirrer   thermometer

1   FOCUS

■ Ask: **How does the weather affect you?** *Different weather conditions affect our dress, plans, and moods.*

2   TEACH

■ Have the title and introductory paragraph read aloud.

Have You Ever . . .
■ Have students **work cooperatively** in groups of four.
Safety Considerations
■ Caution students to handle the thermometer carefully.
Student Responses
■ Ice in the pitcher caused the water in the air to change from a gas to a liquid. Dew drops form when the water in the air (water vapor) meets the cold surfaces of the ground and plants.

3   APPLY

■ Ask students to think of other places they have seen condensation.

Close
■ Tell the students that they will learn more about what affects weather and climate as they read Chapter 8.

PREPLAN

Lesson Objectives

1. **Define** *water vapor.*
2. **Identify** factors that affect evaporation.
3. **Give examples** of where condensation forms.

Science Background

■ Evaporation requires energy. Heat is usually lost from the surface where evaporation occurs. That is why the body feels cooler as water evaporates from the skin's surface.

■ Condensation occurs when the air cools. Air that has cooled becomes saturated. That is, it can hold no more water vapor. The temperature at which air is saturated is called the dew point.

■ Frost forms when the dew point is below the freezing point of water. The process that forms frost is called sublimation. In sublimation, water vapor changes directly to solid ice crystals without first becoming a liquid.

Lesson Vocabulary

atmosphere
water vapor
dew
frost
Note: The activity on student page 153 may be used for guided discovery before you begin this lesson.

1   FOCUS

■ Ask why people always talk about the weather. Discuss how sunny weather, rainy weather, and cold weather affect what students do after school.

■ Use the goals on student page 148 to establish the purpose for studying this lesson.

Evaporation and Condensation

LESSON 1 GOALS
You will learn
● that water changes from a liquid to a gas during evaporation.
● that two factors affect the speed of evaporation.
● that condensation may take place when water as a gas cools.

"It really got cold fast! I wish I had brought my jacket with me. But it was sunny and warm when I left, so how was I to know?" Does this sound like you? How many times can you remember needing a jacket or an umbrella that you hadn't brought? The weather can change quickly.

Weather changes take place in Earth's atmosphere (AT muh sfihr). The **atmosphere** is all the air around Earth.

What is the atmosphere?

Evaporation

Remember from Lesson 2 in Chapter 3 that evaporation is the change of matter from a liquid to a gas. When water is the matter that is evaporating, the gas formed is called **water vapor.** When water vapor evaporates from oceans, lakes, and rivers, it enters the air. Living plants and animals also give off water vapor.

Water changes to water vapor.

148

TEACHER RESOURCE MASTERS

We can't see water vapor. However, after a storm we can see that puddles grow smaller and finally disappear. [1]How does the drying of puddles show that water vapor forms?

Water can evaporate only where it meets the air. If a large surface meets the air, a lot of water can evaporate. If the surface meeting the air is small, not much water can evaporate.

1. It shows that evaporation is occurring.

How does surface area affect evaporation?

Water evaporates faster from one container.

Look at the two containers in the picture on this page. Both hold the same amount of water. [2]Which one has a larger surface meeting the air? [3]From which container will water evaporate faster?

Warm air speeds evaporation. In Lesson 3 in Chapter 2, you learned that particles of liquids bump into each other. When a liquid is heated, the particles move faster. They bump each other harder then. Some particles are bumped away from the surface of the liquid. These particles become a gas.

2. The flat dish has a larger surface area.
3. It will evaporate faster from the flat dish.

149

2 TEACH

Have students **work cooperatively** to develop a list of places they have seen condensation in their daily activities.
■ Discuss how weather affects outdoor games. Compare games and types of after-school activities done in winter with those of summer.

Guided Practice
■ Check students' understanding of lesson concepts by discussing the Lesson Review questions on student page 152. If necessary, use the **reteaching strategy** in OPTIONS.

Independent Practice
■ Assign the Lesson 1 section of the Teacher Resource Master **Independent Practice,** page 123.

3 APPLY

Place a fresh stalk of celery with leaves in an empty glass. The next day the children should observe the celery drooping. Discuss why it's limp (because the cells lost water by evaporation). Add water to glass and observe how soon the celery will straighten up.

Close
■ Use Summary statements on student page 152 to review lesson concepts.

OPTIONS

Reteaching Strategy
Fill three measuring cups with water in the morning. Place one near a sunny window, one near a heat source, one in the middle of the room. Check them at the end of the day and have students explain the differences they observe.

Resource Options
■ Use Activity Book, "Interpreting Data," pages 23 and 24.

TEACHER RESOURCE MASTERS

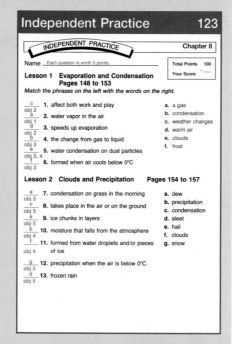

Independent Practice   123

INDEPENDENT PRACTICE   Chapter 8

Name _Each question is worth 5 points._   Total Points 100
Your Score ___

Lesson 1   Evaporation and Condensation
              Pages 148 to 153
Match the phrases on the left with the words on the right.

c   **1.** affect both work and play   a. a gas
obj 2
a   **2.** water vapor in the air   b. condensation
obj 1
d   **3.** speeds up evaporation   c. weather changes
obj 2
b   **4.** the change from gas to liquid   d. warm air
obj 3
e   **5.** water condensation on dust particles   e. clouds
obj 3, 4
f   **6.** formed when air cools below 0°C   f. frost
obj 3

Lesson 2   Clouds and Precipitation   **Pages 154 to 157**

a   **7.** condensation on grass in the morning   a. dew
obj 5
c   **8.** takes place in the air or on the ground   b. precipitation
obj 5
e   **9.** ice chunks in layers   c. condensation
obj 5
b   **10.** moisture that falls from the atmosphere d. sleet
obj 4
f   **11.** formed from water droplets and/or pieces   e. hail
obj 4   of ice   f. clouds
g   **12.** precipitation when the air is below 0°C   g. snow
obj 5
d   **13.** frozen rain
obj 5

OPTIONS

LANGUAGE CONNECTION

■ **Writing:** Give students the following assignment.

Imagine that, as you pick up a can of cola, it slips through your fingers and spills all over the new rug in your living room. Write a letter to your mom explaining why the outside of the can of cola gets so wet. (Water vapor in the air around the can condenses as it is cooled by the cold soda.)

◆ **Reinforcement:** Use two jars that are the same size. Pour very hot water in one jar until it is half full. **CAUTION:** *Be sure to use jars that will not break when the hot water is poured in. Do not let students get too close to the hot water.* Quickly cap the jar. Pour the same amount of cold water in the second jar, and cap it. Have the students observe the jars for five minutes. List the observations they make. Ask them to explain the changes they observed.

Resource Options

■ Show selections from "Change of State," *Mr. Wizard's World of Science Video Library,* Merrill Publishing Company.

---

1. Answers may include shaking hands or rubbing on clothes.

2. Both have warm moving air.

Suppose you hung wet clothes on a clothesline to dry. Would the clothes dry faster on a cool day or on a warm day? Wet clothes will dry faster if the weather is warm, since warm air speeds evaporation.

Moving air speeds evaporation, too. Have you ever washed your hands and then discovered that there were no towels? [1]How did you dry your hands?

Wet hair and clothes dry faster on windy days. On a warm, dry day, where would clothes dry faster—inside a closed garage or out in the windy backyard? Clothes dry faster in the wind, since moving air speeds evaporation. [2]How is a clothes dryer like a warm, dry, windy day?

150

TEACHER RESOURCE MASTERS

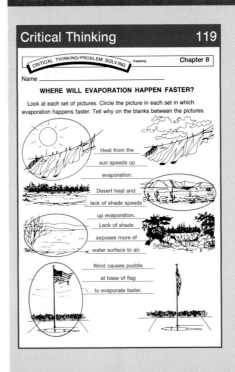

CRITICAL THINKING/PROBLEM SOLVING   Predicting   Chapter 8

Name _____

WHERE WILL EVAPORATION HAPPEN FASTER?

Look at each set of pictures. Circle the picture in each set in which evaporation happens faster. Tell why on the blanks between the pictures.

Heat from the sun speeds up evaporation.

Desert heat and lack of shade speeds up evaporation. Lack of shade exposes more of water surface to air.

Wind causes puddle at base of flag to evaporate faster.

OPTIONS

■ Ask students to compare the properties of liquid water and water vapor.

ART CONNECTION

■ Have students draw pictures showing their activities on days with different kinds of weather, such as rainy weather, warm sunny weather, snowy weather, and so on.

Condensation

Water vapor is a gas, but it can change back to a liquid. In Lesson 2 in Chapter 3, you learned that the change of matter from a gas to a liquid is called condensation. Condensation changes water vapor to liquid water. For water vapor to condense to a liquid, it must become cooler. This cooling and condensation can take place in the air or on the ground.

When water vapor condenses on dust particles in the atmosphere, clouds form. Water vapor may also condense on objects on the ground. **Dew** is a form of condensation. When air cools at night, droplets of water called dew may form on cars and blades of grass.

151

TEACHER RESOURCE MASTERS

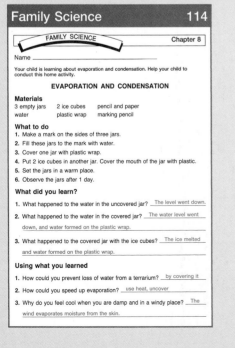

Family Science   **114**

FAMILY SCIENCE   Chapter 8

Name _____

Your child is learning about evaporation and condensation. Help your child to conduct this home activity.

EVAPORATION AND CONDENSATION

Materials
3 empty jars   2 ice cubes   pencil and paper
water   plastic wrap   marking pencil

What to do
1. Make a mark on the sides of three jars.
2. Fill these jars to the mark with water.
3. Cover one jar with plastic wrap.
4. Put 2 ice cubes in another jar. Cover the mouth of the jar with plastic.
5. Set the jars in a warm place.
6. Observe the jars after 1 day.

What did you learn?

1. What happened to the water in the uncovered jar? The level went down.

2. What happened to the water in the covered jar? The water level went down, and water formed on the plastic wrap.

3. What happened to the covered jar with the ice cubes? The ice melted and water formed on the plastic wrap.

Using what you learned

1. How could you prevent loss of water from a terrarium? by covering it

2. How could you speed up evaporation? use heat, uncover

3. Why do you feel cool when you are damp and in a windy place? The wind evaporates moisture from the skin.

OPTIONS

● **Enrichment:** Have students pour equal amounts of water into a glass pie dish and a tall drinking glass. Ask them to predict from which container the most water should evaporate. Place both containers in a location where sun, heat, and wind will not be factors. Allow them to sit for several days. Carefully pour the water from one container into a calibrated cylinder. Measure and record the amount. Repeat this for the second container. Have students compare the actual results with their predictions. Allow students to repeat this experiment with a cover over the pie dish. Allow them to discover how the lid affects evaporation.

▲ **Challenge:** Have students conduct an experiment to find out how wind affects the rate of evaporation. A fan can be used to simulate wind. Have students make predictions before they begin and discuss the conclusions with others.

LESSON REVIEW ANSWERS

1. Water vapor is water as a gas.

2. the water that spilled, because it has more surface meeting the air

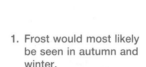

1. Frost would most likely be seen in autumn and winter.
2. It is cold outside when frost forms.

Would You Believe?

Clouds float lower at night than during the day.

When the air cools to below 0°C, water vapor may change to ice without first becoming dew. In that case, the water vapor condenses to form **frost.** [1]In what season would you see frost on cars and blades of grass? [2]Why should you wear a jacket or coat if you see frost?

Lesson Summary

- Evaporation is the change of matter from a liquid to a gas.
- Air temperature and air speed affect the speed of evaporation.
- Condensation is the change of matter from a gas to a liquid.

Lesson Review

1. What is water vapor?

★2. Suppose equal amounts of water are outdoors in two open containers. One is tipped over and spilled onto the sidewalk. The other is not. Which water will evaporate faster? Why?

152

TEACHER RESOURCE MASTERS

When does water evaporate fastest?

What you need

water
3 paper towels
small paper cup
watch
pencil and paper

What to do

1. Make a mark 1 cm from the bottom of the paper cup. Add water to that mark. Then, pour the water on a paper towel.
2. Repeat step 1 for each of the other paper towels.
3. Now, fold the first towel in half. Fold the second in half. Then, fold it in half again.
4. Do not fold the third paper towel.
5. Put all three towels in a warm, dry place.
6. Record how long it takes for each towel to dry.

What did you learn?

1. Which paper towel dried fastest?
2. Which towel took the longest to dry?

Using what you learned

1. How would you hang clothes so they dry quickly?
2. Which will evaporate faster—a cup of water or a spilled cup of water? Why?
3. What could you do to slow down evaporation? When would this be useful?

153

ACTIVITY RESPONSES

What did you learn?
1. The flat paper towel dried fastest.
2. The towel that was folded in quarters took the longest.

Using what you learned
1. The clothes should be hung unfolded so more surface area is exposed to the air.
2. A spilled cup of water will dry faster. It has more surface area exposed to air than the water still in the cup.
3. Expose only a small amount of surface area to the air. This might be useful in keeping clothes damp before ironing or in retaining water in a dish that is being cooked.

Time Allotment: 20 minutes for setup; 5 minutes' observing time each hour for several hours

Process Skills: Observing/Inferring

Objectives

1. **Demonstrate** how the amount of surface exposed to the air determines the rate of evaporation.
2. **Predict** how changing variables will affect the rate of evaporation.

Setup

■ Place large plastic bags over work areas.
■ Have extra towels for cleanup.

Cooperative Grouping: threes—Assign roles as explained on page T24.

1 FOCUS

■ Ask: **Where will a wet bath towel dry faster—on the towel bar or in a heap on the floor?** *on the towel bar due to a larger surface area*

2 TEACH

■ Try the activity before class begins. If a significant puddle of water is left under the paper towel when it is picked up, you are using too much water. Reduce the amount for the activity.
■ Have students use the Teacher Resource Master **Activity Worksheet,** pages 115 and 116, to record their data and answers.

2 APPLY

■ Compare the results with the rates of evaporation from a puddle, pond, river, lake, and ocean.

Close

■ Discuss the activity and questions with the class.

PREPLAN

Lesson Objectives

4. Operationally define *dew, frost, clouds, fog,* and *precipitation.*

5. List the forms of precipitation and **tell** how they are different.

Science Background

■ Clouds are made of millions of tiny condensed water droplets and/or tiny ice crystals. When warm, moist air is cooled, a cloud may form.

■ Fog is formed when warm, moist air passes over a cold surface or when cold air passes over warmer water.

■ Much of the rain in temperate zones actually starts out as snow. Many clouds in the temperate zones are a mixture of very cold water droplets and ice crystals. If the ice crystals fall to the ground in cold air, we call it snow. If they melt on the way down, we call it rain. Sleet occurs when small raindrops pass through a cold layer of air near the ground and freeze, forming small pellets of ice. Hail falls from giant cumulonimbus thunderheads.

Lesson Vocabulary

clouds
cirrus
cumulus
stratus
precipitation

Note: The activity on student page 157 may be used for guided discovery before you begin this lesson.

1 FOCUS

■ Ask students if they have ever walked or traveled through fog. Ask: **What did you see?** *Students should realize that the mist they saw was millions of tiny droplets of water, that is, a cloud.*

■ Use the goals on student page 154 to establish the purpose for studying this lesson.

Clouds and Precipitation

> **LESSON 2 GOALS**
> You will learn
> ● how clouds form.
> ● the names of types of clouds.
> ● that precipitation falls from the atmosphere.

Are you a cloud watcher? Sometimes clouds can look like people's faces, imaginary animals, or even the hills and valleys of an undiscovered land. Have you ever wondered why clouds form and change?

In Lesson 1 you learned that water vapor can't be seen. But when water vapor condenses on tiny particles of dust in the air, droplets of water form. If the air is cold, water vapor condenses to tiny pieces of ice instead of droplets of water. These water droplets, pieces of ice, or both together make **clouds.**

Cirrus (SIHR us) clouds are thin and white with fuzzy edges. They look like feathers. Cirrus clouds are made of ice crystals. They form high above the ground. You can often see cirrus clouds during nice weather.

What are cirrus clouds made of?

Cirrus clouds

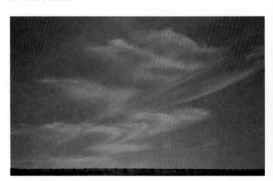

154

TEACHER RESOURCE MASTERS

Cumulus (KYEW myuh lus) clouds are large and puffy. They are much thicker and lower than cirrus clouds. Cumulus clouds may change shape on a windy day. During nice weather you'll often see scattered, puffy, white cumulus clouds. Low, dark, gray cumulus clouds can bring rain.

Clouds that cover the whole sky are **stratus** clouds. Low, thick stratus clouds may bring rain or snow. A stratus cloud close to the ground is called *fog.*

When can cumulus clouds be seen?

Cumulus clouds

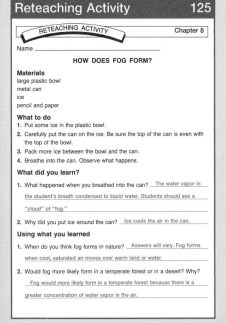

Fog is a stratus cloud.

Precipitation

The water droplets and pieces of ice in clouds are so small that they usually stay in the air. Sometimes the droplets or pieces of ice become large very quickly and fall to the ground. Moisture that falls from the atmosphere is called **precipitation** (prih sihp uh TAY shun).

155

TEACHER RESOURCE MASTERS

Reteaching Activity 125

```
┌─ RETEACHING ACTIVITY ───────── Chapter 8
Name _____

           HOW DOES FOG FORM?

Materials
large plastic bowl
metal can
ice
pencil and paper

What to do
1. Put some ice in the plastic bowl.
2. Carefully put the can on the ice. Be sure the top of the can is even with
   the top of the bowl.
3. Pack more ice between the bowl and the can.
4. Breathe into the can. Observe what happens.

What did you learn?
1. What happened when you breathed into the can?  The water vapor in
   the student's breath condensed to liquid water. Students should see a
   "cloud" of "fog."

2. Why did you put ice around the can?  Ice cools the air in the can.

Using what you learned
1. When do you think fog forms in nature?  Answers will vary. Fog forms
   when cool, saturated air moves over warm land or water.

2. Would fog more likely form in a temperate forest or in a desert? Why?
   Fog would more likely form in a temperate forest because there is a
   greater concentration of water vapor in the air.
```

Independent Practice 123

```
┌─ INDEPENDENT PRACTICE ───────── Chapter 8
Name  Each question is worth 5 points.      Total Points  100
                                            Your Score  ____
Lesson 1  Evaporation and Condensation
          Pages 148 to 153
Match the phrases on the left with the words on the right.

_c_   1. affect both work and play         a. a gas
obj 2
_a_   2. water vapor in the air            b. condensation
obj 1
_d_   3. speeds up evaporation             c. weather changes
obj 2
_b_   4. the change from gas to liquid     d. warm air
obj 3
_e_   5. water condensation on dust particles  e. clouds
obj 3, 4
_f_   6. formed when air cools below 0°C   f. frost
obj 3

Lesson 2  Clouds and Precipitation     Pages 154 to 157

_a_   7. condensation on grass in the morning   a. dew
obj 5
_c_   8. takes place in the air or on the ground  b. precipitation
obj 5
_e_   9. ice chunks in layers              c. condensation
obj 5
_b_  10. moisture that falls from the atmosphere  d. sleet
obj 4
_f_  11. formed from water droplets and/or pieces  e. hail
obj 4     of ice
                                          f. clouds
_g_  12. precipitation when the air is below 0°C  g. snow
obj 5
_d_  13. frozen rain
obj 5
```

---

2 TEACH

■ Have students conduct a cloud watch for three days. Identify the cloud types.

Cloud Type	Day
	Monday
	Tuesday
	Wednesday

■ Compare the kinds of weather often associated with each cloud type. Add a section called "Weather" to the chart.

Guided Practice

■ Check students' understanding of lesson concepts by discussing the Lesson Review questions on student page 156. If necessary, use the **reteaching strategy** in OPTIONS.

Independent Practice

■ Assign the Lesson 2 section of Teacher Resource Master **Independent Practice, page 123.**

3 APPLY

■ Collect pictures of common clouds. Identify them and the associated weather.

Close

■ Use Summary statements on student page 156 to review lesson concepts.

OPTIONS

Reteaching Strategy

Put water into the lower section and water and ice cubes into the upper section of a glass double boiler. Boil the water in the lower section. Have students observe the steam collecting and changing into "rain." Discuss. **CAUTION:** *Only the teacher should conduct this experiment.*

Resource Options

■ Use Activity Book, "Predicting," pages 25 and 26.

OPTIONS

SCIENCE AND . . . MATH

- **Skill:** Solve problems with metric units.

- **Student Response:** C

MATH CONNECTION

- Write the following question on a chalkboard or overhead transparency.

What customary units would you use to measure snowfall: pounds, inches, quarts, or miles? (inches)

♦ **Reinforcement:** Pour about 240 mL of water into a large, glass jar. Get a large, round, rubber balloon. Cut off the neck of the balloon. Strike a wooden match and allow it to burn briefly within the jar. Blow it out, but keep it in the jar for a moment. Quickly fasten the balloon onto the jar with rubber bands. Have two students hold the jar down tightly while another student quickly pulls up the balloon. In bright light a cloud is easily visible. **CAUTION:** *Do not allow students to get too close to the hot match.*

● **Enrichment:** Bring a piece of dry ice to class. Allow students to observe it as it sublimates. Discuss. **CAUTION:** *Don't allow students near the dry ice. Use gloves.*

▲ **Challenge:** Ask students to find out what causes tornadoes and hurricanes. They should explain the cloud structure of each.

LESSON REVIEW ANSWERS

1. cirrus–high, thin, white, feathery clouds with fuzzy edges, made of ice crystals; cumulus–large, puffy clouds.
2. Both are forms of precipitation. Sleet is frozen rain. Hail is layered ice chunks.

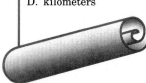

SCIENCE AND . . .
Math
What units would you use to measure how much snow has fallen?
A. grams
B. liters
C. centimeters
D. kilometers

1. People could be injured by the hailstones.

Rain and snow are two kinds of precipitation. When the air is warmer than 0°C, liquid water falls as rain. When the air is 0°C or colder, the water vapor forms ice particles and falls as snow. Sleet and hail are two other kinds of precipitation. Sleet is frozen rain. Hail is ice chunks made of many layers.

If you're a cloud watcher, you may also watch storms. Storm watchers often like to do their watching outdoors where they can see the whole sky. Look at the different sizes of the hailstones in the picture on this page. [1]Why might it be dangerous to be outdoors during a hailstorm?

Hailstones may be different sizes.

Lesson Summary

- Water vapor condenses on tiny dust particles to form clouds.
- Cirrus, cumulus, and stratus are three types of clouds.
- Rain, snow, sleet, and hail are four kinds of precipitation.

Lesson Review

1. How are cirrus clouds different from cumulus clouds?
★2. How are sleet and hail similar? different?

156

TEACHER RESOURCE MASTERS

Language Arts Connection   121

Math Connection   122

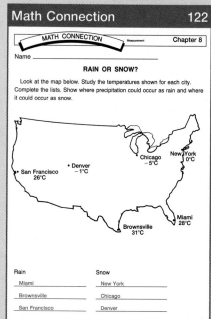

How do amounts of precipitation compare?

What you need
precipitation graphs
pencil and paper

What to do
1. Look at the graphs.
2. Compare the monthly precipitation for Denver and Honolulu.

What did you learn?
1. Which city has the most precipitation during June, July, and August?
2. During what month is Denver driest? Honolulu driest?
3. Which city has the greatest change in amount of precipitation from one month to the next?

Using what you learned
1. What season is Honolulu's "wet season"?
2. What other information is important when comparing climates?

Denver, Colorado

Honolulu, Hawaii

157

ACTIVITY RESPONSES

What did you learn?
1. Denver
2. January, June
3. Honolulu

Using what you learned
1. winter
2. temperature, wind, location, and so on

PREPLAN

Time Allotment: 30 minutes
Process Skill: Interpreting data
Objectives
1. **Interpret** graphs to find precipitation amounts.
2. **Compare** precipitation data for two different areas.

Setup
Cooperative Grouping: twos—Assign roles as explained on page T24.

1   FOCUS

■ Have students locate Denver and Honolulu on a map and then determine which climate zones they are in.

2   TEACH

■ The following are figures for the graph:
Denver (millimeters precipitation)
Jan. 12, Feb. 14, Mar. 28, Apr. 52,, May 62, June 36, July 42, Aug. 36, Sept. 26, Oct. 26, Nov. 16. Dec 16
Honolulu (millimeters precipitation)
Jan. 87, Feb. 102, Mar. 81, Apr. 53, May 35, June 21, July 26, Aug. 31, Sept. 37, Oct. 45, Nov. 86, Dec. 99.
■ Have students use the Teacher Resource Master **Activity Worksheet**, pages 117 and 118, to record their data and answers.

2   APPLY

■ Review the factors that affect the climates of each city. Denver is on the dry side of the mountains, in the center of the continent, and farther north than Honolulu. Honolulu is closer to the equator and surrounded by water.

Close
■ Discuss the activity and questions with the class.

PREPLAN

Lesson Objectives

6. **Define** *climate*.
7. **Identify** the climate zones in the world.
8. **Explain** how large bodies of water, mountains, and cities can affect weather.

Science Background

■ Climates around the world are determined by a number of factors. The most significant factor is latitude. Generally speaking, areas that are located at high latitudes will experience colder climates. Warmer climates are found near the equator.

■ Another factor for determining climate is altitude. Areas located on plateaus or in mountainous regions will experience a cold climate similar to climates of high latitude regions.

■ Bodies of water tend to have a moderating effect on climate. Areas located near oceans will experience mild temperatures all year.

■ Terrain also affects climate. Areas located on the leeward side of mountain ranges will experience continuous dry weather conditions.

Lesson Vocabulary

climate	Polar zones
tropics	temperate zones

1 FOCUS

Ask: **How does the climate affect you?**

■ Use the goals on student page 158 to establish the purpose for studying this lesson.

Climate

LESSON 3 GOALS
You will learn
● that there are three climate zones.
● that climate is affected by three factors.

What are the three major climate zones?

Did you need a heavy, warm coat last winter? If you did and if you haven't moved, then you're likely to need your heavy, warm coat this winter, too.

From one year to the next, the weather in one place stays pretty much the same. The usual weather in a place year after year is its **climate** (KLI mut).

There are three kinds of climate, or climate zones, on Earth. Look at the picture of Earth on this page. In the far northern and far southern parts of the world are the polar zones. In the **polar zones,** the temperatures are always cold. Centered over the middle of Earth is a climate zone called the **tropics.** Here the temperatures are always hot. The rest of the world lies in the two **temperate zones,** where the weather changes during the four seasons of the year.

Earth has three climate zones.

158

TEACHER RESOURCE MASTERS

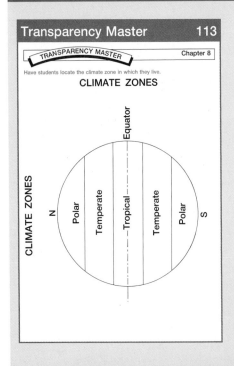

Transparency Master   113

TRANSPARENCY MASTER   Chapter 8

Have students locate the climate zone in which they live.

CLIMATE ZONES

Different places have different climates because they have different temperatures and amounts of water. The temperatures and amounts of water are affected by three factors.

One of these factors is large bodies of water. Places near oceans or large lakes often receive a lot of rain or snow. These places do not usually have very hot summers or very cold winters. Instead, they are likely to have mild temperatures all year long. These mild temperatures happen because large bodies of water stay cooler in summer and warmer in winter than nearby land areas. Air moving across the water toward land makes the summers cooler and the winters warmer. Temperatures year round are more even. Places far from oceans or large lakes, on the other hand, change greatly in temperature from season to season.

159

TEACHER RESOURCE MASTERS

Independent Practice 124

INDEPENDENT PRACTICE Continued Chapter 8

Name _____

Lesson 3 Climate Pages 158 to 163
Complete the sentences using the words below.

climate temperate zone winds polar zone
country tropics year after year

14. The usual weather for an area is called its __climate__ obj 6

15. Areas with a hot climate all year are located in the __tropics__ obj 7

16. The weather of an area changes daily while the climate is the same __year after year__ obj 6

17. During the day, it gets warmer in the city than in the __country__ obj 8

18. Mountains can affect climate by changing the pattern of the __winds__ obj 8

19. During the four seasons of the year, weather changes in the __temperate zone__ obj 7

20. The climate is always cold in the __polar zone__ obj 7

2 TEACH

Find the high and low temperatures for yesterday in the local newspaper. Place these temperatures on the chalkboard or an overhead transparency. Show the students how an average temperature for the day is determined by adding them together and dividing by two. It is not necessary that your students be able to do these calculations. The concept of average is what is important here.

■ Stress the difference between climate and weather.

Guided Practice

■ Check students' understanding of lesson concepts by discussing the Lesson Review questions on student page 162. If necessary, use the **reteaching strategy** in OPTIONS.

Independent Practice

■ Assign the Lesson 3 section of the Teacher Resource Master **Independent Practice,** page 124.

3 APPLY

■ Use Application Activity, "Who Will Stop the Rain?" on student pages 355 and 356.

Close

■ Use the summary statements on student page 162 to review the lesson concepts.

OPTIONS

Reteaching Strategy

■ Have children guess what place you are describing by using climate clues.

Resource Options

■ Use Activity Book, "Who Will Stop the Rain?" pages 45, 46.

OPTIONS

MATH CONNECTION

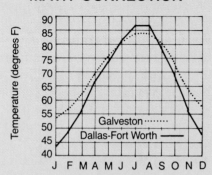

Draw and have students review the monthly temperature graphs of two Texas cities. Ask which one is near a large body of water. (Galveston) Ask how they can tell. (less variation in temperature year-round)

♦ **Reinforcement:** Display a large map of the United States. Have the students locate Pierre, South Dakota, and Olympia, Washington. Have them explain why the climate for Pierre has greater temperature extremes than that for Olympia. Ask which state is likely to have more rain and snow. Allow them to check their predictions by using reference material.

● **Enrichment:** Have students work in **cooperative groups.** Ask them to pretend they will take a trip during December. They may select any city in the world to visit. Have students locate their city on a world map. After studying its position with respect to water, mountains, and latitude, students should prepare a list of clothing to take and explain their choices by using what they have learned in this lesson.

▲ **Challenge:** Have students work in **cooperative groups** to draw a climatic map of the world showing the polar, tropic, and temperate zones.

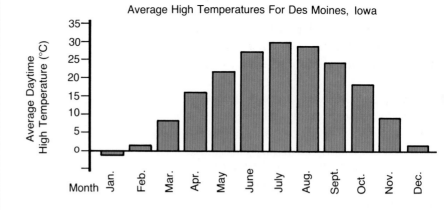

Look at the graph on this page. It has temperature information about Des Moines, Iowa. Study the graph carefully. Notice the change in high temperatures during the year. [1]Using this information, would you say that Des Moines is located near a large body of water or not? [2]Why?

The second factor that can affect climate is mountains. They change the wind's pattern. One side of the mountains may get a lot of rain or snow. The other side may have much less precipitation.

1. Des Moines is not near water.
2. The temperatures vary greatly during the year.

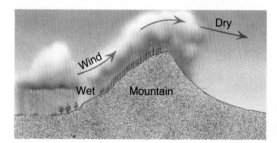

Mountains can affect climate.

160

TEACHER RESOURCE MASTERS

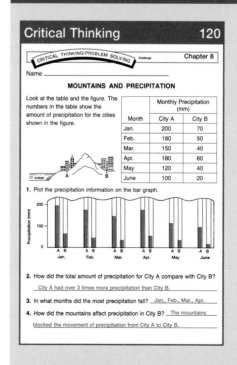

The third factor affecting climate is large cities. The number of tall buildings made of concrete and steel in large cities can absorb more energy from the sun than the open areas found in the country. That means that large cities become warmer during the day and stay warm longer at night than open areas of country. Also, the buildings in large cities are often built close together and may cause a change in wind patterns. On windy days the wind may become very strong, making it hard to walk near some buildings. These changes can affect the climate of areas that have several large cities.

How do large cities affect climate?

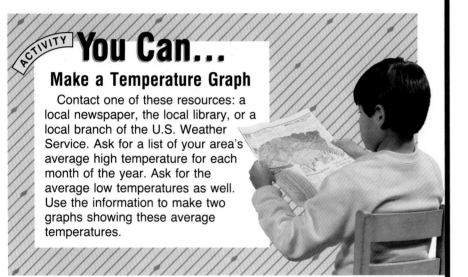

You Can...

ACTIVITY

Make a Temperature Graph

Contact one of these resources: a local newspaper, the local library, or a local branch of the U.S. Weather Service. Ask for a list of your area's average high temperature for each month of the year. Ask for the average low temperatures as well. Use the information to make two graphs showing these average temperatures.

161

OPTIONS

YOU CAN . . . MAKE A TEMPERATURE GRAPH

Process Skill: Communicating

Objective: Develop a graph to compare average temperatures.

Setup/Teach

■ Local telephone directory
   envelope
   first-class postage stamp
   paper and pencil

■ Students can work individually, or you may want to select a few students to act as class representatives when contacting local resources for the information.

■ Students may get the temperatures as Fahrenheit readings. If so, use them. Do not try to have them convert to Celsius.

■ Students may choose to do line graphs or bar graphs to illustrate the temperatures.

Science and Technology: Use "I WANT TO KNOW ABOUT . . . a Solar Collector," student page 163, with this lesson.

TEACHER RESOURCE MASTERS

OPTIONS

SOCIAL STUDIES CONNECTION

Have students use the library to find out about the climate of the area in which they live. Ask them to research what types of agriculture, industry, and recreation are common to the area. Discuss how the climate affects agriculture, industry, and recreation.

LESSON REVIEW ANSWERS

1. Climate is the usual weather in an area year after year.
2. Answers may vary. Most students would prefer to be near a lake on a hot day because it would be cooler.

Now that you know something about climate, where on Earth do you think the climate is the best? Would you enjoy living in a large city? on the side of a mountain? in the middle of an ocean? See what climates your friends like best. Their answers may not match yours!

Lesson Summary

- The polar zones, tropic zone, and temperate zones are three climate zones in the world.
- Water, mountains, and large cities can affect climate.

Lesson Review

1. What is climate?
★2. Would you want to be near a lake on a hot day? Why or why not?

162   Use with Application Activity on pages 355, 356.

TEACHER RESOURCE MASTERS

I WANT TO KNOW ABOUT...

A Solar Collector

Polar bears live in the northern polar climate zone. The temperature there is always very cold. Have you ever wondered how polar bears keep warm when it's cold?

Polar bears have fur that keeps them warm. Scientists have found that their fur does a good job of collecting the sun's rays to warm the bear.

Scientists have taken what they learned from studying polar bear fur and used it to make better solar collectors.

A solar collector is a dark material covered by glass. The sun's rays pass through the glass. The dark material absorbs and collects heat from the sun's rays.

Scientists have found that they can collect more heat from the sun's rays if they use fibers that are like the hairs in polar bear fur. When the fibers are put between the glass and the dark material in a solar collector, it allows the dark material to collect more heat.

Science and Technology

163

TEACHER RESOURCE MASTERS

Feature Background

■ Polar bear fur is 95 percent efficient at converting the sun's rays to heat, according to scientists at Northeastern University in Boston. The scientists have found that polar bear fur absorbs nearly all the sun's ultraviolet rays for heat.

■ One study showed that fibers placed between the glass and the dark-colored collector increased the efficiency of the solar panels by 50 percent.

■ Solar collectors are often used to conserve energy. They collect heat from sunlight. The collected heat is then used to heat water and homes.

Feature Vocabulary

fibers
solar collector

Teaching Suggestions

■ Discuss climate conditions in the polar zone.

■ Explain that latitude is the primary factor affecting climate in the polar zone.

■ Have students locate the polar zones on a map or globe.

■ Ask students to describe solar collectors if they have seen them on roofs of houses.

■ Explain how solar collectors collect energy from the sun.

Summary

Chapter Closure: Ask students to compose questions based on the information contained in the summary statements. Divide the class into two teams. Use the questions written by the students to orally quiz the teams. The team scoring the most correct answers earns the right to be called "Weather and Climate Experts."

Science Words

Reproduce a 15 × 15 unit grid. Have students use each science word to produce a "Seek-and-Find" puzzle. Other weather words may also be used. Remind students to list each word used in the puzzle. Tell them that random letters should be used to fill in all the leftover squares. Allow students to exchange and solve each other's puzzles.

Student Responses

1. frost
2. cumulus
3. water vapor
4. clouds
5. tropics
6. precipitation
7. dew
8. atmosphere

CHAPTER REVIEW 8

Summary

Lesson 1
- Evaporation is the change of matter from a liquid to a gas.
- Air temperature and air speed affect speed of evaporation.
- Condensation is the change of matter from a gas to a liquid.

Lesson 2
- Water vapor condenses on small particles to form clouds.

- Three types of clouds are cirrus, cumulus, and stratus.
- Rain, snow, sleet, and hail are four kinds of precipitation.

Lesson 3
- The three climate zones are the polar zones, tropic zones, and temperate zones.
- Water, mountains, and large cities affect climate.

Science Words

Fill in the blank with the correct word or words from the list.

atmosphere   stratus
water vapor   precipitation
dew   climate
frost   polar zones
clouds   tropics
cirrus   temperate zones
cumulus

1. Ice that forms from water vapor is called ___ .

2. Thick, puffy clouds are called ___ .
3. ___ is water as a gas.
4. Water droplets, pieces of ice, or both form ___ .
5. Clouds that cover all the sky are called ___ .
6. Moisture that falls from the atmosphere is called ___ .
7. Drops of condensed water on grass are called ___ .
8. The air around Earth is the ___ .

164

TEACHER RESOURCE MASTERS

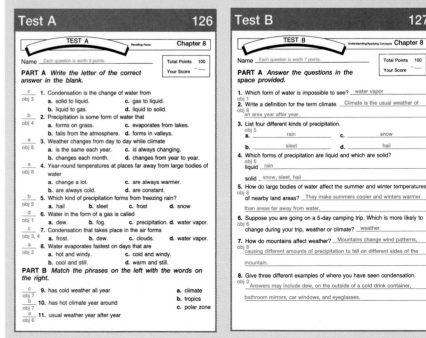

Questions

Recalling Ideas

Correctly complete each of the following sentences.

1. The change of matter from a gas to a liquid is
   (a) precipitation.
   (b) condensation.
   (c) evaporation.
   (d) water vapor.
2. Precipitation that is made of layers of ice is
   (a) rain.   (c) sleet.
   (b) snow.   (d) hail.

3. The climate zone centered over the middle of Earth is the
   (a) polar zone.
   (b) temperate zone.
   (c) tropics.
   (d) Antarctic.
4. In the atmosphere, condensation forms on
   (a) sun rays.   (c) rain drops.
   (b) clouds.   (d) dust particles.

Understanding Ideas

Answer the following questions using complete sentences.

1. How do mountains and large bodies of water affect the climate?
2. Compare the different forms of precipitation.

Thinking Critically

Think about what you have learned in this chapter. Answer the following questions using complete sentences.

1. On what kind of day will clothes dry fastest? Why?
2. How do weather changes affect our lives?

165

Questions

Recalling Ideas

1. b
2. d
3. c
4. d

Understanding Ideas

1. The amount of precipitation on either side of a mountain is different. Mountains change wind patterns. Places near large bodies of water have more even temperatures during the year and usually greater amounts of precipitation than places farther inland.
2. Rain is liquid water that falls when the air is warmer than 0°C. Snow is ice particles formed from water vapor in the air. Snow forms when the air is 0°C or colder. Sleet is frozen rain. Hail is chunks of ice made of many layers.

Thinking Critically

1. Clothes will dry fastest on warm, dry, windy days. Warm, moving air speeds evaporation.
2. Weather changes affect the comfort and safety of people. Weather changes affect how we dress, the speed with which we travel, how we travel, and so on.

TEACHER RESOURCE MASTERS

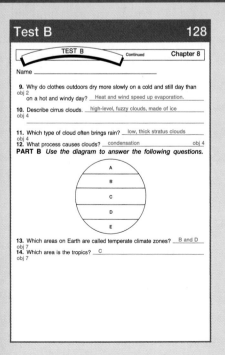

Test B   128

TEST B   *Continued*   **Chapter 8**

Name _____

9. Why do clothes outdoors dry more slowly on a cold and still day than
obj 2   on a hot and windy day? __Heat and wind speed up evaporation.__

10. Describe cirrus clouds. __high-level, fuzzy clouds, made of ice__
obj 4

11. Which type of cloud often brings rain? __low, thick stratus clouds__
obj 4
12. What process causes clouds? __condensation__   obj 4

PART B *Use the diagram to answer the following questions.*

13. Which areas on Earth are called temperate climate zones? __B and D__
obj 7
14. Which area is the tropics? __C__
obj 7

Water

Planning Guide

Lessons	Objectives	Vocabulary
Chapter Introduction pp. 166, 167		
Lesson 1 The Water Cycle pp. 168–173	1. **Identify** the importance of water in daily life. 2. **Give examples** of water at different stages in the water cycle.	water cycle
Lesson 2 Runoff and Groundwater pp. 174–179	3. **Operationally define** *runoff* and *groundwater*. 4. **Understand** the effect of gravity on runoff and groundwater.	runoff groundwater
Lesson 3 Earth's Water Storage pp. 180–185	5. **Identify** different places for water storage. 6. **Explain** the effects of pollution on the water cycle.	
Chapter Review pp. 186, 187		
Unit Review pp. 188, 189		

Planning Guide

Text Activities		Teacher Resource Masters	Other Components
Title/Skill	**Materials per Group**		
Have You Ever . . . Followed the Rain? p. 167 Predict/Operationally Define Time Allotment: 30 minutes	paper pencil		**Activity Center:** "Let Your Fingers Do the Drilling"; "The Days of the Drop"; "Down the Drain"; "Mack and Bill"; "How Can You Clean It?"
You Can . . . Compare Water Evaporation, p. 170 Separating/Controlling Variables Time Allotment: 5 minute setup/observe every two hours for six hours	2 flat, plastic dishes water pencil and paper	Independent Practice, pp. 139, 140 Activity Worksheet, pp. 131, 132 Transparency Master, p. 129 Critical Thinking, p. 135 Language Arts Connection, p. 137 ◆ Reteaching Activity, p. 141	Mr. Wizard's World of Science Video Tape 16 Color Transparency #7
What Is the Water Cycle? p. 173 Observing Time Allotment: 30 minutes	clear, plastic glass oven mitt hot water plastic dish 5 ice cubes pencil and paper		
Which Soil Soaks Up More Water? p. 179 Measuring/Observing/Inferring Time Allotment: 35 minutes	2 different kinds of soil 2 large, clear plastic jars masking tape marking pen water small paper cup stopwatch pencil and paper	Independent Practice, pp. 139, 140 Activity Worksheet, pp. 133, 134 ◆ Family Science, p. 130 ▲ Critical Thinking, p. 136	Poster #4
		Independent Practice, pp. 139, 140 Health Connection, p. 138	
		Test A, p. 142 Test B, pp. 143, 144	
			Unit Test

◆ **Basic** / ▲ **Advanced** / All other masters are for use by all students.

CHAPTER 9

Water

ESL/LEP

Chapter 9/Lesson 1, Page 168

Have students list all the ways they use water. Let them ask questions of one another about how they use water.

Help students act out the water cycle. Let some students belong to the group called **Water Vapor.** Others will belong to the group called **Water Droplets.** Assign one student to be **Evaporation** and another to be **Condensation.** Another student will be the **Announcer,** saying "The Water Cycle will begin." **Evaporation** approaches the **Water Droplet** Group and makes appropriate gestures as if warming the **Water Droplets. Evaporation** tells the **Water Droplets:** "You are evaporating." The **Water Droplets** begin to move toward the **Water Vapor** group. Each one says "I was once a **Water Droplet. Evaporation** is turning me into **Water Vapor.**" Then **Condensation** approaches the now larger **Water Vapor** group. **Condensation** blows on them, making them colder. **Condensation** says, "You are condensing!" Each one of the **Water Vapor** group goes toward the place where the **Water Droplet** group had been before, while saying, "I used to be **Water Vapor. Condensation** is making me a **Water Droplet.**" **Evaporation** then begins the cycle all over again. The drama ends with the **Announcer** saying: "The **Water Cycle** goes on and on. It never ends."

Chapter 9/Lesson 2, Page 174

Have students trace the path of runoff until it reaches the ocean. Ask them to write sentences about the water cycle.

Chapter 9/Lesson 3, Page 180

Ask students to memorize Robert Louis Stevenson's poem about the rain. Have them write their own poems about rain.

Ask students to list ways that water is polluted. Let each of them state how he or she can keep the water supply clean.

Gifted

Chapter 9/Lesson 1, Page 169

Propose this situation to your gifted students. Without warning, your entire community is without water for an entire day. Discuss the various problems people would face and ways they might solve these problems. The end product could be an original story, skit, or role play.

Mainstreamed

Chapter 9/Lesson 1, Page 172

Developmentally Handicapped: Write these words in column A: evaporation, condensation, precipitation, and storage. In column B, write these words or phrases: brings water from the air to Earth, stores water, changes water vapor to liquid, and water vapor rises into the air. Have students match the water cycle process in column A with the description in column B.

Whole Class Science Project

Students should consult encyclopedias or contact a local weather station to obtain information about different climates in the United States. They may obtain weather maps from a weather station or from the Superintendent of Documents, Washington, DC 20025. Choose well-known cities across the United States that represent different kinds of climate (arid, humid, hot, cold, and others). Compare the average rainfall, kinds of seasons, average yearly temperature, average summer and winter temperatures, and kinds of vegetation found in these locations. Devise a chart to record the information. The class could be divided into groups with each group being responsible to research one type of climate. Have groups report to the class in order to compile their information.

Science Fair Projects

Individual students could do one of the following projects:

1. Using a gram of soap in 20 cc of denatured alcohol as a test solution, and by adding about 10 drops of this to different kinds of water (rainwater, distilled water, faucet water, and others), determine the hardness of water by observing the amount of foam occurring after the addition of drops and shaking the solution.
2. Determine the relationship between the amount of stored underground water and the amount of rainfall in a certain area. Draw pictures and display findings on a poster board.
3. Research to determine the location of the major source of underground water. Draw pictures of the area explaining why this area is able to store so much water.
4. Using a number of planted seeds in small containers and giving them a different amount of water and frequency of watering, determine if plants grow better with small amounts of water often, or larger amounts less often, and the maximum amount of water seeds can receive and still flourish.

CHAPTER 9

pages 166–187

Chapter Concepts

■ Evaporation, condensation, and precipitation are all parts of the water cycle.
■ Precipitation results in groundwater and runoff.
■ There are both natural and people-made places for water storage.

Chapter Background

■ If all the water vapor present in the atmosphere could be precipitated, an average depth of only 2.5 centimeters of liquid water would result.
■ New water is constantly added to the atmosphere through evaporation, at a rate of about 5×10^{17} liters/year.
■ The average evaporation rate from oceans is nearly twice that over land.

Looking Ahead

■ Arrange a trip to a reservoir, such as a body of water, well, or water tower. Another idea may be a field trip to a facility that studies and records climate.

Look for These Symbols

—Hands-on activity
—Cooperative learning
—Overhead transparency
◆ —Basic/Reinforcement
● —Average/Enrichment
▲ —Advanced/Challenge
—Calculator Practice

SCIENCE
In Your World

166

CHAPTER 9

Water

Earth's water is always moving. You have seen it in a variety of places — running out the tap in your bathtub, whistling out of a steamy teakettle, or dripping down the windowpane on a cold morning. Wherever you see water, you see just a small part of the big picture.

Have You Ever...

Followed the Rain?

Have you ever listened to the rain against the windowpane and wondered where it came from? Think about one of the raindrops on your windowpane. Imagine all the places the raindrop has been. How did it get on the window? Where was it before? Has it always been a drop of water? Imagine where it will go when it falls from the window. Write a poem or a story about a raindrop.

167

PREPLAN

Time Allotment: 30 minutes

Objectives
1. **Predict** the ways that water moves on Earth and through the atmosphere.
2. **Operationally define** the water cycle.

Setup
■ You will need the following materials for each student or activity group:
paper   pencil

1 FOCUS

■ Lead students in a discussion about how the illustration might give us a hint about what is happening to the water.

2 TEACH

■ Ask: **In what other places have you seen water changing place or form?** Answers may include evaporation from puddles, melting ice, hail, and so on.

Have You Ever . . .
Use this activity as an introduction to the water cycle.
Have students **work cooperatively** in groups of four.
■ **Student Responses**
When the water boils in a pan, the water changes form and, in this way, moves from the pan to the air. In a waterfall, we see the water moving from a mountaintop to a lowland stream.

3 APPLY

■ Have students elaborate on the idea that Earth's water is always moving.

Close
■ Have students save their poems or stories and rewrite them at the end of the chapter, adding vocabulary and concepts they have learned.

PREPLAN

Lesson Objectives

1. Identify the importance of water in daily life.

2. Give examples of water at different stages in the water cycle.

Science Background

■ All of the water on Earth, no matter what its phase, is part of the hydrosphere. This water is in continuous movement. It moves from the oceans to the air, to the land, and back to the oceans again. The continuous movement of water is called the hydrologic cycle. Energy for the continuation of the cycle comes from the sun. It is the sun's energy that causes evaporation of water from the oceans.

■ Movement of water in the hydrologic cycle causes many changes on Earth's surface. Rivers and streams carry weathered and eroded rocks and soil to different areas where they are deposited to form new geologic formations.

Lesson Vocabulary

water cycle

Note: The activity on student page 173 may be used for guided discovery before you begin this lesson.

1   FOCUS

■ Discuss the concept of a cycle with students. Emphasize that in a cycle something happens over and over again. Have students create a list of cycles they know. Answers may include seasons of the year, days of the week, and so on.

■ Use the goals on student page 168 to establish the purpose for studying this lesson.

LESSON 1 GOALS
You will learn
● that water is important to living things.
● the four stages of the water cycle.

1. Answers may include no water for drinking or bathing.

The Water Cycle

Think of all the ways you will use water today. Will you wash your hands? Will you brush your teeth? Will you have a drink of water after recess or before you go to bed? Will you give your plants or your pets a drink, too? Chances are you will use water and not even think about it. Suppose there was no water in your home or school for one day. [1]How would your life change?

Water is Earth's most important resource. Every living thing on Earth needs water to survive. Without drinking water in some form, you would not be able to live for more than a few days. Think of all the people, plants, and animals near your home. They all need water to survive.

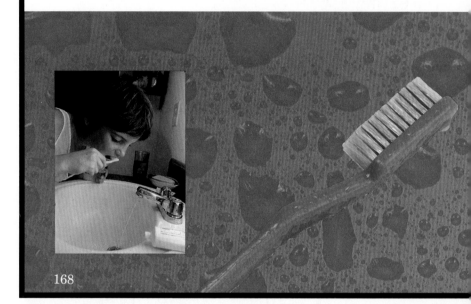

168

TEACHER RESOURCE MASTERS

You may be surprised to know that we use the same water over and over. Even though you know that water dries up after a rain, it doesn't just go away. The water just changes form. Water can be solid ice, liquid water, or a gas vapor. In Chapter 8, you learned about evaporation, condensation, and precipitation. Each of these activities is a different part of the **water cycle**. The storage of water on Earth is also part of the water cycle.

What are four stages of the water cycle?

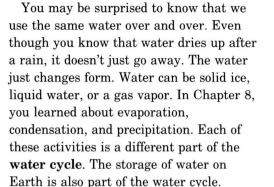

Living things need water.

169

TEACHER RESOURCE MASTERS

Independent Practice   **139**

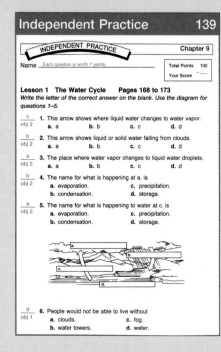

INDEPENDENT PRACTICE   Chapter 9

Name ___ Each question is worth 7 points.   Total Points   100
       Your Score ___

Lesson 1   The Water Cycle   Pages 168 to 173
Write the letter of the correct answer on the blank. Use the diagram for questions 1–5.

_c_   **1.** This arrow shows where liquid water changes to water vapor.
obj 2   **a.** a   **b.** b   **c.** c   **d.** d

_b_   **2.** This arrow shows liquid or solid water falling from clouds.
obj 2   **a.** a   **b.** b   **c.** c   **d.** d

_a_   **3.** The place where water vapor changes to liquid water droplets.
obj 2   **a.** a   **b.** b   **c.** c   **d.** d

_b_   **4.** The name for what is happening at a. is
obj 2   **a.** evaporation.   **c.** precipitation.
       b. condensation.   **d.** storage.

_a_   **5.** The name for what is happening to water at c. is
obj 2   **a.** evaporation.   **c.** precipitation.
       b. condensation.   **d.** storage.

_d_   **6.** People would not be able to live without
obj 1   **a.** clouds.   **c.** fog.
       b. water towers.   **d.** water.

2   TEACH

■ Have students list all of the places they have seen the results of condensation. (cold soft drink glasses or cans, breath on a mirror, mirrors in bathrooms, dew). Relate these to the formation of clouds.

Guided Practice
■ Check students' understanding of lesson concepts by discussing the Lesson Review questions on student page 172. If necessary, use the **reteaching strategy** in OPTIONS.

Independent Practice
■ Assign the Lesson 1 section of the Teacher Resource Master **Independent Practice,** page 139.

3   APPLY

Problem Solving: Have students **work cooperatively** in groups of four and brainstorm other events that happen in cycles. Ask student groups to make a chart to illustrate one of the cycles they name. Student suggestions may include the rock cycle, life cycle, seasons, and so on.

Close
■ Use Summary statements on student page 172 to review lesson concepts.

OPTIONS

Reteaching Strategy
Have students **work cooperatively** to find pictures that show a part of the water cycle and explain that part of the water cycle.

Resource Options
■ Show selections from "Change of State," *Mr. Wizard's World of Science Video Library,* Merrill Publishing Company.
Use Color Transparency #7, "The Water Cycle."

OPTIONS

YOU CAN . . . COMPARE WATER EVAPORATION

Process Skill: Separating and controlling variables

Objective: Identify factors that affect evaporation.

Setup/Teach:

■ Make sure students keep all other variables the same. The only difference is that one dish is placed in the sun and one in the shade.

■ Students should see that water in the sun will evaporate faster because of the higher temperature.

LANGUAGE CONNECTION

Reading: Have students work in **cooperative groups** to discuss the water cycle and to respond to the following. **What happens when water vapor cools after rising into the air?** *The water vapor condenses to liquid droplets.* **What happens next?** *The droplets join to form rain or snow.*

◆ **Reinforcement:** Only fresh water moves through the water cycle. To demonstrate that this is true, dissolve salt in a pan half filled with warm water. Choose three students to taste this salty water. Place the pan on a hot plate and heat the water until it boils. **CAUTION:** *Do not let students approach the heat source while it is working.* Place a lid over the boiling water. When water has condensed on the lid, remove it and place it upside down to cool. Choose three students to taste the water on the lid. Use a dropper to put 2 or 3 drops on each student's tongue. Ask them to compare its taste with the taste of the water in the pan.

You Can...

Compare Water Evaporation

Pour a cup of water into two identical flat dishes. Place one dish in the shade. Put the other in direct sunlight. Mark and record the water level in each dish every two hours for a total of six hours. Use the data to write a conclusion. How does direct sunlight affect the speed at which water evaporates?

Water vapor

Plants lose water vapor.

You know that a bicycle or a motorcycle moves by spinning its wheels in a circle. The water cycle is the movement of water in a big circle. Water evaporates from oceans, lakes, and streams to form water vapor. Water even evaporates from plants and animals. Heat from the sun provides the energy for this evaporation.

170

TEACHER RESOURCE MASTERS

Reteaching Activity   141

RETEACHING ACTIVITY   Chapter 9

Name _____

WHAT SPEEDS UP EVAPORATION?

Materials

2 flat dishes	facial tissue	crayon	meter stick
dropper	paper fan	watch	
water	masking tape	pencil and paper	

What to do

1. Use masking tape and a crayon. Label the dishes A and B. Place a piece of facial tissue on each dish.
2. Put five drops of water on each tissue.
3. Place the dishes at least one meter apart.
4. Use the paper fan. Make a gentle breeze over dish A. Do not fan dish B.
5. Measure and record how long it takes for the tissues in each dish to dry.

What did you learn?

1. Which tissue dried first? _The tissue in dish A dried first._

2. Why do you think this happened? _The fan moved the air above dish A and speeded up the rate of evaporation._

Using what you learned

1. Do clothes dry faster on windy or calm days? _Clothes air dry faster on a windy day (assuming humidity is similar)._

2. How does wind affect how long it takes clothes to dry? _The wind speeds up the rate of evaporation._

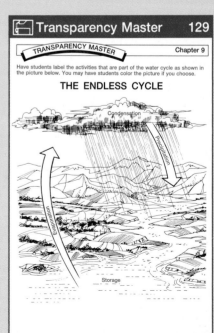

Transparency Master   129

TRANSPARENCY MASTER   Chapter 9

Have students label the activities that are part of the water cycle as shown in the picture below. You may have students color the picture if you choose.

THE ENDLESS CYCLE

Water vapor then rises into the air. It cools as it rises. Cooling causes it to condense. Condensation changes water vapor to liquid droplets. These droplets join to form rain or freeze to form snow. When the rain or snow falls, water returns to the ground. The water from precipitation flows back into the ground or into streams, lakes, and oceans. Then the cycle is ready to start again. It repeats itself over and over.

Water that gets to our homes was first water that fell to Earth. Then the water may have flowed across the ground or soaked into the ground. Finally it was stored and cleaned for our use.

What changes water vapor to liquid droplets?

OPTIONS

● **Enrichment:** Discuss how temperature affects the water cycle. Water will evaporate faster as the temperature rises. When the water vapor reaches a certain height in the air, it becomes cooler and condenses. If the air is warm enough, rain will form from the condensed water drops. If the air is cold, snow will fall. Temperature also determines how water will be stored. Cold weather means water is stored as ice or snow. Warm weather means water is stored in the liquid state.

▲ **Challenge:** Have students **work cooperatively** to make a three-dimensional model of the water cycle. Label where each stage of the water cycle is taking place.

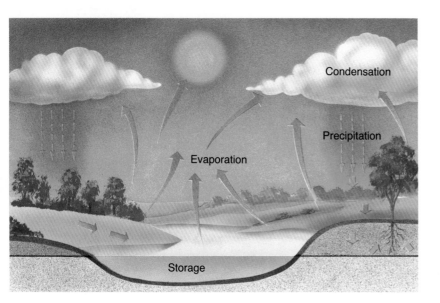

171

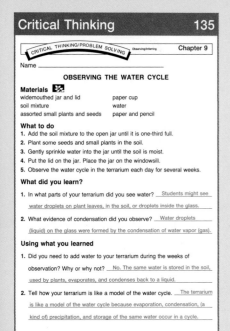

TEACHER RESOURCE MASTERS

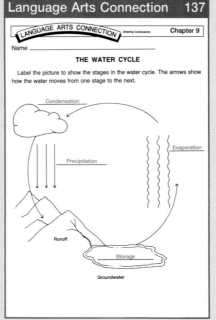

OPTIONS

■ Reproduce this drawing on the chalkboard. Ask for volunteers to print the terms *evaporation, condensation, precipitation,* and *storage* on the drawing where they fit best.

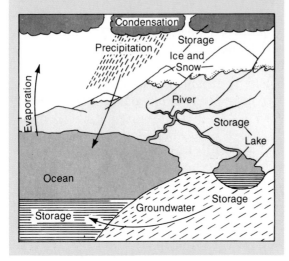

LESSON REVIEW ANSWERS

1. Every living thing needs water to survive.

2. Water evaporates and the water vapor rises into the air. Cooling condenses the water vapor, and it falls back to Earth, flows along or into the ground, and the cycle continues.

Would You Believe?

Even though rain rarely falls in the Atacama Desert in Chile, plants grow!

Lesson Summary

- All living things must have water to live.
- Evaporation, condensation, precipitation, and storage are stages of the water cycle.
- Earth's supply of water is used over and over in the water cycle.

Lesson Review

1. Why is water our most important resource?

★2. How does the water cycle work?

Energy from sun

172

TEACHER RESOURCE MASTERS

What is the water cycle?

What you need

clear plastic glass
oven mitt
hot water
plastic dish
5 ice cubes
pencil and paper

What to do

1. Hold the glass with the oven mitt. Fill the glass two-thirds full of hot water.
2. Tilt the glass to wet the sides to the top.
3. Put some ice in a dish.
4. Set the dish on top of the glass.
5. Observe what happens.

What did you learn?

1. What happened in the glass?
2. Where did evaporation take place?
3. Where did condensation take place?

Using what you learned

1. How does this activity show what happens to some lake water?
2. How does the activity show how clouds form?
3. What process is needed to make this activity a complete water cycle?

173

ACTIVITY RESPONSES

What did you learn?

1. Water collected on the insides of the glass and under the dish filled with ice. Some of the water dripped back into the hot water in the glass.
2. Some of the hot water in the glass evaporated.
3. The water drops on the inside of the glass and on the bottom of the dish were condensation.

Using what you learned

1. Some lake water evaporates. Later, the water will condense into a cloud and then fall back to Earth as some form of precipitation.
2. Water drops formed on the bottom of the dish. The water vapor condensed because the dish was cool. Water vapor in the air also condenses and forms clouds.
3. Precipitation is needed to complete the water cycle.

PREPLAN

Time Allotment: 30 minutes
Process Skill: Observing

Objectives

1. **Identify** the processes that are part of the water cycle.
2. **Compare** the results of this activity with all the changes in the water cycle.

Setup

■ Boil the water prior to starting the activity. Let it cool a few minutes before giving it to students.

Cooperative Grouping: fives—Assign roles as explained on page T24.

1 FOCUS

Review the definitions of the terms *evaporation*, *precipitation*, and *condensation*.

2 TEACH

■ **Safety Consideration:** Caution students to use care when handling and pouring the hot water.
■ Have students use the Teacher Resource Master **Activity Worksheet,** pages 131 and 132, to record their data and answers.

3 APPLY

■ Compare the model water cycle in this activity to a terrarium. Have students point out where the following processes are taking place in the terrarium: evaporation, condensation, precipitation, runoff, groundwater, storage (as groundwater).

Close

■ Discuss the activity and questions with the class.

pages 174–179

PREPLAN

Lesson Objectives
3. Operationally define *runoff* and *groundwater*.
4. Understand the effect of gravity on runoff and groundwater.

Science Background
- Water used in communities is taken from rivers, lakes, and soil or rock. This water comes from precipitation.
- Water can only soak into soil or rock that is permeable. Permeability is the ability of a substance to allow water to flow through it. Permeable soil or rock has a large number of connected pore spaces. Some rock material is not very permeable, even though it has many connected pore spaces. If the spaces are very tiny, it is difficult for the water to move through them.
- Water stored in a saturated layer of permeable rock is called groundwater. The top of this saturated zone of groundwater is called the water table.

Lesson Vocabulary
runoff   groundwater

Note: The activity on student page 179 may be used for guided discovery before you begin this lesson.

1 FOCUS

- Ask: **Where does water go after a rain?** List the ideas on the board or overhead and discuss them. Students should recall from Chapter 8 that condensation and evaporation help circulate water from Earth to the atmosphere.
- Use the goals on student page 174 to establish the purpose for studying this lesson.

Runoff and Groundwater

> **LESSON 2 GOALS**
> You will learn
> ● that water moves across and through the ground.
> ● that gravity causes water to move downward.

Much of the water from rain and melted snow soaks into the ground. Some water flows across the ground instead of soaking in. Water that flows across the ground is called **runoff**. The water running down your street or road after a heavy storm is runoff.

Gravity causes runoff to flow downhill. It flows into small ponds or streams. The streams flow into rivers. Rivers become bigger as more streams flow into them. Finally the rivers flow into oceans. All water on Earth flows toward the ocean.

Where does runoff finally collect?

Runoff

174

TEACHER RESOURCE MASTERS

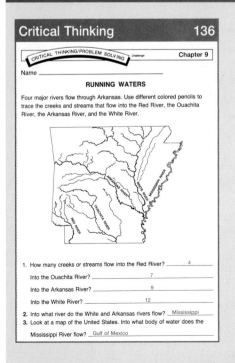

Critical Thinking   136

CRITICAL THINKING/PROBLEM SOLVING   Challenge   Chapter 9

Name _____

RUNNING WATERS

Four major rivers flow through Arkansas. Use different colored pencils to trace the creeks and streams that flow into the Red River, the Ouachita River, the Arkansas River, and the White River.

1. How many creeks or streams flow into the Red River? _____ 4
   Into the Ouachita River? _____ 7
   Into the Arkansas River? _____ 9
   Into the White River? _____ 12
2. Into what river do the White and Arkansas rivers flow? _Mississippi_
3. Look at a map of the United States. Into what body of water does the Mississippi River flow? _Gulf of Mexico_

Melting snow and precipitation cause runoff. A long, heavy rain can cause a lot of runoff. Melting snow increases runoff. When all this runoff fills streams and rivers, it flows over the banks, flooding the land. Floodwater can carry away soil, trees, and even houses.

Floods cause damage.

Runoff from rain

175

TEACHER RESOURCE MASTERS

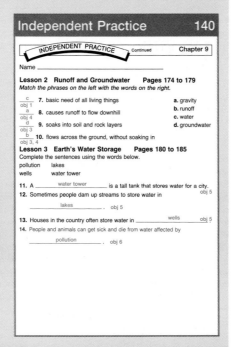

Independent Practice 140

INDEPENDENT PRACTICE Continued   Chapter 9

Name _____

Lesson 2 Runoff and Groundwater   Pages 174 to 179
Match the phrases on the left with the words on the right.

__c__ **7.** basic need of all living things
obj 1
__a__ **8.** causes runoff to flow downhill
obj 4
__d__ **9.** soaks into soil and rock layers
obj 3
__b__ **10.** flows across the ground, without soaking in
obj 3, 4

a. gravity
b. runoff
c. water
d. groundwater

Lesson 3 Earth's Water Storage   Pages 180 to 185
Complete the sentences using the words below.

pollution   lakes
wells   water tower

11. A _____water tower_____ is a tall tank that stores water for a city. obj 5

12. Sometimes people dam up streams to store water in _____lakes_____. obj 5

13. Houses in the country often store water in _____wells_____ obj 5

14. People and animals can get sick and die from water affected by _____pollution_____. obj 6

2 TEACH

Ask students for examples of where they have seen water running over sidewalks, driveways, or street gutters. Have them **work cooperatively** to identify the source of water for each example and trace where this water goes.

- Discuss what causes floods.

Guided Practice

- Check students' understanding of lesson concepts by discussing the Lesson Review questions on student page 178. If necessary, use the **reteaching strategy** in OPTIONS.

Independent Practice

- Assign the Lesson 2 section of the Teacher Resource Master **Independent Practice,** page 140.

3 APPLY

- Tie information about your local reservoir and water treatment plant to health hazards associated with untreated drinking water and sewage.

Close

- Use Summary statements on student page 178 to review lesson concepts.

OPTIONS

Reteaching Strategy

Ask: **How does water soak into rocks?** Find and record the mass of a piece of concrete. Place the concrete in a container of water for several minutes. Remove the concrete and re-mass it. Repeat the procedure for a piece of shale. Ask why the concrete has more mass wet than dry. Have students calculate the mass of water that soaked into the concrete. Explain that shale is an impermeable rock.

Resource Options

- Use Poster #4, "Island in a Sea of Floodwater."

Chapter 9   175

OPTIONS

MATH CONNECTION

Have students work individually or in **cooperative groups** to solve the following problem.

Rosa, her two brothers, and her three sisters took showers before school. Rosa read the meter later to find they had used 54 gallons of water. About how many gallons did each person use? (9 gallons)

♦ **Reinforcement:** To demonstrate how plant life affects runoff, fill two fruit baskets with soil. Wrap sack cloth around the sides and bottoms. Plant fast-growing seeds, such as rye grass, in one of the baskets. Leave the other basket bare of plants. Put the baskets in the sun. Water when necessary. When the plants are 5 to 7 cm tall, place both baskets in separate pans. Prop one end of each basket up 3 cm. Hold a sprinkling can about 15 cm away from the plants and water as fast as the water will flow. Save the runoff in a jar. Repeat this with the same amount of water and the second basket. Allow the runoff in both jars to settle. Ask the students which box had the most runoff and to explain why. Allow students to examine the plants' roots. Ask how they think runoff can be controlled.

Groundwater

If you dig a hole in the ground, you will find that deep down the soil is wet. This is because much of the precipitation does not become runoff. **Groundwater** is the water that soaks into the ground.

Gravity causes groundwater to move slowly down into the soil and rock. Water can soak into rock layers deep under the soil. Some groundwater is trapped in spaces in rocks. But most of it moves until it reaches places where it can flow back onto Earth's surface. Lakes, rivers, springs, and swamps are places where water flows back onto Earth's surface. There it may evaporate back into the air or flow toward the ocean.

At what places does groundwater reach the surface?

Lake

Flow of groundwater

176

TEACHER RESOURCE MASTERS

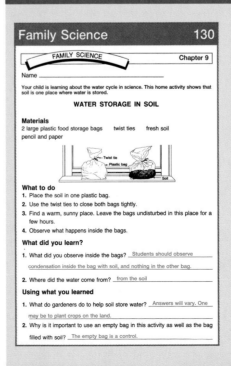

Family Science   130

FAMILY SCIENCE   Chapter 9

Name _____

Your child is learning about the water cycle in science. This home activity shows that soil is one place where water is stored.

WATER STORAGE IN SOIL

Materials
2 large plastic food storage bags   twist ties   fresh soil
pencil and paper

What to do
1. Place the soil in one plastic bag.
2. Use the twist ties to close both bags tightly.
3. Find a warm, sunny place. Leave the bags undisturbed in this place for a few hours.
4. Observe what happens inside the bags.

What did you learn?
1. What did you observe inside the bags? _Students should observe_ _condensation inside the bag with soil, and nothing in the other bag._

2. Where did the water come from? _from the soil_

Using what you learned
1. What do gardeners do to help soil store water? _Answers will vary. One_ _may be to plant crops on the land._

2. Why is it important to use an empty bag in this activity as well as the bag filled with soil? _The empty bag is a control._

Most of us don't think about water very much. We add ice to our drinks. We water the grass. We wash our dishes. And we go swimming without thinking about the water cycle. But if you had a chance to ride the water cycle, you would see things differently. The water cycle would take you on a journey around the world.

Enjoying water

177

OPTIONS

● **Enrichment:** Floodwaters are generally destructive; however, the flooding of the Nile River is considered beneficial. Some students may want to **work cooperatively** to research how the yearly flooding of the Nile produces a fertile area in the middle of a desert.

▲ **Challenge:** Have students **work cooperatively** to calculate the number of liters of water used per day by one person. Include the following water uses.

   drinking liquids—6 glasses/day
   brushing teeth—2 times/day
   washing hands and face—estimate
     number of times
   bathing—1/day
   flushing toilet—4/day
   dishwashing—1 or 2 times/day
   other
The national average is about 328 liters/person/day for all domestic use— including washing clothes and cars, watering lawns, and so on.

TEACHER RESOURCE MASTERS

OPTIONS

■ Discuss the impact of improved sewage treatment plants on improved public health. Ask a school nurse to discuss diseases and illnesses that used to be more common and still are common in some countries.

LESSON REVIEW ANSWERS

1. Gravity causes water to flow downward, either downhill or into the ground.
2. A great amount of precipitation causes a lot of runoff, which can overflow streams and rivers and flood the land.

Water flows downward

Lesson Summary

- Runoff is water that flows across the ground.
- Gravity causes runoff to flow downhill.
- Groundwater is water that moves through the ground.

Lesson Review

1. How does gravity affect runoff and groundwater?
★2. How does runoff cause floods?

178

TEACHER RESOURCE MASTERS

Dams hold back water.

Water for people in big cities is often stored in big lakes near the cities. Sometimes people have created these lakes by damming up water from streams or springs. Other times cities are built around lakes or other water sources.

Some ponds, streams, and rivers also store water. Water is often filtered and then pumped through large pipes to tanks in towns and cities. Near your home, you may have noticed a tall tower with a big tank on the top of it. Sometimes the town or city name is written on the tower. These tall tanks are called water towers. Some big buildings have water towers on their roofs. Gravity helps move the water from the tower when it is needed.

181

TEACHER RESOURCE MASTERS

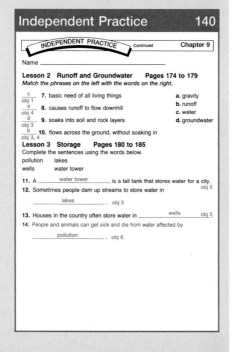

Independent Practice   140

INDEPENDENT PRACTICE Continued   Chapter 9

Name _____

Lesson 2 Runoff and Groundwater   Pages 174 to 179
Match the phrases on the left with the words on the right.

___c___ **7.** basic need of all living things   **a.** gravity
obj 1
___a___ **8.** causes runoff to flow downhill   **b.** runoff
obj 4
___d___ **9.** soaks into soil and rock layers   **c.** water
obj 3
___b___ **10.** flows across the ground, without soaking in   **d.** groundwater
obj 3, 4
Lesson 3 Storage   Pages 180 to 185
Complete the sentences using the words below.
pollution   lakes
wells   water tower

11. A ___water tower___ is a tall tank that stores water for a city.
                                      obj 5
12. Sometimes people dam up streams to store water in

___lakes___ . obj 5

13. Houses in the country often store water in ___wells___ obj 5
14. People and animals can get sick and die from water affected by

___pollution___ . obj 6

2   TEACH

■ Display a road map that shows your town and nearby water bodies. Have students take turns pointing to examples of nearby lakes, ponds, streams, and rivers. Display three clear glasses of water on a table or desk. Mix a few drops of dark-colored oil with the water in one glass, and a spoonful of soil with the water in a second glass. Have the class vote which glass of water would be best to drink.

Guided Practice
■ Check students' understanding of lesson concepts by discussing the Lesson Review questions on student page 184. If necessary, use the **reteaching strategy** in OPTIONS.

Independent Practice
■ Assign the Lesson 3 section of the Teacher Resource Master **Independent Practice,** page 140.

3   APPLY

■ Have students draw a simple map of your area showing places where water is stored. Help students label all water bodies properly. Display the map on a bulletin board.

Close
■ Use Summary statements on student page 184 to review lesson concepts.

OPTIONS

Reteaching Strategy
■ Display a globe and ask students to point to and name different places where water is stored on Earth. Have students locate your city or state on the globe and trace the closest river system. Ask students to explain why pollution of a lake or a river is harmful to an ocean. (Polluting a lake or a river will pollute the water in which it drains or merges. All river systems eventually empty into an ocean.)

OPTIONS

LANGUAGE CONNECTION

■ **Writing:** Have students rewrite the following passage. Instruct them to make complete sentences, to break up run-on sentences, and to use correct punctuation. (Answers appear in parentheses.)

■ Precipitation falls? (delete ?) As (as) rain or snow. It becomes runoff (.) gravity (Gravity) causes runoff to flow downhill into rivers. Where do rivers flow. (?)

◆ **Reinforcement:** Display a diagram of the water cycle. Guide students to review and trace the four steps of the cycle in order: precipitation, evaporation, condensation, and storage. Then have students add black stickers to represent acid precipitation falling to Earth and oil and sewage flowing into clean water bodies. Ask students to name the step in the water cycle affected by each kind of water pollution. (precipitation; storage) Then ask students to tell how water pollution harms the living things in the diagram.

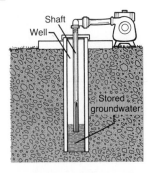

You know that groundwater is often trapped between layers of rock or in holes in rocks. Wells are drilled to get to the stored water. Pumps pull the water to the surface. Many farms and houses in the country get their water from wells.

Water Pollution

Because we use Earth's supply of water over and over, we must store and use it wisely. Each one of the four steps of the water cycle is important: precipitation, evaporation, condensation, and storage. Problems for living things happen when pollution of any of these stages takes place.

Water pollution

182

TEACHER RESOURCE MASTERS

For example, water vapor may condense on particles found in some smoke. Then the droplets join and fall to Earth as precipitation. These particles mix with water on Earth through runoff or groundwater. This water can make you and other animals and plants sick or die.

Pollution of lakes, rivers, streams, and other water sources is also a problem for living things. When substances such as oil or sewage get into these sources, the supply of clean water is affected. When any water is polluted, the amount of clean water decreases. The normal supply of clean water cannot be replaced without the pollution first causing harm to living things. The polluted water must be cleaned thoroughly before it can be used again.

SCIENCE AND . . .
Writing

Your scout troop is studying harmful rain caused by smoke from factories in the next state. Your job is to make a speech to a scout troop in that state. Write your speech to explain how smoke from their state produces rain that is harming your state.

Air pollution kills plants.

183

OPTIONS

SCIENCE AND . . . WRITING

■ **Skill:** Delete superfluous information to address the purpose and audience more effectively.

■ **Student Response:** Answers may vary.

Language Arts Skill: Use "I WANT TO KNOW ABOUT . . . Summarizing the Main Idea," student page 185, with this lesson.

● **Enrichment:** Discuss with students how temperature affects water storage. Cold weather means water is stored as ice or snow. Warm weather means water is stored in its liquid state. Display a globe and have students predict in which form water is stored in different climate regions.

▲ **Challenge:** Help students find the location of a nearby water reservoir, water treatment plant, and water tower on a local road map. Then encourage students to draw their own maps showing the route that water takes through pipes from the reservoir to their home while it is cleaned. Ask students to use their maps to explain to a friend or family member the path water takes to their home.

LESSON REVIEW ANSWERS

1. in big lakes near the city

2. from smoke in the air, from sewage, and from oil

2. Answers may include that there would not be a normal supply of clean water, some people and animals could get sick, people would spend a lot of time and money cleaning the water.

Why is Earth's water so important?

Because there is so much water on Earth, a lot of people think there will always be enough clean water for everyone. Now you know that our water supply is limited. It is important that our water remain clean for our use today and tomorrow. Your help in making sure this happens is important.

Lesson Summary

- Lakes, wells, and water towers are examples of places where water is stored.
- Water in any stage of the cycle must remain unpolluted.

Lesson Review

1. Where do people in large cities often store their water?
2. How does water get polluted?
★3. What would happen if your water supply became polluted?

184

TEACHER RESOURCE MASTERS

Health Connection   138

HEALTH CONNECTION   Personal Health   Chapter 9

Name _____

WATER AND YOUR HEALTH

Most people never think about how important water is to their lives. For one entire day, keep track of all the water that you use. In the chart, record each activity that uses water. Also record the number of times you do each activity.

1. How many times did you drink a glass of water? _Answers will vary._

2. What activity do you think used the most water? _Students may suggest_ bathing or flushing toilets.

3. How would your life be different if you could use only 4 liters of water each day? _Answers will vary. Students should note that many of their_ daily activities would change.

I WANT TO KNOW ABOUT...

Summarizing the Main Idea

When you write a story, you may use a lot of details to explain what you want to say. But you probably have one main idea in your writing. This is the idea you want your reader to remember. For example, you may tell about a pet you have. But your main idea is that your pet is lovable.

Sometimes writers put the main idea in one sentence. Other times the reader needs to figure out the main idea.

Read the following paragraph. Discuss with your classmates what you think the main idea is.

Drinking water often comes from lakes or rivers. Large pipes carry the water to a water treatment plant. The water is sent through tubes of sand and charcoal to remove the dirt. Chemicals are added to kill germs. The water is then piped to a new, clean storage area. When you need it, clean water is ready.

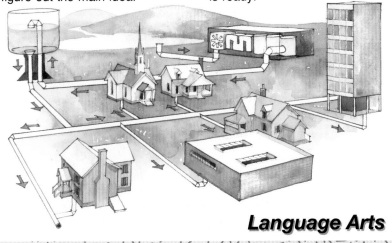

Language Arts

185

Feature Background
■ Finding the main idea is an important skill that students will use in studying all subjects.

Teaching Suggestions
■ After students successfully find the main idea in this paragraph, have them practice using other paragraphs from this lesson.

TEACHER RESOURCE MASTERS

Summary

🏠 **Chapter Closure:** Have students choose one of the summary statements. In **cooperative groups,** they should write three more sentences that explain, prove, or are examples of the statement chosen. Allow students to share and discuss the paragraphs they have written. Summary statements that were not chosen may be developed by the whole class to review the material they contain.

Science Words

Have students use all the science words in drawings to demonstrate their understanding of the meanings.

Student Responses

1. groundwater
2. runoff
3. water cycle

CHAPTER REVIEW

9

Summary

Lesson 1
- Living things need water.
- There are four stages of the water cycle.

Lesson 2
- Water runs across the ground and soaks into the ground.

- Gravity moves water downhill.

Lesson 3
- Water is stored in lakes, ponds, streams, and between layers of rock.
- Polluted water hurts living things.

Science Words

Fill in the blank with the correct word or words from the list.

water cycle   **runoff**
groundwater

1. Water that soaks into the ground is ___.
2. Water that flows across the ground is ___.
3. Evaporation, condensation, precipitation, and storage are parts of the ___.

186

TEACHER RESOURCE MASTERS

Test A   142

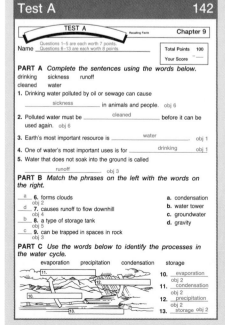

TEST A   Recalling Facts   Chapter 9

Questions 1–5 are each worth 7 points.
Name   Questions 6–13 are each worth 8 points.

Total Points 100
Your Score

PART A *Complete the sentences using the words below.*

drinking   sickness   runoff
cleaned   water

1. Drinking water polluted by oil or sewage can cause

    sickness   in animals and people. obj 6

2. Polluted water must be ___ cleaned ___ before it can be used again. obj 6

3. Earth's most important resource is ___ water ___ . obj 1

4. One of water's most important uses is for ___ drinking ___ obj 1

5. Water that does not soak into the ground is called
    runoff   obj 3

PART B *Match the phrases on the left with the words on the right.*

a 6. forms clouds
   obj 2
d 7. causes runoff to flow downhill
   obj 4
b 8. a type of storage tank
   obj 5
c 9. can be trapped in spaces in rock
   obj 3

   a. condensation
   b. water tower
   c. groundwater
   d. gravity

PART C *Use the words below to identify the processes in the water cycle.*

evaporation   precipitation   condensation   storage

10. ___ evaporation ___
    obj 2
11. ___ condensation ___
    obj 2
12. ___ precipitation ___
    obj 2
13. ___ storage obj 2

Test B   143

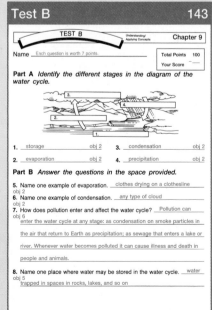

TEST B   Understanding/Applying Concepts   Chapter 9

Name   Each question is worth 7 points.

Total Points 100
Your Score

Part A *Identify the different stages in the diagram of the water cycle.*

1. ___ storage ___ obj 2
2. ___ evaporation ___ obj 2
3. ___ condensation ___ obj 2
4. ___ precipitation ___ obj 2

Part B *Answer the questions in the space provided.*

5. Name one example of evaporation. ___ clothes drying on a clothesline ___
obj 2
6. Name one example of condensation. ___ any type of cloud ___
obj 2
7. How does pollution enter and affect the water cycle? ___ Pollution can ___
obj 6
   enter the water cycle at any stage: as condensation on smoke particles in
   the air that return to Earth as precipitation; as sewage that enters a lake or
   river. Whenever water becomes polluted it can cause illness and death in
   people and animals.

8. Name one place where water may be stored in the water cycle. ___ water ___
obj 5
   trapped in spaces in rocks, lakes, and so on

Questions

Recalling Ideas

Correctly complete each of the following sentences.

1. Water first returns to the ground as
   (a) evaporation.
   (b) gravity.
   (c) storage.
   (d) precipitation.
2. Liquid water becomes water vapor through
   (a) precipitation.
   (b) evaporation.
   (c) storage.
   (d) condensation.
3. Water vapor changes to liquid droplets through
   (a) evaporation.
   (b) condensation.
   (c) precipitation.
   (d) storage.
4. Lakes, wells, and water towers are kinds of
   (a) water storage.
   (b) runoff.
   (c) groundwater.
   (d) tanks.
5. Water in wells comes from
   (a) gravity.   (c) groundwater.
   (b) tanks.   (d) rivers.

Understanding Ideas

Answer the following questions using complete sentences.

1. Describe the flow of runoff as it is affected by gravity.
2. Describe the possible movement(s) of water that soaks into the ground as groundwater.
3. How are plants and animals part of the water cycle?
4. How does pollution affect the water cycle?

Thinking Critically

Think about what you have learned in this chapter. Answer the following questions using complete sentences.

1. How is water important to you?
2. Draw a picture to show the water cycle. Label each stage of the water cycle.

187

Questions

Recalling Ideas

1. d
2. b
3. b
4. a
5. c

Understanding Ideas

1. Gravity causes runoff to flow downhill. It flows into small streams or ponds. These streams flow into larger bodies of water such as rivers. Finally, rivers flow into oceans.
2. Sometimes, groundwater is trapped in spaces in the rocks. Most of the time, however, the water continues moving through the soil and rock layers. When it reaches places where it can flow back onto Earth's surface, it may evaporate into the air.
3. Both plants and animals add water vapor to the air.
4. Pollutants such as oil or sewage may enter reservoirs. The supply of clean water is then affected. Pollutants also may enter the water cycle in the atmosphere when precipitation forms.

Thinking Critically

1. Answers will vary. Answers may include its importance in providing fluid for body cells, or in personal hygiene.
2. Ask students to label each stage of the water cycle using science words and the terms *evaporation, condensation, precipitation,* and *storage.*

TEACHER RESOURCE MASTERS

Test B   144

> **TEST B** *Continued* **Chapter 9**
>
> Name _____
>
> **9.** What are two things that can cause increased runoff and floods?
> obj 3
>   heavy rains
>   snow melting in spring
>
> **10.** How does gravity affect runoff? Groundwater? Gravity causes runoff to
> obj 4
>   flow downhill and into ponds and streams. Gravity causes groundwater to
>   soak slowly into rock layers under the soil.
>
> **11.** What is the water cycle? The water cycle is all of Earth's water
> obj 2
>   changing from solid to liquid to gas and back again. The cycle never
>   ends.
>
> **12.** Why is water so important in our daily lives? All living things need
> obj 1
>   water to live. We need it to drink, for cooking, to bathe, and so on.
>
> **13.** What is groundwater? water that soaks into soil and rock layers
> obj 3
> **14.** Where does well water come from? groundwater held in rock layers
> obj 5

pages 188, 189

Checking for Understanding

1. Glaciers carry rocks that scratch the surfaces of other rocks as the glaciers move. This changes the surfaces of these rocks and also wears down the rocks carried by the glaciers.

2. Metamorphic rock is formed when rocks are exposed to heat and pressure.

3. Igneous rocks formed from lava have small minerals, and those formed from slowly cooled magma have larger minerals.

4. Water can change rocks by smoothing them, by breaking them (as when water freezes), or by dissolving the minerals that make up rocks.

5. Water evaporates to form water vapor that rises into the air. As it rises, it cools and condenses. The water vapor becomes droplets that form rain and return to the ground. Part of the water becomes groundwater and soaks into the ground. Part becomes runoff that flows into bodies of water. The cycle then repeats itself over and over.

6. Land near large bodies of water tends to have more constant temperatures than land that is inland. Mountains change wind patterns that change climate. Large cities are usually warmer than areas of open country because concrete absorbs and retains energy from the sun for a longer period of time. A city's buildings also change wind patterns.

7. Runoff is water that flows across the ground. Groundwater is water that soaks into the ground.

8. Clouds are formed from millions of water droplets, or very small pieces of ice, or both water droplets and ice.

9. Erosion is the movement of soil and rocks to new places. Weathering is the breaking down or wearing away of rocks.

10. Dew and frost are two forms of condensation.

11. Answers will vary but may include rock layers holding groundwater, wells, ponds, or lakes.

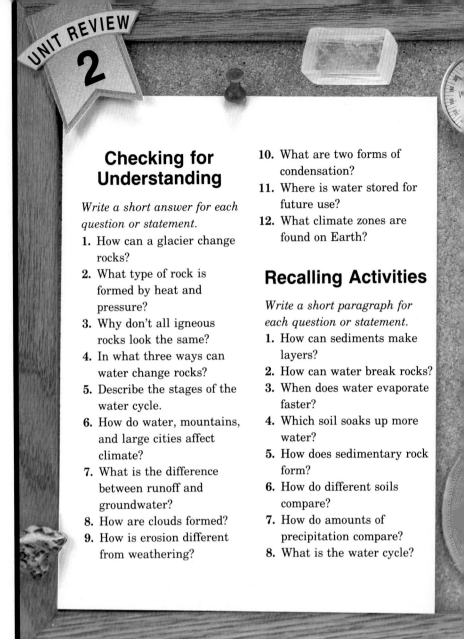

UNIT REVIEW 2

Checking for Understanding

Write a short answer for each question or statement.

1. How can a glacier change rocks?
2. What type of rock is formed by heat and pressure?
3. Why don't all igneous rocks look the same?
4. In what three ways can water change rocks?
5. Describe the stages of the water cycle.
6. How do water, mountains, and large cities affect climate?
7. What is the difference between runoff and groundwater?
8. How are clouds formed?
9. How is erosion different from weathering?
10. What are two forms of condensation?
11. Where is water stored for future use?
12. What climate zones are found on Earth?

Recalling Activities

Write a short paragraph for each question or statement.

1. How can sediments make layers?
2. How can water break rocks?
3. When does water evaporate faster?
4. Which soil soaks up more water?
5. How does sedimentary rock form?
6. How do different soils compare?
7. How do amounts of precipitation compare?
8. What is the water cycle?

TEACHER RESOURCE MASTERS

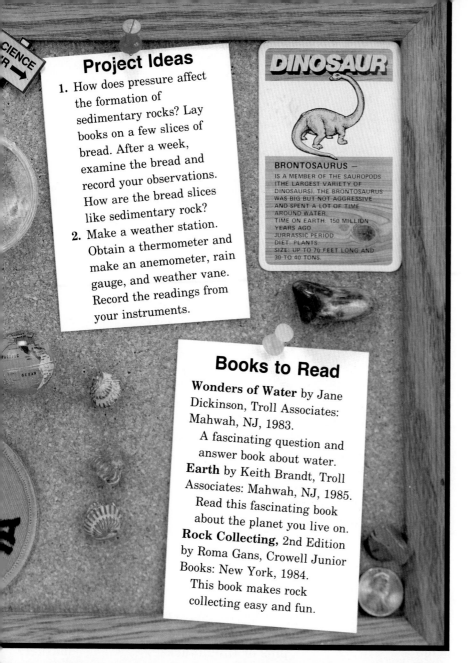

Project Ideas

1. How does pressure affect the formation of sedimentary rocks? Lay books on a few slices of bread. After a week, examine the bread and record your observations. How are the bread slices like sedimentary rock?

2. Make a weather station. Obtain a thermometer and make an anemometer, rain gauge, and weather vane. Record the readings from your instruments.

DINOSAUR

BRONTOSAURUS —
IS A MEMBER OF THE SAUROPODS (THE LARGEST VARIETY OF DINOSAURS). THE BRONTOSAURUS WAS BIG BUT NOT AGGRESSIVE AND SPENT A LOT OF TIME AROUND WATER.
TIME ON EARTH: 150 MILLION YEARS AGO.
JURRASSIC PERIOD.
DIET: PLANTS.
SIZE: UP TO 70 FEET LONG AND 30 TO 40 TONS.

Books to Read

Wonders of Water by Jane Dickinson, Troll Associates: Mahwah, NJ, 1983.
A fascinating question and answer book about water.
Earth by Keith Brandt, Troll Associates: Mahwah, NJ, 1985.
Read this fascinating book about the planet you live on.
Rock Collecting, 2nd Edition by Roma Gans, Crowell Junior Books: New York, 1984.
This book makes rock collecting easy and fun.

TEACHER RESOURCE MASTERS

12. Climate zones in the world are the polar zones, tropics and temperate zones.

Recalling Activities

1. Sediments make layers when they settle out of water. Larger particles settle out and form layers first. Smaller particles settle out later and form layers on top of the larger particles.

2. Water expands when it freezes. Water that gets into cracks in a rock and freezes pushes the rock apart.

3. Water evaporates faster when a larger surface area is directly exposed to air. Water in an unfolded paper towel evaporates faster than water in a folded paper towel.

4. Soil that has the most space between its particles will soak up the most water.

5. Sedimentary rock forms when sediments are pressed together. A cementing solution can harden the sediments, turning them into sedimentary rock.

6. Soils vary in color and feel. Dark soils rich in decayed plants and animals are good for growing plants.

7. Different geographic locations receive different amounts of precipitation. Precipitation graphs can be used to compare precipitation.

8. The water cycle is the process in which water is used over and over again through evaporation, condensation, precipitation, and storage.

Project Ideas

Have students work individually or in **cooperative groups** to complete one of the projects listed.

Books to Read

♦ *Earth*
● *Rock Collecting*
▲ *Wonders of Water*

Life Science

Classroom Centers

Bulletin Board

Goals: This bulletin board will illustrate the relationships between producers and consumers, between predators and prey, and among decomposers, scavengers, and the rest of a community. Students will learn the importance of the sun as a source of energy for life within a community, such as can be found in a forest.

Materials: colored construction paper   scissors
markers   crayons
pins or thumbtacks   paste

Procedure: Cut out the outline of the forest trees from green and brown construction paper. On white paper, draw outlines of various predator and prey animals. Have students **work cooperatively** in groups to color these. Draw a fallen log and have students cut out decomposers and scavengers from colored construction paper to paste onto the log. Ask other students to cut strips of green paper and paste them to the forest floor as woodland plants. Some students may cut out a shrub, red berries for the shrub, or a circle for the sun. Provide students with the labels *predator, prey, producer, consumer, scavenger,* and *decomposer.* Explain that these are consumers.

Science Center

Goals: Students will match a variety of animals with their appropriate shelters.

Materials: colored construction paper   scissors
pins or thumbtacks   markers
3 × 5 cards   crayons
plain paper   paste
reference books

Procedure: Arrange the materials in the science center as suggested. Choose reference books that show animals in their habitats and in their particular homes. Have students: (1) fold a sheet of plain paper lengthwise, (2) write the label *animal* at the top of one column, (3) write the label *shelter* at the top of the second column, (4) write the letters A to J down the left side of the animal column, (5) look at each animal on the board and match it with a shelter by writing the number of the shelter in the right column next to the letter of the animal in the left column.

Provide other pictures of animals and shelters on 3 × 5 cards with a number or letter on the back as shown in the picture. Students may wish to add to these to test their classmates.

Places to Go, People to See

Field Trip Ideas

Visit a zoo to observe a variety of animals in different habitats. You may also arrange a trip to a nature preserve or state park where animals and plants are seen in natural habitats.

Speakers and Visitors

Contact a zoologist or ecologist from the local zoo or from the local division of wildlife.

Invite a conservation officer from the Department of Natural Resources to discuss how people are changing animal habitats in your area.

Audiovisuals for the Students

Films and Filmstrips

Animals That Build, 16 mm, 15 min., color, National Geographic Society.

Forest in the Clouds, 16 mm, 20 min., color, National Geographic Society.

Videotapes

Animals That Build, VHS and Beta, 15 min., color, National Geographic Society.

Computer Software

Outdoor Biology   Two programs include simulations of a food chain in a lake, the feeding conditions of various forest animals, predator/prey relationships, and ecological systems.
Type: Simulations, Tutorial
Hardware: Commodore 64, TRS-80 Color
Supplier: MECC

Life Science Series: Green Plants   Students learn parts of green plants; food chains and pyramids; flowers and reproduction; and plants from parts.
Type: Tutorial
Hardware: Apple II+, IIe, IIc
Supplier: Educational Activities, Inc.

Resources for the Teacher

Materials at Little/No Cost

National Wildlife Federation
School Programs
1400 16th St., NW
Washington, DC 20036

TAMU-SG-81-504
The Marine Information Service
Sea Grant College Program
Texas A&M University
College Station, TX 77843-4115

Write for the free pamphlet *How to Set Up and Maintain a Saltwater Aquarium*

Resource Books for Teachers

Durrell, Gerald with Lee Durrell. *The Amateur Naturalist.* New York: Alfred A. Knopf, Inc., 1983.

Forsyth, Adrian and Kenneth Miyata. *Tropical Nature.* New York: Charles Scribner Sons, 1984.

Headstrom, Richard. *Suburban Wildlife: An Introduction to the Common Animals of Your Backyard and Local Park.* Englewood Cliffs, NJ: Prentice-Hall, 1984.

Mochi, Ugo and Dorcas MacClintock. *African Images.* New York: Charles Scribner Sons, 1984.

Peters, Roger. *Dance of the Wolves.* New York: McGraw-Hill, 1985.

UNIT 3

Life Science

UNIT CONCEPTS

Chapter 10

■ All living things need food, water, and air to live. Plants are the first link in the food chain and are producers of food.

■ Consumers are those living things that cannot produce their own food.

■ Scavengers feed on and remove dead organisms. Scavengers are important because they reduce the amount of organic litter. Decomposers break down dead organisms and return nutrients to the soil.

■ The producers and consumers living together in one area make up a community. A producer uses energy from the sun to grow, and this energy is passed on through the food chain.

■ A food web is composed of all the food chains in a community.

Chapter 11

■ Each living thing is adapted to its own particular habitat.

■ Plants and animals whose needs are alike live together in polar, tundra, desert, or grassland habitats.

■ There are three kinds of forest habitats and two kinds of water habitats.

■ People make changes to habitats; people must also protect habitats.

Chapter 12

■ Animals must be able to find food and protect themselves; adaptations help animals survive.

■ Body coverings such as scales, feathers, and fur are adaptations for warmth and protection from the environment.

■ Specific adaptations to feet, wings, mouthparts, and teeth are adaptations for protection and obtaining food.

■ Behavior is anything an animal does in response to any change in its environment. Animals are born with some behavior that is hard to change, and some behavior is learned by experience and can be changed.

■ An animal is born with reflex behavior and instinct.

Life Science

190

Feather or fur
Come crawling
Creeping
Some come peeping
Some by night
and some by day.

from "Feather Or Fur"
John Becker

191

ACTIVITY CENTER

For fun, hands-on, independent activities that integrate reading, writing, math, and technology with the chapters in this unit, have students complete some or all of the Activity Center Activities below. Look for specific chapter references in the Lesson Planning Guides.

Reading: 8 Who's Chained to Whom? **9** The Habitat of Peter Rabbit, **10** Super Hero Adaptations
Writing: 8 Food for Thought, **9** Home is Where the Habitat Is, **10** A Bird in the House
Math: 8 Green Thumb, **9** Dear Deer, **10** Desert Days
Technology: 8 Inside a Seed, **9** Eagle Eye, **10** Not a Fit Night for Man Nor Beast

CONNECTING LITERATURE TO SCIENCE

Understanding the Selection

■ Lead students in a discussion about animals. Ask: **Which animals have fur? Which have feathers?** Possible answers include *ducks, birds, dogs, cats.*
■ Read the poem aloud. Then have students read the poem aloud with you.
■ Ask: **How did the poet say feather and fur would come?** *Feather or fur would come crawling, creeping, peeping. Some by night and some by day.*
■ Ask for examples of animals that crawl, that creep, that are seen mainly at night, and that are seen mainly during the day.

Relating the Selection to Unit Concepts

■ Ask students why they think animals have coverings like feathers or fur. *Animals have coverings like feathers or fur for protection.*
■ Discuss adaptations that animals have made in order to protect themselves and to find food. Ask: **What does a porcupine have that helps it to protect itself?** *A porcupine has quills.* Ask: **What does a turtle have to protect itself?** *A turtle has a shell.*

Relating the Selection to the Student's World

■ Have students look at the photograph and tell what living thing they see. *a duck*
■ Ask: **How does this animal protect itself? What does it do to get food?** *The duck can swim. It has feathers that protect it from the weather. It can go underwater for food and to get away from its enemies.*
■ Have students **work cooperatively** in small groups to discuss other ways that animals protect themselves or have adapted to their surroundings. Then allow time for the groups to share their findings.

Food for Living Things

Planning Guide

Lessons	Objectives	Vocabulary
Chapter Introduction pp. 192, 193		
Lesson 1 Food Producers pp. 194–197	1. **Communicate** that living things have life needs such as food, space, proper temperature, and water. 2. **Tell** what happens to food made by plants.	producer
Lesson 2 Consumers pp. 198–201	3. **Operationally define** *consumers, predators,* and *prey.* 4. **Group** animals as plant eaters, animal eaters, or consumers of plants and animals.	consumer predator prey
Lesson 3 Scavengers and Decomposers pp. 202–205	5. **Operationally define** *scavenger* and *decomposer.*	scavenger decomposer
Lesson 4 Food in a Community pp. 206–209	6. **Operationally define** *community* and *food chain.* 7. **Communicate** that energy from the sun is used by producers to make food.	community food chain
Lesson 5 Food Webs pp. 210–213	8. **Operationally define** *food web.* 9. **Describe** the flow of energy in a food web.	food web
Chapter Review, pp. 214, 215		

Planning Guide

Text Activities		Teacher Resource Masters	Other Components
Title/Skill	Materials per Group		
Have You Ever . . . Played the String Game? p. 193 Formulating a Model	space enough for class to form circle sticky name tags large ball of thick yarn scissors	**Activity Center:** "Who's Chained to Whom?"; "Food for Thought"; "Green Thumb"; "Dear Deer"; "Inside a Seed"	
What Does the Plant Factory Need? p. 197 Observing/Experimenting	3 healthy bean plants 2 to 3 weeks old small watering can water pencil and paper	Independent Practice, pp. 155, 156 Activity Worksheet, pp. 147, 148	Poster #5
What Plant Part Is Eaten? p. 201 Observing	glass or wire cage animal bedding mixed seeds lettuce carrot water jar or dish small plant-eating animal pencil and paper	Independent Practice, pp. 155, 156 Activity Worksheet, pp. 149, 150 ◆ Reteaching Activity, p. 157 Social Studies Connection, p. 154 Critical Thinking, p. 151	Poster #6 Activity Book, pp. 27, 28
		Independent Practice, pp. 155, 156	
You Can . . . Make a Food Chain, p. 209 Classifying/Communicating	20 cards ball of yarn crayons paper punch scissors	Independent Practice, pp. 155, 156 ◆ Family Science, p. 146 Transparency Master, p. 145	Color Transparency #8
		Independent Practice, pp. 155, 156 Language Arts Connection, p. 153 ▲ Critical Thinking, p. 152	Color Transparency #9
		Test A, p. 158 Test B, pp. 159, 160	Software: "Astro Farmer"

◆ Basic / ▲ Advanced / All other masters are for use by all students.

CHAPTER 10

Food for Living Things

ESL/LEP

Chapter 10/Lesson 1, Page 195
Ask students to divide a sheet of paper into five columns. Have them write the following headings for the columns: **Roots, Stems, Leaves, Fruits, Seeds.** Ask them to list as many foods from plants as possible that belong in each column. Have students share their lists. Ask them to write sentences about foods in their lists.

Chapter 10/Lesson 3, Page 203
Write the following words on the chalkboard: **scavenger, decomposer.** Discuss with students the meaning of words. Ask them to list animals that are scavengers. Have them tell why each is a scavenger. Ask students to list several decomposers. Have them write a sentence telling why scavengers and decomposers are important.

Chapter 10/Lesson 4, Page 208
Ask students to draw a food chain. Have them label the producers and consumers. Give each student five index cards. Direct them to write the name of each plant and animal in their food chain on a seperate card. Tell them to mix the cards and see if their partner can put them in proper order for a food chain.

Chapter 10/Lesson 5, Page 212
Ask students to work together to form webs from their food chains. Help them to see how food chains are related. Let three students share their index cards to produce food webs.

Gifted

Chapter 10/Lesson 2, Page 200
Challenge your gifted students to invent a tag game based on predator-prey relationships in a given community of animals. Encourage them to base the rules of their game on real predator-prey relationships. For example, some students would only be allowed to tag certain other students. Suggest that they test and critique their game rules several times before having the class play the game.

Mainstreamed

Chapter 10/Lesson 3, Page 205
Physically Handicapped: Make the statement "A consumer is a living thing that cannot make its own food." Then conduct a brainstorming session to generate a variety of unique ways in which animals obtain food from other living things. For example, some spiders build webs, lions stalk and hunt, condors scavenge. Use the categories of desert, forest, and sea animals. Write the lists on large easel paper and post them in the classroom.

Whole Class Science Project

Explain that plants are producers. Plants need light, air, and water to make their own food. Have students design an experiment to show how light is important to photosynthesis. To show that plants need light to make food, grow plants in a dark area of the classroom. Have students consider how they can show that food is produced by a plant kept in the light, but not by a plant kept in the dark. After a week of plant growth, provide students with a demonstration in which the chlorophyll is removed from a leaf by boiling it in alcohol. The leaf can then be softened by dropping it in boiling water, and a test for starch using iodine can be carried out. Use a plant with variegated leaves, such as ivy or geranium, to show the importance of chlorophyll in photosynthesis.

 Science Fair Projects

Individual students could do one of the following projects:

1. Capture some flies. Put them in a jar with a small amount of meat and seal the jar with muslin. Observe the life cycle of a fly, which takes about 21 days.
2. Cover a potted plant with a box to show how the plant responds to light from a hole on one side of the box.
3. Set up a small aquarium and find out what kinds of food water snails will eat.

Chapter Concepts

■ All living things need food, water, and air to live. Plants are the first link in the food chain and are producers of food.

■ Consumers are those living things that cannot produce their own food. Animals are classified according to their eating habits, which can be determined by the type of teeth they have.

■ Scavengers feed on and remove dead organisms. Scavengers are important because they reduce the amount of organic litter. Decomposers break down dead organisms and return nutrients to the soil.

■ The producers and consumers living together in one area make up a community. A producer uses energy from the sun to grow, and this energy is passed on through the food chain.

■ A food web is composed of all the food chains in a community. Less and less energy is passed on from one consumer to another.

Chapter Background

■ The requirements of life for organisms are food, water, air, space, and proper temperatures.

■ The sun is the primary source of energy.

■ All the organisms living together make up a community.

■ A community is composed of producers, consumers, food chains, and food webs.

Looking Ahead

■ Contact a zoologist or ecologist from the local zoo or from the local division of wildlife.

Look for These Symbols

　　　—Hands-on activity

　　　—Cooperative learning

　　　—Overhead transparency

◆　—Basic/Reinforcement

●　—Average/Enrichment

▲　—Advanced/Challenge

　　—Calculator Practice

SCIENCE
In Your World

192

CHAPTER 10

Food for Living Things

As humans, we get our food from many sources—
sometimes from plants and sometimes from meat.

ACTIVITY

Have You Ever...

Played the String Game?

With a ball of yarn, you can see how living
things on Earth provide food for one another.
Write the names of an animal or plant on sticky
name tags and give one name tag to each student.
Now stand in a circle. Choose one person to be
"the sun." That person wraps the yarn around his
or her finger. The "the sun" tosses the ball of
yarn to a plant that makes food because of light. In
turn, that person wraps the yarn around his or her
finger and asks "Who do I provide food for?" Toss
the yarn from a food provider to a food consumer
until everybody has had a turn. What does the circle
look like when the game is over?

193

PREPLAN

Time Allotment: 30 minutes

Objectives
1. **Identify** some of the sources where
humans get their food.
2. **Make** a model of a food web.

Setup
■ You will need the following materials
for each student or activity group:
a large open space
sticky name tags
a large ball of thick yarn

1   FOCUS

■ Discuss what the people pictured might
be eating. Emphasize the variety of foods
that humans consume.

2   TEACH

■ Ask: **Name some other examples of
plants and animals that provide food
for one another.** *Answers will vary, but
may include a small fish eats algae, a
large fish eats the small fish, and a fisher-
man catches the large fish and eats it.*

Have You Ever . . .
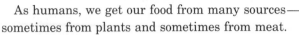 Use this activity as an introduction to
producers and consumers in a food web.
Have students **work cooperatively**
in groups of four.
■ Be certain that there is a piece of yarn
strung between every possible connection.

3   APPLY

■ Transfer the name tags and yarn connections to a bulletin board for students
to have a visual model of a food web.

Close
■ Tell students they will learn more
about the food living things need as they
read Chapter 10.

PREPLAN

Lesson Objectives

1. **Communicate** that living things have life needs such as food, space, proper temperature, and water.
2. **Tell** what happens to food made by plants.

Science Background

■ Green plants make food by the process of photosynthesis, in which the sun's energy, carbon dioxide, and water combine to form food and release oxygen.

■ Food is stored in plant parts in the form of sugar, starch, protein, or fats and is used by plants to build and repair cells.

■ Animals are classified according to their eating habits as herbivores, or plant eaters; carnivores, or meat eaters; and omnivores, or animals that eat both plants and meat.

Lesson Vocabulary

producer

Note: The activity on student page 197 may be used for guided discovery before you begin this lesson.

1 FOCUS

Set up a special pet day and ask students to bring in their pets or pictures of their pets. Have students tell about the type of food, amount of food and water, shelter, space required, and other needs of each pet. **CAUTION:** *Canvass students for allergies to animals before allowing animals in the classroom.*

■ Use the goals on student page 194 to establish the purpose for studying this lesson.

Food Producers

LESSON 1 GOALS
You will learn
● that living things need food to live.
● that green plants are food producers.

Think of a time you were really hungry or thirsty. Your body was telling you that you needed food or water. If you don't get these things, you can't live very long. What other things do you need to live?

Just like you, all living things need food and water to live. You also need oxygen to breathe, the right amount of space, and proper temperature. If a living thing's needs are not met, it can't live.

When you think about food, you probably think about foods that taste good. But we don't eat food just because it tastes good. Food is one of the most important needs of living things. Food provides energy for plants and animals. The energy keeps the parts of each living thing working.

194

TEACHER RESOURCE MASTERS

Think of all the different foods you eat. Many of these foods are plants or made from plants. You may like peanuts, potato chips, tomatoes, walnuts, rice, green beans, apples, or cherries. Some people even like spinach. All of these foods are from plants.

Green plants make or produce their own food. A **producer** (proh DEW sur) is a living thing that makes its own food. Plants use their green leaves to make food. They need sunlight, water, and carbon dioxide to make this food. Carbon dioxide is a gas that is in air and water. Plants often make more food than they can use. The extra food is stored in the roots, stems, leaves, fruits, and seeds of plants. Think of the plant foods you like to eat. Are they the roots, stems, leaves, fruits, or seeds of plants?

What do green plants use to make food?

195

TEACHER RESOURCE MASTERS

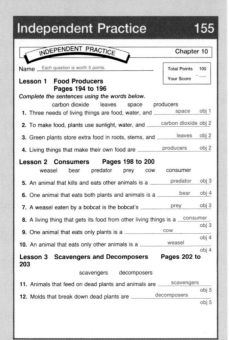

2 TEACH

By using a daily needs chart, have students work in **cooperative groups** to compare the amounts of food eaten daily by a large and small pet.

■ Write the term *producer* on the chalkboard and discuss its meaning.

Guided Practice

■ Check students' understanding of lesson concepts by discussing the Lesson Review questions on student page 196. If necessary, use the **reteaching strategy** in OPTIONS.

Independent Practice

■ Assign the Lesson 1 section of the Teacher Resource Master **Independent Practice,** page 155.

3 APPLY

Have students bring in a plant-produced food they like to eat. Have students **work cooperatively** to make a graph showing what part of the plant they eat—root, stems, leaves, fruits, or seeds.

Close

■ Use the summary statements on student page 196 to review the lesson concepts.

OPTIONS

Reteaching Strategy

■ Collect pictures of living things that make their own food and things that don't. Ask students which pictures show the producers.

Resource Options

■ Use Poster #5, "Sunflowers."

OPTIONS

MATH CONNECTION

■ Have students draw a number line from zero to 100 in increments of five. Then have them locate the following fruits and vegetables along the number line according to the calories of each: apple, 80; banana, 100; carrot, 30; grapefruit, 45, lettuce, 5; and orange, 65. (lettuce, carrot, grapefruit, orange, apple, banana)

♦ **Reinforcement:** Encourage students to work in **cooperative groups** to create and present a puppet show in which the topic is the needs of living things.

● **Enrichment:** Have students select a grassy area in the schoolyard that gets full sunlight. Place a box upside down to cover this area. Leave the box in place for approximately five days. At the end of this treatment, have students explain why the grass appears yellowed.

▲ **Challenge:** Ask students to bring in empty seed packets, read the planting directions, and prepare a chart listing the name of the plant, space needed between seeds, amount of sunlight needed, and when to thin the seedlings.

LESSON REVIEW ANSWERS

1. Food provides energy for life processes.
2. producer
3. Answer may include roots such as carrots, beets, and peanuts; stems such as celery, potatoes, and broccoli; leaves such as cabbage and lettuce; seeds such as almonds, peas, and corn; and fruits such as oranges, apples, grapes, and tomatoes.

The next time you eat, think about the types of plants you are eating. Thanks to these producers, you won't be hungry for long.

Food is stored in many plant parts.

Lesson Summary

• Plants and animals need food for energy to live.
• Green plants can produce their own food.

Lesson Review

1. Why do living things need food?
2. What do you call a plant that makes its own food?
★3. Name foods we eat that come from plant roots, leaves, fruits, and seeds.

196

TEACHER RESOURCE MASTERS

What does the plant factory need?

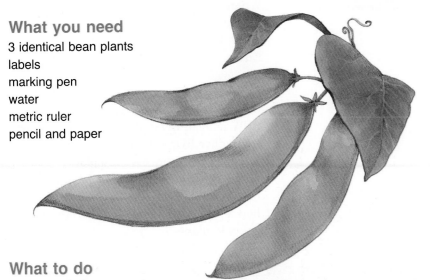

What you need
3 identical bean plants
labels
marking pen
water
metric ruler
pencil and paper

What to do
1. Label the plants **A**, **B**, and **C**.
2. Add water to **plant A** until the soil is moist. Put **plant A** in a dark place.
3. Add the same amount of water to **plant B**. Put **plant B** in bright sunlight.
4. Do not water **plant C**. Put **plant C** in bright sunlight.
5. Add a little water to **A** and **B** every other day. Measure each plant for 10 days. Record your observations.

What did you learn?
1. Which plant is tall and healthy after ten days?
2. Which plant is tall but doesn't look healthy?
3. Which plant grew the least?

Using what you learned
1. What do plants need to grow?
2. What would happen if you kept the soil soaked with water all of the time?

197

ACTIVITY RESPONSES

What did you learn?
1. The plant that had sun and water (plant B) should look very tall and healthy.
2. The plant with water in the reduced light (plant A) should be tall but have limited foliage. It may also be pale green or yellow.
3. The plant without water (plant C) probably died.

Using what you learned
1. The needs of the plants are varied; however, all plants need water and light in order to make food and to grow.
2. Too much water will also produce a problem for the plants. Roots standing in water have difficulty acquiring nutrients they need from the soil in order to grow.

PREPLAN

Time Allotment: 20 minutes for setup; 5-minute observation times each day for ten days

Process Skills: Observing/Experimenting

Objectives
1. **Control** the variables.
2. **Record** the plant data.
3. **Infer** what plants need to grow.

Setup
■ Two to three weeks before beginning this activity, plant enough bean seeds in small milk cartons to supply all of the groups.

Cooperative Grouping: threes—Assign roles as explained on page T24.

1 FOCUS

■ Discuss why plants are sometimes referred to as factories. Explain that all factories change raw materials into finished products.

2 TEACH

■ Before starting the activity, decide where these plants will be placed. Both light and dark areas are required.
■ Plant A needs to be in an area with limited light but not totally in the dark.
■ Have students use the Teacher Resource Master **Activity Worksheet,** pages 147 and 148, to record their data.

3 APPLY

■ Make a large chart and compile a summary of all data. Discuss what they discovered using their own data and the group observations.

Close
■ Discuss the activity and questions.

pages 198–201

PREPLAN

Lesson Objectives

3. Operationally define *consumers,* *predators,* and *prey.*

4. Group animals as plant eaters, animal eaters, or consumers of plants and animals.

Science Background

■ All living things or organisms that cannot produce their own food are consumers.

■ A consumer eats food produced by plants and then converts it into energy for life processes.

■ Animals are classified according to their eating habits into herbivores, or plant eaters; carnivores, or meat eaters; and omnivores, or animals that eat both plants and meat.

■ Animals that kill and eat other animals are classified as predators. The animal that is eaten is the prey.

■ Predator-prey relationships are an important part of the balance in nature.

■ The eating habits of animals can be determined by characterizing their mouth parts, teeth, and other structures.

Lesson Vocabulary

consumer   predator   prey

Note: The activity on student page 201 may be used for guided discovery before you begin this lesson.

1   FOCUS

Prepare a card file of a variety of different kinds of plants and animals. Have each student draw a card and identify the plant or animal. Have each student determine the food the living thing uses for energy. Encourage students to suggest ways each living thing uses food for energy.

■ Use the goals on student page 198 to establish the purpose for studying this lesson.

LESSON 2 GOALS
You will learn
● what consumers are.
● the difference between predators and prey.
● the difference between plant eaters and predators.

Consumers

If you were going to make yourself something to eat, what would you make? Where would you get the food? You might have grown some of it in a garden. Or you might have to go out to buy the food. Either way, your body doesn't make its own food.

Like you, other animals can't make their own food. An animal is a **consumer** (kun SEW mur), a living thing that gets its food from other living things.

Some consumers eat only plants. You may have fed squirrels or some birds with bread crumbs or seeds. Deer, cows, sheep, horses, rabbits, and many other animals eat only plants.

198

TEACHER RESOURCE MASTERS

Critical Thinking   151

CRITICAL THINKING/PROBLEM SOLVING Classifying   Chapter 10

Name _____

PLANT EATERS

Read the list of animals that eat plants. List one plant each animal might eat. Fill in what plant part is eaten.   Answers will vary. Examples are given.

Animal	Plant Eaten	Plant Part
1. cow	grass	stem
2. bird	corn	seed
3. rabbit	lettuce	leaves
4. people	carrot	root
5. squirrel	nuts	seed
6. caterpillar	tomato	fruit
7. giraffe	tree	leaves
8. deer	grass	stem
9. elephant	grass	stem
10. gerbil	sunflower	seed

Some animals eat only other animals. An animal that kills and eats other animals is called a **predator** (PRED ut ur). Think of some predators you know about. Weasels, hawks, sharks, and bobcats might be on your list. Their food might include rabbits, mice, birds, fish, and other animals.

What is a predator?

Animals eaten by predators are called **prey.** Plant eaters are often the prey of predators. But predators can also be the prey of other predators. For example, a weasel might be eaten by a bobcat.

Some animals, like people, eat both plants and animals. Think of some of these animals. You may know that raccoons and bears eat fruit as well as meat. You might have seen robins eating insects, worms, and fruits.

Scientists can group some animals as plant eaters or predators by looking at their teeth. The teeth of plant eaters are broad and flat like the back teeth in your mouth. These teeth can mash leaves and grains.

Would You Believe?
The teeth of a white shark are as hard as steel.

199

TEACHER RESOURCE MASTERS

Independent Practice   155

INDEPENDENT PRACTICE   Chapter 10

Name _____ Each question is worth 5 points. _____   Total Points 100
                                                    Your Score ___

Lesson 1   Food Producers
Pages 194 to 196
Complete the sentences using the words below.
      carbon dioxide   leaves   space   producers
1. Three needs of living things are food, water, and _____ space _____ obj 1
2. To make food, plants use sunlight, water, and _____ carbon dioxide obj 2
3. Green plants store extra food in roots, stems, and _____ leaves _____ obj 2
4. Living things that make their own food are _____ producers _____ obj 2

Lesson 2   Consumers   Pages 198 to 200
      weasel   bear   predator   prey   cow   consumer
5. An animal that kills and eats other animals is a _____ predator _____ obj 3
6. One animal that eats both plants and animals is a _____ bear _____ obj 4
7. A weasel eaten by a bobcat is the bobcat's _____ prey _____ obj 3
8. A living thing that gets its food from other living things is a _____ consumer
                                                                         obj 3
9. One animal that eats only plants is a _____ cow _____
                                                    obj 4
10. An animal that eats only other animals is a _____ weasel _____
                                                          obj 4

Lesson 3   Scavengers and Decomposers   Pages 202 to 203
      scavengers   decomposers
11. Animals that feed on dead plants and animals are _____ scavengers
                                                            obj 5
12. Molds that break down dead plants are _____ decomposers
                                                    obj 5

2   TEACH

■ Write the term *consumer* on the chalkboard or overhead. Encourage students to give examples of consumers in the classroom, in the schoolyard, and at home.
■ Ask: **Are people producers or consumers?** *consumers* Make it clear that people cannot make food in the same way that producers make food.

Guided Practice
■ Check students' understanding of lesson concepts by discussing the Lesson Review questions on student page 200. If necessary, use the **reteaching strategy** in OPTIONS.

Independent Practice
■ Assign the Lesson 2 section of the Teacher Resource Master **Independent Practice,** page 155.

3   APPLY

Have students list animals on the board. Independently or in **cooperative groups,** have them decide if the animals are predators, prey or both. Discuss answers as a group.

Close
■ Use the summary statements on student page 200 to review the lesson concepts.

OPTIONS

Reteaching Strategy
■ Have students make a list of animals that are predators. For each predator, request that students list one or more animals that are its prey. Have them put a star next to the names of prey that are predators that feed on other animals.

Resource Options
■ Use Poster #6, "Leaf-Cutter Ants."
■ Use Activity Book, "Using Numbers," pages 27 and 28.

OPTIONS

MATH CONNECTION

Bluebird	🦋	🦋	🦋	🦋	🦋
Cardinal	🦋	🦋	🦋	🦋	
Dove	🦋	🦋	🦋	🦋	🦋 🦋
Robin	🦋	🦋	🦋		
Blue Jay	🦋	🦋	🦋	🦋	

Each 🦋 means 10 flies eaten

Have students study the picture graph and answer the following questions.
1. How many more flies did the dove eat than the robin? (35)
2. Which two birds ate a total of 60 flies? (cardinal and robin)

◆ **Reinforcement:** Have students find out how hunting helps control animal populations that would otherwise increase to unhealthy levels.

● **Enrichment:** Encourage students to research various ways prey protect themselves from predators. Have students use a photograph for each example as they report their findings to other students.

▲ **Challenge:** Some predators have bad reputations because of the animals they hunt. For example, wolves, coyotes, foxes, and eagles are considered harmful predators. Encourage students to select one of the predators. In one column they should list examples of how predators are harmful and in the second how the predators are helpful.

LESSON REVIEW ANSWERS

1. A consumer can't make its own food, but a producer can.
2. A predator is an animal that hunts and eats other animals. A prey is an animal eaten by predators.
3. A scientist can study the dinosaur's teeth.

How are the teeth of plant eaters and predators different?

Predators have pointed teeth like some of your front teeth. These teeth are sharp and can tear meat. Scientists study the teeth of ancient animals such as dinosaurs to tell what kinds of foods they ate.

Producers, consumers, predators, and prey are all important in nature. Almost everything in nature has a natural predator. If birds stopped eating grasshoppers, think of how many more there would be! The grasshoppers would soon eat up all of their plant food. Though birds eat some grasshoppers, they are really helping them survive.

Lesson Summary

- Animals are consumers because they eat other plants or animals.
- Some animals are hunted and eaten by other animals.
- Plant eaters have broad, flat teeth while predators have sharp, pointed teeth.

Lesson Review

1. How is a consumer different from a producer?
2. Explain the difference between predators and prey.
★3. How can scientists tell whether a dinosaur was a plant eater or a predator?

200

TEACHER RESOURCE MASTERS

Social Studies Connection 154

SOCIAL STUDIES CONNECTION Reference Materials Chapter 10

Name _____

ANIMALS OF THE WORLD

Below is a list of animals found in different parts of the world. Use resource books to find the part of the world in which they live. Also find out whether they are plant eaters, predators or both.

Animal	Where Animal Lives	Plant eater or Predator?
tapir	South America, Malaya	plant eater
aye-aye	Madagascar	both
hedgehog	Europe, Asia	both
Koala	Australia	plant eater
flying fox	Asia, Australia	plant eater
hyrax	Africa	plant eater
peccary	North and South America	both
wolverine	North America	predator
serval	Africa	predator
aardwolf	Africa	predator
yak	Tibet	plant eater
okapi	Africa	plant eater
coatis	North Central and South America	both
pangolin	Africa, Asia	predator
pika	North America, Asia	plant eater

Reteaching Activity 157

RETEACHING ACTIVITY Chapter 10

Name _____

WHERE DO YOU GET YOUR FOOD?

Materials
newspaper grocery store ad
paper
pencil

What to do
1. List five foods from the ad that are plant parts or plant products.
2. List five foods from the ad that are animal parts or animal products.

What did you learn?

1. Which foods in the ad are plant parts or plant products? _Answers will vary._

2. Which foods in the ad are animal parts or animal products? _Answers will vary._

Using what you learned
1. Make a list of the foods you ate for breakfast that are plant parts or plant products. Which are animal parts or animal products? _Answers will vary._

2. Why might it be correct to say that we eat plants in some form at every meal? _All the food a person eats is part of a food chain and all food chains begin with plants (producers)._

What plant part is eaten?

What you need

glass or wire cage
animal bedding
mixed seeds
lettuce
carrot
water
jar or dish
small, plant-eating animal
pencil and paper

What to do

1. Prepare a cage for the animal.
2. Place plant parts in the cage.
3. Gently put the animal in the cage.
4. Observe and record what, when, and how the animal eats for two or three days.
5. Clean the cage each day and add fresh food and water.

What did you learn?

1. What did the animal eat?
2. When did the animal eat?
3. How did it hold its food?

Using what you learned

1. Suppose your animal got out of its cage. How could information in this activity help you catch the animal?
2. Some animals eat only one kind of plant. If your animal eats many kinds of plants, why is it able to live in more areas than an animal that eats only one kind of plant?

201

ACTIVITY RESPONSES

What did you learn?

1. Answers will vary depending on type of animal used.
2. Answers will vary depending on type of animal used.
3. Answers will vary depending on type of animal used.

Using what you learned

1. The food could be used to lure the animal back to its cage. Students could also place the food the animal likes in a place where it could be caught when it started to eat.
2. Answers will vary. The plants that make up the variety eaten by an animal can usually be found in more than one area. If only one kind of plant is eaten, the animal is limited to living only where that plant grows.

PREPLAN

Time Allotment: 20 minutes for setup; several 10-minute observation periods on following days
Process Skill: Observing

Objectives

1. **Prepare** and **maintain** a proper home for a plant-eating animal.
2. **Choose** the proper diet for the animal and **record** data on the eating habits of the animal.

Setup

■ Check to see if any student is allergic to specific animals.

■ **Cooperative Grouping:** tens—Assign roles as explained on page T24.

1 FOCUS

■ Encourage students to discuss eating habits of animals.

2 TEACH

■ Before obtaining the animal, have the students decide how it should be properly housed and cared for.
■ **Safety Consideration:** Animals may become frightened if handled improperly.
■ Have students use the Teacher Resource Master **Activity Worksheet,** pages 149 and 150, to record their data.

3 APPLY

■ Discuss how to determine whether an animal is a plant eater or a meat eater considering the shape of the animal's teeth. Have them name an animal and discuss the type of teeth it has to determine whether it is a plant eater, meat eater, or if it eats both plants and meat.

Close

■ Discuss the activity and questions.

PREPLAN

Lesson Objective

5. Operationally define *scavenger* and *decomposer*.

Science Background

■ Scavengers feed on and remove dead organisms. Examples of scavengers are crows, coyotes, hyenas, crabs, and maggots.

■ Scavengers are important to the environment because they reduce the amount of organic litter.

■ Bacteria are used as decomposers in many waste disposal plants.

■ Dead organisms are broken down in the soil by decomposers. The nutrients required by plants are derived from these decomposed organisms.

Lesson Vocabulary

scavenger   decomposer

1   FOCUS

■ Before the lesson, place a piece of raw meat in a protected area of the schoolyard. Allow students to observe this dead animal part. Have them identify scavengers feeding on the meat. Encourage students to predict what will happen to the meat. Have them collect data to test their predictions.

■ Use the goals on student page 202 to establish the purpose for studying this lesson.

Scavengers and Decomposers

What do you do with rotten fruits and vegetables? You probably throw these foods away in the trash. A garbage truck may take them to a landfill. They are buried with lots of other trash. Do you know what happens to dead plants and animals in nature?

You know that green plants are producers and that plant eaters and predators are consumers. Two other kinds of living things are also consumers. They help remove dead matter from Earth's surface.

A **scavenger** (SKAV un jur) is a consumer that looks for and feeds on dead plants and animals. Many animals, such as the buzzard, hyena, crab, catfish, and crow, are scavengers. They don't usually kill things. They look for animals that have already died.

What does a scavenger eat?

Scavengers eat dead animals.

202

TEACHER RESOURCE MASTERS

A **decomposer** (dee kum POH zur) is a consumer that changes dead plants and animals into simpler matter. You may have seen molds on bread or other spoiled food. These molds change the color and smell of dead plants or animals as decay takes place. Molds are decomposers.

You may have seen a piece of wood that has been broken down so that it crumbles like soil. Farmers and gardeners depend on decomposers to break down leaves, grass, or other mulch into soil. Some bacteria are decomposers. They break down dead matter into very small parts that are returned to the soil.

Decomposers break down dead matter.

203

TEACHER RESOURCE MASTERS

Independent Practice 155

INDEPENDENT PRACTICE   Chapter 10

Name _Each question is worth 5 points._   Total Points 100   Your Score

Lesson 1 Food Producers
Pages 194 to 196
Complete the sentences using the words below.

carbon dioxide   leaves   space   producers

1. Three needs of living things are food, water, and ___space___ obj 1

2. To make food, plants use sunlight, water, and ___carbon dioxide___ obj 2

3. Green plants store extra food in roots, stems, and ___leaves___ obj 2

4. Living things that make their own food are ___producers___ obj 2

Lesson 2 Consumers   Pages 198 to 200

weasel   bear   predator   prey   cow   consumer

5. An animal that kills and eats other animals is a ___predator___ obj 3

6. One animal that eats both plants and animals is a ___bear___ obj 4

7. A weasel eaten by a bobcat is the bobcat's ___prey___ obj 3

8. A living thing that gets its food from other living things is a ___consumer___ obj 3

9. One animal that eats only plants is a ___cow___ obj 4

10. An animal that eats only other animals is a ___weasel___ obj 4

Lesson 3 Scavengers and Decomposers   Pages 202 to 203

scavengers   decomposers

11. Animals that feed on dead plants and animals are ___scavengers___ obj 5

12. Molds that break down dead plants are ___decomposers___ obj 5

2   TEACH

■ **Problem Solving:** Ask students how we can recognize a decomposer. Arrange a field trip to find examples of decomposers. **CAUTION:** *Warn students not to touch or collect any specimens, as many fungi are poisonous.* Have students choose a fungus and observe how and where it grows. Ask students to describe the effects the fungus has on its surroundings.

Bring in a slice of bread and let it mold. Make a wet-mount slide of a bit of mold and have students view it under a microscope.

Guided Practice

■ Check students' understanding of lesson concepts by discussing the Lesson Review questions on student page 205. If necessary, use the **reteaching strategy** in OPTIONS.

Independent Practice

■ Assign the Lesson 3 section of the Teacher Resource Master **Independent Practice,** page 155.

3   APPLY

Bring to class a piece of fruit, vegetable, or perishable food. Have students observe and chart the change in the food as the food grows bacteria. Use the microscope to show the different stages of bacteria growth.

Close

■ Use Summary statements on student page 205 to review lesson concepts.

OPTIONS

Reteaching Strategy

■ Invite a guest speaker who is knowledgeable about recycling leaves, grass clippings, and other mulch to discuss why this has become an area of concern to people.

OPTIONS

LANGUAGE CONNECTION

■ **Reading:** Assist students with the following comparison of the word *decomposer* with a musical *composer*. How is the word *decomposer* the opposite of the word *composer*? Consider a musical composer. What things does he or she bring together to create a piece of music? (musical scale, notes) What would a musical decomposer do? How does this relate to the decomposers in this lesson? (break down organic matter)

♦ **Reinforcement:** Have students work in **cooperative groups** to make a food chain with pictures of animals pasted onto cards. Have them sort the cards into the categories of producers, plant eaters, meat eaters, decomposers, and scavengers. Have students identify possible predator-prey relationships.

● **Enrichment:** Have students line up in groups of five to ten. Show them quarter measuring cups full of corn meal. Pour the corn meal into the cupped hands of the first student in each line. Have that student pass it on to the second student in the line and so on down the line. The student at the end of the line should carefully pour the remaining corn meal into the original measuring cup. The corn meal represents energy being passed through a food chain. The energy that is used in the life processes of each consumer is represented by the corn that was dropped during transfer from one person to the next.

Many decomposers are too small to see with your eyes. For a long time, the decay of plants and animals was a mystery to people. About four hundred years ago, the microscope (MI kruh skohp) was invented. The word *micro* means "small," and *scope* means "to look." A microscope is an instrument used to make small things look larger. The microscope showed people that there is a world of very small living things. Using a microscope, you can see decomposers at work.

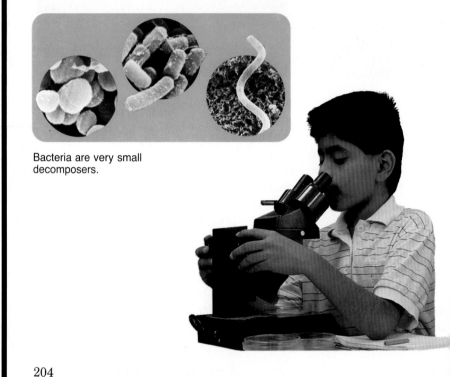

Bacteria are very small decomposers.

204

TEACHER RESOURCE MASTERS

You may think scavengers and decomposers do unpleasant work. But their work is very important. They get energy by feeding on dead matter and return that energy to nature. Decomposers put chemicals that were once in living things back into the soil. Without these chemicals, plants could not get the energy to grow and produce food for the rest of us.

Lesson Summary

- Scavengers eat dead plants and animals.
- Decomposers break down dead plants and animals into simpler matter.

Lesson Review

1. Name two animals that are scavengers.
2. Name two decomposers.
3. Why are decomposers important?

Why are decomposers important to plants?

SCIENCE AND . . .
Math

In 10 spins, what living thing will the spinner probably point to most?

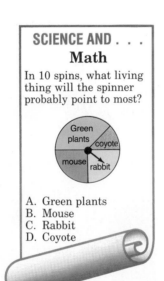

A. Green plants
B. Mouse
C. Rabbit
D. Coyote

205

SCIENCE AND . . . MATH

- **Skill:** Determine possible outcomes in a given situation.
- **Student Response:** A

▲ **Challenge:** Encourage students to prepare a decomposition chamber by placing two centimeters of moist soil in an aquarium. Use representative left-over food from lunch and scatter the food over the moist soil. After three hours, cover and seal the aquarium. Provide a five-minute observation period for each student to observe and record data for seven days. Discuss how the food was decomposed during the observation period, and identify the decomposers, if possible. After the activity, take the aquarium outside to open and clean. **CAUTION:** *Some students may be allergic to mold and should avoid exposure to the opened aquarium.*

LESSON REVIEW ANSWERS

1. Answers may include crows, crabs, or hyenas.
2. Answers may include bacteria or mold.
3. Decomposers are important in breaking down dead matter into smaller parts that are used by plants for their growth.

TEACHER RESOURCE MASTERS

PREPLAN

Lesson Objectives

6. Operationally define *community* and *food chain.*

7. Communicate that energy from the sun is used by producers to make food.

Science Background

■ The life of each species depends on other species that live in the same community.

■ Producers such as green plants use solar energy to make food by the process of photosynthesis. Producers are always the first link in a food chain.

■ Consumers that eat producers are primary consumers (herbivores). Consumers that eat herbivores are secondary consumers (carnivores). Consumers that eat only carnivores are tertiary consumers. Omnivores eat both plants and animals. Decomposers break down dead plants and animals.

Lesson Vocabulary

community   food chain

1   FOCUS

■ Draw green marks representing grass across the bottom of the chalkboard. Above this have students write names of animals that eat grass. Above this have them write animals that eat these animals, and so on. Draw arrows from the thing eaten to all the animals that eat it. Discuss the resulting food web.

■ Use the goals on student page 206 to establish the purpose for studying this lesson.

LESSON 4 GOALS

You will learn
● what a food community and food chain are.
● how the sun is important to all living things.
● that energy is transferred from plants to animals.

Food in a Community

You live in a community. It may be a suburban community, a farm community, or a city community. A community is a group of people living together in a neighborhood. But you are also part of a nature community.

In nature, a **community** is a group of producers and consumers living together in one area. Every living thing in a community is important. Think of all the living things that might live in a pond community. You might name green plants, insects, fish, frogs, snakes, and bacteria. All of these living things live and work together in the pond community.

206

TEACHER RESOURCE MASTERS

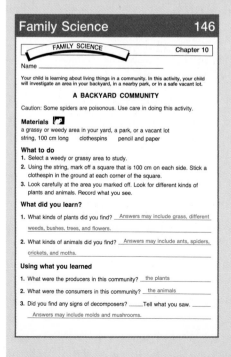

Family Science   146

FAMILY SCIENCE   Chapter 10

Name _____

Your child is learning about living things in a community. In this activity, your child will investigate an area in your backyard, in a nearby park, or in a safe vacant lot.

A BACKYARD COMMUNITY

Caution: Some spiders are poisonous. Use care in doing this activity.

Materials
a grassy or weedy area in your yard, a park, or a vacant lot
string, 100 cm long   clothespins   pencil and paper

What to do
1. Select a weedy or grassy area to study.
2. Using the string, mark off a square that is 100 cm on each side. Stick a clothespin in the ground at each corner of the square.
3. Look carefully at the area you marked off. Look for different kinds of plants and animals. Record what you see.

What did you learn?
1. What kinds of plants did you find? _Answers may include grass, different weeds, bushes, trees, and flowers._
2. What kinds of animals did you find? _Answers may include ants, spiders, crickets, and moths._

Using what you learned
1. What were the producers in this community? _the plants_
2. What were the consumers in this community? _the animals_
3. Did you find any signs of decomposers? ___Tell what you saw. ___ _Answers may include molds and mushrooms._

Food supplies the energy for living things. But where does this energy come from in the first place? Plants need energy from the sun to grow and live. They use the sun's energy to make food. This energy is then passed on to animals when they eat the plants. The sun is the major source of energy on Earth.

Why is energy from the sun important?

The producers in a pond community are the green plants that use the sun's energy to grow and make food. Some of the energy is passed on to an insect when it eats the plants. The energy that the insect doesn't use is passed on to the frog when it eats the insect. Some energy is then passed on to the snake when it eats the frog.

When the snake dies, bacteria break down the body of the dead snake. The bacteria get some of the energy. Plants then use this energy and more energy from the sun to begin the process again. The insects, fish, frogs, snakes, and bacteria are all consumers in the community.

207

TEACHER RESOURCE MASTERS

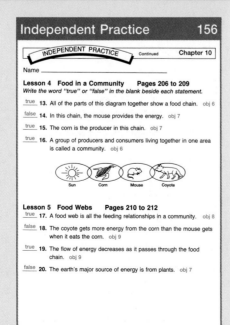

2 TEACH

■ Have students list all living things in a school community. Discuss how the composition of the school community is like a forest community, a pond community, or a seashore community.
■ Have students make drawings of one or two animals and plants that make up a food chain.

Guided Practice
■ Check students' understanding of lesson concepts by discussing the Lesson Review questions on student page 209. If necessary, use the **reteaching strategy** in OPTIONS.

Independent Practice
■ Assign the Lesson 4 section of the Teacher Resource Master **Independent Practice,** page 156.

3 APPLY

Use pictures from magazines or have students draw animals and plants that make up a food chain. Have students working in **cooperative groups** each pick a picture and stand in the order of a food chain. The other groups can decide if they are correct.

Close
■ Use Summary statements on student page 209 to review lesson concepts.

OPTIONS

Reteaching Strategy
■ Have students decide what type of community they live in—city, farm, suburban. Have them list all living things found in their community and compare their community to another. Discuss what is similar and different.

Resource Options
Use Color Transparency #8, "A Food Chain."

OPTIONS

LANGUAGE CONNECTION

Reading: Have students determine whether each statement is **Fact** or **Opinion**.

A. Weasels eat mice. (Fact)

B. Each living thing is food for the next link in a food chain. (Fact)

C. Every living thing in a community is important. (Opinion)

D. Plants use energy from the sun to grow. (Fact)

MATH CONNECTION

■ Have students review the 3-dimensional figure. Ask them to identify the 2-dimensional shape of each side (triangle), the bottom (square), and each of the lower four side sections (trapezoid). Then ask students to identify the entire 3-dimensional shape of the figure (pyramid).

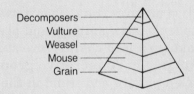

♦ **Reinforcement:** Ask students to cut out pictures of plants and animals. When students have free time, allow them to make food chains using the pictures.

● **Enrichment:** Provide students with an illustrated guide to insects and have them make a list of the different feeding habits of each kind of insect.

What is passed on through the food chain?

The energy moves or transfers from one living thing in the community to another. It starts with the sun, then goes to the producers and on to the consumers. All of these living things are connected like a chain necklace. The plant, insect, fish, frog, snake, and bacteria are all links in a **food chain.** Energy, in the form of food, passes through the food chain.

There are many different food chains in each community. Each food chain can have few or many links. A girl eating lettuce from a salad is part of a short food chain. A longer food chain might start with a mouse eating grain. A weasel then eats the mouse. Later, the weasel dies. A vulture eats the dead weasel. When the vulture dies, the decomposers break it down into the soil.

As you take your next bite of food, think about the food chain that you are part of. Is it a long chain or a short chain? What is your role in it?

A person eating a salad is part of a food chain.

208

TEACHER RESOURCE MASTERS

📖 Transparency Master   145

You Can...

Make a Food Chain

Use 20 cards, yarn, crayons, and a paper punch. Write the name and draw a picture of a plant or animal on each card. Punch a hole in each end of the card. Use the yarn to join the cards together to make food chains. Compare food chains with your classmates. What happens to energy in your chain?

Lesson Summary

- A community is a group of producers and consumers living together in one area.
- The sun is Earth's major source of energy.
- A food chain is the transfer of energy from one living thing to another through food.

Lesson Review

1. What is a community in nature?
2. What is the sun's role in a food chain?
3. A boy drinks milk from a cow that ate clover. Who are the consumers in this food chain? What is the producer?

209

TEACHER RESOURCE MASTERS

OPTIONS

YOU CAN . . . MAKE A FOOD CHAIN

Process Skill: Classifying/Communicating

Objective: Construct a food chain and **identify** the type of organism that is always the first link in the chain.

Setup/Teach

■ You may want to have cards with different plants and animals already listed for students to use.

■ See which organisms are part of more than one food chain. Discuss why this can happen.

■ Encourage students to make a food chain that includes a producer, consumer (plant eater), consumer (animal eater), consumer (plant and animal eater), and a decomposer.

■ Be certain students understand that energy is used for the life processes of each organism before it is transferred from link to link.

Student Responses

■ The amount of energy decreases as more links are added to the chain.

▲ **Challenge:** Have students research those plants that are carnivorous. Have them describe the mechanism of catching insects used by one of these plants. They should also attempt to suggest a possible explanation for this kind of adaptation. Point out that these are both producers and consumers.

LESSON REVIEW ANSWERS

1. A community is a group of producers and consumers living together in one area.

2. The sun provides Earth's major source of energy.

3. The boy and the cow are the consumers; clover is the producer.

PREPLAN

Lesson Objectives
1. **Operationally define** *food web*.
2. **Describe** the flow of energy in a food web.

Science Background
■ The size of a population is limited by the sizes of the populations on which it feeds.
■ The energy passed through a food web is used for life activities or is lost as body heat.
■ All the possible feeding relationships in a community make food chains that are the strands of a food web.

Lesson Vocabulary
food web

1 FOCUS

■ Draw a web on the board and have students tell you what it is. Agree that it does look like a spider web, but label it as a FOOD WEB. Discuss how energy is generated throughout the strings, which represent feeding relationships.
■ Use the goals on student page 210 to establish the purpose for studying this lesson.

LESSON 5 GOALS
You will learn
● what a food web is.
● how energy flows in a food web.

What is a food web?

Food Webs

Looking closely at a community, you can see many different food chains. Different animals may eat the same plant. Many predators may hunt the same animal. Consumers eat more than one kind of food. All plants and animals are part of more than one food chain.

In a spider's web, you can see many fine strings that are all connected. All the food chains put together in a community make a giant web. A **food web** is all the feeding relationships in a community. A food web shows which animals are predators and which are prey. It also includes the scavengers and decomposers.

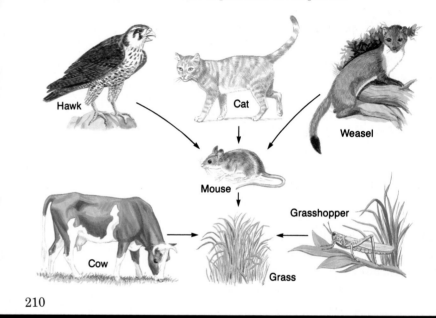

Hawk　Cat　Weasel　Mouse　Grasshopper　Cow　Grass

210

TEACHER RESOURCE MASTERS

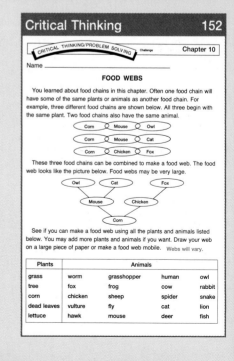

Critical Thinking 152

CRITICAL THINKING/PROBLEM SOLVING — Challenge — Chapter 10

Name _____

FOOD WEBS

You learned about food chains in this chapter. Often one food chain will have some of the same plants or animals as another food chain. For example, three different food chains are shown below. All three begin with the same plant. Two food chains also have the same animal.

Corn — Mouse — Owl
Corn — Mouse — Cat
Corn — Chicken — Fox

These three food chains can be combined to make a food web. The food web looks like the picture below. Food webs may be very large.

Owl　Cat　Fox
Mouse　Chicken
Corn

See if you can make a food web using all the plants and animals listed below. You may add more plants and animals if you want. Draw your web on a large piece of paper or make a food web mobile. Webs will vary.

Plants	Animals			
grass	worm	grasshopper	human	owl
tree	fox	frog	cow	rabbit
corn	chicken	sheep	spider	snake
dead leaves	vulture	fly	cat	lion
lettuce	hawk	mouse	deer	fish

In each food chain within a food web, green plants produce food. But consumers don't receive all of the energy in this food. The plant uses part of the energy as it grows. The consumer that eats the plant uses part of the energy. Less of the energy from the plant is available to other consumers in the food chain. The energy doesn't go away. It changes its form and isn't available to other consumers.

In a forest community, for example, energy is stored in food made by a green plant. Only some of that energy becomes stored in the body of a deer that eats the green plant. An even smaller part of the plant's energy is then available to a wolf that eats the deer. As energy passes through the food web, living things use a large part of it.

What happens to energy as it passes through the food web?

211

2 TEACH

Plan a trip to the schoolyard or nearby park. Have students **work cooperatively** in pairs. Each pair should place a wire coat hanger on the ground and identify the different types of producers and consumers within the area. As a class, tabulate the number of each type of producer and each type of consumer. Discuss the relationship of the number of producers compared with the number of consumers.

Guided Practice
■ Check students' understanding of lesson concepts by discussing the Lesson Review questions on student page 212. If necessary, use the **reteaching strategy** in OPTIONS.

Independent Practice
■ Assign the Lesson 5 section of the Teacher Resource Master **Independent Practice,** page 156.

3 APPLY

■ Have students write a poem or paragraph to describe the importance of food webs.

Close
■ Use Summary statements on student page 212 to review lesson concepts.

OPTIONS

Reteaching Strategy
■ Display pictures of drought areas, flooded land, forest fires, and unexpected cold in the South. Discuss how these natural disasters affect the food chain in the community—higher prices, scarcity of fruits or vegetables, poor quality.

Resource Options
Use Color Transparency #9, "A Food Web."

TEACHER RESOURCE MASTERS

Language Arts Connection 153

LANGUAGE ARTS CONNECTION   Critical Reading   Chapter 10

Name _____

A FOOD WEB

This story about a food web is made of sentences that are not in order. Read the story and answer the questions.

[1]In the autumn the grass and the insects died. [2]The grasses used the sunlight, carbon dioxide and water to make food. [3]The light from the sun was shining on the field of grasses. [4]Mold grew on the dead grass and insects and caused them to decay. [5]Suddenly a spider jumped on one insect and ate it. [6]It was springtime. [7]Many small insects chewed on the leaves of grasses. [8]The lizard ate the spider and crawled away to look for more things to eat. [9]The spider moved quickly through the grass, but was caught by a lizard.

1. Write the numbers of the sentences in the story in correct order.

   6, 3, 2, 7, 5, 9, 8, 1, 4

2. Name the living things that are:

   producers _____ grasses

   consumers ____ insect, spider, lizard

   decomposers _____ mold

3. What was the source of energy for all the living things?

   sun

4. Draw the food web described in the story.

   sunlight ⟶ grass ⟶ insect ⟶ spider ⟶ lizard
                              ↳ mold

Independent Practice 156

INDEPENDENT PRACTICE   Continued   Chapter 10

Name _____

Lesson 4   Food in a Community   Pages 206 to 209
Write the word "true" or "false" in the blank beside each statement.

true 13. All of the parts of this diagram together show a food chain. obj 6

false 14. In this chain, the mouse provides the energy. obj 7

true 15. The corn is the producer in this chain. obj 7

true 16. A group of producers and consumers living together in one area is called a community. obj 6

Sun   Corn   Mouse   Coyote

Lesson 5   Food Webs   Pages 210 to 212

true 17. A food web is all the feeding relationships in a community. obj 8

false 18. The coyote gets more energy from the corn than the mouse gets when it eats the corn. obj 9

true 19. The flow of energy decreases as it passes through the food chain. obj 9

false 20. The earth's major source of energy is from plants. obj 7

OPTIONS

LANGUAGE CONNECTION

Writing: Assign students the following writing assignment.

Draw a web with yourself at the center. Draw the different strings from the center of your web to show the many different communities to which you belong. Include such communities as family, school, church, neighborhood, sports, music, and so on. Arrange these different strings into a written composition that describes how you are important to each community.

Science and Technology: Use "I WANT TO KNOW ABOUT . . . Artificial Reefs," student page 213, with this lesson.

● Enrichment: Mimeograph a handout with the names of the following living things: grass, trees, antelope, flies, ticks, hyenas, shrubs, sedges, vultures, giraffes, lions, zebras, storks. Have students work in **cooperative groups** and paste the names of each living thing onto index cards. Have them use yarn to construct a food web of the index cards. Exhibit the collage food web and discuss the relationships.

LESSON REVIEW ANSWERS

1. A food chain is a particular group of producers and consumers. A food web is all of the feeding relationships in a community.

2. The amount of energy available from producers decreases as it is passed from one consumer to another.

Every living thing in a community is important. They can be members of several different food chains, which make up a food web. Changes in a community cause changes in the food chains and food webs, too. You are a member of your community. The way you live your life makes a big difference to many other living things.

Lesson Summary

- A food web is made up of all the food chains within a community.
- The total amount of available energy from producers is less and less as it flows through a food web.

Lesson Review

1. What is the difference between a food chain and a food web?
★2. How does energy flow in a food web?

212

TEACHER RESOURCE MASTERS

I WANT TO KNOW ABOUT...

Artificial Reefs

Do you like seafood? Have you ever had shrimp or tuna? These animals live and find food in the sea. The seafood you see in the grocery store was caught in the ocean and shipped to the store. People who fish are like farmers. They harvest seafood for people to eat. Because seafood is popular, people are looking for new ways to catch more.

Most animals in the ocean live near reefs. Scientists think that if there were more reefs, there would be more seafood to eat. To make an artificial reef, old ships, cars, and even playground equipment have been lowered into the ocean.

Small animals and plants quickly begin to grow on the sunken objects. Soon, crabs and other animals move in, finding food and shelter in the new reefs. Over 400 reefs have been built along the coasts of the United States.

Science and Technology

213

TEACHER RESOURCE MASTERS

Feature Background

■ For comprehensive articles on artificial reefs, refer to *National Wildlife* magazine, February/March, 1986, and *Science News,* July 16, 1986.

Feature Vocabulary

reef

Teaching Suggestions

■ Set up an aquarium in the classroom. Place a small aquarium building that has openings in it on the floor of the tank.
■ Have children suggest other small, weighted objects that could serve as reefs in the aquarium. **Safety Considerations:** *Avoid objects that contain lead.* Try some of their suggestions.
■ Have students observe the amount of time small fish spend in and around the building.
■ Show photographs of sea life in the Great Barrier Reef.

Summary

Chapter Closure: Assign each summary statement to groups of two or three students. Ask students to **work cooperatively** to use the summary statements they have been assigned as the main idea of a paragraph. Tell them to write at least three more sentences that explain or are examples for the summary statement. Allow groups to share their paragraphs.

Science Words

Have students illustrate each of the science words. Have them use the science words to label their drawings.

Student Responses

1. food web
2. community
3. decomposer
4. consumer
5. scavenger
6. predator
7. food chain
8. producer

CHAPTER REVIEW 10

Summary

Lesson 1
- Living things need food.
- Green plants produce food.

Lesson 2
- Consumers cannot make food.
- Predators eat prey.
- Plant eaters and predators have different types of teeth.

Lesson 3
- Scavengers eat dead things.
- Decomposers break down dead plants and animals.

Lesson 4
- A community is a group of producers and consumers.
- The sun is the major source of energy.
- Energy moves through the food chain.

Lesson 5
- A food web is all the food chains in a community.
- Energy decreases as it passes through the food web.

Science Words

Fill in the blank with the correct word or words from the list.

**producer   decomposer
consumer   community
predator   food chain
prey   food web
scavenger**

1. A ___ is all the feeding relationships in a community.
2. Plants and animals live together in a ___ .

3. Dead plants and animals are broken down by a ___ .
4. A living thing that cannot make its own food is a ___ .
5. An animal that eats dead plants and animals is a ___ .
6. A ___ kills and eats other animals.
7. Energy in the form of food passes through the ___ .
8. A ___ makes its own food.

214

TEACHER RESOURCE MASTERS

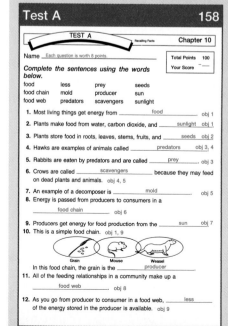

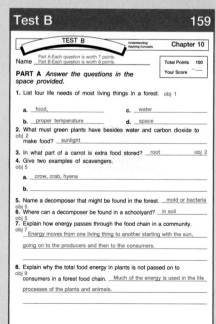

Questions

Recalling Ideas

Correctly complete each of the following sentences.

1. An example of a decomposer is a
   - (a) root.
   - (b) mold.
   - (c) nutrient.
   - (d) prey.

2. Producers make food with energy from the
   - (a) air.
   - (b) water.
   - (c) soil.
   - (d) sun.

3. All living things need
   - (a) light.
   - (b) food.
   - (c) exercise.
   - (d) carbon dioxide.

Understanding Ideas

Answer the following questions using complete sentences.

1. Tell about the flow of energy through a food web.

2. How do plants make food? Where is it stored?

3. List some animals that are plant eaters, some that are animal eaters, and some that consume both.

Thinking Critically

Think about what you have learned in this chapter. Answer the following questions using complete sentences.

1. Tell about a food web that includes people.

2. A plant—an insect—a frog—a snake is an example of a food chain. Which is the producer and which are consumers?

215

Questions

Recalling Ideas

1. b
2. d
3. b

Understanding Ideas

1. The energy in a food web begins with the plant or producer. Part of the energy is used by the plant as it grows, and then part is passed on to the consumer that eats the plant. As energy is passed on in the food web, it is gradually used up. A large part of the energy is used by the producer and the consumer(s) as they live.

2. Plants make their own food by using sunlight, water, and carbon dioxide. The food is then stored in roots, stems, leaves, fruits, and seeds.

3. Answers will vary. Students may list squirrels, birds, and deer as plant eaters; weasels, hawks, and sharks as animal eaters; raccoons and bears as consumers of both plants and animals.

Thinking Critically

1. Answers will vary. Students may talk about food webs in which people eat producers such as those mixed in a salad. Other food webs might include those in which people eat other consumers such as the meat of cattle.

2. The plant is the first link, or producer, and the insect, frog, and snake are the consumers, or other links of the food chain.

TEACHER RESOURCE MASTERS

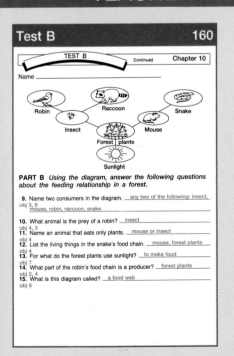

Test B   160

TEST B   Continued   Chapter 10

Name _____

Robin   Raccoon   Snake   Insect   Mouse   Forest plants   Sunlight

PART B *Using the diagram, answer the following questions about the feeding relationship in a forest.*

9. Name two consumers in the diagram. __any two of the following: insect,__
obj 3, 6 __mouse, robin, raccoon, snake__

10. What animal is the prey of a robin? __insect__
obj 4, 3

11. Name an animal that eats only plants. __mouse or insect__
obj 4

12. List the living things in the snake's food chain. __mouse, forest plants__
obj 4

13. For what do the forest plants use sunlight? __to make food__
obj 7

14. What part of the robin's food chain is a producer? __forest plants__
obj 2, 4

15. What is this diagram called? __a food web__
obj 8

CHAPTER 11

Habitats

Planning Guide

Lessons	Objectives	Vocabulary
Chapter Introduction pp. 216, 217		
Lesson 1 Habitats Are Important pp. 218–223	1. **Operationally define** *habitat.* 2. **Communicate** why all living things need space and why animals need shelter. 3. **Communicate** why some animals live in groups.	habitat shelter
Lesson 2 Polar, Tundra, Desert, and Grassland Habitats pp. 224–229	4. **Operationally define** *polar region, tundra, desert,* and *grassland.* 5. **Tell** how examples of plants and animals in these habitats are adapted to the habitat.	polar region tundra desert grassland
Lesson 3 Forest and Water Habitats pp. 230–237	6. **Operationally define** *coniferous, temperate,* and *rain forests.* 7. **Communicate** how animals of these habitats adapt to their habitats. 8. **Identify** the living things in freshwater and saltwater habitats.	coniferous forest temperate forest rain forest freshwater habitats saltwater habitat
Lesson 4 People Adapt to Habitats pp. 238–241	9. **Communicate** how people make changes to habitats. 10. **Operational define** the term *wildlife conservation.* 11. **Infer** why people should conserve wildlife and natural habitats.	wildlife conservation
Chapter Review pp. 242, 243		

Planning Guide

Text Activities		Teacher Resource Masters	Other Components
Title/Skill	**Materials per Group**		
Have You Ever . . . Visited a Pet Shop? p. 217 Observing/Formulating a Model Time Allotment: 30 min.	nonfiction books about animals the students have selected to research	**Activity Center:** "The Habitat of Peter Rabbit"; "Home Is Where the Habitat Is"; "Desert Days"; "Eagle Eye"	
How Can You Make a Land Habitat? p. 223 Observing/ Formulating a Model Time Allotment: 45 min. set up/5-10 minutes daily for two weeks	large jar paper cup lid with rocks holes plants metric ruler water dish gravel small animal potting soil food, water	Independent Practice, pp. 171, 172 ◆ Family Science, p. 162 Activity Worksheet, pp. 163, 164	
		Independent Practice, pp. 171, 172 ▲ Critical Thinking, p. 168	
What Animals Live Around You? p. 237 Observing/Inferring Time Allotment: 30 minutes on two consecutive days	rake mixed bird seed bread crumbs peanuts carrots flour metric ruler resource book on animal tracks pencil and paper	Independent Practice, pp. 171, 172 Activity Worksheet, pp. 165, 166 Art Connection, p. 170 Transparency Master, p. 161 Critical Thinking, p. 167 Language Arts Connection, p. 169 ◆ Reteaching Activity, p. 173	Activity Book, pp. 29, 30 Color Transparency #10 Poster #6
You Can . . . Create a Puppet Show, p. 239 Formulating Models/ Communicating Time Allotment: Two 30 minute periods **Protect Yourself,** p. 357 Observing/Inferring Time Allotment: 20 to 30 minutes; 2 to 3 days to gather materials	old magazines containing animal pictures drawing paper crayons animal books glue cardboard material for scenery students choose materials	Independent Practice, pp. 171, 172	Activity Book, pp. 47, 48
		Test A, p. 174 Test B, pp. 175, 176	

◆ Basic / ▲ Advanced / All other masters are for use by all students.

Habitats

For Exceptional Students

ESL/LEP

Chapter 11/Lesson 1, Page 218
Have students play a guessing game in which one student thinks of an animal. In a version of Twenty Questions, other students begin asking questions about the animal's habitat. The interrogation should steer them to the leading question **Are you thinking of a ____?** Ask students to describe the habitat of the animal guessed.

Chapter 11/Lesson 2, Page 224
Ask students if they would like to live in a polar region. Have them list three reasons why they wouldn't want to live there. Ask them to name three animals that apparently like to live there.

Have students list these habitats: polar, tundra, desert, or grassland. Ask them to pretend they are an animal that lives in each of these habitats. Have them tell what makes each place a good environment for them.

Chapter 11/Lesson 4, Page 238
Discuss with students the need to protect the habitats of animals which are in or near their own habitat. Ask students how people can change their habitat. Have them point out how some changes people make are harmful to animal habitats. Ask students to write a few sentences about protecting animal habitats. Help students with this task when necessary.

Gifted

Chapter 11/Lesson 1, Page 222
Have each of your gifted students choose a small pet or plant that someone their age might enjoy caring for. Using outside sources, have students find out about proper care of and appropriate habitat for the plant or animal based on its needs. Suggest that students design a creative shelter for the living thing. The final product could be a pamphlet, photo essay, or poster describing proper care of the plant or animal.

Mainstreamed

Chapter 11/Lesson 2, Page 228

Developmentally Handicapped: Prepare an overhead transparency titled "Tundra Habitats, Adaptation/Survival Chances." In Column A, list several animals/plants including small plants, palm trees, caribou, robins, and lions. Title Column B "Likely/ Unlikely." Using progressive disclosure with the overhead transparency, show the first item. Ask students to indicate the adaptation/survival chances of the plant or animal. Place an **X** under the appropriate column. Ask students to explain their selection. Repeat for other habitats in the lesson.

Whole Class Science Project

Discuss some animals that are adapted to living in saltwater habitats. Have groups of students research information on saltwater wetlands such as mangrove swamps or salt marshes. Provide the class with small, clear containers to raise their own brine shrimp. Supply each group of students with a few brine shrimp eggs and a hand lens. Brine shrimp eggs can be bought at most pet stores. Ask students to examine and draw what they observe. Explain that these are the eggs of an animal that is found naturally in saltwater lakes. Have students determine how salty the water must be for the brine shrimp to survive by planning and carrying out an experiment to test their ideas. Have them set up a series of containers that have increasing amounts of salt in water. Use aged tap water. For a standard mixture, use one tablespoon of salt mixed with one cup of water. The eggs should hatch in a day or two. Have students observe which concentration of salt water the brine shrimp are best adapted to. They should make regular observations and drawings to record the stages of growth in brine shrimp. Challenge students to find out more about brine shrimp during this experiment.

 ## Science Fair Projects

Individual students could do one of the following projects.
1. Set up an experiment to observe and record the effects of touch on different areas of the specialized leaves of the carnivorous Venus flytrap. Find out what causes the trap to shut.
2. Construct a microhabitat using lichens, molds, ferns, mosses, or water plants. Observe and record the effects a change in temperature or moisture level has on the habitat.

pages 216–243

Chapter Concepts

■ Each living thing is adapted to its own particular habitat; animals find shelters in their habitats.

■ Plants and animals whose needs are alike live together in polar, tundra, desert, or grassland habitats.

■ There are three kinds of forest habitats and two kinds of water habitats; each habitat has living things adapted to it.

■ People make changes to habitats so that they can live in different kinds of habitats; people must also protect habitats.

Chapter Background

■ All organisms need air, food, water, space, and proper growing conditions.

■ Organisms adapt to a specific environment.

■ All organisms living together form a community.

■ A population is made up of organisms of the same species.

■ A habitat is the place where the populations live and grow.

■ Organisms and the environment in which they live make up large habitats known as ecosystems. An ecosystem is one or more communities of organisms.

Looking Ahead

■ Arrange a visit to a zoo to observe a variety of animals in different habitats.

■ You may also arrange a trip to a nature preserve or state park where animals and plants are seen in natural habitats.

Look for These Symbols

　　—Hands-on activity

　　—Cooperative learning

　　—Overhead transparency

◆　—Basic/Reinforcement

●　—Average/Enrichment

▲　—Advanced/Challenge

　　—Calculator Practice

SCIENCE
In Your World

216

CHAPTER 11

Habitats

Everybody tries to find a home. Ants find a home in the soil. Birds find a home in the trees and cliffs. Fish find a home in the streams and seas. Every living thing needs a place to live.

ACTIVITY

Have You Ever...

Visited a Pet Shop?

The animals in a pet shop originally came from different places around the world. Go to a pet shop and look at the animals that are there. Find out more about one of the animals by answering these questions:

1. Where did the animal come from originally?
2. What is the climate and weather like there?
3. What are the dangers to the animal in its home?
4. Where would the animal go to find safety?

Using this information, describe the kind of place you would need to provide to give this animal a home.

217

TEACHER RESOURCE MASTERS

PREPLAN

Time Allotment: 30 minutes

Objectives
1. **Observe** that every living thing needs a place to live.
2. **Explain** some of the elements of habitats.

Setup
■ You will need the following materials for each student or activity group: non-fiction books about animals

1   FOCUS

■ Ask: **What does the photograph tell us about the kind of home this animal comes from?** where the animal might find food and shelter, what the climate is like

2   TEACH

■ Ask: **Describe the place where a rattlesnake lives. Where does a squirrel live? How are they different? What does this tell you about these animals?** *a desert, a wooded area The desert is dry. A squirrel couldn't live in the desert because it's too dry.*

Have You Ever . . .
Use this activity as an introduction to *habitats*.
Have students **work cooperatively** in groups of four.
■ **Student Responses**
Answers will vary with the animal.

3   APPLY

■ Use the discussion to begin to outline the characteristics of different habitats.

Close
■ Review lesson concepts by comparing habitats of animals discussed.

pages 218–223

PREPLAN

Lesson Objectives

1. **Operationally define** *habitat.*
2. **Communicate** why all living things need space and why animals need shelter.
3. **Communicate** why some animals live in groups.

Science Background

■ A forest is one small ecosystem with communities of organisms in the canopy or on the ground. There are many habitats within each of these areas.

■ A habitat is one place in an ecosystem where a population of organisms lives and grows.

■ The habitat contains the life needs of the organism such as proper food, water, air, temperature, pressure, space, soil, and shelter.

Lesson Vocabulary

habitat   shelter

Note: The activity on student page 223 may be used for guided discovery before you begin this lesson.

1   FOCUS

Encourage students to work individually or in small **cooperative groups** to think of a brain teaser. Have students begin by writing the names of several plants or animals on pieces of paper and placing them in environments in which they don't belong. Then have students trade the brain teaser with another student so he or she can tell why the plant or animal wouldn't be able to live in that habitat.

■ Use the goals on student page 218 to establish the purpose for studying this lesson.

LESSON 1 GOALS
You will learn
● that each plant or animal lives in a habitat.
● that all living things have special needs.
● that animals can find protection in habitats.

What does a habitat provide?

Habitats Are Important

Could you live underwater in a cave? Could you live in a nest of sticks on the side of a cliff? Of course not! But an octopus lives underwater, and an eagle can live in a nest on a cliff. Could an eagle or an octopus live where you do?

Plants and animals live in all parts of the world. Living things are found in hot as well as cold places. They live in areas that have dry or wet climates. Each living thing lives in a **habitat** (HAB uh tat), a place where its needs are met. A habitat provides the food, temperature, and living space that each plant or animal needs.

218

TEACHER RESOURCE MASTERS

There are many kinds of habitats. A robin may have a nest in a tree. A fish may live in part of a sunken ship. A beach pea plant grows near an ocean. The nest and tree are part of the robin's habitat. The ship is part of the fish's habitat. The sandy soil is part of the pea plant's habitat. These habitats are different, but each one meets the needs of different living things.

Each living thing is fit for, or adapted to, its habitat. The water lily and the mole in the pictures on this page are adapted to different habitats. The water lily is adapted to life in the water. [1]How is the mole adapted to life underground?

All living things need air, food, and water. They also need space. If too many plants or animals are in one place, the needs of each living thing cannot be met.

1. The mole has sensitive hairs on its nose. It also has front feet adapted for digging.

219

---

2 TEACH

■ Discuss the meaning of *adaptation* as any characteristic of a living thing that improves its chances of survival in a particular habitat.

■ Have students list all of the things that must be found in the habitat in order for plants and animals to live (food, water, air, temperature, pressure, soil, and space).

Guided Practice

■ Check students' understanding of lesson concepts by discussing the Lesson Review questions on student page 222. If necessary, use the **reteaching strategy** in OPTIONS.

Independent Practice

■ Assign the Lesson 1 section of the Teacher Resource Master **Independent Practice,** page 171.

3 APPLY

■ Have students name an animal, tell the type of habitat in which it would be found, and list the other plants and animals that could be found there.

Close

■ Use the summary statements on student page 222 to review the lesson concepts.

OPTIONS

Reteaching Strategy

Make a list of living things found in the schoolyard or nearby park. Write the name of each living thing on an index card and have each student choose a card. The student should tell how the selected living thing fulfills its needs for life and how the living things interrelate in this habitat.

TEACHER RESOURCE MASTERS

Independent Practice   171

INDEPENDENT PRACTICE   Chapter 11

Name ___ Each question is worth 4 points. | Total Points   100 | Your Score ___

Lesson 1   Habitats Are Important
Pages 218 to 223
Complete the sentences using the words below.
groups   shelter   space   needs

1. A place where the ___ needs ___ of living things are met is called a habitat. obj 1
2. The need for food and water by living things cannot be met unless they have enough ___ space ___. obj 2
3. Animals need ___ shelter ___ to protect them from wind, rain, hot or cold weather, and predators. obj 2
4. Some animals are protected from predators by living in ___ groups ___ obj 3

Lesson 2   Polar, Tundra, Desert, and Grassland Habitats
Pages 224 to 229
Complete the sentences using the words below.
desert   polar region   water   tundra   underground   plants

5. A cold, dry habitat with a layer of soil that is usually frozen is called a ___ tundra ___. obj 4
6. A cactus is adapted to desert life by its ability to store ___ water ___ obj 5
7. An area of ice and snow located near the North or South Pole is called a ___ polar region ___. obj 4
8. A habitat that has little moisture is called a ___ desert ___ obj 4
9. One way animals in the desert have adapted to their climate is by living ___ underground ___ obj 5
10. Most of the ___ plants ___ in a grassland are grasses. obj 5

OPTIONS

 SCIENCE AND . . . MATH

- **Skill:** Determine missing elements in patterns.
- **Student Response:** C

LANGUAGE CONNECTION

Reading: Organize students into **cooperative groups** to discuss and respond to the following activity. Have each group select one plant and one animal. Then have each group describe the habitats (place) of its plant and its animal during each season (time). Be certain each group includes food, temperature, and living space in its habitat.

◆ **Reinforcement:** Have students make clay models of plants or animals. Encourage them to use old shoe boxes and pictures from old magazines to construct appropriate habitats for the clay models. Provide the opportunity for students to share their creations with the other students.

● **Enrichment:** Encourage students to work in **cooperative groups** to make science centers for different types of habitats. The centers should include resource books, pictures, photographs, writings, or dioramas related to the particular habitat. Have students take turns presenting their centers to the class.

SCIENCE AND . . .
Math

Dimitri planted 4 seeds in the first row of his garden, 7 in the second, 10 in the third, and 13 in the fourth. If he continues this pattern, how many seeds will be in the sixth row?
A. 15
B. 16
C. 19
D. 22

Suppose you planted vegetables in a garden. Not knowing any better, you poured one hundred seeds onto a small area of garden soil. All of the seeds sprouted. At first, all the seedlings grew well. The next week, some of the plants began to turn yellow and wilt. Soon those plants died. The other plants didn't look healthy. The problem was that too many plants were in one small area. No plant had enough water, food, and light.

The same thing would be true if too many foxes were in one habitat. There would not be enough water and food in the space. Not all of the foxes could live there.

Plants need space

220

TEACHER RESOURCE MASTERS

Within each living space, animals find shelters. A **shelter** is a place or object that protects an animal. Animals use shelters for protection from wind, rain, and hot or cold weather. They also use shelters to hide from predators. Think about some animals that are prey. [1]What shelters could protect these animals from predators? [2]List as many shelters as you can.

Some animals use caves as shelters. Bats, for example, hang from walls inside caves during the daytime. Other animals use holes in trees or rocks, or ledges under the water. Some animals such as insects and spiders hide in the leaves and flowers of plants. Other animals dig burrows or tunnels. Shelters are a part of an animal's habitat.

What is a shelter?

1. Answers may include burrows, nests, ledges.

2. Students should list various kinds of shelters. Answers may include trees, rocks, eaves of roofs.

Bats in a cave

Birds in trees

221

OPTIONS

■ Write the term *shelter* on the chalkboard. Have students discuss the term and list as many shelters as they can.
■ Have students choose an animal and tell in what habitat it would be found and what shelter it would seek.

◆ **Reinforcement:** Encourage students to make a picture book or collage called "Living Things and Their Shelters." Students should cut out pictures of animals and their shelters to construct the book or the collage. Have them share their work with the other students.

● **Enrichment:** Have students prepare a matching game bulletin board for a science center. Provide them with pictures of animals and pictures of animal shelters. Provide yarn and tape so students can connect the animal with the shelter. Have students change the matching game every few days.

TEACHER RESOURCE MASTERS

OPTIONS

▨▲**Challenge:** Encourage students to brainstorm to make a list of animals that live in a group such as a pack of wolves or a pod of whales. Have them find the proper group name for each animal listed and tell how the group protects the individual from predators. Have students make a chart to show their findings.

LESSON REVIEW ANSWERS

1. a place where the needs of living things are met
2. The seeds would be too crowded to get the proper food, water, and light.
3. A group helps to protect animals from predators; wind and precipitation have less effect on animals huddled in a group.

School of fish

Some animals are protected from predators by living in groups. Herds, flocks, packs, prides, pods, and schools are some names for animal groups. Most predators do not attack animals in a group. They look for prey that is alone. The group, therefore, is like a shelter for each animal.

A group can also protect some animals from storms. Wind and precipitation have less effect on each animal when the animals are huddled together. In this way, too, the group acts like a shelter.

The world has millions of different places to live. For each habitat, there are different plants and animals that are adapted to it.

Lesson Summary

- Each plant or animal is adapted to a habitat, a place where its needs are met.
- Air, food, water, and space are life needs.
- Shelters protect animals from predators and hot, cold, wet, or windy weather.

Lesson Review

1. What is a habitat?
2. Why would sixty seeds planted in a small area probably not grow well?
★3. How are some animals protected by living in a group?

222

TEACHER RESOURCE MASTERS

Family Science 162

FAMILY SCIENCE   Chapter 11

Name _____

Your child is learning about plants and animals in science. This home activity will show the wide variety of plants and animals that live nearby.

PLANT AND ANIMAL TREASURE HUNT

Take a walk around your neighborhood. Look for the plants and animals that are described in each sentence below. Check each sentence when you find a plant or animal that fits it. Then, write the name of the plant or animal in the blank.

Check here: Answers will vary.

Name of Plant or Animal

___ **1.** A plant that is taller than you are. _____
___ **2.** A plant that grows on another plant. _____
___ **3.** A plant that lives in or near water. _____
___ **4.** A plant that is food for a small ground animal. _____
___ **5.** A plant that grows in a shady place. _____
___ **6.** A plant that grows in a sunny place. _____
___ **7.** A plant that is food for a flying animal. _____
___ **8.** A plant that is food for a large animal. _____
___ **9.** An animal that lives in a tree or bush. _____
___ **10.** An animal that lives in the grass. _____
___ **11.** An animal that lives in water. _____
___ **12.** An animal that eats seeds or nuts. _____

How can you make a land habitat?

What you need

large jar	plants
lid with holes	water
metric ruler	water dish
gravel	small animal
potting soil	animal food
paper cup	pencil
rocks	paper

What to do

1. Add a 3-cm layer of gravel to the jar. Add an 8-cm layer of soil on top of the gravel. Set a few small rocks on the soil.
2. Place the plants in the soil and add water.
3. Add food to the jar.
4. Put the animal in the jar. Replace the lid.
5. Add food and water as needed. Record your observations.

What did you learn?

1. What was the animal's shelter?
2. How do you know if the needs of the plants and animals were met?

Using what you learned

1. How is this habitat the same as or different from the animal's natural habitat?
2. What would happen if you planted these plants in an aquarium filled with water? Why?

223

ACTIVITY RESPONSES

What did you learn?

1. The plants or rocks were shelter for the animal.
2. As long as the plants and animal stayed healthy, their needs were met.

Using what you learned

1. Answers will vary. Some may be that the habitat is the same because it provides food, water, and shelter for the animals. It is different because it is smaller in size and is contained within a jar.
2. The plants would probably die because they would get too much water.

PREPLAN

Time Allotment: One 45-minute period to set up the terrarium and a 5- to 10-minute period daily for two weeks.

Process Skill: Observing, Formulating a Model

Objectives

1. **Build** a land habitat terrarium.
2. **Identify** the living things that are introduced into this habitat.

Setup

■ Chameleons or other small lizards, frogs, or toads are good animals to use for this activity.

Cooperative Grouping: tens—Assign roles as explained on page T24.

1   FOCUS

■ Provide copies of *National Geographic* for students to look through. Have students select a habitat of interest, then devise a plan for the construction of the model habitat in the jar.

2   TEACH

■ **Safety Consideration:** Remind students to take care when handling glass jars and any animals.
■ Have the students construct a graph or chart and record changes in plant height.
■ Have students use the Teacher Resource Master **Activity Worksheet, pages 163 and 164,** to record their data.

3   APPLY

■ Discuss how the materials and living things were used to make a model of the habitat. Encourage students to make suggestions for improving their habitat.

Close

■ Discuss the activity and questions.

PREPLAN

Lesson Objectives

4. Operationally define *polar region, tundra, desert,* and *grassland.*

5. Tell how examples of plants and animals in these habitats are adapted to the habitat.

Science Background

■ The growing season is short and the permafrost layer in the tundra prevents the development of root systems necessary for large plants.

■ Lichens, mosses, polar bears, mice, musk oxen, foxes, and a variety of birds are found in the tundra.

■ Deserts have a wide daily temperature range.

■ Cacti, yuccas, kangaroo rats, snakes, and scorpions are found in the desert.

■ Grasses, snakes, zebras, rabbits, bison, and lions are found in grasslands.

Lesson Vocabulary

polar region   tundra   desert   grassland

1   FOCUS

⬛ Have students locate the polar regions, deserts, and grasslands on a world map or globe. Have them draw pictures to show the plant and animal life living in each habitat.

■ Use the goals on student page 224 to establish the purpose for studying this lesson.

Polar, Tundra, Desert, and Grassland Habitats

Imagine a cactus trying to live in the Arctic. Its needs would not be met there. Neither could a polar bear meet its needs if it lived in a hot, dry desert. Plants and animals whose needs are alike live together in the same type of habitat.

Polar and Tundra Habitats

Two areas in the far northern and southern parts of the world have very cold climates and are called polar regions. A **polar region** is an area of ice and snow located near the North or South Pole. Very few plants live in the polar regions.

Climate zones

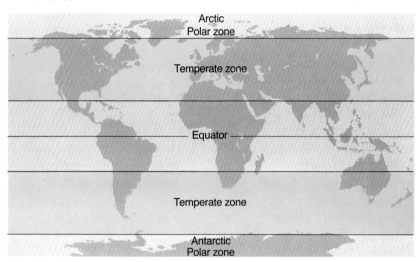

224

TEACHER RESOURCE MASTERS

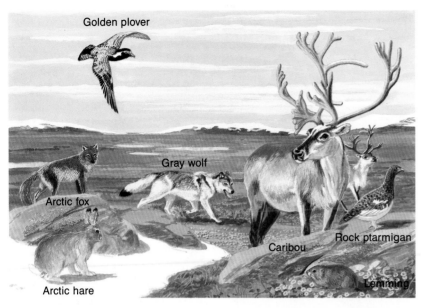

Golden plover

Gray wolf

Arctic fox

Arctic hare

Caribou

Rock ptarmigan

Lemming

Animals of the Arctic tundra

Fish, whales, and seals live in the salt water within both polar regions. Walruses live only in the northern region. Penguins live only in the southern region.

Many kinds of animal life and some plant life are found on frozen land surrounding the ice of the northern polar region. This habitat is called the Arctic tundra (TUN druh). **Tundra** is a cold, dry habitat with a layer of soil that is usually frozen. The tundra is covered with snow more than half the year. The climate is too cold for tall trees to grow. However, small plants such as grasses and mosses do grow in the tundra.

Why aren't trees found in the tundra?

225

TEACHER RESOURCE MASTERS

Independent Practice 171

INDEPENDENT PRACTICE   Chapter 11

Name _Each question is worth 4 points._   Total Points 100
                                           Your Score __

Lesson 1   Habitats Are Important
             Pages 218 to 223
Complete the sentences using the words below.
groups   shelter   space   needs

1. A place where the _____needs_____ of living things are met is called a habitat. obj 1
2. The need for food and water by living things cannot be met unless they have enough _____space_____. obj 2
3. Animals need _____shelter_____ to protect them from wind, rain, hot or cold weather, and predators. obj 2
4. Some animals are protected from predators by living in ___groups___
                                                              obj 3
Lesson 2   Polar, Tundra, Desert, and Grassland Habitats
             Pages 224 to 229
Complete the sentences using the words below.
desert   polar region   water   tundra   underground   plants
5. A cold, dry habitat with a layer of soil that is usually frozen is called a _____tundra_____
                                                  obj 4
6. A cactus is adapted to desert life by its ability to store ___water__ obj 5
7. An area of ice and snow located near the North or South Pole is called a _____polar region_____. obj 4
8. A habitat that has little moisture is called a _____desert___ obj 4
9. One way animals in the desert have adapted to their climate is by living _____underground_____
                                              obj 5
10. Most of the _____plants_____ in a grassland are grasses.
                                              obj 5

2 TEACH

■ Write the term *polar region* on the chalkboard and have students discuss why plant growth is limited in this area.
■ Discuss the term *tundra* with the students, teaching the concept that tundra is also located on the tops of high mountains such as the mountains of Colorado and the Andes.

Guided Practice

■ Check students' understanding of lesson concepts by discussing the Lesson Review questions on student page 229. If necessary, use the **reteaching strategy** in OPTIONS.

Independent Practice

■ Assign the Lesson 2 section of the Teacher Resource Master **Independent Practice,** page 171.

3 APPLY

■ Have students name plants and animals that could live in the polar or tundra habitat and tell how they have adapted to these habitats.

Close

■ Use Summary statements on student page 229 to review lesson concepts.

OPTIONS

Reteaching Strategy

Encourage students to focus on the artwork and photographs in the text for the polar and tundra habitats. Have them **work cooperatively** to construct a chart that labels the habitat, gives examples of producers and consumers, names common predators, describes where the habitat is located and tells how plants and animals are adapted to the habitat.

OPTIONS

MATH CONNECTION

Reproduce the above drawing of penguins and present students with the following problem.

What fraction of the penguins in the drawing is facing left? (6/8) What fraction is facing right? (2/8) Write these fractions in simplest terms. (3/4, 1/4)

◆ **Reinforcement:** Encourage students to collect pictures of plants and animals for each of the three habitats. Have them cut out and mount the pictures on tag board. Use a coat hanger, tag board, yarn, and the mounted pictures to make a plant and animal collage for each habitat. Be certain to label the collages. Exhibit the collages in the classroom and have students continue to add pictures of living things to the appropriate collage.

● **Enrichment:** Encourage students to research the topic of how native Americans used the bison. Have them make a drawing of a bison and use yarn to connect parts of the animal to an information card on how this bison part was used. Discuss the findings of the project.

Reindeer

Arctic tern

Musk oxe

The tundra also contains a great variety of animal life. Reindeer, musk oxen, wolves, mice, and the Arctic tern are some animals that live in the tundra.

Some animals living in the tundra grow thick fur in winter and then shed much of the fur in summer. Some animals are adapted to seasonal changes in other ways. Animals such as the Arctic hare have lighter-colored fur in winter than in summer. [1]How does this color change protect the Arctic hare?

1. The color change helps the hare blend in with its surroundings.

226

TEACHER RESOURCE MASTERS

Desert Habitat

Another type of habitat is the desert. A **desert** is a habitat that has little moisture. Some deserts are hot and dry. Other deserts are cold and dry. Living things there are adapted to life with little water. Some animals, such as rattlesnakes, get all the water they need from their food. Other animals, such as the camel, drink a lot of water at one time. They can live for many days without drinking again.

Desert plants are also adapted to a dry climate. Some plants such as cacti store water in their stems or roots. Many desert plants have small leaves that lose very little water to the air. These plants are able to live for a long time without taking up water.

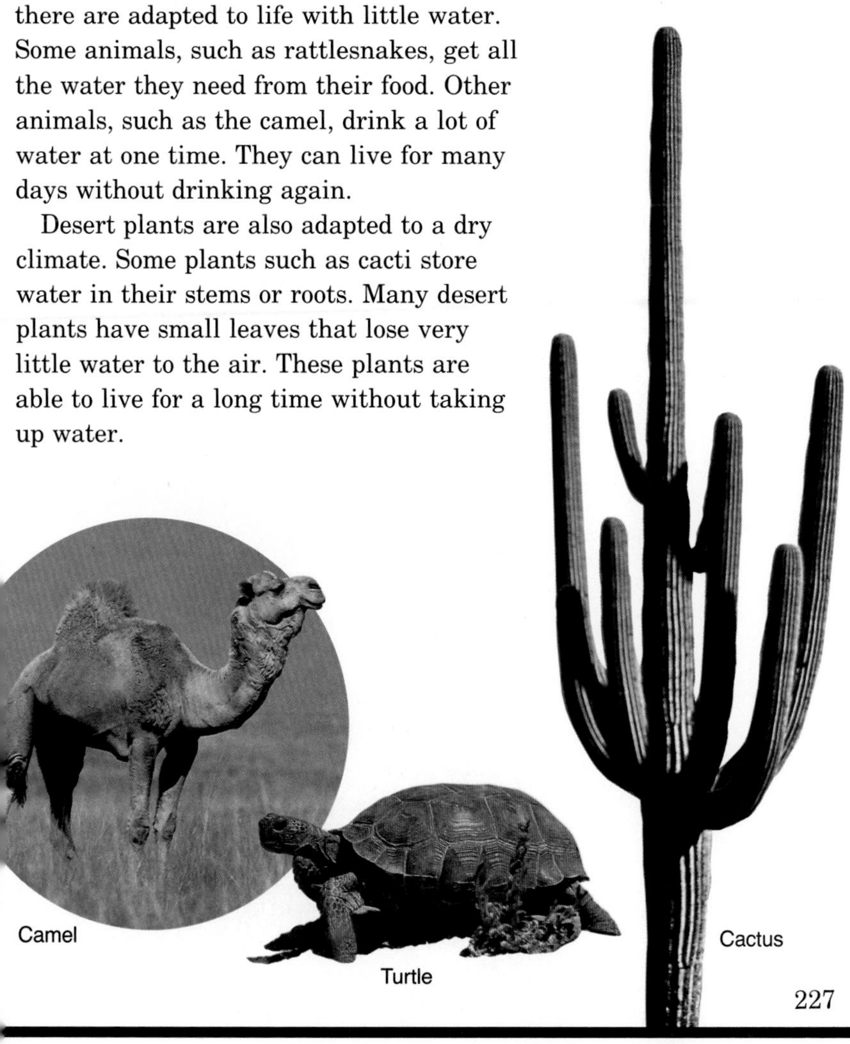

Camel

Turtle

Cactus

227

OPTIONS

▲ **Challenge:** Challenge students to research the topic of protective coloration of animals in each of the habitats. Have them compare the findings for each habitat and share the results with the other students.

■ Discuss the operational definition of the term *desert*.

■ Help students realize that the desert has little precipitation. Organisms must store moisture or get it from food they eat.

TEACHER RESOURCE MASTERS

OPTIONS

■ Discuss the many terms that are synonymous with *grassland*—steppe, prairie, plain, pampas, veldt, and savanna.

■ Encourage students to bring in photographs of grassland habitats from magazines. Have them list the living things they are able to observe and identify in the grassland pictures. Ask students to find out what makes a grassland. They should discuss that grasslands are made up of several species of grasses. Discuss how the living things on all grasslands are alike and how they are different.

Would You Believe?

An elephant can run as fast as 40 kilometers per hour.

Animals in the desert are adapted to a dry habitat. Living underground is one way animals stay cool in the desert. Small size is an important adaptation to desert life. Small living things find it easier to escape desert heat than do large animals.

Grassland Habitat

Another type of habitat is the grassland. A **grassland** is a habitat where most of the plants are grasses. Some animals that live in grasslands are prairie dogs, pronghorn antelope, foxes, hawks, lions, and kangaroos. Some of the fastest animals on Earth live there. Grasslands are usually large, open spaces. Speed is necessary to escape from predators or to catch prey.

228

TEACHER RESOURCE MASTERS

Critical Thinking   168

CRITICAL THINKING/PROBLEM SOLVING   Challenge   Chapter 11

Name _____

ANIMALS OF THE GRASSLAND

On each continent there are animals that are adapted for living in grasslands. Use resource books to find examples of grassland animals and complete the chart below. Answers will vary, the following are examples.

	Running Predators	Running Plant-eaters	Running Flightless Birds	Burrowing Plant-eaters	Jumping Plant-eaters
NORTH AMERICA	coyote wolf	pronghorn bison		prairie dog	jack rabbit
SOUTH AMERICA	bush dogs pampas fox	guanaco	rhea	Patagonian cavy plains vizcachas	
AFRICA	cheetah lion	zebra gazelle	ostrich	ground squirrel	springhaas
ASIA	tiger	saiga wild horse		hamster	jerboa
AUSTRALIA	Tasmanian wolf		emu	wombat	kangaroo

Lesson Summary

- The polar regions, tundra, desert, and grassland are four types of habitats.
- Each type of habitat contains a variety of plants and animals that are adapted to that habitat.

Lesson Review

1. How are the northern polar and Arctic tundra regions different?
2. Describe a plant and an animal that live in a desert habitat.
3. Give an example of an animal that lives in the grasslands, and tell how it is adapted to life there.

Animals of the grasslands

LESSON REVIEW ANSWERS

1. More plants and animals live in the tundra because there is soil and it is not always frozen.

2. Answers may include plants that store water in their stems or roots and animals that are small, live underground, and don't need a lot of water.

3. Answers may include animals such as an antelope that is fast or a fox that can hide in tall grass.

229

TEACHER RESOURCE MASTERS

PREPLAN

Lesson Objectives

6. Operationally define *coniferous, temperate,* and *rain forests.*

7. Communicate how animals of these habitats adapt to their habitats.

8. Identify the living things in freshwater and saltwater habitats.

Science Background

■ Coniferous forests include pines, larches, moose, deer, rodents, and a variety of birds.

■ Temperate forests include maples, oaks, spring wildflowers, bears, squirrels, and many birds.

■ Tropical rain forests include vines, palms, tree ferns, monkeys, ants, and reptiles.

■ Algae are the major producers in freshwater and saltwater habitats.

■ Most ocean life is near the surface because of light limitations.

Lesson Vocabulary

coniferous forest   temperate forest
rain forest   freshwater habitats
saltwater habitat

Note: The activity on student page 237 may be used for guided discovery before you begin this lesson.

1   FOCUS

📖 Display photographs of different kinds of forests. Ask students to observe and predict the different types of consumers that would inhabit each type of forest. Show them where each type of forest would be located on a world map or globe.

■ Use the goals on student page 230 to establish the purpose for studying this lesson.

Forest and Water Habitats

LESSON 3 GOALS
You will learn
● that there are three kinds of forest habitats.
● that there are two kinds of water habitats.

When you think of the word *forest*, what picture comes to mind? Do you see pine trees, maple trees with bright fall colors, or very tall trees? Do you picture moose and owls, deer and cardinals, or monkeys and parrots? All these living things and more can be found in different kinds of forests.

There are three kinds of forest habitats. Each kind of forest contains plants and animals that are adapted to it.

A **coniferous** (kuh NIHF rus) **forest** is a habitat in many northern regions of the world. The growing season is short, and the weather is very cold. These forests have trees with needle-shaped leaves. Most coniferous trees stay green all year. Spruce and fir are two kinds of evergreen trees found in coniferous forests.

Coniferous forest

230

TEACHER RESOURCE MASTERS

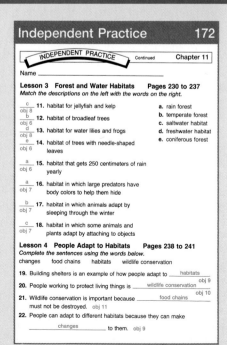
Temperate forest

A variety of animals live in coniferous forests. These animals include mice, beavers, moose, owls, wolves, and woodpeckers.

A **temperate** (TEM prut) **forest** is a habitat that has four seasons—spring, summer, autumn, and winter. Temperate forests contain mostly broadleaf trees that lose their leaves in autumn. New leaf growth does not take place until spring. Oak, maple, and elm trees are examples of broadleaf trees that are common in many temperate forests. Smaller plants such as wildflowers, mosses, and ferns are also found in these forests.

231

OPTIONS

MATH CONNECTION

■ Have students complete the following problem.

The rainiest place on Earth is Mount Waialeale, Hawaii. It receives about 1,165.86 centimeters of rain each year. What number is in the tenths place of this amount? (8) What number is in the hundredths place? (6)

♦ **Reinforcement:** Divide the class into two groups. Encourage each group to construct plant or animal flashcards using mounted photographs. The name of the habitat for the living thing should be written on the back of the flashcard. Play the game "Where Does It Live?" Show pictures (one at a time) to a member of the opposite team. If that member correctly identifies the habitat in which the organism lives, the team gets one point. If the member is incorrect, the other team gets the point. Continue until all the pictures are correctly identified.

● **Enrichment:** Encourage students to invent their own plant or animal that would be adapted to life in the rain forest. Have them make a model of the living thing. Have students present their model to the class and tell about its natural history. Be certain students specify how the living thing is adapted to the habitat.

Resource Options

Use Color Transparency #10, "The Temperate Forest."

■ Use Poster #6, "Leaf-Cutter Ants."

Animals living in temperate forests are adapted to a year with four seasons. Most of the year, they have a good supply of food. In winter, there is less food. Deer, rabbits, mice, and some birds find food under the snow. Other birds must leave their habitats and fly to warmer places where they can find food. Some forest animals such as insects, salamanders, frogs, chipmunks, and bears sleep through most of the winter.

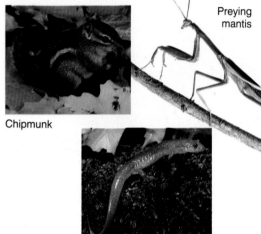

Preying mantis

Chipmunk

Bear

Salamander

Animals of temperate forests

Where are rain forests found?

The third kind of forest habitat is the rain forest. A **rain forest** is a habitat that receives about 250 centimeters of rain a year. Rain forests are found in South America, Malaysia, and Africa and are hot and wet.

232

TEACHER RESOURCE MASTERS

Plants grow quickly in rain forests. They are adapted to daily rainfall and even temperatures. Many evergreen plants with broad leaves grow closely together. Most trees grow tall and are covered with vines.

Animals of rain forests

Animals in rain forests are adapted to life among tall plants. Monkeys use their long tails and arms to swing from tree to tree. Large predators have body colors that help them hide when they hunt prey. Look at each animal in the picture on this page. [1]How is each animal adapted to life in a rain forest?

1. Jaguar's color helps it blend into foliage. Macaw's bright colors blend in with flowering plants. Anaconda's color helps it hide. Spider monkey swings from trees.

233

OPTIONS

■ Have students name consumers found in temperate forests, giving several ways they are adapted to the cold winters.

■ Compare and contrast the types of consumers found in the rain and temperate forest habitats. Explain that there are more kinds of plants and animals in a tropical rain forest than in any other habitat. Point out that animal life is most abundant in the treetops.

TEACHER RESOURCE MASTERS

Art Connection 170

ART CONNECTION — Creating Pictures — Chapter 11

Name

ANIMALS IN THE FORESTS

Inside each box draw the habitat to which each animal has adapted.

rain forest	rain forest
temperate forest	temperate forest
coniferous forest	coniferous forest

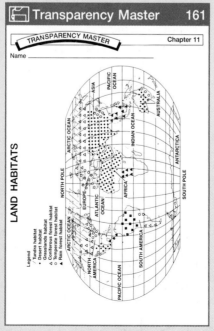

Transparency Master 161

TRANSPARENCY MASTER — Chapter 11

Name

LAND HABITATS

OPTIONS

▲ **Challenge:** Encourage interested students to prepare and maintain a saltwater or freshwater aquarium in the classroom. Information on setting up and maintaining the aquarium can be obtained from a local pet store, library, or by writing for the pamphlet: *How to Set Up and Maintain a Saltwater Aquarium.* TAMU-SG-82-504, The Marine Information Service, Sea Grant College Program, Texas A&M University, College Station, Texas 77843.

Water Habitats

Much of Earth is covered with water. On Earth there is more water than land. There are two types of water habitats. There are different kinds of plants and animals that are adapted to living in each of them.

Freshwater habitats are found in ponds, bogs, swamps, lakes, and rivers. Each freshwater habitat has many kinds of plants and animals living there. Some plants and animals live in very cold waters. Others live in warm waters. Some plants and animals are adapted to waters that flow fast. Others are adapted to still water. Water lilies are freshwater plants. Freshwater animals include largemouth bass, beavers, clams, and frogs.

Where is fresh water found?

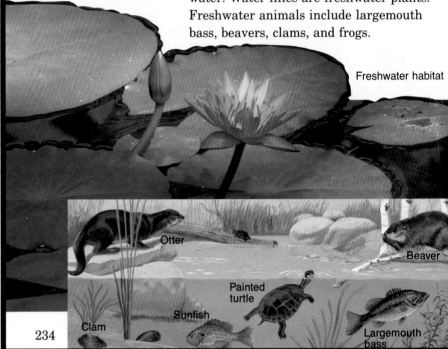

Freshwater habitat

Otter

Beaver

Painted turtle

Sunfish

Clam

Largemouth bass

234

TEACHER RESOURCE MASTERS

Critical Thinking 167

CRITICAL THINKING/PROBLEM SOLVING Chapter 11

Name _____

COME LIVE WITH ME

Look at the pictures. Put a ✔ under the habitat in which each animal lives. Draw the habitat.

	Land	Water	Habitat Drawing
		✓	stream or river
	✓		grassland
	✓		rain forest
	✓		forest
	✓		desert
	✓	✓	pond

The larger of the two types of water habitats is the ocean or **saltwater habitat.** Large numbers of living things are found in salt water. Some animals such as sharks, jellyfish, sea bass, and whales move freely through the salt water. Sea anemones and sea squirts are attached to objects and do not move away.

Earth has many habitats. Every habitat, even a polar region covered with ice and snow, supports life. All living things are adapted to their own habitats.

Saltwater habitat

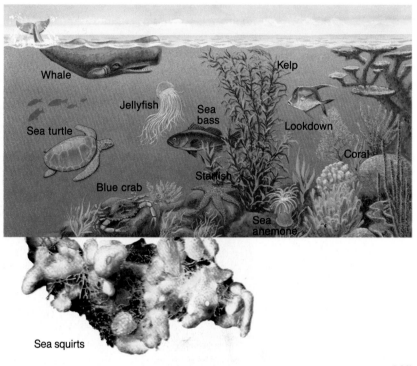

Whale

Kelp

Jellyfish

Sea
bass

Sea turtle

Lookdown

Coral

Blue crab

Starfish

Sea
anemone

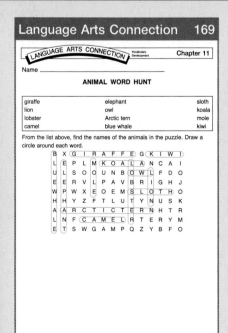

Sea squirts

235

OPTIONS

■ Using a world map or globe, have students compare the amount of land to the amount of water on Earth's surface. Encourage students to compare the size of ocean surfaces to the size of freshwater surfaces by locating the oceans of the world and large freshwater bodies such as lakes and rivers.

■ Encourage students to brainstorm all the ocean and saltwater habitats they can name and list these on the chalkboard. Examples would be seas, bays, and estuaries. Have students name a plant or animal that would live in each habitat named.

■ Repeat the process with freshwater habitats. Examples would be ponds, puddles, creeks, streams, and rivers.

■ Have students brainstorm what all freshwater and saltwater living things have in common. The discussion should include life needs and similar structure-function relationships.

TEACHER RESOURCE MASTERS

Language Arts Connection 169

LANGUAGE ARTS CONNECTION   Vocabulary Development   Chapter 11

Name _____

ANIMAL WORD HUNT

giraffe	elephant	sloth
lion	owl	koala
lobster	Arctic tern	mole
camel	blue whale	kiwi

From the list above, find the names of the animals in the puzzle. Draw a circle around each word.

```
B X G I R A F F E G K I W I
L E P L M K O A L A N C A I
U L S O O U N B O W L F D O
E E R V L P A V B R I G H J
W P W X E O E M S L O T H O
H H Y Z F T L U T Y N U S K
A A R C T I C T E R N H T R
L N F C A M E L R T E R Y M
E T S W G A M P Q Z Y B F O
```

Reteaching Activity 173

RETEACHING ACTIVITY   Chapter 11

Name _____

WHAT LIVING THINGS WOULD YOU FIND IN THESE HABITATS?

Materials
pictures of polar, desert, grassland, forest, mountain, and water habitats
12 sheets of drawing paper   crayons   pencil and paper

What to do
1. Draw a picture of a plant that lives in each habitat listed above. Label the plant and the habitat where it lives.
2. Draw a picture of an animal that lives in each habitat listed above. Label the animal and the habitat where it lives.

What did you learn?
1. Which picture would you name polar? Desert? Grassland? Forest? Mountain? Water habitat? Answers will depend on the pictures.

2. Name the plants that live in each habitat. Answers will vary.
_____

3. Name the animals that live in each habitat. Answers will vary. Examples are: polar bear - polar area; camel - desert; bison - grassland; bear - forest; goat - mountains; whale - water

Using what you learned
1. How can people live in each one of the habitats listed above? People are able to provide food and shelter for themselves in most environments.

2. What would you need to live in each habitat? You would need food, shelter, water, and space to live in each place.

CHAPTER 11/LESSON 3

pages 230–237

LESSON REVIEW ANSWERS

1. Trees of coniferous forests have needle-shaped leaves; most trees of temperate forests have broad leaves; trees of rain forests grow very tall, close together, and are covered with vines.

2. Answers may include bears that sleep most of the winter in temperate forests, and owls or woodpeckers that live in trees of the coniferous forests.

3. Monkeys use their long tails and arms to swing through the trees.

4. Answers may include a turtle with flippers and large whales in salt water; beavers that build dams and turtles that have feet in fresh water.

Lesson Summary

- Northern coniferous forests, temperate forests, and rain forests are three kinds of forest habitats.
- Freshwater and saltwater habitats are the two kinds of water habitats.

Lesson Review

1. Compare the types of trees that grow in northern coniferous forests, temperate forests, and rain forests.
2. Tell about animals that live in temperate forests and coniferous forests.
3. How is a monkey adapted to living in a rain forest?
★4. Describe two animals that live in salt water and two animals that live in fresh water.

236

TEACHER RESOURCE MASTERS

236   Chapter 11

ACTIVITY

What animals live around you?

What you need

rake
mixed bird seed
bread crumbs
peanuts
carrots
flour
metric ruler
resource book on
  animal tracks
pencil and paper

What to do

1. Select a place on the ground where you think an animal lives or visits.
2. Rake leaves away from the area.
3. Measure an area one meter long and one meter wide.
4. Spread flour over the area.
5. Place a variety of foods in the middle of the area.
6. Return the next day and observe any tracks in the flour. Record which foods were eaten.

What did you learn?

1. How many different types of tracks did you find?
2. Where do you think the animal(s) came from?
3. Which food did the animal(s) eat?

Using what you learned

1. What animal(s) made tracks in the flour?
2. How could you use this activity to find out if an animal has made a home in your yard?

237

ACTIVITY RESPONSES

What did you learn?

1. Answers may vary.
2. Answers may include from shelters close by. This can be determined by the directions and positions of the tracks.
3. Answers will vary. Carrots would be eaten by rabbits, peanuts by squirrels, and crumbs and birdseed by mice and birds.

Using what you learned

1. The food may attract a variety of consumers including woodchucks, snakes, ants, rabbits, ground squirrels, mice, birds, and worms.
2. The same process used in the activity is appropriate for detecting an animal in another locale, such as a yard.

PREPLAN

Time Allotment: 30 minutes on two consecutive days

Process Skills: Observing/Inferring

Objectives

1. **Construct** the study site.
2. **Observe** evidence of animal movement based upon tracks.
3. **Infer** the types of animals that live in the habitat.
4. **Tell** where the animal that visited the study site lives.

Setup

■ Locate several active sites to use.
■ Have resource books available to identify animal tracks.

Cooperative Grouping: fives—Assign roles as explained on page T24.

1   FOCUS

■ Construct a pictorial puzzle showing several different types of animal footprints. Have students describe each animal based on the footprints, tell what the animal was doing when the footprints were made, and give evidence for their interpretations.

2   TEACH

■ Have students make before and after drawings for comparison.
■ Have students use the Teacher Resource Master **Activity Worksheet,** pages 165 and 166, to record their data.

3   APPLY

■ Discuss the presence of a variety of living things in one habitat.

Close

■ Discuss the activity and questions.

PREPLAN

Lesson Objectives

9. Communicate how people make changes to habitats.

10. Operationally define the term *wildlife conservation*.

11. Infer why people should conserve wildlife and natural habitats.

Science Background

■ Conservation is the wise use of resources including preservation or proper, controlled utilization.

■ The preservation of natural habitats and natural resources requires public support.

■ People are invaders of habitats and have the ability to improve or destroy them.

■ The conservation of water, air, land, plants, animals, and space is important to the future of life on Earth.

Lesson Vocabulary

wildlife conservation

1 FOCUS

Obtain current pictures of the area where you live and pictures of the same area 50 or 100 years ago. Encourage students to cite observed changes in the photograph series and suggest several hypotheses for the population changes over the years. Encourage students to draw pictures and suggest changes that will occur in the next 50 or 100 years. Discuss students' suggestions.

■ Use the goals on student page 238 to establish the purpose for studying this lesson.

People Adapt to Habitats

You've learned that monkeys live in rain forests, sharks live in salt water, and reindeer live in the tundra. Where do people live?

Most plants and animals live in only one kind of habitat. People, however, live in different kinds of habitats. They adapt to different habitats because they can make changes to them. People can build shelters to protect them from predators and the weather. They can grow and eat different kinds of food. People can make their own clothes. People, like some other animals, can move from one habitat to another. The pictures on this page show different habitats where people live.

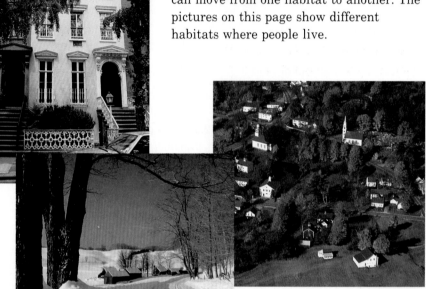

Different habitats

238

TEACHER RESOURCE MASTERS

ACTIVITY

You Can...

Create a Puppet Show

Use old magazines. Cut out three animals that live in different habitats. You might want to draw your own animals if you can't find pictures you like. Glue each animal to cardboard and attach a cardboard handle. Write a puppet show about each animal. Create scenery for your shows to illustrate each animal's habitat.

Although people make changes to habitats, they must be careful not to harm a habitat. Habitats should remain healthy places for plants and animals. Some people work to protect habitats. Their work is called wildlife conservation. **Wildlife conservation** is the protection that is given to living things and their habitats.

What is wildlife conservation?

Protecting animals

239

2 TEACH

■ Discuss the ways people can change or improve the habitat in which they live. Write the word *conservation* on the chalkboard or overhead and discuss its meaning. Relate the word to looking after, protecting, saving, or preserving a valuable possession. Encourage students to provide examples of wise use of their habitat.

Guided Practice

■ Check students' understanding of lesson concepts by discussing the Lesson Review questions on student page 240. If necessary, use the **reteaching strategy** in OPTIONS.

Independent Practice

■ Assign the Lesson 4 section of the Teacher Resource Master **Independent Practice,** page 172.

3 APPLY

■ Use Application Activity, "Protect Yourself," on student pages 357 and 358.

Close

■ Use Summary statements on student page 240 to review lesson concepts.

OPTIONS

Reteaching Strategy

Divide students into **cooperative groups.** Bring in some plants from a local forest preserve or nature center. Each group will transplant and chart the progress of its plants. Students with hands-on experience will be able to infer why the plants are not doing well out of the habitat.

Resource Options

■ Use Activity Book, "Protect Yourself," pages 47, 48.
■ Refer to page 240 for teaching strategies for **You Can . . . Create a Puppet Show**

TEACHER RESOURCE MASTERS

Independent Practice   172

INDEPENDENT PRACTICE   Continued   Chapter 11

Name _____

Lesson 3   Forest and Water Habitats   Pages 230 to 237
Match the descriptions on the left with the words on the right.

___c___ **11.** habitat for jellyfish and kelp
obj 8

___b___ **12.** habitat of broadleaf trees
obj 6

___d___ **13.** habitat for water lilies and frogs
obj 8

___e___ **14.** habitat of trees with needle-shaped
obj 6   leaves

___a___ **15.** habitat that gets 250 centimeters of rain
obj 6   yearly

___a___ **16.** habitat in which large predators have
obj 7   body colors to help them hide

___b___ **17.** habitat in which animals adapt by
obj 7   sleeping through the winter

___c___ **18.** habitat in which some animals and
obj 7   plants adapt by attaching to objects

a. rain forest
b. temperate forest
c. saltwater habitat
d. freshwater habitat
e. coniferous forest

Lesson 4   People Adapt to Habitats   Pages 238 to 241
Complete the sentences using the words below.
changes   food chains   habitats   wildlife conservation

19. Building shelters is an example of how people adapt to ___habitats___
obj 9

20. People working to protect living things is ___wildlife conservation___
obj 10

21. Wildlife conservation is important because ___food chains___
must not be destroyed. obj 11

22. People can adapt to different habitats because they can make
___changes___ to them. obj 9

OPTIONS

YOU CAN . . . CREATE A PUPPET SHOW

Process Skill: Formulating Models/ Communicating

Objective: Identify the types of animals that live in different habitats.

Setup/Teach:

Have students **work cooperatively** in small groups. Provide some magazines with animal pictures. Students can use library books and draw their own animals if they choose.

■ Students might enjoy sharing their shows with students in earlier grades.

LANGUAGE CONNECTION

Reading: Organize students into **cooperative groups** to discuss and respond to the following activity. Have each group describe the habitats of each of its members as their habitats exist today. Then have each group identify past changes that have been made in each habitat. Finally, have each group determine if their habitats have or have not remained healthy places for plants and animals.

Career: Use "I WANT TO KNOW ABOUT . . . A Zoo Worker," student page 241, with this lesson.

LESSON REVIEW ANSWERS

1. build shelters, grow food, make their own clothes

2. If people destroy producers, they have destroyed the basis of a food chain.

Wildlife conservation should be a concern for everyone. People need to make sure that food chains are not destroyed. Everyone must remember that producers are the basis of every food chain in the world.

Lesson Summary

• People can build shelters, grow food, and travel to different habitats.

• Wildlife conservation concerns the protection of habitats.

Lesson Review

1. What are some examples of changes that people make to habitats?

★2. Why is the conservation of producers especially important?

240　　Use with Application Activity on pages 357, 358.

TEACHER RESOURCE MASTERS

I WANT TO KNOW ABOUT...

A Zoo Worker

Bill Toone takes care of birds at a large zoo. He is working with California condors, the largest flying bird in the United States. They are seriously endangered.

Condors have lost some of their habitat to humans. Many condors have become sick from eating poison by mistake. The sick adults can't care for their young. People are trying to help.

Some people are carefully taking condor eggs from the nests of sick adults. The eggs are carefully packed and flown by helicopter to the zoo. When a chick hatches, Bill makes sure that it is cared for properly.

Biologists like Bill are working hard to save the California condor. Bill wants to increase the number of condors at the zoo. These birds can later be released to the wild.

Career

241

TEACHER RESOURCE MASTERS

Feature Background

■ A list of endangered and threatened wildlife and plants can be obtained from the local field offices of the United States Department of the Interior, Fish and Wildlife Service.

■ Information on the condor program can be obtained through the National Audubon Society, Boulder, CO 80302.

Feature Vocabulary

condor   endangered

Teaching Suggestions

■ Define the term *endangered*.

■ Obtain a photograph of a California condor from a bird guide or wildlife journal.

■ Discuss the impact of pollution problems, such as lead poisoning of condors.

■ Have interested students find out what animals are endangered in your state.

Summary

Chapter Closure: Tell students to write a question for each of the summary statements. They should leave space between their questions for answers. When students have completed this assignment, have them exchange papers and answer each of the questions. Students should check their own papers by referring to the text and to the question writer.

Science Words

Have students write each of the science words in vertical form. Beside each word, they should write the name of a plant or animal associated with it. Allow students to work in teams to complete this assignment. The team that finds the most words may be declared "Scientists of the Week."

Student Responses

1. temperate forest
2. habitat
3. wildlife conservation
4. rain forest
5. shelter
6. tundra
7. freshwater habitats
8. grassland
9. desert
10. polar region

Summary

Lesson 1
- Habitats provide the air, food, water, and space that living things need.
- Groups can be shelters.

Lesson 2
- The polar regions, tundra, desert, and grassland are four types of habitats.
- Plants and animals are adapted to each habitat.

Lesson 3
- Three types of forest habitats are coniferous, temperate, and rain forests.
- Freshwater and saltwater habitats are two kinds of water habitats.

Lesson 4
- People change habitats.
- Wildlife conservation concerns the protection of habitats.

Science Words

Fill in the blank with the correct word or words from the list.

habitat, shelter, polar region, tundra, desert, grassland, coniferous forest, temperate forest, rain forest, freshwater habitats, saltwater habitat, wildlife conservation

1. A forest that has four seasons is called a(n) ___.
2. A place where a plant or animal lives is a(n) ___.
3. The protection given to living things is called ___.
4. A kind of forest with a hot, wet climate is a(n) ___.
5. A place or object that protects an animal is a(n) ___.
6. A habitat with soil that is usually frozen is ___.

242

TEACHER RESOURCE MASTERS

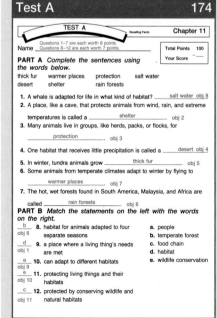

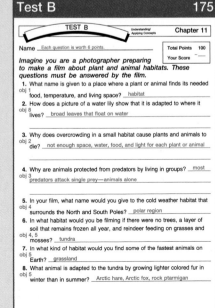

7. Habitats found in rivers and ponds are called ___.

8. A habitat with large, open spaces covered with grass is ___.

9. A dry habitat that receives little moisture is a ___.

10. A habitat that is covered by snow and ice all year is a ___.

Questions

Recalling Ideas
Correctly complete each of the following sentences.

1. Animals live in groups to
  (a) attract predators.
  (b) protect themselves.
  (c) build shelters.
  (d) have more space.

2. The tundra is a habitat that does NOT have
  (a) snow.   (c) soil.
  (b) tall trees. (d) animals.

3. A rain forest is a habitat that is
  (a) cold.   (c) hot and dry.
  (b) dry.   (d) hot and wet.

Understanding Ideas
Answer the following questions using complete sentences.

1. Why do living things need space?

2. How are the two water habitats the same? different?

Thinking Critically
Think about what you have learned in this chapter. Answer the following questions using complete sentences.

1. Describe a plant or animal that lives in each of the land habitats and tell how it is adapted to that habitat.

2. Why should people be concerned about wildlife conservation?

243

Questions

Recalling Ideas
1. b
2. b
3. d

Understanding Ideas
1. All living things need space so that there is enough water, food, and light for all living things in an area.
2. Both freshwater and saltwater habitats have plants and animals that are adapted to life in water. Freshwater habitats are found in ponds, bogs, swamps, lakes, and rivers. Plants and animals living in this habitat must adapt to waters that may be very warm or very cold, fast flowing or still. In saltwater habitats, there are a large number of plants and animals. Some animals move freely through the water while others are attached to objects.

Thinking Critically
1. Answers will vary. Answers may include polar bears and penguins in polar regions. Tundras contain grasses, mosses, and animals such as caribou and snowy owls. Deserts contain plants such as cacti and animals such as camels and rattlesnakes. Grasslands contain mostly grasses and animals such as antelope. Coniferous forests contain needle-leaved trees such as fir and spruce and animals such as beavers and moose. Temperate forests contain broad-leaved trees and smaller plants such as wildflowers. Animals such as deer and rabbits live in temperate forests. Rain forests contain many broad-leaved evergreen trees and animals such as monkeys, jaguars, and macaws.
2. People should be concerned about wildlife conservation because each living thing in a habitat is part of the food chain. If one link of the food chain is destroyed, the whole food chain will be affected. People must make sure that all habitats remain healthy places for the plants and animals.

TEACHER RESOURCE MASTERS

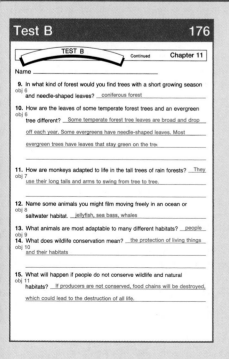

Test B 176

TEST B
Continued   Chapter 11

Name _____

9. In what kind of forest would you find trees with a short growing season
obj 6
and needle-shaped leaves? __coniferous forest__

10. How are the leaves of some temperate forest trees and an evergreen
obj 6
tree different? __Some temperate forest tree leaves are broad and drop__
off each year. Some evergreens have needle-shaped leaves. Most
evergreen trees have leaves that stay green on the tree

11. How are monkeys adapted to life in the tall trees of rain forests? __They__
obj 7
use their long tails and arms to swing from tree to tree.

12. Name some animals you might film moving freely in an ocean or
obj 8
saltwater habitat. __jellyfish, sea bass, whales__

13. What animals are most adaptable to many different habitats? __people__
obj 9
14. What does wildlife conservation mean? __the protection of living things__
obj 10
and their habitats

15. What will happen if people do not conserve wildlife and natural
obj 11
habitats? __If producers are not conserved, food chains will be destroyed,__
which could lead to the destruction of all life.

CHAPTER 12

Animal Adaptations

Planning Guide

Lessons	Objectives	Vocabulary
Chapter Introduction pp. 244, 245		
Lesson 1 Adaptations pp. 246–249	1. **Define** *adaptation*. 2. **Recognize** that all animals have skin.	adaptation fur skin reflex scales instinct feathers
Lesson 2 Scales, Feathers, and Fur pp. 250–253	3. **Explain** that some animals have a covering over the skin. 4. **Give examples** of animal body coverings and **understand** how they help the animal survive.	
Lesson 3 Specific Adaptations pp. 254–259	5. **Give examples** of different animal adaptations. 6. **Understand** the importance of adaptations for animal survival.	
Lesson 4 Animal Behavior pp. 260–263	7. **Define** *behavior*. 8. **Recognize** that some behavior is learned. 9. **Explain** that animals are born with behavior.	behavior learned behavior
Lesson 5 Reflexes and Instincts pp. 264–271	10. **Define** and **identify** examples of a reflex. 11. **Define** and **give examples** of instinctive behavior.	
Chapter Review pp. 272, 273		
Unit Review pp. 274, 275		

Planning Guide

Text Activities		Teacher Resource Masters	Other Components
Title/Skill	**Materials per Group**		
Have You Ever . . . Wondered About Life at the North Pole? p. 245 Inferring Time Allotment: 30 min.	paper pencil crayons	Activity Center: "Super Hero Adaptations"; "A Bird In the House"; "Not a Night Fit for Man Nor Beast"	
		Independent Practice, pp. 187, 188 Transparency Master, p. 177	
How Do Fish Scales Look Under a Microscope? p. 253 Observing/Classifying Time Allotment: 35 min. **Blending Right In,** p. 359 Observing/Inferring/ Measuring/Interpreting Data Time Allotment: 60 min.	fish scales (from 2 different fish) microscope coverslip glass slide tweezers old clothing disposable cloth pieces scissors string	Independent Practice, pp. 187, 188 Activity Worksheet, pp. 179, 180 ▲ Critical Thinking, p. 184	
		Independent Practice, pp. 187, 188 ♦ Family Science, p. 178 Language Arts, p. 185	Activity Book, pp. 31, 32 Activity Book, pp. 49, 50
		Independent Practice, pp. 187, 188 Critical Thinking, p. 183 Math Connection, p. 186	Color Transparency #11
You Can . . . Build a Nest! p. 268 Formulating Models Time Allotment: 25 min. **Do Mealworms Like Light or Dark Places?** p. 270 Observing Time Allotment: 35 minutes	grass leaves sticks mud drawing paper index card mealworm	Independent Practice, pp. 187, 188 Activity Worksheet, pp. 181, 182 ♦ Reteaching Activity, p. 189	
		Test A, p. 190 Test B, pp. 191, 192	
			Unit Test

♦ **Basic** / ▲ **Advanced** / All other masters are for use by all students.

CHAPTER 12

Animal Adaptations

For Exceptional Students

ESL/LEP

Chapter 12/Lesson 1, Page 246
Write the word **adaptation** on the chalkboard. Discuss its meaning with students. Ask them if people have to adapt to their surroundings. Have them write two or three sentences describing how people learn to adapt when they come to live in a new country.

Chapter 12/Lesson 2, Page 250
Ask students how scales, feathers, and fur are alike. (They are all part of the skin.) Have them name two animals that have each of these coverings. Have them make up humorous statements about these coverings, using the negative. Give them an example: A fish does not have fur because fur is harder to dry out than scales.

Chapter 12/Lesson 3, Page 254
Have students list the animals mentioned in the lesson. Next to each animal have students list an adaptation of the animal. Ask them to write sentences about five of the animals on their list.

Chapter 12/Lesson 4, Page 260
Have students talk about their pets. Question them about typical behaviors of the pets. Let students practice conversations by asking one another questions about their pets' behavior.

Chapter 12/Lesson 5, Page 264
Write the words **reflex** and **instinct** on the chalkboard. Discuss with students the meaning of these words. Ask them to list examples of animal reflexes and instincts. Ask them whether sitting up is an instinct, a reflex, or a learned behavior in a dog.

Tell them to think of a certain animal behavior. Have them ask another student whether the behavior is a reflex, an instinct, or a learned behavior in that particular animal.

Gifted

Chapter 12/Lesson 2, Page 252
Students should research and compile a list of fur-bearing animals. They could construct a chart with four columns with the following heads: Name of Animal; Past Use of Fur; Present Use of Fur; and Endangered. Students could also research animals that have become extinct through exploitation of their fur. This exercise will enable students to determine the uses of fur in our society, the names and types of animals with fur, and those animals that are endangered because of unwise use of their pelts. (Obtain information from library books and encyclopedias, or the *Endangered Species Handbook* available through The Animal Welfare Institute, P.O. Box 3650, Washington, DC, 20007—Library of Congress Card Number 82-072956.

Mainstreamed

Chapter 12/Lesson 3, Page 258
Learning Disabled: Provide students with cards that show the names (or pictures) of several animals. Play the game "What Am I?" by giving clues related to the adaptive features of the animal. Students should hold up the response card associated with the clue.

Whole Class Science Project

Have students choose a habitat (desert, grassland, forest, polar, or water), research to find out what type of vertebrates and invertebrates live there, and report their findings to the class. Students should tell about animal adaptations, including skin, scales, feathers, fur, feet and wings, mouthparts, teeth, camouflage, countershading, warning coloration, or mimicry, and tell what advantage the adaptation is for each animal. Working in **cooperative groups,** students could select one habitat and research all animals found in their chosen habitat from various parts of the world. For example, the adaptations of animals found in the grasslands of North America, South America, Europe, and other countries can be compared. Students could refer to a world atlas or other reference books for information. Display the results from each group on a world map.

Science Fair Projects

Individual students could do one of the following projects.

1. Using a labeled chart, students may research ways that insects defend themselves. Examples may include: carabid beetle—odor; larva of American sawfly—watery fluid; swallowtail butterfly—odor; puss moth—formic acid; oil beetle—yellow blood; caterpillars—hairs protect, some emit fluid; honeybee—sting; wasp—sting.

2. To explore camouflage, students might tell about insects that escape detection from their enemies by passively resembling their surroundings. They could depict this in a picture display.

3. Students may draw different types of beaks illustrating specializations due to the environment or types of food eaten.

4. On a chart, students may describe and itemize body parts different animals use to search for food, and tell how these body parts are used for food gathering.

5. By displaying different types of body coverings and telling about their function, students may determine the purpose of the adaptation of these body coverings.

CHAPTER
12

pages 244–273

Chapter Concepts

- Animals must be able to find food and protect themselves. Adaptations help animals survive.
- Body coverings such as scales, feathers, and fur are adaptations for warmth and protection from the environment.
- Specific adaptations to feet, wings, mouthparts, and teeth are adaptations for protection and obtaining food.
- Behavior is anything an animal does in response to any change in its environment. Animals are born with some behavior that is hard to change, and some behavior is learned by experience and can be changed.
- The two types of behavior an animal is born with are reflex behavior and instinct.

Chapter Background

- Specialized body parts such as feet, wings, and mouthparts are adaptations for protection and obtaining food.
- Camouflage, countershading, warning coloration, and mimicry are all modifications of body covering that help animals adapt.

Looking Ahead

- Invite a conservation officer from the Department of Natural Resources to discuss how people are changing animal habitats in your area.
- Take a trip to a zoo to observe the behavior of animals. Have students choose two animals and compare their behaviors.

Look for These Symbols

- —Hands-on activity
- —Cooperative learning
- —Overhead transparency
- ◆ —Basic/Reinforcement
- ● —Average/Enrichment
- ▲ —Advanced/Challenge
- —Calculator Practice

SCIENCE
In Your World

244

CHAPTER 12

Animal Adaptations

Think about getting dressed this morning. Did you put on a jacket or a sweater? How do you dress if the weather is very hot? How do you dress if the weather is very cold? Wearing different clothes is one way that we adapt to our environment.

Have You Ever...

Wondered About Life at the North Pole?

If you lived at the North Pole, how would you adapt to protect yourself from the extreme cold? What kinds of animals would you expect to find? How would they be different from the animals where you live? Pretend you're a zoologist who has discovered a new animal at the North Pole. Make a diagram of the animal you have found and make some notes about how the animal survives in the cold climate.

245

PREPLAN

Time Allotment: 30 minutes

Objectives
1. **Describe** how people dress for different weather conditions.
2. **Identify** some of the ways that animals adapt to their environments.

Setup
■ If you wish to perform this activity, you will need the following materials for each student or activity group:

paper   pencil   crayons

1 FOCUS

■ Ask: **What are ways that Alaskans adapt to the cold weather conditions in which they live?** *They wear fur clothing, eat a high fat diet, and build warm houses to protect themselves from the cold.*

2 TEACH

■ Ask: **What are other ways that we adapt to our environment?** *heat and air condition our homes, eat different foods in different seasons*

Have You Ever . . .
▨ Have students **work cooperatively** in groups of four.
Student Responses
A human would wear protective clothing and build an insulated shelter. Polar bears, whales, seals, and penguins have more fat and fur/feathers to protect them from the cold than animals in warmer climates.

3 APPLY

■ Ask: **How do people adapt to space travel?** *They wear insulated suits, carry food, carry oxygen tanks, and so on.*

Close
■ Ways animals adapt to their environment will be discussed in Chapter 12.

pages 246–249

PREPLAN

Lesson Objectives

1. **Define** *adaptation*.
2. **Recognize** that all animals have skin.

Science Background

■ An animal will live successfully when it is adapted to its environment.

■ Adaptations include any body covering, body part, or behavior that helps an animal survive in its environment.

Lesson Vocabulary

adapatation	skin	feathers
scales	reflex	instinct
fur		

1 FOCUS

■ Ask students to list four or five different environments in which animals live. Considering each environment one at a time, ask: **What problems would an animal living here face? What could the animal do to overcome these problems?** Encourage students to be as imaginative as possible with their answers.

■ Use the goals on student page 246 to establish the purpose for studying this lesson.

Adaptations

Brrr! Joel shivered, looking out the car window at the wind tossing the treetops. "It looks like a thunderstorm is coming," he thought. "I hope all the wild animals are snug in their beds tonight." Then Joel chuckled. He knew that wild animals don't have beds like his. He began to wonder, "How *do* wild things stay alive in bad weather?" The answer begins with adaptations.

For an animal to live in its environment, it must be able to protect itself and find food. When an animal is adapted to its environment, it is able to live successfully.

Joel decided to go to the library to find out about how animals adapt.

246

TEACHER RESOURCE MASTERS

Adaptation

Any body part, body covering, or behavior that helps an animal live in its environment is called an **adaptation** (ad ap TAY shun). Body coverings help protect body organs. Look at the armadillo in the picture on this page. Notice that a hard, protective armor covers its back. The armor is attached in rows so that the armadillo can curl into a ball. This protects its legs and belly if it is disturbed.

What is an adaptation?

247

TEACHER RESOURCE MASTERS

2 TEACH

■ Have on hand a number of tools with which students are familiar (a fork, hand lens, drinking straw, or pliers). Discuss the uses that people have for these tools. Have students try to think of animals that use comparable "tools."

■ Have students decide what the word *environment* means. Environment is everything that affects an organism.

Guided Practice

■ Check students' understanding of lesson concepts by discussing the Lesson Review questions on student page 249. If necessary, use the **reteaching strategy** in OPTIONS.

Independent Practice

■ Assign the Lesson 1 section of the Teacher Resource Master **Independent Practice,** page 187.

3 APPLY

■ Ask: **How are dogs adapted to being good watchdogs?** *Dogs have ears which can stand up straight to catch the slightest sound. They can turn their ears toward the sound, which helps them to hear even better. Dogs are territorial, which makes them want to defend their habitat. They also bark when an intruder appears.*

Close

■ Use Summary statements on student page 249 to review lesson concepts.

OPTIONS

Reteaching Strategy

■ Ask: **How have whales, porcupines, and skunks adapted to their environment?** *Whales have blubber for body warmth; porcupines have quills for protection; skunks have a strong scent that is sprayed when predators approach.*

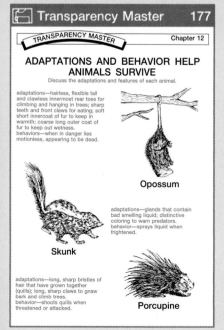

Transparency Master 177

TRANSPARENCY MASTER   Chapter 12

ADAPTATIONS AND BEHAVIOR HELP ANIMALS SURVIVE

Discuss the adaptations and features of each animal.

adaptations—hairless, flexible tail and clawless innermost rear toes for climbing and hanging in trees; sharp teeth and front claws for eating; soft short innercoat of fur to keep in warmth; coarse long outer coat of fur to keep out wetness.
behaviors—when in danger lies motionless, appearing to be dead.

Opossum

adaptations—glands that contain bad smelling liquid; distinctive coloring to warn predators.
behavior—sprays liquid when frightened.

Skunk

adaptations—long, sharp bristles of hair that have grown together (quills); long, sharp claws to gnaw bark and climb trees.
behavior—shoots quills when threatened or attacked.

Porcupine

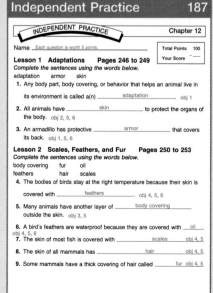

Independent Practice 187

INDEPENDENT PRACTICE   Chapter 12

Name _Each question is worth 5 points._ ____

| Total Points | 100 |
| Your Score | — |

Lesson 1 Adaptations   Pages 246 to 249
Complete the sentences using the words below.
adaptation   armor   skin

1. Any body part, body covering, or behavior that helps an animal live in its environment is called a(n) ____adaptation____. obj 1

2. All animals have ____skin____ to protect the organs of the body. obj 2, 5, 6

3. An armadillo has protective ____armor____ that covers its back. obj 1, 5, 6

Lesson 2 Scales, Feathers, and Fur   Pages 250 to 253
Complete the sentences using the words below.
body covering   fur   oil
feathers   hair   scales

4. The bodies of birds stay at the right temperature because their skin is covered with ____feathers____. obj 4, 5, 6

5. Many animals have another layer of ____body covering____ outside the skin. obj 3, 5

6. A bird's feathers are waterproof because they are covered with ____oil____. obj 4, 5, 6

7. The skin of most fish is covered with ____scales____. obj 4, 5

8. The skin of all mammals has ____hair____. obj 4, 5

9. Some mammals have a thick covering of hair called ____fur____. obj 4, 5

OPTIONS

MATH CONNECTION

Assign students the following math problem. The largest tree frog was found in the Dominican Republic and measured 14.3 cm. The smallest tree frog was found in the southeastern United States and measured 1.6 cm. How much longer was the largest tree frog than the smallest? (12.7 cm)

◆ **Reinforcement:** Ask: **How do fingernails help you adapt to your environment?** Answers may include the following: *Fingernails help you pick up things and handle delicate objects. They help you scratch your skin if it itches.* Ask students to think of other adaptations people make. Examples may include eyelids to protect the eyes, hair to protect the head and keep it warm, and sweat glands to cool the body.

● **Enrichment:** Ask: **What adaptations do pets have that help them to live in their environment?** Answers may include the following: *A dog has a keen sense of smell, which helps it to find its master easily. It also has a strong sense of loyalty. A bird has claws for grasping and holding onto a perch. A cat has padded feet for walking silently and retractable claws. A cat's tongue has a rough surface that can be used for grooming its coat.*

▲ **Challenge:** Have interested students do research to find out how a porcupine's quills are an adaptation that helps the animal defend itself.

Skin

Animals need adaptations of body coverings to stay alive. **Skin** is the outer covering of an animal's body. Skin is a body system that protects the organs inside. It also helps some animals keep the correct body temperature. Skin can sense touch and changes in temperature. Skin can hold or release water as needed.

The skin of some animals provides all the protection they need. A frog's skin gives off a liquid that makes its body slimy and hard to hold. Some toads have organs that make poison in their skins. These organs give off a liquid that may harm animals that try to eat them.

Joel smiled. He had learned a little about how wild things stay alive in bad weather. He decided to read more.

248

TEACHER RESOURCE MASTERS

LESSON REVIEW ANSWERS

1. Adaptations help animals find food and protect themselves.
2. An animal's organs are protected by the skin.

Lesson Summary

- An animal must be able to find food and protect itself.
- An adaptation helps an animal live in its environment.
- An animal's skin protects the organs of the body.

Lesson Review

1. What are two ways adaptations help animals survive?
★2. How does skin help an animal survive?

249

TEACHER RESOURCE MASTERS

PREPLAN

Lesson Objectives

3. Explain that some animals have a covering over the skin.

4. Give examples of animal body coverings and **understand** how they help the animal survive.

Science Background

■ Body coverings take a number of different forms. They may be hard and armor-like, or they may be soft and warm. They may provide protection from predators or protection against extreme environmental conditions.

Note: The activity on student page 253 may be used for guided discovery before you begin this lesson.

1 FOCUS

■ Provide various feathers for examination. For each type of feather, ask: **What do you think this feather might be used for?** *to help the bird, fly, float, keep warm*

■ Use the goals on student page 250 to establish the purpose for studying this lesson.

Scales, Feathers, and Fur

What are scales?

Joel decided that wild animals must have adaptations of their skins that help them stay alive. Joel was right.

Many animals have another layer of body covering outside the skin. This layer may be scales, feathers, or hair. Although scales, feathers, and hair look different from each other, they are all part of the skin. The extra layer of body covering gives more protection to an animal.

Scales are small, thin plates that cover the skin of some animals. There are different kinds of scales. In fish, scales can be smooth, rough, or pointed. They are slippery and help fish glide through water.

Snakes have scales that are dry. Most snakes have scales that overlap and stretch apart when the snake moves. Snakes shed their scaly skins as they grow, leaving them in one piece.

250

TEACHER RESOURCE MASTERS

Feathers

Feathers are the strong, lightweight outer covering of birds. The close-up picture on this page shows what a feather looks like. Notice how the parts of the feather lock together somewhat like the parts of a zipper. Very little air can pass through a feather.

You may have seen baby chicks covered with soft, fluffy feathers called down. In older birds, down feathers form a layer close to the skin. Down feathers keep a bird's body at the correct temperature, even when it flies through very cold air.

What is the purpose of down feathers?

Many birds must dive or swim in water to find food. The feathers of these birds are covered with a layer of body oil. Oil makes the feathers waterproof. These oily feathers keep a bird's skin dry, keep its body warm, and keep the bird afloat in water.

251

TEACHER RESOURCE MASTERS

Independent Practice   187

INDEPENDENT PRACTICE   Chapter 12

Name _____ Each question is worth 5 points.   Total Points 100
                                                          Your Score   ____

Lesson 1 Adaptations   Pages 246 to 249
Complete the sentences using the words below.
adaptation   armor   skin

1. Any body part, body covering, or behavior that helps an animal live in
   its environment is called a(n) _____ adaptation _____. obj 1

2. All animals have _____ skin _____ to protect the organs of
   the body. obj 2, 5, 6

3. An armadillo has protective _____ armor _____ that covers
   its back. obj 1, 5, 6

Lesson 2 Scales, Feathers, and Fur   Pages 250 to 253
Complete the sentences using the words below.
body covering   fur   oil
feathers   hair   scales

4. The bodies of birds stay at the right temperature because their skin is
   covered with _____ feathers _____. obj 4, 5, 6

5. Many animals have another layer of _____ body covering _____
   outside the skin. obj 3, 5

6. A bird's feathers are waterproof because they are covered with _____ oil _____
   obj 4, 5, 6

7. The skin of most fish is covered with _____ scales _____ obj 4, 5

8. The skin of all mammals has _____ hair _____ obj 4, 5

9. Some mammals have a thick covering of hair called _____ fur obj 4, 5

2 TEACH

■ Small lizards, such as anoles, are easily kept in a classroom terrarium. Instructions for their care are available from pet shops. They make good subjects for the study of scales as adaptations.

■ Obtain pictures of different birds from magazines such as *National Wildlife* or *Audubon*. Impress upon the class the variety of sizes, shapes, and colors of feathers, such as the eyelashlike feathers of an ostrich's eyelids; the shiny feathers of a hummingbird; the short, furlike feathers of a penguin; or the stiff, pointed feathers of a woodpecker's tail.

Guided Practice

■ Check students' understanding of lesson concepts by discussing the Lesson Review questions on student page 252. If necessary, use the **reteaching strategy** in OPTIONS.

Independent Practice

■ Assign the Lesson 2 section of the Teacher Resource Master **Independent Practice,** page 187.

3 APPLY

■ Ask students to list the different body coverings that have been discussed and to provide one example of an animal that has that type of covering.

Close

■ Use Summary statements on student page 252 to review lesson concepts.

OPTIONS

Reteaching Strategy

■ Provide a number of different animal field guides. Have the class review these guides and then, as a group, devise a "field guide" to the animals living in your area. Each page could have a heading such as "Animals with Fur" or "Animals with Slimy Skin."

OPTIONS

SCIENCE AND . . . READING

■ **Skill:** Recall supporting facts and details.

■ **Student Response:** B

MATH CONNECTION

Have students **work cooperatively** to solve the following geometry problem. Michelle wants to raise baby chicks. Her mom is helping her build a pen. They have already measured off a rectangular piece of their land 5 meters wide and 12 meters long. Find how many meters of fencing Michelle needs around the perimeter of her pen. (34 meters)

◆ **Reinforcement:** Put these headings on the bulletin board: SKIN, SCALES, FEATHERS, and FUR. Have students bring in pictures of animals that have a particular adaptation of one of these body coverings. Have them attach their picture to a sheet of paper and write a paragraph or two about the animal's adaptation.

● **Enrichment:** Have students research the advancements in warm clothing that have resulted from today's technology.

▲ **Challenge:** Have students make a list comparing natural adaptations of animals to "borrowed" ones that humans use.

LESSON REVIEW ANSWERS

1. scales, feathers, and fur
2. The parts of a bird's feather lock together trapping warm air and keeping it next to the body.

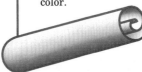

SCIENCE AND . . .
Reading

How does a polar bear's fur keep it warm when diving into cold water?
A. The fur is covered with a layer of oil.
B. The fur traps air.
C. A layer of down is under the fur.
D. The fur changes color.

Fur

All mammals have hair. In some mammals, the hair is a thick covering of soft hairs called **fur.** Fur protects animals from bites and scratches from predators and helps keep them warm. A polar bear is one example. A polar bear lives in a very cold environment where temperatures are often below freezing. The thick fur of a polar bear traps air and helps keep it warm, even when it dives into very cold water.

Some animals are the same color as their environment. This makes them hard to see, because their body colors blend into their surroundings. The snowshoe hare has a brown coat for most of the year. But in winter, the hare grows a white one.

Lesson Summary

● Scales, feathers, and fur are three types of skin coverings.

● An animal's body covering helps keep it warm and provides protection.

Lesson Review

1. Name three types of body coverings that are part of the skin tissue.
★2. How do feathers keep birds warm?

252   Use Application Activity on pages 359, 360.

TEACHER RESOURCE MASTERS

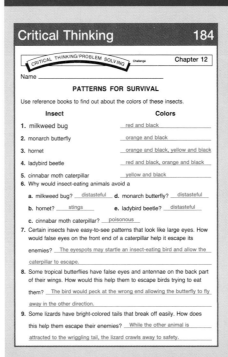

Critical Thinking   184

CRITICAL THINKING/PROBLEM SOLVING   Challenge   Chapter 12

Name _____

PATTERNS FOR SURVIVAL

Use reference books to find out about the colors of these insects.

Insect	Colors
1. milkweed bug	red and black
2. monarch butterfly	orange and black
3. hornet	orange and black, yellow and black
4. ladybird beetle	red and black, orange and black
5. cinnabar moth caterpillar	yellow and black

6. Why would insect-eating animals avoid a

a. milkweed bug? _distasteful_   d. monarch butterfly? _distasteful_

b. hornet? _stings_   e. ladybird beetle? _distasteful_

c. cinnabar moth caterpillar? _poisonous_

7. Certain insects have easy-to-see patterns that look like large eyes. How would false eyes on the front end of a caterpillar help it escape its enemies? _The eyespots may startle an insect-eating bird and allow the caterpillar to escape._

8. Some tropical butterflies have false eyes and antennae on the back part of their wings. How would this help them to escape birds trying to eat them? _The bird would peck at the wrong end allowing the butterfly to fly away in the other direction._

9. Some lizards have bright-colored tails that break off easily. How does this help them escape their enemies? _While the other animal is attracted to the wriggling tail, the lizard crawls away to safety._

How do fish scales look under a microscope?

What you need

fish scales (from two
   different fish)
microscope
glass slide
coverslip
tweezers
pencil and paper
eyedropper

What to do

1. Prepare 4 slides, one for scales from the upper body and one for scales from the lower body of each fish.
2. Put 2 drops of water on each glass slide. Use the tweezers to put a fish scale in the water. Hold it in place on the slide with a coverslip.
3. Observe each slide under the microscope, first under low power and then under high power.
4. After each viewing, make a drawing of what you saw.

What did you learn?

1. How do the scales look different under the microscope compared to seeing them with the unaided eye?
2. Compare upper and lower scales from the same fish.

Using what you learned

1. Compare the scales of the two different fish you observed.
2. How are scales an adaptation for survival?

253

ACTIVITY RESPONSES

What did you learn?
1. The scales of a fish have rough surfaces that can't be seen without a microscope.
2. The upper scales are larger and rougher than the lower scales.

Using what you learned
1. One fish had larger (smaller) scales, rougher (smoother) scales, and so on. Observations may vary.
2. Scales allow the fish to glide through the water as it swims. Scales also provide protection.

PREPLAN

Time Allotment: 35 minutes
Process Skills: Observing/Classifying

Objectives
1. **Recognize** the difference between the scales from two different kinds of fish.
2. **Distinguish** between upper body scales and lower body scales.

Setup
■ Try to get scales from two different fish species. Examples are carp vs. trout. Tell students what types of fish were used.

■ **Cooperative Grouping:** fives—Assign roles as explained on page T24.

1   FOCUS

■ Ask students if they've ever been fishing or seen fish in an aquarium. Review the procedure for removing scales from a freshly caught fish.

2   TEACH

■ **Safety Considerations:** Caution students about the use of glass slides and coverslips.

■ **Troubleshooting:** Review microscope procedures.

■ Have students use the Teacher Resource Master **Activity Worksheet,** pages 179 and 180, to record their data and answers.

3   APPLY

■ Reinforce the idea that fish scales are a special outer layer of a fish's skin. Scales differ in shape, size, and texture depending on the type of fish and the places on the body where the scales are found. Scales serve as an adaptation.

Close
■ Discuss the activity and questions.

PREPLAN

Lesson Objectives
5. Give examples of different animal adaptations.
6. Understand the importance of adaptations for animal survival.

Science Background
■ The animals mentioned in the lesson have several different kinds of teeth adapted to the kinds of food which the animal eats. Although cats, wolves, and dogs have large canines for tearing meat, they also have molars and incisors. Elephants have enlarged incisors called tusks in addition to molars. Many fish and most reptiles, in contrast, have teeth which are all about the same size and shape. Their teeth are adapted to catching and holding prey.

1 FOCUS

■ Review the five senses. Ask: **How does an animal find food?** *by using its senses* Discuss ways different animals find food.
■ Use the goals on student page 254 to establish the purpose for studying this lesson.

What two things must an animal do to survive?

Specific Adaptations

Marlene was carefully trimming the claws of her cat, Woodsmoke. "Are these claws made of the same material as my fingernails?" she wondered. "But they really look different. They're curved, and they come to a point. When her claws get too long, Woodsmoke can scratch her scratching post and remove the whole top layer. It's just like pulling off the top cup in a stack of bathroom cups." Marlene decided she would learn more about cat claws at the library.

To stay alive in its environment, an animal must protect itself as well as find and catch food. The feet or wings of animals are often adapted for protection and food gathering.

254

TEACHER RESOURCE MASTERS

Some body parts that are adapted for protection may also be used for food gathering. For example, an animal might use sharp claws and teeth to protect itself. The animal may also use its claws and teeth for catching food. The eagle in the picture has large wings, sharp talons, and strong foot muscles to catch prey and carry it off.

Some animals, such as the lynx, the arctic fox, and the snowshoe hare, grow extra-long, thick hair on their feet. This increases the size of their feet and helps them move about easily on soft snow to escape their enemies or catch their prey.

The picture of a duck's foot shows how its feet are particularly well adapted for swimming in water in search of food.

255

TEACHER RESOURCE MASTERS

Independent Practice   188

INDEPENDENT PRACTICE   Continued   Chapter 12

Name _____

Lesson 3   Specific Adaptations   Pages 254 to 259
Complete the sentences using the words below.
adaptation   bill   claws   teeth

10. The mouth part of a bird is called a _____ bill _____ obj 6

11. Some animals have sharp teeth and _____ claws _____ to catch food and _____ themselves. obj 5, 6

12. Mouth parts used to bite, tear, crush, and grind food are called _____ teeth _____ obj 6

13. The _____ adaptation _____ of an animal to its environment is important for its survival. obj 6

Lesson 4   Animal Behavior   Pages 260 to 263
Match the phrases on the left with the words on the right.

___b___ 14. a living thing's response to any change in
obj 7   its environment
___a___ 15. a behavior changed by experience
obj 8
___c___ 16. a behavior that can't be changed very
obj 9   easily

a. learned behavior
b. behavior
c. born behavior

Lesson 5   Reflexes and Instincts   Pages 264 to 271
Match the phrases on the left with the words on the right.

___b___ 17. simple type of behavior an animal is born
obj 10   with
___c___ 18. an example of an instinct
obj 11
___d___ 19. complex type of born behavior
obj 11
___a___ 20. an example of a reflex
obj 10

a. blinking eyes
b. reflex
c. migration
d. instinct

2   TEACH

■ The raccoon has only four digits on its front paws, yet it can handle small food items skillfully. Let students play "raccoon" for a short time by taping their thumbs in place to the side of their hand. Encourage them to attempt tasks such as writing, combing hair, or lifting a book.

Guided Practice
■ Check students' understanding of lesson concepts by discussing the Lesson Review questions on student page 259. If necessary, use the **reteaching strategy** in OPTIONS.

Independent Practice
■ Assign the Lesson 3 section of the Teacher Resource Master **Independent Practice,** page 188.

3   APPLY

■ Use Application Activity, "Blending Right In," on student page 359.

Close
■ Use Summary statements on student page 259 to review lesson concepts.

OPTIONS

Reteaching Strategy
■ Play a game with students to help them recall the specific adaptations of the animals mentioned in the lesson. (bird, sea lion, cat, snowshoe hare, eagle, lynx, arctic fox, duck, woodpecker, finches, wolves, dogs, giraffes, horses, mice, squirrels) Pass out slips of paper, each with the name of one of these animals. Have students make up a riddle in which the adaptations of their animal are mentioned.

Resource Options
■ Use Activity Book, "Interpreting Data," pages 31, 32.

OPTIONS

MATH CONNECTION

■ Assign students the following geometry problem. Bradley and his dad want to dig a small duck pond. Before starting with digging equipment, they have drawn the following diagram of the pond.

Each square is one square meter. What will be the area of Bradley's pond? (36 sq. meters)

♦ **Reinforcement:** Put animal names on slips of paper. Have students pick slips randomly. Have the student read the name of the animal. Discuss with the class what kind of food it eats. Then have the student tell how the mouthparts of the animal are adapted to the kind of food it eats.

Resource Options

■ Use Activity Book, "Blending Right In," pages 49, 50.

Mouth Parts

Some animals, such as sea lions, swallow their food whole. Others have mouth parts for tearing, grinding, or spearing food. The mouth part of a bird is called a bill. Woodpeckers have hard, pointed bills, which they use to chisel or cut into the bark of a tree. Woodpeckers also have long tongues to reach into small openings for insects beneath the bark. Some finches have short, cone-shaped, hard bills. The size, shape, and strength of their bills help finches break open seeds.

256

TEACHER RESOURCE MASTERS

Some birds, such as ducks, eat water plants and small insects. These birds have bills with strainers to sift food from the mud and water. Look at the pictures of the different birds. Try to decide from the shapes of the bills which birds are seed eaters, water plant eaters, spearers, or fish-eaters.

257

OPTIONS

● **Enrichment:** Make a list of characteristics that enable animals to survive in different environments. Allow students to randomly choose three of these characteristics. Have them describe the animal that would have these characteristics and tell for what kind of environment it would be adapted. The animal might not have characteristics that would be very good for survival in another environment. If this is the case, have students explain. Discuss the animals with the class. This will reinforce the principle that adaptations must be beneficial in order to help the animal survive.

▲ **Challenge:** A bird-feeding station can be an excellent way to observe animal adaptations. Have interested students make simple feeders from milk containers, plastic onion bags, or pine cones filled with a peanut butter birdseed mix. Provide a variety of foods: suet, whole peanuts, sunflower seeds, raisins, or cranberries. When observing the birds at the station, have students take note of the shapes and sizes of the birds' bills and the types of food the birds eat most often.

OPTIONS

■ Contact a nearby zoo to make arrangements for a zookeeper or curator to visit your class. Request a program that includes a demonstration of how food is prepared for a zoo full of animals. Perhaps a safe, live animal can be brought to class and its food-getting adaptations discussed.

■ A high school or college biology laboratory may have samples of different animals' skulls that may be borrowed. Before identifying each skull, ask students to deduce the types of food the animal may have eaten.

Teeth are mouth parts that are used to bite, tear, crush, and grind food. Two long, chisel-shaped teeth at the front of the mouth are found in animals such as mice and squirrels. These teeth are used for biting and gnawing. Cats, wolves, and dogs have long, pointed teeth to stab and tear the meat they eat. Giraffes, horses, and sheep have flat teeth for crushing and grinding plants. What types of teeth do you have? 1

Marlene was interested by what she had studied about some animal adaptations. "Now, I wonder," she said to Woodsmoke, "if I can find a library book to tell me more about you."

1. People have teeth for biting, tearing, and grinding food.

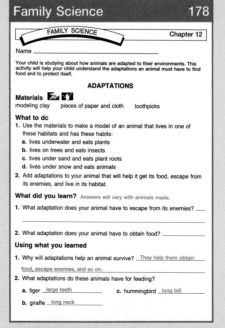

258

TEACHER RESOURCE MASTERS

Family Science   178

FAMILY SCIENCE   Chapter 12

Name _____

Your child is studying about how animals are adapted to their environments. This activity will help your child understand the adaptations an animal must have to find food and to protect itself.

ADAPTATIONS

Materials
modeling clay   pieces of paper and cloth   toothpicks

What to do
1. Use the materials to make a model of an animal that lives in one of these habitats and has these habits:
   a. lives underwater and eats plants
   b. lives on trees and eats insects
   c. lives under sand and eats plant roots
   d. lives under snow and eats animals
2. Add adaptations to your animal that will help it get its food, escape from its enemies, and live in its habitat.

What did you learn? Answers will vary with animals made.

1. What adaptation does your animal have to escape from its enemies? ____

_____

2. What adaptation does your animal have to obtain food? _____

Using what you learned

1. Why will adaptations help an animal survive? They help them obtain

food, escape enemies, and so on.

2. What adaptations do these animals have for feeding?

   a. tiger large teeth   c. hummingbird long bill

   b. giraffe long neck

Language Arts Connection   185

LANGUAGE ARTS CONNECTION Using Reference Materials   Chapter 12

Name _____

SURVIVAL

Use reference books to find out about the unique adaptations these animals have to survive in their environment. Answers may vary; these are possible responses.

1. Box turtle hard shell covers body

2. Polar bear white color to blend in with snow

3. Fawn spotted color, no odor

4. Walking stick resembles stick

5. Rough green snake resembles vine

6. Poison arrow frog poisonous skin secretions

7. Tiger swallowtail caterpillars bright colors to warn that it is poisonous

8. Bee fly resembles bee; predators avoid it

9. Io moth eyespots to startle predators

10. Flounder changes color to match surroundings

11. Anole lizard changes color to match surroundings

12. Octopus shoots inklike substance to aid escape

13. Camel able to live in desert without drinking each day

14. Owl keen hearing, sharp claws

15. Flying fish leaps from water and uses fins to glide away from enemies

LESSON REVIEW ANSWERS

1. feet, mouthparts, and teeth

2. Answers may vary. A cat's teeth are sharp and help it stab and tear meat. Its paws have claws that help it catch and hold onto its prey.

Lesson Summary

- Feet, wings, and mouth parts are three types of animal adaptations.
- Animals must be able to protect themselves and find food in their environment in order to survive.

Lesson Review

1. What are three adaptations that help animals survive?

★2. Explain how a cat's teeth and claws help it survive.

259

TEACHER RESOURCE MASTERS

PREPLAN

Lesson Objectives

7. Define *behavior.*
8. Recognize that some behavior is learned.
9. Explain that animals are born with behavior.

Science Background

■ Understanding of animal behavior is important when trying to raise a pet. For example, parrot owners are sometimes puzzled by their pet's biting behavior. Parrots bite when they are afraid, nervous, upset, angry, and sometimes when they are happy or playful. It could be that the bird is biting when its owner tries to force it to do something it does not want to do. The best way to correct this problem is for the trainer to teach the bird to do what the owner wants by offering a treat. With rewards, learned behavior more easily supplants the bird's normal behavior.

Lesson Vocabulary

behavior   learned behavior

1 FOCUS

■ Learning is an important part of human behavior. Discuss the many things that people learn. Illustrate the ways a learned behavior can change by citing a familiar example. A 2-year-old learns to hold a crayon and scribble on paper. By first grade, that same child can print and, as he or she grows older, will learn to write in the cursive style.
■ Use the goals on student page 260 to establish the purpose for studying this lesson.

LESSON 4 GOALS
You will learn
● about animal behavior.
● about animal behavior that is learned.
● about behavior that animals are born with.

Animal Behavior

Have you ever tried to train a dog? Dogs can easily be trained to do some things, such as sitting up, begging for food, and chasing thrown sticks. But it isn't so easy to train a dog not to jump up and lick your face or not to eat food left on the coffee table. Why are some things easy and some things hard for dogs to learn?

Everything an animal does is part of its behavior. **Behavior** is a living thing's response to any change in its environment. Anything in the environment, such as light, sound, touch, or smell, can cause a living thing to respond. There are two kinds of behavior. An animal is born with one kind. The other kind is behavior that an animal learns. Both kinds of behavior help an animal survive in its environment.

TEACHER RESOURCE MASTERS

Learned behavior is behavior that is changed by experience. Learned behavior can be changed. A dog may learn to sit up when its trainer gives a command. Because sitting up is a learned behavior, it can be changed. The sitting-up behavior can be "unlearned." The dog can then learn to do another action when the same command word is spoken. The dog could learn to roll over or put its paw in the trainer's hand in response to the old command. An animal learns a behavior by repeating the same action many times.

What kind of behavior can be changed?

261

2 TEACH

■ Discuss the five senses and how these senses influence behavior.
■ Talk about what a stimulus is. Compile a list of stimuli that an animal might be exposed to in a typical day.

Guided Practice

■ Check students' understanding of lesson concepts by discussing the Lesson Review questions on student page 263. If necessary, use the **reteaching strategy** in OPTIONS.

Independent Practice

■ Assign the Lesson 4 section of the Teacher Resource Master **Independent Practice,** page 188.

3 APPLY

■ Ask students to notice certain behaviors of their pets. For example, a dog may turn around several times before lying down. This behavior is a throwback to its ancestors, the wolves and wild dogs, which trample leaves as a bed to lie on.

Close

■ Use Summary statements on student page 263 to review lesson concepts.

OPTIONS

Reteaching Strategy

■ Ask students to list five unlearned and five learned behaviors common to their pets. Ask them why the pets were able to learn certain behaviors and not others. Have them recall the learned behaviors of some circus animals. Ask: **How were circus animals trained?** *First, the animals' natural behaviors were understood. Behaviors the animals were taught were often based on their natural behaviors.*

Resource Options

Use Color Transparency #11, "Animal Behavior."

TEACHER RESOURCE MASTERS

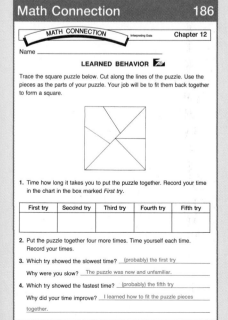

Math Connection	186

MATH CONNECTION — Interpreting Data — Chapter 12

Name _____

LEARNED BEHAVIOR

Trace the square puzzle below. Cut along the lines of the puzzle. Use the pieces as the parts of your puzzle. Your job will be to fit them back together to form a square.

1. Time how long it takes you to put the puzzle together. Record your time in the chart in the box marked *First try.*

First try	Second try	Third try	Fourth try	Fifth try

2. Put the puzzle together four more times. Time yourself each time. Record your times.
3. Which try showed the slowest time? __(probably) the first try__
   Why were you slow? __The puzzle was new and unfamiliar.__
4. Which try showed the fastest time? __(probably) the fifth try__
   Why did your time improve? __I learned how to fit the puzzle pieces together.__

Independent Practice	188

INDEPENDENT PRACTICE — Continued — Chapter 12

Name _____

Lesson 3 Specific Adaptations   Pages 254 to 259
Complete the sentences using the words below.
adaptation   bill   claws   teeth

10. The mouth part of a bird is called a ___bill___ obj 6
11. Some animals have sharp teeth and ___claws___ to catch food and _____ themselves. obj 5, 6
12. Mouth parts used to bite, tear, crush, and grind food are called ___teeth___. obj 6
13. The ___adaptation___ of an animal to its environment is important for its survival. obj 6

Lesson 4 Animal Behavior   Pages 260 to 263
Match the phrases on the left with the words on the right.

___b___ 14. a living thing's response to any change in its environment   **a.** learned behavior
obj 7
___a___ 15. a behavior changed by experience   **b.** behavior
obj 8   **c.** born behavior
___c___ 16. a behavior that can't be changed very easily
obj 9

Lesson 5 Reflexes and Instincts   Pages 264 to 271
Match the phrases on the left with the words on the right.

___b___ 17. simple type of behavior an animal is born with   **a.** blinking eyes
obj 10   **b.** reflex
___c___ 18. an example of an instinct   **c.** migration
obj 11   **d.** instinct
___d___ 19. complex type of born behavior
obj 11
___a___ 20. an example of a reflex
obj 10

OPTIONS

MATH CONNECTION

■ Have students continue the following problem from Lesson 3.

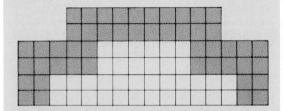

Bradley and his dad decided that they would pile the soil they dug out of their duck pond around the pond for runoff. They added the shaded area above to their first diagram. How can they find the area that the soil will cover for runoff? (Count the shaded squares.)

◆ **Reinforcement:** Discuss with students why they eat, drink, and stop for DON'T WALK signs. Explain that all these actions are behaviors and the things that cause a person to do them are stimuli.

● **Enrichment:** Have students make a list of the behaviors they have experienced that day. Discuss with them that getting up, eating breakfast, catching the school bus, and raising their hands to answer questions are all behaviors. Beside the behaviors, have them list the stimulus that caused the behavior. Have them decide whether the stimuli were from inside or outside their bodies.

On the other hand, animals are born with some behaviors. Ducklings follow their mother. The mother duck leads the ducklings to water. The ducklings can swim without being taught. The picture shows ducklings following their mother to go to swim. Following and swimming are behaviors the ducklings are born with. Behaviors animals are born with can't be changed very easily.

262

TEACHER RESOURCE MASTERS

Critical Thinking   183

CRITICAL THINKING/PROBLEM SOLVING   Chapter 12

Name _____

Choose a partner and find a place to do some bird watching. Use a field guide and the bird-watching checklist found below. Choose one bird and record as many observations as you can. Describe and compare your observations with other students.

BIRD-WATCHING CHECKLIST

All answers will vary.

1. Where was the bird? Circle your answer(s).   ground   tree   shrub

   water   air   field   marsh   suburb   city   other _____

2. What activities did you observe?   walking   hopping   running
   flapping flight   gliding flight   wading   swimming   sitting

   sleeping   feeding   other _____

3. How did the bird communicate?   calling   singing   other _____

4. What color(s) was the bird? _____

5. What body shape did the bird have? Draw your answer on the back.

6. What color patterns did the bird's body have? Draw your answer on the back.

7. What beak shape did the bird have? Draw your answer on the back.

8. What wing shape did the bird have? Draw your answer on the back.

9. What did the bird eat? _____

10. What protective adaptations did you observe? _____

11. What behaviors did you observe? _____

12. What is the name of the bird you observed? _____

Lesson Summary

- An animal's behavior is everything the animal does.
- Some behavior is learned.
- Animals are born with some behavior.

Lesson Review

1. What are two kinds of behavior a duckling is born with?
2. What are two kinds of behavior a dog can learn?

Following and swimming are behaviors ducklings are born with.

263

pages 260–263

OPTIONS

▲ **Challenge:** Have students observe a pet for 30 minutes recording the behaviors it exhibits during that time. Have them hypothesize the stimulus for the behaviors exhibited. Discuss their ideas in class.

LESSON REVIEW ANSWERS

1. following and swimming
2. Answers may vary. A dog can be taught to sit, beg, shake hands, and roll over.

TEACHER RESOURCE MASTERS

pages 264–271

PREPLAN

Lesson Objectives

10. Define and **identify** examples of a reflex.

11. Define and **give examples** of instinctive behavior.

Science Background

■ Inborn behavior, such as reflex behavior and instinct, is not easily changed. Ducklings instinctively know how to swim without being taught. Our eyes respond reflexively to changes in light intensity. Inborn behaviors such as these can be performed very shortly after an animal is born.

■ Migration, nest building, and web spinning are examples of instincts. Instincts usually involve several different actions and, therefore, are more complex behaviors than reflexes.

Note: The activity on student page 270 may be used for guided discovery before you begin this lesson.

1 FOCUS

■ Ask: **What happens when you touch a hot stove or come too close to a match flame?** *You jerk your hand away immediately; you don't have to think about it.*

■ Use the goals on student page 264 to establish the purpose for studying this lesson.

What is a reflex?

Reflexes and Instincts

A baby animal doesn't have to be shown how to drink milk. It already knows. In fact, if you touch a baby animal's nose or mouth, it will try to drink. This is called a reflex action. A reflex (REE fleks) is a simple type of behavior an animal is born with. A **reflex** is the reaction of an animal to something in its environment.

For example, when an animal suddenly sees a very bright light, the animal's eyes blink. This blinking is a reflex action. It's automatic. The animal can't help blinking.

264

TEACHER RESOURCE MASTERS

Your eyes have this reflex, too. The reflex happens without your thinking about it. You can see it happen by watching a classmate. You could take pictures of your classmate using a camera with a flash attachment. In all cases, your classmate's eyes will blink.

You have other reflexes, too. For example, you may remember how you jerked your hand away when you touched something hot. This reflex protected you from getting burned. A reflex usually happens very quickly.

Blinking is a reflex action.

265

TEACHER RESOURCE MASTERS

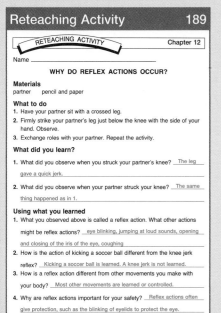

Reteaching Activity 189

RETEACHING ACTIVITY — Chapter 12

Name _____

WHY DO REFLEX ACTIONS OCCUR?

Materials
partner   pencil and paper

What to do
1. Have your partner sit with a crossed leg.
2. Firmly strike your partner's leg just below the knee with the side of your hand. Observe.
3. Exchange roles with your partner. Repeat the activity.

What did you learn?
1. What did you observe when you struck your partner's knee? _The leg gave a quick jerk._
2. What did you observe when your partner struck your knee? _The same thing happened as in 1._

Using what you learned
1. What you observed above is called a reflex action. What other actions might be reflex actions? _eye blinking, jumping at loud sounds, opening and closing of the iris of the eye, coughing_
2. How is the action of kicking a soccer ball different from the knee jerk reflex? _Kicking a soccer ball is learned. A knee jerk is not learned._
3. How is a reflex action different from other movements you make with your body? _Most other movements are learned or controlled._
4. Why are reflex actions important for your safety? _Reflex actions often give protection, such as the blinking of eyelids to protect the eye._

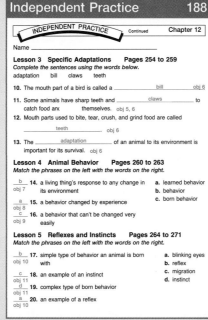

Independent Practice 188

INDEPENDENT PRACTICE   Continued   Chapter 12

Name _____

Lesson 3   Specific Adaptations   Pages 254 to 259
Complete the sentences using the words below.
adaptation   bill   claws   teeth

10. The mouth part of a bird is called a _____ bill _____ obj 6
11. Some animals have sharp teeth and _____ claws _____ to catch food and _____ themselves. obj 5, 6
12. Mouth parts used to bite, tear, crush, and grind food are called _____ teeth _____. obj 6
13. The _____ adaptation _____ of an animal to its environment is important for its survival. obj 6

Lesson 4   Animal Behavior   Pages 260 to 263
Match the phrases on the left with the words on the right.

_b_ 14. a living thing's response to any change in its environment   a. learned behavior
obj 7   b. behavior
_a_ 15. a behavior changed by experience   c. born behavior
obj 8
_c_ 16. a behavior that can't be changed very easily
obj 9

Lesson 5   Reflexes and Instincts   Pages 264 to 271
Match the phrases on the left with the words on the right.

_b_ 17. simple type of behavior an animal is born with   a. blinking eyes
obj 10   b. reflex
_c_ 18. an example of an instinct   c. migration
obj 11   d. instinct
_d_ 19. complex type of born behavior
obj 11
_a_ 20. an example of a reflex
obj 10

2   TEACH

■ Explain to students that humans exhibit many easily observed reflexes. We blink at a sudden noise or jump when someone startles us. A person automatically begins breathing again after holding his or her breath for too long. Ask students to think of other human reflexes.

■ Point out that during a medical checkup, a doctor will shine a small light into a patient's eyes to test the response of the iris to the light. The doctor is checking the patient's reflexes. If the response is too slow, the doctor may need to make further tests to determine why the reflex response was slow.

Guided Practice
■ Check students' understanding of lesson concepts by discussing the Lesson Review questions on student page 269. If necessary, use the **reteaching strategy** in OPTIONS.

Independent Practice
■ Assign the Lesson 5 section of the Teacher Resource Master **Independent Practice,** page 188.

3   APPLY

■ Ask students to think about ways in which animals respond to different stimuli. Discuss these responses in terms of reflexes and instincts.

Close
■ Use the summary statements on student page 269 to review the lesson concepts.

Reteaching Strategy
Ask students to imagine themselves as small animals living in a forest. Ask: **What sorts of instinctive behaviors might help you survive?** *Seeking food and shelter without having to learn to find those things might be appropriate responses.*

OPTIONS

LANGUAGE CONNECTION

Reading: Organize students into pairs of **cooperative groups** to complete the following activity. Discuss the meanings of the words *reflex* and *instinct*. (reflex: the action of an animal to something in its environment; instinct: a complex type of behavior an animal is born with)

Language Arts Skill: Use "I WANT TO KNOW ABOUT . . . Writing the Results," student page 271, with this lesson.

Instinct

What is an instinct?

Instinct (IHN stingt) is a complex type of behavior an animal is born with. It is different from a reflex because an instinct includes more than one action. It is also a behavior that can't easily be changed.

Many birds migrate in groups or flocks. The Canada geese flying in a V-shaped formation in the picture are migrating. How do they know where to go? Birds may use landmarks, stars, and the sun to help them find their way. Other animals, such as seals, whales, salmon, and reindeer, also migrate in search of food and a safe place to live and raise their young. How do they know where to go? Instinct tells them.

266

TEACHER RESOURCE MASTERS

Spinning a web is an instinct in spiders. They spin webs to capture food to eat. Different kinds of spiders spin different kinds of webs. A spider does not learn to spin a web. Spiders spin perfect webs the first time they try.

Why do spiders spin webs?

267

TEACHER RESOURCE MASTERS

OPTIONS

♦ **Reinforcement:** Show students a wildlife film about insects. After the film ask students to identify animal reflexes or instincts which were shown in the film. Students should recognize the complicated behavior of insects as being the result of instinct.

● **Enrichment:** To help students understand that all living things have their own forms of behavior, have students observe a species of protozoan after a drop of vinegar has been added at the edge of the coverslip. Students should determine that the protozoan reaction is a behavior.

▲ **Challenge:** Ask students to do research to find out the behavioral patterns of a particular animal in which they are interested. They should write a report which they will share with the class. They may wish to illustrate their reports.

■ Inform students that other examples of animals relying on their instincts include salmon swimming back to the same stream in which they were hatched; baby horses knowing how to stand up within a short time of birth; or songbirds becoming quiet and still when a hawk flies near. Challenge the class to think of more examples.

OPTIONS

YOU CAN . . . BUILD A NEST!

Process Skill: Formulating Models

Objective: Construct a bird's nest and **compare** it to a real one.

Setup/Teach:

■ Talk about different kinds of nests. Some are made only with twigs. Others are grass and mud. Sparrows use mainly grasses. Help students to gain an appreciation of nests. Local museums frequently have nests of birds common to your area.

■ **Student Response:** Responses will vary. Encourage thoughtful observations and inferences.

Nest building in birds is an instinct. If a bird's nest is destroyed by wind or by another animal during nest building, the bird will build a new nest in the same place. This action may be repeated several times until the young are raised. The bird does *not* learn to build its nest in a new and safer place.

ACTIVITY You Can...

Build a Nest!

For birds, building nests is an instinctive behavior. You can build a nest, too. Select grass, sticks, leaves, and some mud. Use these materials to create your own bird's nest. Look at examples of real birds' nests. How does yours compare? What kind of bird would most likely make a nest like yours?

268

TEACHER RESOURCE MASTERS

Reflexes and instincts are stronger in animals than in humans, but we have them, too. They help us stay alive when there isn't time to think what to do. Animals think much less than humans, but they use reflexes and instincts all the time to tell them what to do next.

Lesson Summary

- Reflex behavior is a simple type of behavior an animal is born with. Reflex behavior is caused by something in the surroundings.
- Instinct is a complex type of behavior an animal is born with. Instinctive behavior includes more than one action.

Lesson Review

1. What are two animal reflex behaviors?
★2. What are two animal instinctive behaviors?

Would You Believe?

A rodent's teeth never stop growing; they are worn down as the rodent gnaws on bark or other plants.

269

pages 264–271

LESSON REVIEW ANSWERS

1. Answers may include blinking in bright light, making drinking motions, and moving away from something hot.
2. Answers may include: animals migrating, spinning a web, and nest building.

TEACHER RESOURCE MASTERS

PREPLAN

Time Allotment: 35 minutes

Process Skill: Observing

Objectives

1. **Observe** instinctive behavior.
2. **Recognize** that data needs to be collected using more than one trial.

Setup

■ Mealworms can be obtained at pet stores or bait shops.

■ **Cooperative Grouping:** twos—Assign roles as explained on page T24.

1 FOCUS

■ Remind students that all animals exhibit forms of behavior. Distribute a mealworm to each group. Observe the mealworms and discuss their characteristics.

2 TEACH

■ Some mealworms may be approaching the pupa stage and will not be active. Give the student a different mealworm.

■ Have students use the Teacher Resource Master **Activity Worksheet,** pages 181 and 182, to record their data and answers.

3 APPLY

■ Ask students to define "instinctive behavior." How do they know that this is not learned behavior?

Close

■ Discuss the activity and questions.

Do mealworms like light or dark places?

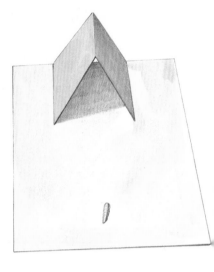

What you need

drawing paper
index card
mealworm

What to do

1. Place the paper on a table. Fold the card to look like a tent and put it at one end of the paper.
2. Put a mealworm at the other end of the paper. Observe and record its movements for 3 minutes.
3. Exchange mealworms with another group of students. Repeat step 2 three more times.

What did you learn?

1. Where did the first mealworm go? the second?
2. How did different mealworms behave?

3. What did other groups discover about how mealworms behave?

Using what you learned

1. What might happen if you had a light shining on the mealworm?
2. How could you set up an activity to find out if mealworms prefer a certain color? Try it and find out.

270

ACTIVITY RESPONSES

What did you learn?

1. Mealworms will probably move to the darker area.
2. Not all mealworms behave the same. Several trials with each mealworm will demonstrate this behavior. Some mealworms may not move. Some will be very active.
3. Not every group will have exactly the same information. However, with a greater amount of data from a variety of groups, a pattern of the mealworms moving to dark areas should become apparent.

Using what you learned

1. A flashlight introduces heat and light. Sometimes, the mealworm becomes more active. The students may infer that the brighter light encourages the mealworm to locate a darker place more quickly.
2. Students could set up a series of two or three different-colored paper tents to see if the mealworms consistently go to one color.

I WANT TO KNOW ABOUT...

Writing the Results

People who study animals spend a lot of time just watching them. They take notes about everything the animals do. Writing these notes acts as a measure of what they see.

Knowing about different kinds of behavior helps in measuring animal actions. All of this information helps people form opinions about how animals behave. The results of their work help people understand why animals behave in certain ways.

Study the picture below and answer the questions that follow.
- What is the brown dog doing?
- Is this a behavior that the dog was born with or has learned?
- What is the cat on the fence doing? Why?
- Is this behavior a reflex or an instinct?

The answers to these questions give general ideas about the actions of different animals. The answers are the results of your study.

Language Arts

271

TEACHER RESOURCE MASTERS

Feature Background
- Animal behaviorists make observations of animal responses to changes in their environment related to temperature, sound, light, water, oxygen, carbon dioxide, plants, and other animals.
- Studies show that birds respond to high temperatures by remaining dormant until the temperature drops. An animal behaviorist would try to find out at what temperature a certain species of bird becomes dormant and at what temperature it is aroused from its dormancy.
- People often wonder why moths are attracted to light. Animal behavior studies reveal that moths respond to the light of the sun in order to find their way. They do not distinguish between the light of the sun and artificial lights and therefore fly toward any light—even if it results in their getting burned.

Feature Vocabulary
results

Teaching Suggestions
- An interesting activity in which students can assume the role of animal behaviorist involves setting up a metal tray which is divided by a strip of wide masking tape. Fill one paper cup with ice cubes, and place it in the middle of the left side of the tray. Fill another cup with warm water, and place it in the middle of the right side of the tray. Release six healthy earthworms on the masking-tape strip. Have students record the time it takes the earthworms to move to one side of the tray or the other. (*The earthworms should move toward the colder side.*)
- Have students brainstorm in **cooperative groups** to determine another behavior they might observe in earthworms. For example, they might decide to study how earthworms respond to light or moisture. Have students also brainstorm how they will carry out their experiment.
- Ask students to write two or three sentences telling why they might like to become an animal behaviorist.

Summary

Chapter Closure: Review the major concepts listed on this page in a class discussion. Survey the class about other adaptations in animals they have observed.

CHAPTER REVIEW

12

Summary

Lesson 1
- An animal must be able to protect itself and find food in order to live in its habitat.
- Anything that helps an animal live in its environment is called an adaptation.

Lesson 2
- Animals have a skin covering of scales, feathers, or hair.
- Skin coverings protect animals and keep them warm.

Lesson 3
- Feet, wings, and mouth parts are three types of adaptations.
- Adaptations help animals stay alive.

Lesson 4
- Behavior is everything an animal does.
- Learned behavior is caused by experience; learned behavior can be changed.

Lesson 5
- An animal is born with reflex behavior, which is caused by something in its surroundings.
- Animals are born with instinctive behavior.

Science Words

Fill in the blank with the correct word or words from the list.

adaptation behavior
skin learned behavior
scales reflex
feathers instinct
fur

1. A complex type of behavior an animal is born with is called ___.
2. An animal reacts quickly to something with a ___.

272

TEACHER RESOURCE MASTERS

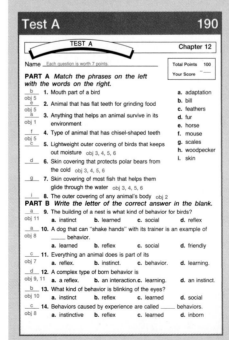

Test A 190

TEST A — Chapter 12

Name _Each question is worth 7 points._ — Total Points 100 / Your Score ___

PART A *Match the phrases on the left with the words on the right.*

- _b_ obj 5 **1.** Mouth part of a bird
- _e_ obj 5 **2.** Animal that has flat teeth for grinding food
- _a_ obj 1 **3.** Anything that helps an animal survive in its environment
- _f_ obj 5 **4.** Type of animal that has chisel-shaped teeth
- _c_ **5.** Lightweight outer covering of birds that keeps out moisture obj 3, 4, 5, 6
- _d_ **6.** Skin covering that protects polar bears from the cold obj 3, 4, 5, 6
- _g_ **7.** Skin covering of most fish that helps them glide through the water obj 3, 4, 5, 6
- _i_ **8.** The outer covering of any animal's body obj 2

a. adaptation
b. bill
c. feathers
d. fur
e. horse
f. mouse
g. scales
h. woodpecker
i. skin

PART B *Write the letter of the correct answer in the blank.*

- _a_ obj 11 **9.** The building of a nest is what kind of behavior for birds?
  a. instinct b. learned c. social d. reflex
- _a_ obj 8 **10.** A dog that can "shake hands" with its trainer is an example of _____ behavior.
  a. learned b. reflex c. social d. friendly
- _c_ obj 7 **11.** Everything an animal does is part of its
  a. reflex. b. instinct. c. behavior. d. learning.
- _d_ obj 9, 11 **12.** A complex type of born behavior is
  a. a reflex. b. an interaction. c. learning. d. an instinct.
- _b_ obj 10 **13.** What kind of behavior is blinking of the eyes?
  a. instinct b. reflex c. learned d. social
- _c_ obj 8 **14.** Behaviors caused by experience are called _____ behaviors.
  a. instinctive b. reflex c. learned d. inborn

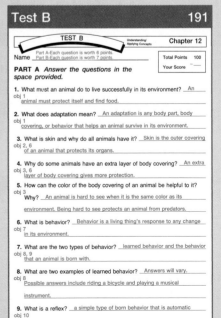

Test B 191

TEST B — Understanding/Applying Concepts — Chapter 12

Name _Part A-Each question is worth 6 points._ _Part B-Each question is worth 7 points._ — Total Points 100 / Your Score ___

PART A *Answer the questions in the space provided.*

1. What must an animal do to live successfully in its environment? _An animal must protect itself and find food._ obj 1

2. What does adaptation mean? _An adaptation is any body part, body covering, or behavior that helps an animal survive in its environment._ obj 1

3. What is skin and why do all animals have it? _Skin is the outer covering of an animal that protects its organs._ obj 2, 6

4. Why do some animals have an extra layer of body covering? _An extra layer of body covering gives more protection._ obj 3, 6

5. How can the color of the body covering of an animal be helpful to it? Why? _An animal is hard to see when it is the same color as its environment. Being hard to see protects an animal from predators._ obj 3

6. What is behavior? _Behavior is a living thing's response to any change in its environment._ obj 7

7. What are the two types of behavior? _learned behavior and the behavior that an animal is born with_ obj 8, 9

8. What are two examples of learned behavior? _Answers will vary. Possible answers include riding a bicycle and playing a musical instrument._ obj 8

9. What is a reflex? _a simple type of born behavior that is automatic_ obj 10

3. Any body part, body covering, or behavior that helps an animal live in its environment is called a(n) ____.

4. A living thing's response to any change in its environment is ____.

5. Behavior that can be changed is called ____.

6. Small, thin plates covering the skin of some animals are called ____.

Questions

Recalling Ideas

Correctly complete each of the following sentences.

1. An added layer of covering some animals have on their skin is
   (a) bone. (c) wings.
   (b) feet. (d) scales.

2. Learned behavior can be
   (a) skin. (c) an instinct.
   (b) changed. (d) a reflex.

Understanding Ideas

Answer the following questions using complete sentences.

1. What are three extra layers of body covering that come from skin tissue?

2. What is the difference between behavior an animal is born with and learned behavior?

3. Give two examples of a reflex.

4. Give an example of an animal instinct.

5. How does being the same color as its environment help an animal to survive?

Thinking Critically

Think about what you have learned in this chapter. Answer the following questions using complete sentences.

1. How does a cat avoid predators?

2. Describe how one particular animal is adapted for food getting and protection.

273

TEACHER RESOURCE MASTERS

Test B   **192**

| TEST B | Continued | Chapter 12 |

Name _____

10. What are some examples of a reflex? __Answers will vary. Possible__
obj 10 __answers include blinking, breathing, and jerking one's hand away from__
__something hot.__

11. What is instinct? __a complex type of born behavior that includes more__
obj 11 __than one action and that can't be easily changed__

12. What are some examples of instincts? __Answers will vary. Possible__
obj 11 __answers include migrating, spinning a web, and building a nest.__

Part B *Complete the chart.*

Animal	Body covering	Adaptations for getting food Answers may vary.
13. Snake obj 4, 5, 6	scales	mouth with jaw that can open; wide curved teeth
14. Duck obj 4, 5, 6	feathers	webbed feet for swimming; bill for grasping and sifting food
15. Horse obj 4, 5, 6	hair or fur	teeth with flat surfaces for grinding food
16. Woodpecker obj 4, 5, 6	feathers	hard pointed bill and long tongue to eat insects that live under the bark

Science Words

Students can practice quick word recognition with a game called "cover up." In large letters, print each science word on a file card. In class, cover the word and then slowly uncover it. Ask students to raise their hands as soon as they know the word.

Student Responses

1. instinct
2. reflex
3. adaptation
4. behavior
5. learned behavior
6. scales

Questions

Recalling Ideas

1. d
2. b

Understanding Ideas

1. Possible responses are fur, scales, and feathers.
2. Behavior an animal is born with can't be changed easily; learned behavior can be changed.
3. Sneezing and the change in size of the pupil in light and dark are two examples of reflexes.
4. Migration, web spinning, and nest building are three examples of instincts.
5. It makes them hard to see because they blend into their surroundings.

Thinking Critically

1. A cat can make its hair stand out so that it looks larger to its predators. This frightens off the threatening animal. It also uses its sharp teeth and claws for protection.
2. A lion uses its sharp claws and teeth to get its food and also to protect itself. Its fur protects it from bumps and scratches. It has long, thick growths of hair around its neck where injuries would be very serious. This is one possible answer. Students' answers will vary.

Checking for Understanding

1. air, food, water, and space

2. A producer can make its own food. A consumer must obtain food from producers or other consumers.

3. an animal that kills and eats other animals—a lion or wolf; animals eaten by predators—mice and rabbits

4. Both habitats are large open spaces. The tundra is covered with a frozen layer of soil. Only small grasses and mosses grow there. The grassland has a warmer climate and is covered with tall grasses.

5. Both are water habitats that have plants and animals adapted to a water habitat. The saltwater habitat is larger. Plants and animals within each type of habitat are different.

6. Accept all reasonable answers related to wildlife conservation.

7. food and protection, among other things

8. Behavior that an animal is born with is not learned and cannot be changed easily. Learned behavior is caused by experience and can be changed.

9. Decomposers break down dead plants and animals into simple matter that becomes part of the soil.

10. A food chain is the transfer of energy from the sun to producers and then to consumers. A food web is all the feeding relationships in a community.

11. The fur of a polar bear traps air that is then warmed by the bear's body. The warm air helps keep the bear's body at an even temperature.

12. The camel can go for days without water; the bear sleeps through most of the winter in the temperate forest; the antelope moves quickly in the grassland; the monkey has long arms and a long tail with which it can move from tree to tree.

13. The energy is used by producers and consumers for their life processes, and the amount of available energy decreases with each consumer in the food chain.

Checking for Understanding

Write a short answer for each question or statement.

1. List four needs of all living things.
2. How are producers and consumers different?
3. What kind of animal is a predator? prey? Give an example of each.
4. How are tundra and grassland habitats alike? different?
5. How are saltwater and freshwater habitats alike? different?
6. How can people help to conserve their habitats?
7. What are some things animals must have to live in their environment?
8. What is the difference between behavior an animal is born with and learned behavior?
9. How do decomposers change dead plants and animals?
10. What is the difference between a food chain and a food web?
11. How does fur protect a polar bear in below zero temperature?
12. Name ways in which the following animals are adapted to life in their habitats: camel, bear, antelope, monkey.
13. What happens to energy as it is passed from the producer to the consumer in a food chain?

Recalling Activities

Write a short paragraph for each question or statement.

1. What plant parts are eaten?
2. How can you make a land habitat?
3. How do fish scales look under a microscope?
4. What does the plant factory need?
5. What animals live around you?
6. Do mealworms like light or dark places?

TEACHER RESOURCE MASTERS

Project Ideas

1. Observe a place with plants and animals. Record your observations. Write a report or give a talk about what you observe.
2. Test the effect of different body coverings on body temperature. Experiment using various types and layers of clothes.
3. Using a plastic bag, show how a cactus loses less water than a woodland plant in sunlight.

Books to Read

All Kinds of Feet by Ron and Nancy Goor, Crowell Junior Books: New York, 1984.
This book describes how animals' feet are suited to their needs.

Fish Facts and Bird Brains: Animal Intelligence by Helen R. Sattler, Lodestar Books: New York, 1984.
Read this book and learn how smart animals are.

Who Knows This Nose by Marlene M. Robinson, Dodd Mead & Co.: New York, 1983.

TEACHER RESOURCE MASTERS

Recalling Activities

1. The animal in the activity may eat lettuce (leaves), carrots (roots), or seeds.
2. Rocks, soil, food, and water may be put in a ventilated jar with a small animal to make a land habitat.
3. The scales have rough surfaces that can't be seen without a microscope. The upper scales are larger and rougher than the lower scales.
4. Plants need water and sunlight to grow. Plants that don't receive enough water or sunlight don't grow.
5. A variety of animals such as birds, squirrels, and mice may leave tracks in the flour.
6. Most mealworms like dark places better. Some show no preference.

Project Ideas

Have students work individually or in **cooperative groups** to complete one of the projects listed.

Books to Read

♦ *Who Knows This Nose?*
● *All Kinds of Feet*
▲ *Fish Facts and Bird Brains*

UNIT 4

Human Body

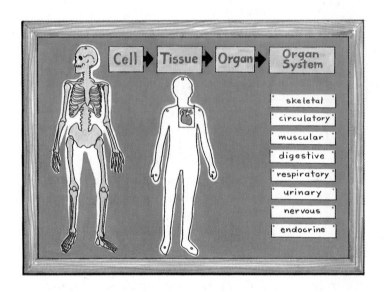

Bulletin Board

Goals: This bulletin board should be built during the course of the chapter on body systems to help students identify various systems and their locations in the body.

Materials: construction/poster paper
markers or crayons
letters
scissors
string or yarn
thumbtacks or pushpins

Procedure: Make cards for the terms *cell, tissue, organ,* and *organ system* and use them to construct a flow chart. Place cards for the various organ systems as the system is introduced and have a student connect the system diagram with the name card by a length of string or yarn. Have students **work cooperatively** to make cut-outs of the heart, digestive organs, lungs, brain, and kidneys. You may wish to use a separate structure showing only the skeleton. A blank body form on which organs will be placed will be needed.

Science Center

Goals: Students are to select a pocket activity to test or expand their knowledge of the unit material on body systems, disease, nutrition, drugs, and poisons. Suggestions are made below.

Materials: reference books   string
markers or crayons   scissors
stethoscope   magazines
construction paper   glue

Procedure: Place appropriate references, magazines, and materials in the science center. Have students select questions from individual pockets. Finished diagrams, answer sheets, or worksheets should be kept in a folder.

Suggested pocket activities are: unscramble body system names and write a complete sentence about the system; use a stethoscope to listen to your own heartbeat and count the number of beats per minute at rest and after running in place one minute; using arrows on a diagram of the respiratory system, show the pathway of oxygen into and carbon dioxide out of the lungs; make a healthful food mobile; list four places where the Poison Control Center telephone number should be placed; use a resource to write a paragraph describing a disease; make a bookmark in the shape of a bone.

Places to Go, People to See

Field Trip Ideas

Arrange a visit to a company where food is processed for resale or restaurant use. Have students notice any health regulations that employees are required to follow or special clothing they have to wear.

Speakers and Visitors

Invite a nurse who works in a hospital and another who works in a doctor's office to talk to students about their different responsibilities in caring for people who are ill.

Audiovisuals for the Students

Films and Filmstrips

Cells of Plants & Animals, 16 mm, 10 min., B&W, Coronet.

Growth and Change, 16 mm, 15 min., color, Professional Research, Inc.

The World of Cells, 3 filmstrips, 3 sound cassettes, 10 min., Society for Visual Education.

Health, 16 mm, 6 min., color, EBEC.

Health-Exercise, Rest and Sleep, 16 mm, 11 min., color, AIMS Media, Inc.

I am Joe's Skin, 16 mm, 25 min., color, Pyramid Films & Video.

Videotapes

Growth and Change, 15 min., color, Professional Research, Inc.

Advice on Lice, 13 min., color, Walt Disney Educational Media Co.

Nutrition for Better Health, 15 min., color, EBEC.

Computer Software

Nutrition Series A three-program series includes Food for Thought; You are What You Eat; and Food Group Puzzles. Can be bought separately. Teaches nutrition and the five basic food groups.

Type: Tutorial, Games

Hardware: Apple II+, IIe, IIc

Supplier: Marshfilm/Marshware Enterprises, Inc.

Cells and Tissues Teaches the basic structure and functions of cells using animated graphics. Three programs include The Structure of Cells; Binary Fission; and From Cells to Tissues. Activity masters included.

Type: Tutorial

Hardware: Apple II+, IIe, IIc

Supplier: Educational Activities, Inc.

Resources for the Teacher

Materials at Little/No Cost

Breakfast Scorecard and Breakfast American-style Kellogg Company

Dept. C-3

Battle Creek, MI 49016

Send a postcard and receive a game and a chart on which students keep a daily breakfast record.

Resource Books

Arnot, Robert. *The Complete Manual of Fitness & Well-Being.* New York: Viking-Penguin, Inc., 1984.

DeDuve, Christian. *A Guided Tour of the Living Cell.* New York: W. H. Freeman, 1985.

Powis, Raymond L. *The Human Body and Why It Works.* Englewood Cliffs, NJ: Prentice-Hall, 1985.

Human Body

UNIT CONCEPTS

Chapter 13

■ Cells are the building blocks of the body.

■ The body is made of cells, tissues, organs, and organ systems.

■ The circulatory system carries food and oxygen; the skeletal system gives shape and support; the muscular system moves body parts.

■ The digestive system processes food, and the respiratory system exchanges the gases oxygen and carbon dioxide.

■ The urinary system removes most of the liquid body wastes. The control systems keep the body working as a unit.

Chapter 14

■ Foods from the five basic food groups provide the nutrients and energy that your body needs to grow and repair damaged cells.

■ Diseases are caused by germs that enter the body. Immunity is gained by having the disease, or through vaccination. Liquids, healthful foods, and rest can help the body heal faster.

■ Drugs used in medicines may be needed to cure or control diseases and must be used safely. Other drugs can be found in some foods, drinks, and tobacco products.

■ Some poisons can be found in the home and should be used safely. Know where to seek help for accidental poisonings.

Five minutes, five minutes more, please!
   Let me stay five minutes more!
Can't I just finish the castle
   I'm building here on the floor?
Can't I just finish the story
   I'm reading here in my book?
Can't I just finish this bead-chain—
   It *almost* is finished, look!

from "Bedtime"
Eleanor Farjeon

277

ACTIVITY CENTER

For fun, hands-on, independent activities that integrate reading, writing, math, and technology with the chapters in this unit, have students complete some or all of the Activity Center Activities below. Look for specific chapter references in the Lesson Planning Guides.

Reading: 11 Good Food? 12 A Well-Rounded Meal
Writing: 11 When I Was Sick and Lay A-Bed, 12 Good and Bad
Math: 11 You Can Do, 12 Who Caught It?
Technology: 11 Heartbeat, 12 Too Sweet!

CONNECTING LITERATURE TO SCIENCE

Understanding the Selection

■ Have students discuss what their bodies need to stay healthy. Tell students that you are going to read a poem about something we all need in order to be strong and healthy.
■ Read the poem aloud. Then have students read the poem aloud with you.
■ Ask: **What is the poem about?** *bedtime* **What did the person in the poem not want to do?** *The person in the poem did not want to go to bed.* Ask: **Is the person in the poem an adult or a child? How do you know?** *a child because the person talks about finishing a castle and making a bead chain.*

Relating the Selection to Unit Concepts

■ Ask students why they think a person needs rest and sleep. Possible answers include *The body needs a rest after it works and plays hard; when a person sleeps, the body uses the time to repair itself.* Ask students what can happen if a person does not get enough rest or sleep. *A person can get sick.*
■ Discuss what a person can do to avoid sickness and what a person should do if he/she gets sick.
■ Ask: **What can you do to stay healthy?** Possible answers include: *eat good foods, get plenty of rest, exercise.*

Relating the Selection to the Student's World

■ Have students look at the photograph and tell what time the clock shows. *8:00*
■ Discuss why eight o'clock is an appropriate bedtime for third graders.
■ Ask: **What are some other healthy habits you should strive for besides getting enough rest?** Possible answers include *exercising, eating properly, washing hands before eating.*

Your Body

Planning Guide

Lessons	Objectives	Vocabulary
Chapter Introduction pp. 278, 279		
Lesson 1 Cells pp. 280–283	1. **Define** *cell* and **infer** that cells are the building blocks of the human body. 2. **Conclude** that most cells grow and replace themselves continuously.	cell
Lesson 2 Tissues Organs, and Organ Systems pp. 284–287	3. **Define** *tissue, organ,* and *organ system.* 4. **Observe** and **communicate** the relationship among cells, tissues, organs, and organ systems.	tissue organ organ system
Lesson 3 Circulatory, Skeletal, and Muscular Systems pp. 288–293	5. **Communicate** the main functions of the circulatory and skeletal systems. 6. **Observe** the function of the muscular system.	circulatory system skeletal system muscular system
Lesson 4 Digestive and Respiratory Systems pp. 294–297	7. **Infer** the movement of food through the digestive system. 8. **Tell** the function of the respiratory system.	digestive system respiratory system
Lesson 5 Urinary and Control Systems pp. 298–301	9. **Identify** and **describe** some parts and functions of the urinary, nervous, and endocrine systems. 10. **Understand** that the body has two control systems.	perspiration urinary system urethra urine nervous system endocrine system
Chapter Review pp. 302–303		

Planning Guide

Text Activities		Teacher Resource Masters	Other Components
Title/Skill	**Materials per Group**		
Have You Ever . . . Tested Your Lung Capacity? p. 279 Measuring/Observing Time Allotment: 30 minutes	dishpan water hose cardboard jar		Activity Center: "When I Was Sick and Lay A-Bed"; "Heartbeat"
What Do Different Body Cells Look Like? p. 283 Observing Time Allotment: 35 minutes	micro-viewer micro-view slides pencil and paper	Independent Practice, pp. 203, 204 Activity Worksheet, pp. 195, 196	
		Independent Practice, pp. 203, 204 Language Arts Connection p. 201 Transparency Master, p. 193 ◆ Family Science, p. 194	Color Transparency #12 Color Transparency #13
How Does Your Pulse Rate Change? p. 293 Measuring Time Allotment: 30 minutes	watch with second hand pencil and paper	Independent Practice, pp. 203, 204 Activity Worksheet, pp. 197, 198 Math Connection, p. 202	Activity Book, pp. 33, 34 Color Transparency #12 Color Transparency #13 Color Transparency #14
You Can . . . See Your Lung Capacity, p. 296 Observing Time Allotment: 15 minutes	balloon	Independent Practice, pp. 203, 204 Critical Thinking, p. 199 ▲ Critical Thinking, p. 200	Color Transparency #13
		Independent Practice, pp. 203, 204 ◆ Reteaching Activity, p. 205	Color Transparency #13
		Test A, p. 206 Test B, pp. 207, 208	

◆ Basic / ▲ Advanced / All other masters are for use by all students.

Your Body

ESL/LEP

Chapter 13/Lesson 1, Page 280
Draw a typical cell on the chalkboard. Ask students to help you label the parts. Have them pronounce the words *nucleus, cytoplasm,* and *cell membrane.* Have students find the same parts in other kinds of cells shown in their science book. Ask students to describe the functions of cells.

Chapter 13/Lesson 3, Page 288
Ask students to explain the function of the circulatory system. Have them use these words in sentences: *heart, blood vessels,* and *blood.*

Chapter 13/Lesson 5, Page 300
Write these words on the chalkboard: *nerves, spinal cord, brain.* Ask students to pinch their arms. Trace the pathway of the message that goes from a nerve in their arm to their spinal cord then to their brain. Have students think of other sensations for which they can trace the pathway to the brain.

Gifted

Chapter 13/Lesson 3, Page 293
Have students collect data from steps 4 through 7 in the *What to do* section of the activity on page 293 from all students in the class. Help them organize the information in a data table. Help them find class averages for each activity. Suggest that they design an experiment to find out if the average pulse rate of children their age is the same as that of an adult. Having collected data from a group of adults, have them suggest reasons for any differences that might be noted.

Mainstreamed

Chapter 13/Lesson 4, Page 297
Physically Disabled: Show students a model or large detailed diagram of the digestive system. Tell them to imagine they are shipmates on a minisubmarine traveling through the digestive system on an expedition. When you say "Up periscope" students should describe where they are located, what they see, and what is going on at that location.

Whole Class Science Project

Have students work in pairs to determine how many breaths each one takes per minute. Have one student count the number of breaths taken by a partner in one minute. Have students record the results. A clock with a second hand will be needed. Have the test student run in place for two minutes and immediately have a recount of the number of breaths per minute. Have the student rest two minutes and have the counter take a third one-minute reading. Then have students reverse roles so that each student in the room has three readings. Discuss the results. Discuss the difference between breathing through the nose and breathing through the mouth. Because the nose is lined with short hairs, particulate matter may be trapped before it passes into the trachea.

Student:	Number of breaths in one minute
resting	
after running in place	
after two-minute rest	

Science Fair Projects

Individual students could do one of the following projects.
1. Find out what happens to a peanut butter and jelly sandwich as it goes through the digestive tract.
2. Using various foods, find out how fast aromas travel.

Chapter Concepts

■ Cells are the building blocks of the body.

■ The body is made of cells, tissues, organs, and organ systems.

■ The circulatory system carries food and oxygen; the skeletal system gives shape and support; the muscular system moves body parts.

■ The digestive system processes food, and the respiratory system exchanges the gases oxygen and carbon dioxide.

■ The urinary system removes most of the liquid body wastes. The control systems keep the body working as a unit.

Chapter Background

■ The human body contains billions of cells. Cells differ in function, size, shape, and contents. All the contents are important for life's activities.

■ Organs are more complicated than tissues and usually contain several types of tissues.

■ Plasma is the liquid part of blood. Plasma contains water, salts, protein, antibodies, and hormones.

■ Muscles move the bones of your body.

■ Digestion chemically changes food to a form that can pass through cell membranes in the small intestines.

■ The brain receives and sends messages to and from the spinal cord and nerves.

Looking Ahead

■ Invite a nurse to talk to students about their different responsibilities in caring for people who are ill.

Look for These Symbols

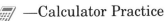 —Hands-on activity

—Cooperative learning

—Overhead transparency

◆ —Basic/Reinforcement

● —Average/Enrichment

▲ —Advanced/Challenge

—Calculator Practice

SCIENCE
In Your World

278

CHAPTER
13

Your Body

Have you ever run in a race with a friend? How did you feel when the race was over? Were your legs tired? Was your heart beating very fast?

Have You Ever...

Tested Your Lung Capacity?

Gather together a dishpan, a jar, a piece of cardboard, and a small length of hose. Pour water into the dishpan until the water is about five centimeters deep. Fill up the jar with water and place the piece of cardboard over its mouth. Put the jar upside down into the dishpan of water. Remove the cardboard and then put the hose up into the jar. Take a deep breath and blow into the hose. What happened to the water in the jar? Why?

279

PREPLAN

Time Allotment: 30 minutes

Objectives
1. **Discuss** the effects of running on the muscular and circulatory systems.
2. **Experiment** to determine lung capacity.

Setup
- You will need the following materials for each student or activity group:
  dishpan   hose   jar
  water   cardboard

1   FOCUS

- Encourage students to tell about their experiences with running and how they may have prepared for a race.

2   TEACH

- Have the title and the introductory paragraph read aloud.
- Discuss student answers to questions.

Have You Ever . . .
Use this activity as an introduction to the respiratory system.
Have students **work cooperatively** in groups of four.

Student Responses
- The water level in the jar goes down because the air blown into the jar forces the water out of the jar and into the pan. The air displaced the water.

3   APPLY

- Ask: **Why might a trained runner be able to displace more water with air?** *His/her lung capacity is greater.*

Close
- Tell students they will learn more about the systems of their bodies as they read Chapter 13.

pages 280–283

PREPLAN

Lesson Objectives

1. Define *cell* and **infer** that cells are the building blocks of the human body.
2. Conclude that most cells grow and replace themselves continuously.

Science Background

■ Each cell is composed of cytoplasm, a jellylike substance similar to egg white. The cytoplasm is surrounded by a cell membrane that permits food, water, and oxygen to enter and wastes to leave the cell.
■ Cells have a nucleus or control center that directs the activities of the cell.
■ The first cell was described by an Englishman, Robert Hooke, in 1665.
■ The electron microscope helps scientists study cells more closely than a light microscope.

Lesson Vocabulary

cell

Note: The activity on student page 283 may be used for guided discovery before you begin this lesson.

1 FOCUS

■ Display a honeycomb for students to examine. Have them describe its structure and function.
■ Use the goals on student page 280 to establish the purpose for studying this lesson.

Cells

LESSON 1 GOALS
You will learn
● that all living things are made of cells.
● that your body has many kinds of cells.
● that cells grow and divide.

Have you ever eaten honey fresh from a honeycomb? A honeycomb is the package that bees build out of wax to hold the honey they make. Each boxlike section of a comb is called a cell. The cells are fastened together and are the building blocks of a honeycomb.

Living things are also made of small units called cells. These cells, though, are made of living matter instead of beeswax and honey. A **cell** is the smallest unit of living matter. Most cells are so small that scientists must use microscopes to look at them.

All living things are made of one or more cells. The picture on this page shows an animal cell. All animal cells contain a nucleus, cytoplasm, and a cell membrane. However, all cells do not look the same. They may be round, long, or thin.

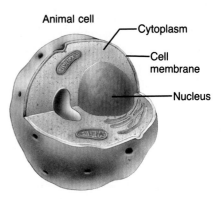

Animal cell — Cytoplasm — Cell membrane — Nucleus

280

TEACHER RESOURCE MASTERS

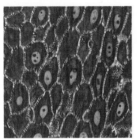
Skin cells

Nerve cells

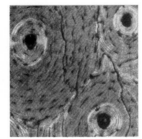
Bone cells

Muscle cells

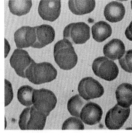
Blood cells

Your body is made of many kinds of cells. Each kind of cell has a different job. A bone cell can't do the job of a skin cell, for example. The pictures on this page show some of the different kinds of cells in your body.

Each person goes through a life cycle that includes birth, growth, aging, and death. Body cells also go through a life cycle. Your body grows larger by adding new cells. New cells form when other cells divide. The new cells grow, divide, age, and die. New cells also replace dead or damaged cells.

281

TEACHER RESOURCE MASTERS

Independent Practice   203

INDEPENDENT PRACTICE   Chapter 13

Name ___ Questions are each worth 4 points.   Total Points 100
                                                Your Score ___

Lesson 1 Cells   Pages 280 to 283
Complete the following sentences.

1. All living things are made up of ___ one or more cells
   obj 1
2. A cell is the ___ smallest unit of living matter
   obj 1
3. Your body grows larger by ___ adding new cells
   obj 2
4. ___ New cells ___ replace dead or damaged cells. obj 2

Lesson 2 Tissues, Organs, and Organ Systems   Pages 284 to 287

5. Cells working together in a group form a ___ tissue
   obj 3
6. ___ Muscle ___ tissue tightens and relaxes to help you move your leg. obj 4
7. An ___ organ ___ is a group of tissues working together. obj 3
8. Two tissues in your heart are ___ muscle ___ tissue and ___ nerve ___ tissue.
   obj 4
9. A group of organs working together is an ___ organ system
   obj 3
10. Organ systems carry out major jobs in the ___ body ___ obj 4

Lesson 3 Circulatory, Skeletal, and Muscular Systems   Pages 288 to 293
Match the description on the left with the words on the right.

___ b ___ 11. pumps blood to all parts of the body   obj 5   a. blood
                                                                b. heart
___ a ___ 12. carries food and oxygen to the body   obj 5   c. skeletal system
                                                                d. muscle
___ c ___ 13. gives body shape and support
___ d ___ 14. shortens when it contracts   obj 6

2 TEACH

Use inflated balloons to demonstrate how cells fit together to form a cluster. Have students infer that the balloons are like groups of cells.

■ Discuss life cycles with students to make sure they understand the concept.

Guided Practice

■ Check students' understanding of lesson concepts by discussing the Lesson Review questions on student page 282. If necessary, use the **reteaching strategy** in OPTIONS.

Independent Practice

■ Assign the Lesson 1 section of the Teacher Resource Master **Independent Practice,** page 203.

3 APPLY

■ Introduce the idea that some snakes shed their skin periodically. Ask: **Why do you think some snakes shed their skin?** *This shedding of skin cells demonstrates the aging, dying, and replacement pattern that all cells experience.*

Close

■ Use Summary statements on student page 282 to review lesson concepts.

OPTIONS

Reteaching Strategy

Divide students into small groups and provide each group with an uncooked egg. Have groups break their eggs into a container. Point out the similarity between the egg and a body cell. Compare the yolk to a nucleus, the white to the cytoplasm, and the shell membrane to a cell membrane.

OPTIONS

MATH CONNECTION

Have students work in pairs or **co-operative groups** to evaluate, discuss, and respond to the picture of honeycomb cells on this page. Pick two honeycomb cells in the picture. Are they similar? (yes, if same shape) Are they congruent? (yes, if same shape and same size) Pick a square section of cells and draw a line of symmetry through the section.

◆ **Reinforcement:** Provide cotton, clay, and plastic boxes for students to use to make a model cell. Help students label the cytoplasm (cotton), nucleus (ball of clay), and cell membrane (plastic box). Place the boxes on a table to form a structure. Encourage students to tell how cells are alike and how cells differ. Save the cells for the section on tissue.

● **Enrichment:** Encourage students to use a prepared slide of a plant cell and an animal cell. Have students observe the cells with a microscope and draw pictures of what they see. Have students compare the cells.

▲ **Challenge:** Have students locate and reproduce on drawing paper a diagram that shows how cells divide during mitosis. Have them explain their diagrams to the class. Discuss why it is important for the cells on the inside of their cheeks or on their hands to be able to make new cells quickly.

LESSON REVIEW ANSWERS

1. They are both building blocks.
2. by adding new cells
3. A cell forms when another cell divides; it then grows, divides, ages, and dies.

Unlike honeycomb cells, body cells don't contain delicious honey. But body cells are also building blocks. They are the building blocks of your body.

Lesson Summary

- A cell is the smallest unit of living matter.
- Different kinds of cells have different jobs within your body.
- New cells grow, divide, age, and die.

Lesson Review

1. How are the cells of your body like honeycomb cells?
2. How does your body grow larger?
★3. What is the life cycle of a cell?

Cells are building blocks.

282

TEACHER RESOURCE MASTERS

What do different body cells look like?

What you need
micro-viewer
micro-view slides (human body cells)
pencil and paper

What to do
1. Place a slide in the micro-viewer.
2. Observe the cells on the slide. Make a drawing of what you see. Label the cell membrane, cytoplasm, and nucleus.
3. Repeat steps 1 and 2. Continue until all the slides have been viewed.

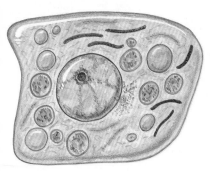

What did you learn?
1. How are all the cells alike?
2. How are the cells different?

Using what you learned
1. Why are there different kinds of body cells?
2. How is a living cell different from a dead cell of the same type?

283

ACTIVITY RESPONSES

What did you learn?
1. All cells have a cell membrane, cytoplasm, and a nucleus.
2. The cells are different sizes and shapes. They may appear different colored as well. The cells may have been stained to help see the features more clearly.

Using what you learned
1. The cells are different because they all carry out different functions. The characteristics of each type of cell are determined by its function.
2. Once a cell dies, the cell membrane collapses and eventually the contents of the cell disappear.

PREPLAN

Time Allotment: 35 minutes
Process Skill: Observing

Objectives
1. **Identify** and **label** cell parts.
2. **Differentiate** between different human cells.

Setup
■ Use microscopes if micro-viewers are not available.
■ Try to get blood, skin, nerve, muscle, and bone cells.
■ **Cooperative Grouping:** fives—Assign roles as explained on page T24.

1 FOCUS

■ Demonstrate the proper use and techniques of the micro-viewer or microscope. Ask students to describe how they think human body cells look.

2 TEACH

■ Review the parts of a cell. All cells have a cell membrane, cytoplasm, and a nucleus. The cell membrane is a thin layer that surrounds the cell and holds the parts of the cell together. The material inside the nucleus directs the activity of the cell. The cytoplasm is a jelly-like material similar to egg white.
■ Have students use the Teacher Resource Master **Activity Worksheet,** pages 195 and 196, to record their data.

3 APPLY

■ Encourage students to speculate on the function of each cell type. Discuss how function could be related to appearance.

Close
■ Discuss the activity and questions.

pages 284–287

PREPLAN

Lesson Objectives

3. Define *tissue, organ,* and *organ system.*

4. Observe and **communicate** the relationship among cells, tissues, organs, and organ systems.

Science Background

■ Epithelial tissue covers organs. Muscular tissue can be voluntary, involuntary, or cardiac. Connective tissue supports and joins other tissues. Nerve tissue comprises the brain, spinal cord, and nerves.

■ An organ such as the eye is composed of all four major tissues. Each tissue performs a different function. The tissues working together allow this organ to respond to light.

■ There are ten body systems. These are the integument or body covering, skeletal, muscular, digestive, circulatory, respiratory, urinary, nervous, endocrine, and reproductive systems.

Lesson Vocabulary

tissue
organ
organ system

1 FOCUS

■ Ask: **How are your body cells like the members of a team?** *They work together to perform a task.* Discuss with students the idea that cells work together to form a larger unit (tissue) which, with other tissue, forms yet larger units.

■ Use the goals on student page 284 to establish the purpose for studying this lesson.

Tissues, Organs, and Organ Systems

> **LESSON 2 GOALS**
> You will learn
> ● that cells form tissues.
> ● that tissues form organs.
> ● that organs form organ systems.

Have you ever watched a school band? All of the members of a band work together as a group so that they all move at the same time. Members of a band are like body cells.

When you raise your hand or breathe in and out, your body cells are working together in groups. Most organisms have more than one kind of cell. Each cell works with others of the same kind. Groups of cells working together are called **tissues** (TIHSH ewz).

Working together

284

TEACHER RESOURCE MASTERS

Language Arts Connection 201

LANGUAGE ARTS CONNECTION   Composition   Chapter 13

Name _____

YOUR ORGAN SYSTEMS

The children in the picture are playing tag. They may not realize how their organ systems help them to run and play. Think about how each of the following organ systems of your body helps you.

circulatory   digestive   nervous   skeletal
muscular   respiratory   urinary   endocrine

Choose one organ system that you think helps you the most. Write a letter to a friend telling why you think the system you chose is so important to you. Tell how you will try to keep that system healthy.

_____
_____
_____
_____
_____
_____

Different kinds of tissues in your body include muscle, bone, skin, nerve, and blood. Muscle tissue tightens and relaxes to perform jobs such as moving a leg or smiling. Other body tissues do different jobs. Nerve tissue carries messages between your brain and other parts of your body. You feel a tap on the shoulder because messages are carried between your skin and your brain.

Organs

Cells form tissues, and tissues form organs. An **organ** is a group of tissues working together. Your heart is an organ. Each kind of tissue has its own job within your heart. One of the tissues in your heart is muscle. Another is nerve tissue. [1]What job do you think muscle tissue has in your heart?

1. Muscle tissue contracts and expands so that the heart can pump blood.

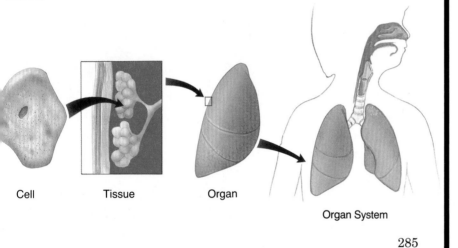

Cell   Tissue   Organ

Organ System

285

2 TEACH

Provide examples of tissues and organs to help students understand these terms.

■ Ask: **What other organ systems are there?** *Answers may include skeletal, circulatory, and muscular.*

Guided Practice

■ Check students' understanding of lesson concepts by discussing the Lesson Review questions on student page 287. If necessary, use the **reteaching strategy** in OPTIONS.

Independent Practice

■ Assign the Lesson 2 section of the Teacher Resource Master **Independent Practice,** page 203.

3 APPLY

■ In pairs, have students tap each other's kneecap to test for the reflex kicking reaction. Ask students to name the kinds of body tissue involved in this one reflex movement (nerve, muscle, skin, bone). Have students explain what role each kind of tissue plays.

Close

■ Use the summary statements on student page 287 to review the lesson concepts.

OPTIONS

Reteaching Strategy

■ Have students create flowcharts to represent the progression from cells to organ systems, listing all the stages. Instruct them to label all the organs that make up the organ system they choose to represent. You may want to post these flowcharts.

Resource Options

Use Color Transparency #12, "Cells to Systems."

TEACHER RESOURCE MASTERS

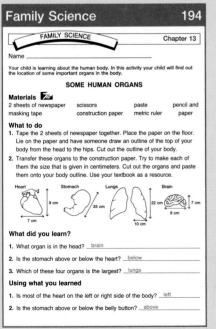

Family Science   194

FAMILY SCIENCE   Chapter 13

Name _____

Your child is learning about the human body. In this activity your child will find out the location of some important organs in the body.

SOME HUMAN ORGANS

Materials

2 sheets of newspaper   scissors   paste   pencil and
masking tape   construction paper   metric ruler   paper

What to do

1. Tape the 2 sheets of newspaper together. Place the paper on the floor. Lie on the paper and have someone draw an outline of the top of your body from the head to the hips. Cut out the outline of your body.

2. Transfer these organs to the construction paper. Try to make each of them the size that is given in centimeters. Cut out the organs and paste them onto your body outline. Use your textbook as a resource.

Heart   Stomach   Lungs   Brain

9 cm   25 cm   22 cm   7 cm

7 cm   10 cm   9 cm

What did you learn?

1. What organ is in the head? _brain_

2. Is the stomach above or below the heart? _below_

3. Which of these four organs is the largest? _lungs_

Using what you learned

1. Is most of the heart on the left or right side of the body? _left_

2. Is the stomach above or below the belly button? _above_

Independent Practice   203

INDEPENDENT PRACTICE   Chapter 13

Name _Questions are each worth 4 points._

Total Points   100
Your Score   ___

Lesson 1 Cells   Pages 280 to 283
Complete the following sentences.

1. All living things are made up of ___ one or more cells
obj 1

2. A cell is the ___ smallest unit of living matter
obj 1

3. Your body grows larger by ___ adding new cells
obj 2

4. ___ New cells ___ replace dead or damaged cells.   obj 2

Lesson 2 Tissues, Organs, and Organ Systems   Pages 284 to 287

5. Cells working together in a group form a ___ tissue
obj 3

6. ___ Muscle ___ tissue tightens and relaxes to help you move your leg. obj 4

7. An ___ organ ___ is a group of tissues working together. obj 3

8. Two tissues in your heart are ___ muscle ___ tissue and
obj 4   ___ nerve ___ tissue.

9. A group of organs working together is an ___ organ system
obj 3

10. Organ systems carry out major jobs in the ___ body   obj 4

Lesson 3 Circulatory, Skeletal, and Muscular Systems   Pages 288 to 293

Match the description on the left with the words on the right.

_b_ 11. pumps blood to all parts of the body   obj 5   a. blood

          b. heart

_a_ 12. carries food and oxygen to the body   obj 5   c. skeletal system

          d. muscle

_c_ 13. gives body shape and support

_d_ 14. shortens when it contracts   obj 6

OPTIONS

LANGUAGE CONNECTION

■ **Writing:** Have students rewrite the following letter using correct capitalization. Answers appear in parentheses.

dear (Dear) terry (Terry),

i (I) have been learning about the human body. did (Did) you know that our organs are made up of tissue? the (The) organs then work together in a system. i (I) am getting a physical examination on may (May) 6. when (When) are you coming to visit?

your (Your) friend,
frankie (Frankie)

♦ **Reinforcement:** Obtain a model of a human torso. Have students locate the major organs. Have them name the organs, tell about their functions, and identify the system to which they belong.

● **Enrichment:** Have interested students find out about skin as an organ. How is new skin formed and what important jobs does this organ perform?

▲ **Challenge:** Encourage students to write a description of the structure and function of a major organ. The report should not identify the organ. The final line of the description should be "What organ am I?" Have students read their descriptions to other students. Use a human anatomy book to check and reinforce the answers.

Resource Options

▢ Use Color Transparency #13, "Organ Systems."

Organ Systems

A group of cells working together forms a tissue. Tissues working together form an organ. A group of organs work together to form an **organ system.** The organs of an organ system carry out a major job in your body. The organs of the respiratory (RES pruh tor ee) system work together to move oxygen from the air you breathe to body cells. Some of the organs of the respiratory system are the windpipe, lungs, and blood vessels. The respiratory system also takes carbon dioxide away from the cells.

What job do all the organs of the respiratory system carry out?

Playing

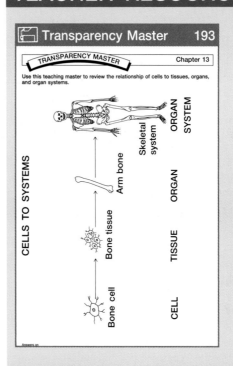

286

TEACHER RESOURCE MASTERS

▢ **Transparency Master**   193

TRANSPARENCY MASTER   Chapter 13

Use this teaching master to review the relationship of cells to tissues, organs, and organ systems.

CELLS TO SYSTEMS

Skeletal system — ORGAN SYSTEM

Arm bone — ORGAN

Bone tissue — TISSUE

Bone cell — CELL

Answers on

Working

Your body is made up of many cells, tissues, organs, and organ systems. They all work together so that you can work and play.

Lesson Summary

- Cells working together in a large group form a tissue.
- A group of tissues working together forms an organ.
- A group of organs working together forms an organ system.

Lesson Review

1. What does nerve tissue do?
2. Why is the heart an organ?
★3. Why is the respiratory system important to your body?

OPTIONS

ART CONNECTION

Have students **work in pairs.** Each pair should draw a body outline of one member on a sheet of paper. The students should draw and cut out the major body organs. Use different body systems. Have students paste the organ models on the paper body outline in the proper relative positions. Discuss and display the students' work.

LESSON REVIEW ANSWERS

1. It carries messages between the brain and parts of your body.
2. The heart is made up of different tissues, such as muscle and nerve tissues, that work together.
3. It moves oxygen from the air you breathe to body cells; it also removes carbon dioxide from the body.

TEACHER RESOURCE MASTERS

PREPLAN

Lesson Objectives
5. **Communicate** the main functions of the circulatory and skeletal systems.
6. **Observe** the function of the muscular system.

Science Background
■ There are about 4.7 liters (5 quarts) of blood in the human body.
■ The heart pumps blood to every part of the body and back again every 30 seconds.
■ There are four main groups of bones in the body: the skull, the spinal column, the ribs, and the limbs. About 18 percent of a person's weight is bone.
■ There are more than 600 muscles in your body. Skeletal muscles work in pairs; one muscle contracts while the other lengthens.
■ Muscles that are exercised regularly are strong, firm, and healthy. Muscles that are not exercised become soft, weak, and flabby. Exercise helps retain the tone and strength of all the muscles, including the cardiac muscle.

Note: The activity on student page 293 may be used for guided discovery before you begin this lesson.

Lesson Vocabulary
circulatory system
skeletal system
muscular system

1   FOCUS

Ask: **What muscles have you used today? Can you feel your heart beating? What would you look like if you didn't have any bones?** Have students talk about these questions with a partner.
■ Use the goals on student page 288 to establish the purpose for studying this lesson.

LESSON 3 GOALS
You will learn
● that the circulatory system is made up of three main parts.
● why the skeletal system is important.
● why the muscular system is important.

Circulatory, Skeletal, and Muscular Systems

The **circulatory** (SUR kyuh luh tor ee) **system** moves blood throughout your body. Your heart pumps blood through blood vessels to all parts of your body with each heartbeat. Blood returns to your heart through other blood vessels. This process is repeated over and over. Blood carries food and oxygen to all parts of your body. It also takes wastes away from body cells.

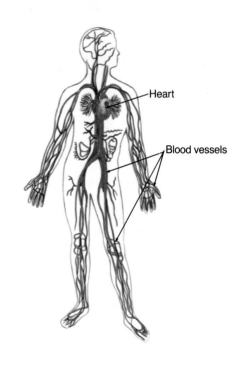

Heart

Blood vessels

288

TEACHER RESOURCE MASTERS

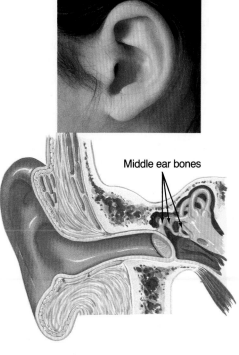

Middle ear bones

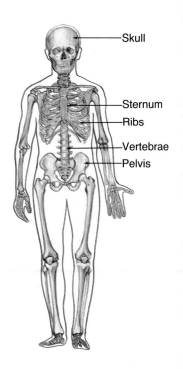

Skull

Sternum

Ribs

Vertebrae

Pelvis

Skeletal System

The **skeletal** (SKEL ut ul) **system** gives your body shape and support. It also protects many organs. The skeletal system is made of bone tissue and other support tissue. Bone tissue forms over 200 bones in your body. Your largest bone is the long bone in your upper leg. The smallest bones are three tiny bones in your middle ear. Bones of your skull protect your brain. Compare the pictures of the body on this page and on page 295. [1]What part of the skeletal system protects the lungs?

1. The ribs and sternum protect the lungs.

289

TEACHER RESOURCE MASTERS

Independent Practice 203

INDEPENDENT PRACTICE   Chapter 13

Name _Questions are each worth 4 points._   Total Points 100
Your Score ___

Lesson 1   Cells   Pages 280 to 283
Complete the following sentences.
1. All living things are made up of _____ one or more cells
obj 1
2. A cell is the _____ smallest unit of living matter
obj 1
3. Your body grows larger by _____ adding new cells
obj 2
4. ____ New cells ____ replace dead or damaged cells.   obj 2

Lesson 2   Tissues, Organs, and Organ Systems   Pages 284 to 287
5. Cells working together in a group form a ____ tissue
obj 3
6. ____ Muscle ____ tissue tightens and relaxes to help you move your leg. obj 4
7. An ____ organ ____ is a group of tissues working together. obj 3
8. Two tissues in your heart are ____ muscle ____ tissue and ____ nerve ____ tissue.
obj 4
9. A group of organs working together is an ____ organ system
obj 3
10. Organ systems carry out major jobs in the ____ body ____ obj 4

Lesson 3   Circulatory, Skeletal, and Muscular Systems   Pages 288 to 293
Match the description on the left with the words on the right.
_b_ 11. pumps blood to all parts of the body   obj 5   a. blood
_a_ 12. carries food and oxygen to the body   obj 5   b. heart
_c_ 13. gives body shape and support   c. skeletal system
_d_ 14. shortens when it contracts   obj 6   d. muscle

2   TEACH

■ Have students point out the main parts of the circulatory system. Identify the arteries in the drawing. Relate that arteries have thick walls and carry blood away from the heart. Veins have thinner walls and carry blood to the heart.

■ Break open a bone and point out the marrow in the center of the bone. This is an excellent time to reinforce students' ideas of cells, tissues, and organs.

Have students feel their biceps as they move the lower arm upward. It gets shorter and thicker. Have them feel their triceps as the lower arm is raised. It becomes longer and thinner. Explain that muscles work together in pairs.

Guided Practice

■ Check students' understanding of lesson concepts by discussing the Lesson Review questions on student page 292. If necessary, use the **reteaching strategy** in OPTIONS.

Independent Practice

■ Assign the Lesson 3 section of the Teacher Resource Master **Independent Practice,** page 203.

3   APPLY

■ Tell students that adults have 206 bones in their bodies. Babies may have as many as 275 bones at birth. Ask them to suggest what happens to the bones of babies to cause this decrease. (They fuse)

Close

■ Use Summary statements on student page 292 to review lesson concepts.

OPTIONS

Reteaching Strategy

Bring in several kinds of bones and joints. Have students observe the structures and characteristics of the bones, ligaments, cartilage, and joints.

OPTIONS

🖩 MATH CONNECTION

■ Have students solve the following addition problem.

The Red Cross needs people to donate blood for other people who are ill and need blood. Local radio stations in Amarillo and Houston held weekend blood drives. The Amarillo station collected 236.55 liters of blood, the Houston station, 229.44 liters. How much total blood did people from both cities donate? (465.99 liters)

◆ **Reinforcement:** Encourage students to research the names and locations of the bones of the skeleton. Have the students make a labeled drawing of their research. Display their drawings and have students describe one part of the human skeleton.

Resource Options

🖳 Use Color Transparencies #12, #13, and #14; "Cells to Systems," "Organ Systems," and "Circulatory System."
■ Use Activity Book, "Interpreting Data," pages 33 and 34.

Muscular System

The **muscular system** is made of muscle tissue. Your body parts move because muscles and bones work together to make them move. You use muscles to walk, talk, and eat. [1]What else can you do because you have muscles?

1. Answers may include run, sit down, jump.

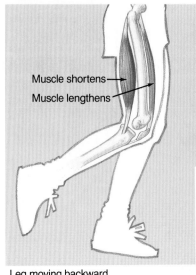

Leg moving backward

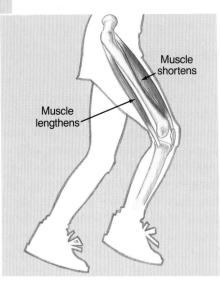

Leg moving forward

290

TEACHER RESOURCE MASTERS

When a muscle moves a part of your body, the muscle either contracts or relaxes. A muscle shortens when it contracts and lengthens when it relaxes. When you bend your leg, some of your leg muscles contract and other leg muscles relax. When you straighten your leg, the contracting and relaxing of these muscles are reversed. Try bending your leg now. Use your other hand to feel some muscles contract. Feel other muscles relax. Straighten out your leg and feel how the muscles reverse their actions.

Using muscles

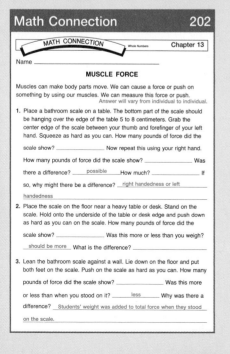

291

OPTIONS

■ Exhibit an X ray of a broken bone. Have students find the broken bone on the skeleton. Discuss why the bones of older people may break more easily.

● **Enrichment: Problem Solving:** Have students research the pulse rates of other animals. Ask: **Is there a relationship between pulse rate and animal size?** Have students make a chart showing the animal, its mass, and its pulse rate. Discuss the results of the research. The pulse rate of an elephant is 35 beats per minute; a chicken, 250-300 beats per minute; and a mouse, 534 beats per minute. Refer to the *Merck Veterinary Manual* or have a veterinarian supply pulse rates for other animals. Not all animals have a pulse at the wrist, as humans do. Pulse is taken in the groin area of dogs and cats.

TEACHER RESOURCE MASTERS

Math Connection   202

MATH CONNECTION   Whole Numbers   Chapter 13

Name _____

MUSCLE FORCE

Muscles can make body parts move. We can cause a force or push on something by using our muscles. We can measure this force or push.
Answer will vary from individual to individual.

1. Place a bathroom scale on a table. The bottom part of the scale should be hanging over the edge of the table 5 to 8 centimeters. Grab the center edge of the scale between your thumb and forefinger of your left hand. Squeeze as hard as you can. How many pounds of force did the scale show? _____ Now repeat this using your right hand.

How many pounds of force did the scale show? _____ Was there a difference? __possible__ How much? _____ If so, why might there be a difference? __right handedness or left handedness__

2. Place the scale on the floor near a heavy table or desk. Stand on the scale. Hold onto the underside of the table or desk edge and push down as hard as you can on the scale. How many pounds of force did the scale show? _____ Was this more or less than you weigh? __should be more__ What is the difference? _____

3. Lean the bathroom scale against a wall. Lie down on the floor and put both feet on the scale. Push on the scale as hard as you can. How many pounds of force did the scale show? _____ Was this more or less than when you stood on it? __less__ Why was there a difference? __Students' weight was added to total force when they stood on the scale.__

OPTIONS

▲ **Challenge:** Using resource materials, describe and diagram how muscles are attached to bones and how bones are joined together. Have students distinguish between a muscle strain and a sprain. Allow students to share their findings with the class.

LESSON REVIEW ANSWERS

1. It pumps blood, which carries food and oxygen, to all parts of the body.
2. It gives the body shape, support, and protection.
3. Some muscles relax, or lengthen, while other muscles contract, or shorten.

Would You Believe?

It takes 17 muscles to smile and 43 to frown.

Now put both hands on your cheeks. Find some of the muscles that contract or relax when you smile. Now frown, and find muscles that contract or relax.

Lesson Summary

- The circulatory system moves blood to all parts of your body, and it is made up of the heart, blood vessels, and blood.
- The skeletal system gives your body shape and support.
- Muscles move body parts.

Lesson Review

1. What does the circulatory system do?
2. In what three ways is the skeletal system important?
★3. What happens to leg muscles when you bend your leg?

292

TEACHER RESOURCE MASTERS

How does your pulse rate change?

What you need
watch with second hand
pencil and paper

What to do
1. Using one hand, gently place your fingers on the side of your neck just below your jaw.
2. Find your pulse.
3. Count your pulse for 10 seconds. Multiply this number by 6 to get your pulse rate for 1 minute.
4. Count your pulse while sitting at your desk.
5. Record this number.
6. Walk quietly around the room for 45 seconds. Repeat steps 3 and 5.
7. Now run in place for 45 seconds. Repeat steps 3 and 5.

What did you learn?
1. When was your pulse the most rapid?
2. When was your pulse the slowest?
3. Compare your results with those of a classmate. How do they compare?

Using what you learned
1. How long does it take for the pulse rate in step 7 to return to that in step 4?
2. Find the pulse at your wrist. Compare this pulse with the pulse at your neck.

293

ACTIVITY RESPONSES

What did you learn?
1. Answers may vary. However, most students should have the most rapid pulse rate after running in place.
2. Answers will vary. However, most students should have the slowest pulse rate while sitting at their desks.
3. Answers will vary depending on the classmate chosen.

Using what you learned
1. Answers will vary. Students should notice a significant drop in pulse rate within 60 seconds.
2. Answers will vary. Students will find that pulse rates are the same but the strength of the pulse is greater at the neck.

PREPLAN

Time Allotment: 30 minutes
Process Skill: Measuring

Objectives
1. **Locate** and **measure** the pulse.
2. **Compare** pulse rate while at rest with pulse rate after exercise.

Setup
■ You will need a stopwatch or a clock with a second hand.
■ Have students work individually.

1 FOCUS

■ Have students place one hand on their chest and feel their heartbeat. Have students run in place for 45 seconds and then place their hand on their chest and feel the heartbeat. Ask: **Is there a difference in how fast your heart is beating? When does it beat faster?** *It beats faster after running in place.*

2 TEACH

■ Inform students that their pulses have the same rhythm as their heartbeats. Review the main parts of the circulatory system.
■ Students will be able to concentrate better if they close their eyes during the pulse location phase of the activity.
■ Have students use Teacher Resource Master **Activity Worksheet,** pages 197 and 198, to record their data.

3 APPLY

■ You may want to extend the activity by having students suggest other times to collect data, such as before they get out of bed in the morning, before they go to bed at night, after various physical activities, or while eating.

Close
■ Discuss the activity and questions.

PREPLAN

Lesson Objectives

7. Infer the movement of food through the digestive system.

8. Tell the function of the respiratory system.

Science Background

■ The digestive tract consists of the mouth, throat, esophagus, stomach, small intestine, and large intestine. The rectum and anus are considered part of the large intestine.

■ The liver, pancreas, and gallbladder are not part of the digestive tract. The liver produces bile for digestion of fatty foods. Bile is stored in the gallbladder. Pancreatic juices are produced to digest starch, fat, and protein.

■ Gastric juice of the stomach is composed of water, pepsin, and hydrochloric acid.

■ The respiratory system consists of the nose, nasal passages, throat, windpipe or trachea, voice box or larynx, the bronchi, the bronchioles, and the lungs.

■ The diaphragm and chest muscles move air into and out of the body.

Lesson Vocabulary

digestive system
respiratory system

1 FOCUS

■ Tell students that when they are eating, they are using two systems of their bodies: digestive and respiratory. Have students work with a partner to list as many steps as they can think of in the digestive process and in the respiratory process. (Alternatively, you may want them to try to name the organs in each system.)

■ Use the goals on student page 294 to establish the purpose for studying this lesson.

LESSON 4 GOALS
You will learn
● what the digestive system does.
● the importance of the respiratory system.

Digestive and Respiratory Systems

The **digestive** (di JES tihv) **system** changes the food you eat so that it can be used by your body. When you eat, your teeth mash, tear, and grind food. The small bits of food then move down a tube and into your stomach. As stomach muscles contract, they mix the food with stomach juices. The stomach juices break down, or digest, some of the food.

The mixture of food and stomach juices passes from your stomach to your small intestine, where the digestion of food is completed. Vitamins, digested food, and water pass into your blood through the walls of your small intestine. The leftover food material that isn't digested moves into your large intestine. This solid waste material passes through your large intestine and is finally moved out of your body by muscles.

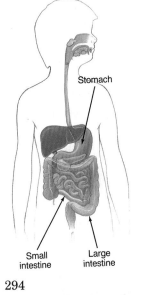

Stomach

Small intestine

Large intestine

294

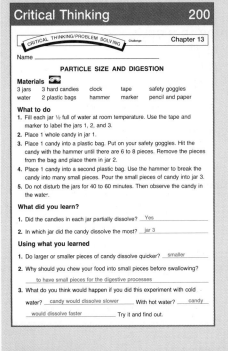

TEACHER RESOURCE MASTERS

Critical Thinking 200

CRITICAL THINKING/PROBLEM SOLVING Challenge   Chapter 13

Name _____

PARTICLE SIZE AND DIGESTION

Materials
3 jars   3 hard candies   clock   tape   safety goggles
water   2 plastic bags   hammer   marker   pencil and paper

What to do
1. Fill each jar ½ full of water at room temperature. Use the tape and marker to label the jars 1, 2, and 3.
2. Place 1 whole candy in jar 1.
3. Place 1 candy into a plastic bag. Put on your safety goggles. Hit the candy with the hammer until there are 6 to 8 pieces. Remove the pieces from the bag and place them in jar 2.
4. Place 1 candy into a second plastic bag. Use the hammer to break the candy into many small pieces. Pour the small pieces of candy into jar 3.
5. Do not disturb the jars for 40 to 60 minutes. Then observe the candy in the water.

What did you learn?
1. Did the candies in each jar partially dissolve? ___Yes___
2. In which jar did the candy dissolve the most? ___jar 3___

Using what you learned
1. Do larger or smaller pieces of candy dissolve quicker? ___smaller___
2. Why should you chew your food into small pieces before swallowing?
   ___to have small pieces for the digestive processes___
3. What do you think would happen if you did this experiment with cold water? ___candy would dissolve slower___ With hot water? ___candy would dissolve faster___ Try it and find out.

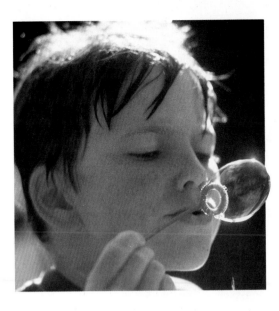

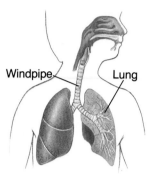

Windpipe   Lung

Respiratory system

Respiratory System

Oxygen and carbon dioxide are important gases. You breathe in oxygen, and you breathe out carbon dioxide. The **respiratory system** makes this exchange of gases happen. All body cells use oxygen to change food into energy. When the energy is formed in the cells, carbon dioxide is made. Carbon dioxide is a waste product. This waste gas is removed from your body when you breathe out.

Why is oxygen important to cells in your body?

295

2 TEACH

■ Have students refer to the diagram of the digestive system in the book and trace the movement of food through the digestive tract.

⛹ Have students take a deep breath and hold it a few seconds. Have them use their hands to feel the air they breathe out. Ask: **What does the air feel like?** *The air is warm and moist.*

Guided Practice

■ Check students' understanding of lesson concepts by discussing the Lesson Review questions on student page 297. If necessary, use the **reteaching strategy** in OPTIONS.

Independent Practice

■ Assign the Lesson 4 section of the Teacher Resource Master **Independent Practice,** page 204.

3 APPLY

■ Bring some cooked vegetables to class. Mash them to simulate chewed food. Place the mashed vegetables in a bowl, and add water and a few drops of hydrochloric acid. Point out that stomach juices have a similar effect in digesting food.

Close

■ Use Summary statements on student page 297 to review lesson concepts.

OPTIONS

Reteaching Strategy

⛹ Divide students into **cooperative groups.** Ask: **How are the digestive and respiratory systems similar?** Have each group write a paragraph comparing the two systems. Each system takes a substance (food or air) into the body, uses what it needs, and gets rid of the waste product.

TEACHER RESOURCE MASTERS

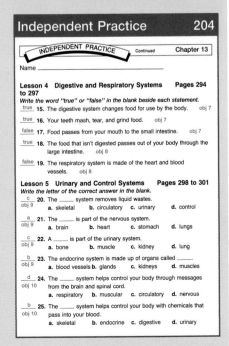

Independent Practice   204

INDEPENDENT PRACTICE   Continued   Chapter 13

Name _____

Lesson 4   Digestive and Respiratory Systems   Pages 294 to 297
Write the word "true" or "false" in the blank beside each statement.

true **15.** The digestive system changes food for use by the body.   obj 7

true **16.** Your teeth mash, tear, and grind food.   obj 7

false **17.** Food passes from your mouth to the small intestine.   obj 7

true **18.** The food that isn't digested passes out of your body through the large intestine.   obj 8

false **19.** The respiratory system is made of the heart and blood vessels.   obj 8

Lesson 5   Urinary and Control Systems   Pages 298 to 301
Write the letter of the correct answer in the blank.

c **20.** The ___ system removes liquid wastes.
obj 9
a. skeletal   b. circulatory   c. urinary   d. control

a **21.** The ___ is part of the nervous system.
obj 9
a. brain   b. heart   c. stomach   d. lungs

c **22.** A ___ is part of the urinary system.
obj 9
a. bone   b. muscle   c. kidney   d. lung

b **23.** The endocrine system is made up of organs called ___.
obj 9
a. blood vessels b. glands   c. kidneys   d. muscles

d **24.** The ___ system helps control your body through messages
obj 10
from the brain and spinal cord.
a. respiratory   b. muscular   c. circulatory   d. nervous

b **25.** The ___ system helps control your body with chemicals that
obj 10
pass into your blood.
a. skeletal   b. endocrine   c. digestive   d. urinary

OPTIONS

YOU CAN . . . SEE YOUR LUNG CAPACITY

Process Skill: Observing

Objective: Observe the amount of air that students can hold in their lungs.

Setup/Teach

- balloon
- You might want to suggest that each person completely blow up a balloon, release the air, and then do the one breath collection. Sometimes it is difficult to start filling a balloon. Once it has been fully stretched, its expansion is more consistent.
- **Safety Consideration:** Caution students not to inhale with their balloons in their mouths.

MATH CONNECTION

Have students estimate the answer to the following addition problem.

Sheryl's mom bought vitamins at the local pharmacy. She bought children's vitamins for Sheryl for $3.50, vitamin C for $2.80, and vitamin E for $4.30. Estimate the total amount in dollars that Sheryl's mom paid for vitamins. ($11.00)

- **Career:** Use "I WANT TO KNOW ABOUT . . . an EMT," student page 301, with this lesson.

Resource Options

Use Color Transparency #13, "Organ Systems."

ACTIVITY You Can...

See Your Lung Capacity

Pull on the sides of a balloon and blow into it several times until it stretches easily. Completely empty the balloon. Now take a deep breath, and blow all your breath into the balloon. Tie the balloon. Look at the size of the balloon. The size shows your lung capacity.

1. Answers may include that the air we breathe out is warmer, the air we breathe in has more oxygen, and the air we breathe out has more carbon dioxide.

When you breathe in, air enters your body through your nose and mouth. It travels through your windpipe to your lungs. In your lungs, oxygen from the air passes to your blood. Blood carries the oxygen through blood vessels to your body cells. Then the blood carries carbon dioxide away from these cells and back to your lungs. When you breathe out, carbon dioxide leaves your body through your nose and mouth. [1]What is one difference between the air you breathe in and the air you breathe out?

296

TEACHER RESOURCE MASTERS

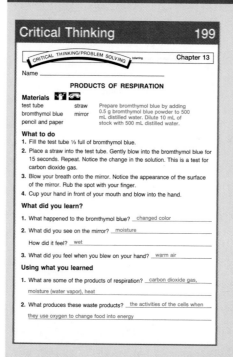

Critical Thinking 199

CRITICAL THINKING/PROBLEM SOLVING Inferring   Chapter 13

Name _____

PRODUCTS OF RESPIRATION

Materials

test tube   straw   Prepare bromthymol blue by adding
bromthymol blue   mirror   0.5 g bromthymol blue powder to 500
pencil and paper   mL distilled water. Dilute 10 mL of
                                stock with 500 mL distilled water.

What to do

1. Fill the test tube ⅓ full of bromthymol blue.
2. Place a straw into the test tube. Gently blow into the bromthymol blue for 15 seconds. Repeat. Notice the change in the solution. This is a test for carbon dioxide gas.
3. Blow your breath onto the mirror. Notice the appearance of the surface of the mirror. Rub the spot with your finger.
4. Cup your hand in front of your mouth and blow into the hand.

What did you learn?

1. What happened to the bromthymol blue? __changed color__
2. What did you see on the mirror? __moisture__

   How did it feel? __wet__
3. What did you feel when you blew on your hand? __warm air__

Using what you learned

1. What are some of the products of respiration? __carbon dioxide gas, moisture (water vapor), heat__
2. What produces these waste products? __the activities of the cells when they use oxygen to change food into energy__

Lesson Summary

- The digestive system changes food so that it can be used by your body.
- The respiratory system brings oxygen into your body and removes carbon dioxide.

Lesson Review

1. Trace food through the digestive system.
2. How is carbon dioxide formed in the body?

Measuring lung capacity

297

TEACHER RESOURCE MASTERS

♦ **Reinforcement:** Obtain a photograph of lungs affected by coal dust, cigarettes, or some other form of pollution (perhaps from a physician) and a photograph of healthy lungs. Let students compare and comment on the difference. Ask students to list ways we can all help keep air cleaner and lungs healthier. (Answers might include not smoking, checking car exhaust systems regularly, working to fight air pollution.)

● **Enrichment:** Encourage students to write to the American Cancer Society for health information about smoking. Each student should use the information to prepare a project to help an adult they care about stop smoking. Have the students implement their project.

▲ **Challenge:** Ask students to describe how a bite of hamburger gets into the bloodstream for use by the body. They should begin with chewing and the formation of saliva, and end with the passing of nutrients through the intestinal wall. Their report should mention each of the digestive organs.

LESSON REVIEW ANSWERS

1. Food enters the digestive system through the mouth, passes into the throat, down a tube, into the stomach, to the small intestine, large intestine, and out of the body.
2. When body cells use oxygen to change food to energy, carbon dioxide is formed as a waste product.

PREPLAN

Lesson Objectives

9. Identify and **describe** some parts and functions of the urinary, nervous, and endocrine systems.

10. Understand that the body has two control systems.

Science Background

- One healthy kidney can do the work of two.
- The urinary bladder stores urine.
- The spinal cord is a thin cable that extends from the base of the brain about two-thirds of the way down the back.
- The nerves and spinal cord carry messages between the brain and other organs.
- The endocrine system glands control many of the body's activities with hormones that are secreted directly into the bloodstream. The endocrine glands and the functions they control are pituitary—growth, thyroid—metabolism, parathyroid—blood, calcium, and phosphorus, adrenal—energy release, islets of Langerhans—blood sugar, and the gonads—reproduction.

Lesson Vocabulary

perspiration	urinary system
urine	urethra
nervous system	endocrine system

1 FOCUS

- Ask students what it means to control something. Some may say that it means keeping something in line, starting or stopping, or keeping still. Accept all reasonable answers.
- Use the goals on student page 298 to establish the purpose for studying this lesson.

Urinary and Control Systems

Your body is always producing waste products that are solids, liquids, and gases. Body systems remove waste products so that you stay healthy. The digestive system moves solid wastes out of the body. The respiratory system removes waste gases from your body.

Body cells also produce liquid wastes. Liquid wastes are picked up by your blood. Some of the liquid wastes are released through sweat glands to the surface of your skin. This liquid waste is called **perspiration** (pur spuh RAY shun).

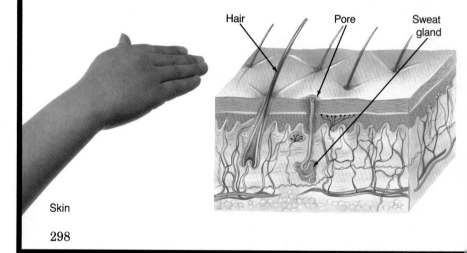

Hair   Pore   Sweat gland

Skin

298

TEACHER RESOURCE MASTERS

Urinary System

Most liquid wastes are removed from your body by the **urinary** (YOOR uh ner ee) **system.** As blood moves through organs called kidneys, wastes and water are removed from the blood. The wastes and water form **urine** (YOOR un). Urine passes from your kidneys through tubes to your bladder. The **urethra** (yoo REE thruh) releases urine from your body.

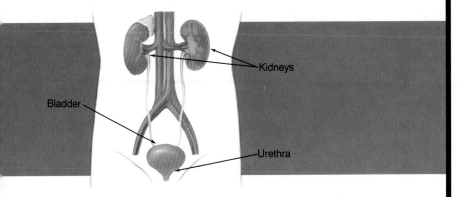

Kidneys

Bladder

Urethra

Control Systems

The control systems of your body keep your body working as one unit. They control your muscles and organs. They control your senses and your thinking. One control system is the **nervous system.** It is made up of the brain, spinal cord, and nerves. The brain and the spinal cord are like message centers.

299

TEACHER RESOURCE MASTERS

Independent Practice   204

INDEPENDENT PRACTICE   Continued   Chapter 13

Name _____

Lesson 4   Digestive and Respiratory Systems   Pages 294 to 297
Write the word "true" or "false" in the blank beside each statement.

true   **15.** The digestive system changes food for use by the body.   obj 7

true   **16.** Your teeth mash, tear, and grind food.   obj 7

false   **17.** Food passes from your mouth to the small intestine.   obj 7

true   **18.** The food that isn't digested passes out of your body through the large intestine.   obj 8

false   **19.** The respiratory system is made of the heart and blood vessels.   obj 8

Lesson 5   Urinary and Control Systems   Pages 298 to 301
Write the letter of the correct answer in the blank.

c   **20.** The _____ system removes liquid wastes.
obj 9   **a.** skeletal   **b.** circulatory   **c.** urinary   **d.** control

a   **21.** The _____ is part of the nervous system.
obj 9   **a.** brain   **b.** heart   **c.** stomach   **d.** lungs

c   **22.** A _____ is part of the urinary system.
obj 9   **a.** bone   **b.** muscle   **c.** kidney   **d.** lung

b   **23.** The endocrine system is made up of organs called _____.
obj 9   **a.** blood vessels **b.** glands   **c.** kidneys   **d.** muscles

d   **24.** The _____ system helps control your body through messages
obj 10   from the brain and spinal cord.
   a. respiratory   **b.** muscular   **c.** circulatory   **d.** nervous

b   **25.** The _____ system helps control your body with chemicals that
obj 10   pass into your blood.
   a. skeletal   **b.** endocrine   **c.** digestive   **d.** urinary

2   TEACH

■ Point out that water makes up most of the human body. It is the most needed nutrient. Ask: **Where do we get the water our bodies need?** *from water itself, fruits, and vegetables*

■ Emphasize that on a hot day, an athlete shouldn't wait to take a drink until he or she feels thirsty.

■ Ask students why a healthy nervous system is important for their safety.

Guided Practice

■ Check students' understanding of lesson concepts by discussing the Lesson Review questions on student page 300. If necessary, use the **reteaching strategy** in OPTIONS.

Independent Practice

■ Assign the Lesson 5 section of the Teacher Resource Master **Independent Practice,** page 104.

3   APPLY

Have students simulate a nervous system by playing the various roles: brain, spinal cord, nerves, as well as muscle and bone tissue. Have them role-play some specific actions controlled by the nervous system.

Close

■ Use Summary statements on student page 300 to review lesson concepts.

OPTIONS

Reteaching Strategy

Provide students with plastic bags, cellophane tape, and drinking straws. Have them construct models of a urinary system. Have students demonstrate with water how liquid passes through this system.

Resource Options

Use Color Transparency #13, "Organ Systems."

OPTIONS

SCIENCE AND . . . MATH

- **Skill:** Estimate with whole numbers.
- **Student Response:** C   2370L

MATH CONNECTION

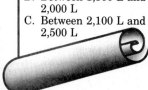 Write the following problem on the chalkboard or an overhead transparency. Have students work in **cooperative pairs** to select the appropriate problem-solving strategy.

The doctor bought 3 jars of tablets for $4 per jar. Each jar holds 100 tablets. To find the cost of the 3 jars, should you add 3 plus 4 plus 100? Should you add 3 plus 4 and then subtract the sum from 100? Should you multiply 3 times 4? Should you multiply 4 times 100? (Multiply 3 times 4)

Reinforcement: Gaseous wastes are removed from our bodies each time we exhale. These wastes are in the form of carbon dioxide. To prove this, prepare fresh limewater by mixing three spoonfuls of calcium hydroxide in a glass of water. Have students inhale deeply and then exhale through a straw into the glass. Repeat this process several times. The limewater will turn milky in appearance because of the presence of carbon dioxide.

LESSON REVIEW ANSWERS

1. The digestive system removes solid wastes; sweat glands remove some as perspiration; the urinary system removes the most.
2. through the respiratory system
3. glands
4. They control all the other organs and systems of the body so that the body works as a unit.

SCIENCE AND . . . Math

If your heart pumps 395 liters of blood each hour, which is the best estimate of the number of liters it pumps in six hours?
A. Less than 500 L
B. Between 1,500 L and 2,000 L
C. Between 2,100 L and 2,500 L

Messages from all body parts are sent through nerves to your spinal cord and brain. Other nerves in the brain and spinal cord carry messages to parts of your body.

The **endocrine** (EN duh krun) **system** is the other control system. It helps the nervous system control your body and is made up of organs called glands. Glands make chemicals that pass into your blood. Some chemicals are important for proper growth. Others help to digest food.

Each system plays a necessary part. Working together, these systems keep your body growing, working, and healthy.

Lesson Summary

- The urinary system removes liquid body wastes.
- The nervous system and endocrine system are the control systems of the body.

Lesson Review

1. How are solid and liquid wastes removed from the body?
2. How are waste gases removed?
3. What organs make up the endocrine system?
★4. Why are the control systems important to the body?

300

TEACHER RESOURCE MASTERS

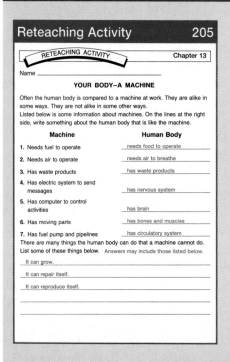

Reteaching Activity   205

RETEACHING ACTIVITY   Chapter 13

Name _____

YOUR BODY–A MACHINE

Often the human body is compared to a machine at work. They are alike in some ways. They are not alike in some other ways.
Listed below is some information about machines. On the lines at the right side, write something about the human body that is like the machine.

Machine	Human Body
1. Needs fuel to operate	needs food to operate
2. Needs air to operate	needs air to breathe
3. Has waste products	has waste products
4. Has electric system to send messages	has nervous system
5. Has computer to control activities	has brain
6. Has moving parts	has bones and muscles
7. Has fuel pump and pipelines	has circulatory system

There are many things the human body can do that a machine cannot do.
List some of these things below. Answers may include those listed below.

It can grow.

It can repair itself.

It can reproduce itself.

I WANT TO KNOW ABOUT...

An EMT

Lily Denbo is an Emergency Medical Technician (EMT). She works as part of an ambulance team. When an emergency call is received, Lily and her partner rush to the scene. After giving first aid, they may take the patient to a hospital.

Lily also teaches cardiopulmonary resuscitation (CPR). When a person's heart and lungs stop working, oxygen doesn't reach body cells. Without a normal supply of oxygen, cells will die.

The person trained in CPR works to save a life by helping to bring back the usual action of the patient's heart and lungs. A person trained in CPR can breathe for a patient who is not breathing. The trained person also knows how to get a patient's heart to start beating again. CPR can sometimes keep a person alive until he or she gets to a hospital.

Lily enjoys teaching CPR. She is happy to help people learn to save lives.

Career

301

TEACHER RESOURCE MASTERS

Feature Background

■ CPR certification is supervised by the American Heart Association. The address for a local chapter can be found in the phone book.

■ Everyone has the opportunity to take CPR instruction. In many areas, all medical personnel, coaches, and aerobic instructors must be CPR certified.

Feature Vocabulary

emergency medical technician (EMT)
cardiopulmonary resuscitation (CPR)

Teaching Suggestions

■ Have an EMT visit the class to describe the training for this profession, or visit a fire station that has an EMT team.

■ Explain cardiopulmonary resuscitation and why it is necessary.

■ Emphasize the importance of knowing first aid.

Summary

Chapter Closure: Copy each summary statement twice onto sentence strips, cut the words apart, and place them into separate envelopes or boxes. Divide the class into two teams. Challenge pairs of students to arrange the words in sentence order quickly. The team finishing first scores a point. Review the concepts contained in each statement by discussing it with the class when the round is completed.

Science Words

Have the students locate a picture in the text that is an example of each of the science words. Use the words to review the structure of the human body in a discussion with the class.

Student Responses

1. organ
2. perspiration
3. cell
4. nervous system
5. tissue
6. digestive system
7. organ system

CHAPTER REVIEW 13

▬ Summary ▬

Lesson 1
- Cells can be found in all living things.
- Different kinds of cells have different jobs.

Lesson 2
- Cells working together in a group form a tissue.
- Tissues working together form an organ.
- Organs working together form an organ system.

Lesson 3
- The circulatory system moves blood through the body.

- The skeletal system gives the body shape and support.
- Muscles move body parts.

Lesson 4
- The digestive system changes food so the body can use it.
- The respiratory system brings oxygen into the body.

Lesson 5
- The urinary system removes liquid body wastes.
- The nervous and endocrine systems are control systems.

▬ Science Words ▬

Fill in the blank with the correct word or words from the list.

cell	skeletal system	urinary system
tissues	muscular system	urine
organ	digestive system	urethra
organ system	respiratory system	nervous system
circulatory system	perspiration	endocrine system

302

TEACHER RESOURCE MASTERS

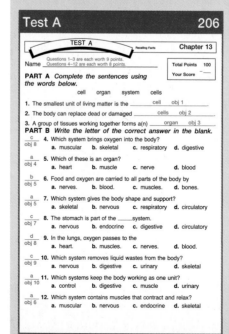

Test A 206

TEST A — Recalling Facts — Chapter 13

Name _____ Questions 1–3 are each worth 9 points. Questions 4–12 are each worth 8 points.

Total Points 100 Your Score ___

PART A *Complete the sentences using the words below.*

cell   organ   system   cells

1. The smallest unit of living matter is the ___ cell ___ obj 1
2. The body can replace dead or damaged ___ cells ___ obj 2
3. A group of tissues working together forms a(n) ___ organ ___ obj 3

PART B *Write the letter of the correct answer in the blank.*

c / obj 8 — 4. Which system brings oxygen into the body?
a. muscular   b. skeletal   c. respiratory   d. digestive

a / obj 4 — 5. Which of these is an organ?
a. heart   b. muscle   c. nerve   d. blood

b / obj 5 — 6. Food and oxygen are carried to all parts of the body by
a. nerves.   b. blood.   c. muscles.   d. bones.

a / obj 5 — 7. Which system gives the body shape and support?
a. skeletal   b. nervous   c. respiratory   d. circulatory

c / obj 7 — 8. The stomach is part of the ____system.
a. nervous   b. endocrine   c. digestive   d. circulatory

d / obj 8 — 9. In the lungs, oxygen passes to the
a. heart.   b. muscles.   c. nerves.   d. blood.

c / obj 9 — 10. Which system removes liquid wastes from the body?
a. nervous   b. digestive   c. urinary   d. skeletal

a / obj 10 — 11. Which systems keep the body working as one unit?
a. control   b. digestive   c. muscle   d. urinary

a / obj 6 — 12. Which system contains muscles that contract and relax?
a. muscular   b. nervous   c. endocrine   d. skeletal

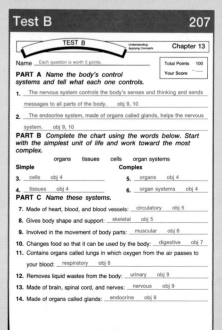

Test B 207

TEST B — Understanding/Applying Concepts — Chapter 13

Name _____ Each question is worth 5 points.

Total Points 100 Your Score ___

PART A *Name the body's control systems and tell what each one controls.*

1. ___ The nervous system controls the body's senses and thinking and sends messages to all parts of the body. obj 9, 10

2. ___ The endocrine system, made of organs called glands, helps the nervous system. obj 9, 10

PART B *Complete the chart using the words below. Start with the simplest unit of life and work toward the most complex.*

organs   tissues   cells   organ systems

Simple	Complex
3. cells obj 4	5. organs obj 4
4. tissues obj 4	6. organ systems obj 4

PART C *Name these systems.*

7. Made of heart, blood, and blood vessels: ___ circulatory ___ obj 5
8. Gives body shape and support: ___ skeletal ___ obj 5
9. Involved in the movement of body parts: ___ muscular ___ obj 6
10. Changes food so that it can be used by the body: ___ digestive ___ obj 7
11. Contains organs called lungs in which oxygen from the air passes to your blood: ___ respiratory ___ obj 8
12. Removes liquid wastes from the body: ___ urinary ___ obj 9
13. Made of brain, spinal cord, and nerves: ___ nervous ___ obj 9
14. Made of organs called glands: ___ endocrine ___ obj 9

1. A group of tissues working together forms a(n) ____.
2. The liquid waste released through sweat glands is called ____.
3. The smallest unit of living matter is a(n) ____.
4. The control system that is made up of the brain, spinal cord, and nerves is the ____.
5. Cells working together in groups form ____.
6. The ____ changes the food you eat so that it can be used by your body.
7. The muscular system is an example of a(n) ____.

Questions

Recalling Ideas
Correctly complete each of the following sentences.

1. Most liquid wastes are removed from the blood by the
   (a) bladder. (c) urethra.
   (b) kidneys. (d) sweat glands.
2. The skeletal system
   (a) sends messages.
   (b) digests food.
   (c) protects body organs.
   (d) pumps blood to the lungs.
3. Food and oxygen are carried to all the parts of your body in the
   (a) blood.
   (b) bone.
   (c) cells.
   (d) air.

Understanding Ideas
Answer the following questions using complete sentences.

1. What are the control systems of the body?
2. Does a person always keep the same cells?
3. What is the function of the muscular system?

Thinking Critically
Think about what you have learned in this chapter. Answer the following questions using complete sentences.

1. Trace some food through the digestive system.
2. What happens to oxygen and carbon dioxide when you breathe in and out?

303

Questions

Recalling Ideas
1. b
2. c
3. a

Understanding Ideas
1. The control systems are the nervous system and the endocrine system.
2. No. New cells form when cells divide and replace dead or damaged cells.
3. Muscles work with bones to make body parts move.

Thinking Critically
1. Food is chewed in the mouth and moves down a tube into the stomach. Stomach juices change some of the food, which then passes to the small intestine. Minerals, vitamins, nutrients from digested food, and some water pass into the blood from the small intestine. Solid matter that is not digested passes through the large intestine and is removed from the body.
2. As you breathe in, air enters your body through your nose and mouth. It travels to your lungs where oxygen from the air passes to your blood. The blood carries the oxygen to your body cells. Carbon dioxide is carried from the cells to your lungs. You breathe out and carbon dioxide leaves your body.

TEACHER RESOURCE MASTERS

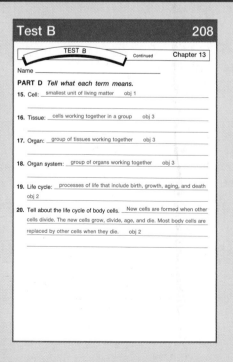

Test B 208

TEST B   Continued   Chapter 13

Name ____

PART D *Tell what each term means.*

15. Cell: smallest unit of living matter   obj 1

16. Tissue: cells working together in a group   obj 3

17. Organ: group of tissues working together   obj 3

18. Organ system: group of organs working together   obj 3

19. Life cycle: processes of life that include birth, growth, aging, and death   obj 2

20. Tell about the life cycle of body cells. New cells are formed when other cells divide. The new cells grow, divide, age, and die. Most body cells are replaced by other cells when they die.   obj 2

CHAPTER 14

Staying Healthy

Planning Guide

Lessons	Objectives	Vocabulary
Chapter Introduction pp. 304, 305		
Lesson 1 Eating Well pp. 306–309	1. **Infer** the need for healthful foods. 2. **Identify** foods in the five healthful food groups.	
Lesson 2 Being Sick pp. 310–313	3. **Define** *immunity* and *disease*. 4. **Tell** why liquids, healthful foods, and rest are important during an illness.	disease immunity vaccine
Lesson 3 Taking Medicines pp. 314–319	5. **Define** *drug*. 6. **Identify** safety rules for taking medicine. 7. **Communicate** the effects of and **describe** products that contain caffeine, alcohol, and nicotine.	drug prescription drug over-the-counter drug caffeine alcohol nicotine
Lesson 4 Poisons pp. 320–325	8. **Operationally define** *poisons*. 9. **Identify** poison safety rules. 10. **Communicate** the function of the Poison Control Center.	poisons
Chapter Review pp. 326, 327		
Unit Review pp. 328, 329		

Planning Guide

Text Activities		Teacher Resource Masters	Other Components
Title/Skill	Materials per Group		
Have You Ever . . . Read a Food Label? p. 305 Inferring Time Allotment: 30 minutes	food wrappers paper and pencil boxes or cans from food	Activity Center: "Good Food?"; "A Well-Rounded Mal"; "Good and Bad"; "You Can Do"; "Who Caught It"; "Too Sweet"	
What Healthful Foods Have You Eaten Today? p. 309 Communicating Time Allotment: 30 minutes **What's For Lunch?** p. 361 Measuring/Interpreting Data Time Allotment: 25 minutes	food group table crayons paper plates pencil and paper play money	Independent Practice, pp. 219, 220 Activity Worksheet pp. 211, 212 ▲ Critical Thinking, p. 216 Language Arts Connection, p. 217	Color Transparency #15 Activity Book, pp. 51, 52
		Independent Practice, pp. 219, 220 Critical Thinking, p. 215 ◆ Reteaching Activity, p. 221	
How Do You Know Which Vaccinations You Need? p. 319 Communicating/Interpreting Data/Inferring Time Allotment: 35 minutes **Read the Labels,** p. 363 Using Numbers/Measuring Time Allotment: 35 minutes	resource books and pamphlets pencil and paper medicine labels	Independent Practice pp. 219, 220 Transparency Master, p. 209 Activity Worksheet, pp. 213–214 Health Connection, p. 218	Color Transparency #16 Activity Book, pp. 53, 54
You Can . . . Design a Poison Warning Sign, p. 324 Communicating Time Allotment: 20 minutes	posterboard paint crayons	Independent Practice, pp. 219, 220 ◆ Family Science, p. 210	
		Test A, p. 222 Test B, pp. 223, 224	
			Unit Test

◆ Basic / ▲ Advanced / All other masters are for use by all students.

For Exceptional Students

ESL/LEP

Chapter 14/Lesson 1, Page 306

Ask students to use the food group chart to plan a nutritious meal they would enjoy eating. Remind them to have at least one serving from each food group. Tell them to name the vegetable, meat, soup, stew, or pasta they would like to eat.

Chapter 14/Lesson 2, Page 310

Have students memorize Robert Louis Stevenson's poem about being sick. Ask them to suggest diseases they have heard about or have had. Write the name of the diseases on the chalkboard and help students pronounce the words. Ask students which diseases are caused by germs and which by other means.

Chapter 14/Lesson 3, Page 314

Ask students to list the names of some over-the-counter drugs they have heard about. Have them write sentences explaining how these medicines help cure diseases. For example: My mother gave me cough medicine when I had a cough. Discuss with students the **Medicine Safety Rules.** Have them memorize the rules.

Have students write sentences telling why caffeine, alcohol, and nicotine can be harmful drugs.

Chapter 14/Lesson 4, Page 320

Discuss with students the **Poison Safety** rules. Have them memorize the rules. Discuss what should be done if someone accidentally takes a poison. Have students role play that they are calling a Poison Control Center. Let pairs of students practice being the caller and the person who has taken the poison accidentally. Questions such as **What did you swallow? How much did you take? How long ago did you swallow the poison?** should be practiced.

Gifted

Chapter 14/Lesson 1, Page 308

Help your gifted students design a survey or questionnaire to find out about the snack habits of the class. They should have a definition of the word *snack* as anything that is eaten other than at a regularly scheduled meal. Using the results of the survey, have them determine whether the class consumes healthful snacks or needs to learn to make more responsible decisions about eating snacks. They may also wish to ask when snacks are most frequently eaten.

Mainstreamed

Chapter 14/Lesson 1, Page 308

Learning Disabled: Have students work in pairs. Blindfold one partner. The other member of the team should serve a small sample of a food on a spoon (apple slice, cereal, cheese, bread). The blindfolded person has to identify the food and indicate the food group to which the sample belongs (grain, milk, meat, fruit/vegetable, or combination). Help students record their results in a simple table. *A separate spoon should be used for each sample for each student.* **CAUTION:** *If toothpicks are used with samples, caution students on their use.*

Whole Class Science Project

Several days before observations are taken give each student a piece of bakery bread (or other bread without preservatives). Have students moisten the bread *slightly* and leave it exposed to the air for a few hours. This will allow spores from the air to settle on the bread. Cover each piece of bread with a jar for a few days. Mold should develop. Have students observe what the mold looks like with the use of a magnifying glass. If microscopes are available, show students how to make a slide and have them observe the mold closely. Have students suggest how the bread became moldy. Was it the water, the bread, or the air? Relate this to their own ability to get diseases. Is there some way they could prevent the bread from getting moldy? How can they protect themselves from getting diseases?

Science Fair Projects

Individual students could do one of the following projects:
1. Find out the effects of caffeine on growing plants.
2. Determine the effect of the color of food on people's appetites.

CHAPTER 14

pages 304–327

Chapter Concepts

■ Foods from the five basic food groups provide the nutrients and energy that your body needs to grow and repair damaged cells.

■ Diseases are caused by germs that enter the body. Immunity is gained by having the disease, or through vaccination. Liquids, healthful foods, and rest can help the body heal faster.

■ Drugs used in medicines may be needed to cure or control diseases and must be used safely. Other drugs can be found in some foods, drinks, and tobacco.

■ Some poisons can be found in the home and should be used safely. Know where to seek help for accidental poisonings.

Chapter Background

■ Some research indicates that a diet adequate in fiber reduces the incidence of colon cancer.

■ Alcoholism affects 20 million people.

■ Cigarette smoking is the single most preventable cause of death in the United States today.

■ The chief causes of poisoning by ingestion are overdose of medicine, ingestion of medicines and household cleaners by children, using alcohol and other drugs at the same time, and using poisons placed in an unlabeled food container.

Looking Ahead

■ Arrange a visit to a company where food is processed for resale or restaurant use. Notice any health regulations that employees are required to follow or special clothing they have to wear.

Look for These Symbols

—Hands-on activity

—Cooperative learning

—Overhead transparency

◆ —Basic/Reinforcement

● —Average/Enrichment

▲ —Advanced/Challenge

—Calculator Practice

CHAPTER 14

Staying Healthy

For your body to accomplish all the work it must do, you must provide it with food that keeps it healthy. Think about the foods that you like to eat. Are they good for you? Healthy foods have ingredients that provide nutrients—the building blocks your body needs to accomplish its work.

Have You Ever...

Read a Food Label?

Read the list of ingredients of some of your favorite foods. On a piece of paper, list the ingredients that you think are good for you. How many ingredients did you list? Do you think that this is a healthful food to eat?

305

PREPLAN

Time Allotment: 30 minutes

Objectives
1. **Discuss** foods that are healthy to eat.
2. **Infer** which foods contribute to good health by reading the label.

Setup
■ If you wish to perform this activity, you will need the following materials for each student or activity group:
ingredients labels from boxes or cans of food
pencil and paper

1 FOCUS

■ Discuss how our bodies need food to grow and stay healthy.

2 TEACH

■ Have the title and introductory paragraph read aloud.

Have You Ever . . .
Use this activity as an introduction to *nutrients.*
Have students **work cooperatively** in groups of four.
■ Provide a variety of food labels. Be certain that students compare the number of ingredients on their lists with the total number of ingredients listed on the label.
■ **Student Responses**
Answers will vary, depending upon the labels that are read.

3 APPLY

■ Discuss the difference between ingredients in food and food nutrients. Ingredients may contain many or no nutrients.

Close
■ Tell students that they will learn more about nutrients in Chapter 14.

PREPLAN

Lesson Objectives

1. **Infer** the need for healthful foods.
2. **Identify** foods in the five healthful food groups.

Science Background

■ The healthful food groups are the milk group, the meat group, the fruit and vegetable group, and the grain group. The Dairy Council chart includes a fifth group, the combination group. This group includes servings or partial servings from the four basic food groups.

■ Water, minerals, carbohydrates, fats, proteins, and vitamins are the six nutrients in foods.

■ A person who eats too much junk food (candy, potato chips, soda pop, sweet rolls, etc.) may have plenty of energy, but does not get all the needed nutrients. This may result in health problems such as malnutrition.

■ Excess food energy is stored in the body as fat.

Note: The activity on student page 309 may be used for guided discovery before you begin this lesson.

1   FOCUS

■ **Problem Solving:** Have students imagine themselves as the person in charge of planning school lunches for a week. They will need to make a large chart of the menus and keep it for the end of the lesson. After completion of the chapter, have them discuss whether or not their meals were healthful.

■ Use the goals on student page 306 to establish the purpose for studying this lesson.

Eating Well

> **LESSON 1 GOALS**
> You will learn
> ● why we need good foods.
> ● which groups of foods are good for us.

What is your favorite food? Do you like pecks of pickled peppers, hot cross buns, or green eggs and ham? You need food to stay alive. But sometimes the foods you like best aren't the best ones for your body.

One way to stay healthy is to eat good foods. Healthful foods provide the energy your body needs to grow and repair cells. Your body uses energy from food to keep tissues, organs, and organ systems working.

The foods you eat affect how you feel every day. People who eat the wrong foods or skip meals may get sick often.

You know that a nutrient is a substance needed by living things for growth. Healthful foods have different nutrients. When you eat, the nutrients are carried to all the cells in your body. Your cells use the nutrients to help you grow and to keep your body healthy.

306

TEACHER RESOURCE MASTERS

Language Arts Connection   217

LANGUAGE ARTS CONNECTION   Using Reference Materials   Chapter 14

Name _____

FOOD SOURCES

We eat a variety of foods each day. These foods come from many sources. They supply us with different nutrients to keep our bodies healthy. Use resource books to find out from where the foods listed below come. Also write one way the food is used. The first example is completed for you.

Answers will vary.

Food	Source	How Used
bread	grains	sandwiches
ham	pigs	sandwiches
apple	tree	pie
milk	cows	drink
peanut butter	plant	sandwiches
rice	plant	breakfast cereal
hamburger	beef cattle	meat patty
tortilla chips	corn	snack
eggs	chicken	fried eggs
ice cream	milk cows	dessert
noodles	grains	stew
cheese	milk cows	sandwiches
beans	plant	soup
lettuce	plant	salad
grits	corn	breakfast food
fillet of sole	fish	dinner food
ketchup	tomatoes	sandwiches
yogurt	milk	snack

Unfortunately, not all foods are healthful. Candy, chips, and other foods that contain a lot of sugar or salt are not healthful. These types of foods have few nutrients and don't help your body grow. In fact, these foods can hurt your body. If you eat too much of them, they can damage your teeth or make you overweight.

Eating different foods helps your body get all the nutrients it needs to grow. Think of the different types of food you can eat. Suggestions for servings from the five food groups are listed. These suggestions will give you an idea of the kinds of foods you should be eating to stay healthy. In which groups are your favorite foods? They may be in more than one group.

SCIENCE AND . . .
Math

Amy eats more than Joy. Joy eats less than Ken. Gus eats more than Amy. What is most reasonable?
A. Gus eats more than Joy.
B. Ken and Amy eat the same amount.
C. Gus eats less than Ken.

Table 1   Food Groups and Suggested Servings for Children

Milk	Meat	Fruit-Vegetable	Grain	Combination
1 Serving: 1 cup milk 1 cup yogurt 1 1/2 slice cheese	**1 Serving:** 2 oz lean meat, fish, poultry 2 eggs 4 tsp peanut butter	**1 Serving:** 1/2 cup juice 1/2 cup cooked vegetable 1 cup raw fruit or vegetable	**1 Serving:** 1 slice bread 1 cup dry cereal 1/2 cup cooked cereal	**1 Serving:** 1 cup soup 1 cup pasta dish 1 cup stew, casserole
Servings: 3	**Servings: 2**	**Servings: 4**	**Servings: 4**	**Servings: ***

*These count as servings or partial servings of the groups from which they are made.

307

TEACHER RESOURCE MASTERS

Critical Thinking   216

CRITICAL THINKING/PROBLEM SOLVING   Challenge   Chapter 14

Name _____

FOOD DETECTIVE

We must be careful to watch what we eat. Too much fat, sugar, and salt are not good for our health. Often we eat foods that have these substances and we do not realize it. Look at the list of ingredients in this food product.

tomatoes, corn sweetener, distilled vinegar, salt, spices and natural flavors

The ingredient that makes up the largest amount of the product is listed first. The last ingredient makes up the smallest amount of the product. The other ingredients are listed in order from most to least. Notice that this food product has a lot of sugar (corn sweetener). Did you guess that this product is ketchup? Check the labels of these products. Answer the questions that follow. Use resource books if you need help.

mayonnaise	chicken soup	butter
barbeque sauce	cola soft drink	hot cocoa mix
margarine	cake mix	milk chocolate
breakfast cereals	potato chips	lemon-lime soft drink

1. What are some forms of sugar found in foods? _corn syrup, corn_
sweeteners, honey, molasses, dextrose, maple syrup

2. What foods are high in sugar? _barbeque sauce, soft drinks, cake mixes,_
hot cocoa mix, milk chocolate, some breakfast cereals, some mustards

3. What foods are high in salt? _chicken soup, potato chips, mustard_

4. What foods are high in fat? _mayonnaise, butter, some margarines_

Independent Practice   219

INDEPENDENT PRACTICE   Chapter 14

Name _Each question is worth 5 points._   Total Points 100
Your Score ___

Lesson 1   Eating Well   Pages 306 to 309
Use the words below to complete the sentences.
food groups   healthy   grain
milk   meat   fruit-vegetable

1. Nutrients in foods help keep your body _healthy_
obj 1
2. To be healthy, you need to eat foods from all five _food groups_
obj 1
3. Cheese comes from the _milk_ food group.
obj 2
4. The _meat_ food group contains eggs.
obj 2
5. One item from the _grain_ food group is bread.
obj 2
6. Carrots and apples represent the _fruit-vegetable_ food group. obj 2

Lesson 2   Being Sick   Pages 310 to 313
immunity   rest   vaccine
disease   liquids   energy

7. The body's protection against certain diseases is called _immunity_
obj 3
8. When you are sick, getting _rest_ and sleep allows your body to heal faster. obj 4
9. A(n) _disease_ is an illness. obj 3
10. Healthful foods give your body _energy_ to repair sick body cells. obj 4
11. Eating healthful foods and drinking _liquids_ help you get well when you are sick. obj 4

2   TEACH

■ Discuss with students how they start each day. Do they eat breakfast? How does a good breakfast affect their morning?

■ Ask students why it is important to eat a wide variety of foods from the five food groups.

Guided Practice
■ Check students' understanding of lesson concepts by discussing the Lesson Review questions on student page 308. If necessary, use the **reteaching strategy** in OPTIONS.

Independent Practice
■ Assign the Lesson 1 section of the Teacher Resource Master **Independent Practice,** page 219.

3   APPLY

■ Use Application Activity, "What's for Lunch?" on student page 361.

Close
■ Use Summary statements on student page 308 to review lesson concepts.

OPTIONS

Reteaching Strategy
Have students imagine they are restaurant managers. Divide them into small **cooperative groups** and have each group devise imaginative restaurant menus featuring meals balanced to represent all the basic food groups. You might want some groups to create breakfast menus, while others do lunch and dinner. Provide cardboard, construction paper, markers, and so on.

Resource Options
Use Color Transparency #15, "Food Groups and Servings for Children."
■ Refer to page 308 for **Science and . . . Math** solution.

OPTIONS

SCIENCE AND . . . MATH

Skill: Evaluate reasonableness.

Student Response: A

♦ **Reinforcement:** Plan a *What Happened to My Pizza?* party. Have students list all the ingredients of a deluxe pizza and figure out the different food groups to which these items belong. Discuss whether certain toppings make a pizza more healthful.

● **Enrichment:** Have students find out what happens to milk when cheese, cottage cheese, or yogurt is made. Have students work in **cooperative groups** to make one of these products in class.

▲ **Challenge:** Have students find the appropriate weights for children age 5 through age 13. Have them define overweight and give reasons people might overeat. Be sensitive to individuals during this activity.

Resource Options

■ Use Activity Book, "What's For Lunch?" pages 51 and 52.

LESSON REVIEW ANSWERS

1. to grow new cells, repair damaged cells, to keep cells, tissues, organs, and organ systems working, and to provide energy the body needs

2. a substance in food that is used by the body for growth

3. It does not contain nutrients that the body needs.

You may have heard that "you are what you eat." If you eat good, healthful foods, chances are your body will be good and healthy, too.

Lesson Summary

● Your body uses healthful foods to grow and to repair damaged cells.

● Foods from the healthful food groups have the nutrients your body needs to live and grow.

Lesson Review

1. Why are healthful foods important for the body?
2. What is a nutrient?
★3. Why is a food high in sugar not healthful?

Use Application Activity on pages 361, 362.

TEACHER RESOURCE MASTERS

What healthful foods have you eaten today?

What you need
food group table
crayons
paper plates
pencil and paper

Meal	Foods eaten	Food groups
Breakfast		
Lunch		

What to do
1. Study Table 1 on page 307. Make a chart like the one shown.
2. List the foods you had for breakfast or lunch in the correct column.
3. Using the crayons and paper plates, make a drawing of the foods you ate.
4. Compare your meal with that of a classmate. Decide whether or not you had a healthful meal.

What did you learn?
1. From which groups did you choose your food?
2. Did you or your classmate have the more healthful meal? How can you tell?

Using what you learned
1. What could you do to make your meal more healthful?
2. Plan a menu of healthful foods for two days.

309

ACTIVITY RESPONSES

What did you learn?
1. Answers will vary depending on what students had for breakfast or lunch.
2. Answers will vary depending on what students had for breakfast or lunch. The meal that contained more choices from the five food groups would be the more healthful.

Using what you learned
1. Answers will vary depending upon the meal selected, but should include foods from all food groups.
2. Answers will vary, but each meal should include the suggested servings from each food group.

PREPLAN

Time Allotment: 30 minutes
Process Skill: Communicating

Objectives
1. **Plan** a healthful meal.
2. **Place** the foods eaten in the proper food groups.

Setup
■ Have the charts already run off for each student.
■ Have students work through the activity individually.

1 FOCUS

■ Review what foods belong in a particular food group and why.

2 TEACH

■ Allow the students to preview this activity the day before actually beginning the collection of data. Otherwise, some students might not have eaten breakfast. The preview will alert students to the activity and allow them to make some decisions prior to starting their charts.
■ Have students use the Teacher Resource Master **Activity Worksheet,** pages 211 and 212, to record their data and answers.

3 APPLY

■ Ask the students to consider how the information from this activity might influence how they choose their foods.

Close
■ Discuss the activity and questions.

PREPLAN

Lesson Objectives

3. Define *immunity* and *disease*.

4. Tell why liquids, healthful foods, and rest are important during an illness.

Science Background

■ Diseases that can be passed from one person to another are called communicable diseases. These include the common cold, influenza, cold sores, fever blisters, and strep throat.

■ Some diseases are inherited at birth and others develop as a person gets older.

■ Skin that remains unbroken, hairs in the nose, cilia in the trachea, eyelashes, and tears help to keep disease-causing organisms from entering the body.

■ Immunity may be natural or acquired through vaccines.

■ Water carries nutrients to all body cells. Body temperature is affected by water.

Lesson Vocabulary

disease
immunity
vaccine

1 FOCUS

■ Discuss with students how they feel when they are ill. Ask: **How do you take care of yourself when you are ill?** *rest, drink juices, take medicine if recommended or prescribed*

■ Use the goals on student page 310 to establish the purpose for studying this lesson.

Being Sick

LESSON 2 GOALS
You will learn
● what disease and immunity are.
● what to do when you are sick.

"When I was sick and lay-a-bed,
I had two pillows at my head,
And all my toys beside me lay
To keep me happy all the day . . ."

Over one hundred years ago, the poet Robert Louis Stevenson wrote these lines about being sick. When was the last time you were really sick? How did you feel? [1]What made you sick? [2]Do you know how you can keep from getting sick again?

1. Answers may include germs or a virus.

2. Answers may include getting enough sleep, eating healthful foods, or dressing for the weather.

Diseases

A **disease** (dihz EEZ) is an illness. Some diseases, like colds, chicken pox, and measles, are caused by germs. Germs are tiny living things that you can't see with your eyes. Other diseases, like heart disease or some cancers, can be caused by smoking or not eating the right kinds of food. No one knows what causes some other diseases.

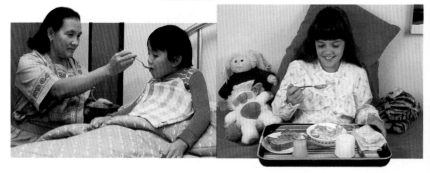

310

TEACHER RESOURCE MASTERS

We know that many diseases caused by germs may be spread from person to person. If someone who has a cold sneezes near you, germs may be spread to you through the air. Your hands can pick up a lot of germs just by touching things that sick people have touched. That's why you should wash your hands often. [1]What can you do to keep your cold or flu from spreading to other people?

1. Answers may include covering your mouth when you cough or sneeze, or washing your hands.

Your Body's Defense

Even if you come in contact with germs, it doesn't mean you will get sick. Your body has ways to defend itself from germs. Your skin helps keep germs from getting into your body. Tears wash away germs that get into your eyes. Getting enough sleep and eating healthful foods can also help your body defend itself against germs.

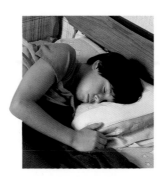

When germs do get into your body, they attack your body and harm cells. Your body fights back by making substances that kill the germs. These substances give your body **immunity** (ihm YEW nut ee), or protection, against certain diseases.

What is immunity?

Your body gets immunity in different ways. You can get some diseases only one time. For example, after you have mumps, your body is always protected against the germs that cause mumps.

311

TEACHER RESOURCE MASTERS

Critical Thinking 215

CRITICAL THINKING/PROBLEM SOLVING Inferring — Chapter 14

Name _____

SPREADING DISEASE

Materials
1 fresh apple warm water paper towel
1 rotting apple soap toothpick

What to do
1. Check the fresh apple to see that there are no holes in the skin or rotting spots. Wash the apple with water and soap. Dry it with paper towels.
2. Push the toothpick into a rotten spot of the rotting apple.
3. Push the same end of the toothpick into the fresh, clean apple.
4. Repeat step 3 several times to be sure some of the rotting apple is poked into the fresh apple.
5. Set both apples in a warm place for 3 to 5 days. Observe the area around the toothpick holes in the fresh apple.

What did you learn?
1. Why was the fresh apple washed with soap and water? _to wash off any germs on the skin_
2. What happened to the fresh apple? _It also got a rotten spot._

Using what you learned
1. How was the rottenness spread from one apple to the other? _by the toothpick_
2. What are some other ways disease might be spread? _by air, water_
3. Why does washing off skin with soap and water help prevent the spread of disease? _The disease germs are killed or washed away._

Independent Practice 219

INDEPENDENT PRACTICE — Chapter 14

Name _____ Each question is worth 5 points. Total Points 100 Your Score ___

Lesson 1 Eating Well Pages 306 to 309
Use the words below to complete the sentences.
food groups healthy grain
milk meat fruit-vegetable

1. Nutrients in foods help keep your body _healthy_ obj 1
2. To be healthy, you need to eat foods from all five _food groups_ obj 1
3. Cheese comes from the _milk_ food group. obj 2
4. The _meat_ food group contains eggs. obj 2
5. One item from the _grain_ food group is bread. obj 2
6. Carrots and apples represent the _fruit-vegetable_ food group. obj 2

Lesson 2 Being Sick Pages 310 to 313
immunity rest vaccine
disease liquids energy

7. The body's protection against certain diseases is called _immunity_ obj 3
8. When you are sick, getting _rest_ and sleep allows your body to heal faster. obj 4
9. A(n) _disease_ is an illness. obj 3
10. Healthful foods give your body _energy_ to repair sick body cells. obj 4
11. Eating healthful foods and drinking _liquids_ help you get well when you are sick. obj 4

2 TEACH

- List ways germs are spread. Answers may include coughing, animals, insects, and water.
- Caution students that only the doctor or a parent should decide whether medicine is to be used.

Allow time for students to use a hand lens to look at their own skin and hairs. Stress how much skin the body has. Ask: **How do germs get through the skin into the body?** *breaks in the skin*

Guided Practice

- Check students' understanding of lesson concepts by discussing the Lesson Review questions on student page 313. If necessary, use the **reteaching strategy** in OPTIONS.

Independent Practice

- Assign the Lesson 2 section of the Teacher Resource Master **Independent Practice,** page 219.

3 APPLY

- Provide students with poster board and markers and divide them into two groups. Have one group work together to create a list of rules to follow to help avoid sickness. Instruct the other group to make a poster listing things to do to help get well when you are sick. Display the completed posters.

Close

- Use Summary statements on student page 313 to review lesson concepts.

OPTIONS

Reteaching Strategy

- Work with students to write a letter to a local physician. Have students explain what they have learned about staying well and recovering from sickness. Ask the doctor for further suggestions on maintaining good health.

OPTIONS

MATH CONNECTION

Write the problem below on the chalkboard or an overhead transparency. Have students select a strategy for solving the following problem.

Masao had the flu and his dad took him to the doctor. The doctor's visit cost $17.75. The shot she gave Masao cost $11.50. On the way home, they stopped to have the doctor's prescription filled. It cost $10.95. How would you find the total cost of the trip? (Add the three dollar amounts.)

■ Have students relate experiences with vaccinations. Ask: **Does it hurt? What could happen if people don't have vaccinations?** *They could get diseases.* Note that not all vaccines are given by injection. Polio vaccine is usually swallowed.

■ Explain that germs need food, warmth, and water to grow. Ask: **Would your bodies be good places for germs to grow? Why?** *Yes, because they provide food, warmth, and water.*

♦ **Reinforcement:** Tell students that more germs are spread by hands than by coughs and sneezes. Demonstrate the proper hand-washing technique.
1. Rinse hands.
2. Apply soap to the palms.
3. Rub front and back of hands briskly for at least 15 seconds.
4. Rinse and dry hands thoroughly.
5. Dispose of paper towels in trash cans at school or in public restrooms. At school, encourage students to wash their hands before lunch and after using the restrooms.

Sometimes you get a **vaccine** (vak SEEN) to get protection from a disease you haven't had. Vaccines are dead or weak germs that give immunity to a disease. A vaccine can come in the form of a liquid, a pill, or a shot. Babies are given vaccines for diseases like whooping cough, polio, and scarlet fever so that they never get those diseases. Your school probably required that you have certain vaccines before you started school. Unfortunately, we do not have a vaccine for every disease.

Vaccines come in different forms.

How do you feel when you get sick? Sometimes all you feel like doing is staying in bed and sleeping. When you are sick, it is important to continue to eat healthful foods, stay warm, get rest, and drink liquids.

312

TEACHER RESOURCE MASTERS

Healthful foods give your body the energy it needs to repair body cells. Rest and sleep allow your body to heal faster and fight the disease. If an illness continues, you should see a doctor. The doctor may give you medicine to help your body fight the disease. After all, the best thing about being sick is getting well.

Lesson Summary

- A disease is an illness that can be caused by germs that enter the body. Immunity is the body's protection against certain diseases.
- Liquids, healthful foods, and rest are needed when you are sick.

Lesson Review

1. How do you get diseases like colds or the flu?
2. How can your body become immune to a disease?
3. What should you do if you are ill?
★4. Why should schools make sure that students have certain vaccines?

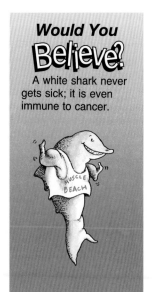

Would You
Believe?
A white shark never gets sick; it is even immune to cancer.

313

OPTIONS

● **Enrichment:** Many students may think a fever is an illness instead of a symptom. Ask students to find out how fevers help the body fight germs.

▲ **Challenge:** Assign a specific body system to each student. Have them report to the class the medical specialist who deals with the system as well as some of the diseases that occur specifically to the system. An example might be circulatory system, cardiologist, and heart attack, respectively. An association game such as connecting words from the left column to the right column would be appropriate.

LANGUAGE ARTS CONNECTION

■ Have students write and illustrate a short story about staying home while sick or a visit to the doctor.

LESSON REVIEW ANSWERS

1. germs
2. You may be immune after you get a disease, or sometimes you get a vaccine to become immune.
3. You should drink liquids, eat healthful foods, and rest.
4. to prevent diseases from being spread to many students.

TEACHER RESOURCE MASTERS

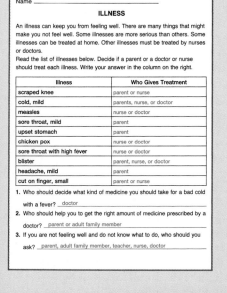

Reteaching Activity 221

RETEACHING ACTIVITY — Chapter 14

Name

ILLNESS

An illness can keep you from feeling well. There are many things that might make you not feel well. Some illnesses are more serious than others. Some illnesses can be treated at home. Other illnesses must be treated by nurses or doctors.

Read the list of illnesses below. Decide if a parent or a doctor or nurse should treat each illness. Write your answer in the column on the right.

Illness	Who Gives Treatment
scraped knee	parent or nurse
cold, mild	parents, nurse, or doctor
measles	nurse or doctor
sore throat, mild	parent
upset stomach	parent
chicken pox	nurse or doctor
sore throat with high fever	nurse or doctor
blister	parent, nurse, or doctor
headache, mild	parent
cut on finger, small	parent or nurse

1. Who should decide what kind of medicine you should take for a bad cold with a fever? _doctor_
2. Who should help you to get the right amount of medicine prescribed by a doctor? _parent or adult family member_
3. If you are not feeling well and do not know what to do, who should you ask? _parent, adult family member, teacher, nurse, doctor_

pages 314–319

PREPLAN

Lesson Objectives

5. Define *drug*.

6. Identify safety rules for taking medicine.

7. Communicate the effects of and **describe** products that contain caffeine, alcohol, and nicotine.

Science Background

■ Two of the most common over-the-counter drugs are aspirin and antihistamines.

■ The over-the-counter drug's purpose is to relieve minor symptoms of illness.

■ Prescription drugs are ordered by a doctor for a specific patient. A pharmacist reads the doctor's orders for medicines and prepares the drugs.

■ Caffeine is habit-forming.

■ Warning labels are required on cigarette packages and bottles of liquor.

■ Evidence shows that smoking causes lung cancer, heart disease, and emphysema.

■ Cigarette advertisements were banned from radio and television in 1970.

Lesson Vocabulary

drug   prescription drug
over-the-counter drug
caffeine
alcohol
nicotine

Note: The activity on student page 319 may be used for guided discovery before you begin this lesson.

1   FOCUS

■ Have students share some of their experiences using medicine. Discuss various OTC drugs.

■ Use the goals on student page 314 to establish the purpose for studying this lesson.

Taking Medicines

If you are sick, you may need some medicine to help you get well. You may have been given medicine the last time you had a cold or the flu. Medicines are drugs.

Medicines

A **drug** is a substance that changes the way your body or mind works. Drugs are used in different ways. There are drugs in medicines that cure some diseases. For example, if germs cause an earache, medicines can kill the germs and your ear will stop hurting.

Drugs in medicines can also control, but not cure, some diseases. People with heart disease or high blood pressure may take medicine to control those diseases.

Drugs in medicines can also just make people feel better when they are sick. Cold medicines, for example, will not cure or control cold germs. But they can ease coughing, sneezing, or a runny nose.

314

TEACHER RESOURCE MASTERS

Medicines are sold in two ways. A doctor must order some medicines. These kinds of medicines should not be taken in the same way by everyone. A **prescription** (prih SKRIHP shun) **drug** is prepared for you after your doctor orders it. An **over-the-counter drug** is one like aspirin and many cough medicines that you can buy without a doctor's order.

Even helpful medicines can be dangerous. It is very important that you follow the safety rules here when taking medicines.

What is a prescription drug?

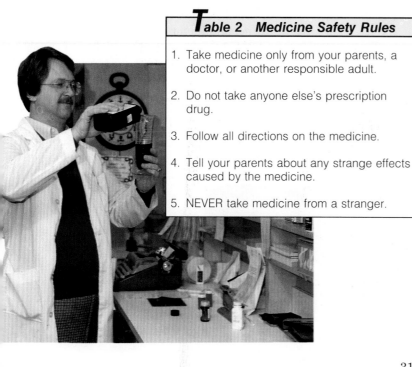

Table 2   Medicine Safety Rules

1. Take medicine only from your parents, a doctor, or another responsible adult.

2. Do not take anyone else's prescription drug.

3. Follow all directions on the medicine.

4. Tell your parents about any strange effects caused by the medicine.

5. NEVER take medicine from a stranger.

315

2   TEACH

■ Discuss the different forms in which medicines are produced—capsules, tablets, liquids, and creams.

■ Differentiate between an over-the-counter and a prescription drug. Explain that over-the-counter drugs can be bought at a variety of stores (grocery, convenience, drug stores, and so on) but prescription drugs can only be bought from a pharmacist at a drug store.

■ Discuss with students the fact that the American Dental Association warns against the use of chewing tobacco. It contributes to cancer and gum disease.

Guided Practice

■ Check students' understanding of lesson concepts by discussing the Lesson Review questions on student page 318. If necessary, use the **reteaching strategy** in OPTIONS.

Independent Practice

■ Assign the Lesson 3 section of the Teacher Resource Master **Independent Practice,** page 220.

3   APPLY

■ Use Application Activity, "Read the Labels," on student page 363.

Close

■ Use Summary statements on student page 318 to review lesson concepts.

OPTIONS

Reteaching Strategy

Using magazines, have students cut out pictures of medicines and make a poster. Discuss where each medicine could have been purchased and its form (capsule, liquid, and so on).

Resource Options

Use Color Transparency #16, "Drugs and our Bodies."

TEACHER RESOURCE MASTERS

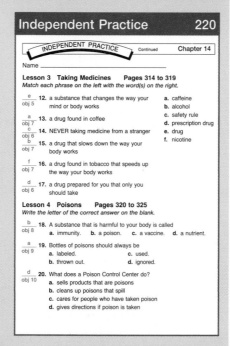

Independent Practice   220

INDEPENDENT PRACTICE   Continued   Chapter 14

Name _____

Lesson 3   Taking Medicines   Pages 314 to 319
Match each phrase on the left with the word(s) on the right.

___e___ **12.** a substance that changes the way your   **a.** caffeine
obj 5   mind or body works   **b.** alcohol

___a___ **13.** a drug found in coffee   **c.** safety rule
obj 7   **d.** prescription drug

___c___ **14.** NEVER taking medicine from a stranger   **e.** drug
obj 6   **f.** nicotine

___b___ **15.** a drug that slows down the way your
obj 7   body works

___f___ **16.** a drug found in tobacco that speeds up
obj 7   the way your body works

___d___ **17.** a drug prepared for you that only you
obj 6   should take

Lesson 4   Poisons   Pages 320 to 325
Write the letter of the correct answer on the blank.

___b___ **18.** A substance that is harmful to your body is called
obj 8   **a.** immunity.   **b.** a poison.   **c.** a vaccine.   **d.** a nutrient.

___a___ **19.** Bottles of poisons should always be
obj 9   **a.** labeled.   **c.** used.
           b. thrown out.   **d.** ignored.

___d___ **20.** What does a Poison Control Center do?
obj 10   **a.** sells products that are poisons
           b. cleans up poisons that spill
           c. cares for people who have taken poison
           d. gives directions if poison is taken

OPTIONS

MATH CONNECTION

Write the following problem on the chalkboard or on an overhead transparency. Have students select a strategy for solving the following problem.

Tonya and Masao are not in school today. Tonya has an ear infection while Masao is home with the flu. Tonya's medicine cost $14.50, Masao's, $10.95. How would you find how much more Tonya's medicine cost than Masao's? (Subtract $10.95 from $14.50.)

♦ **Reinforcement:** Students in your school may be interested in participating in the "Just Say No" program. Invite a representative from this group to your school or classroom to speak to students about this organization and its goals.

● **Enrichment:** Have a pharmacist visit the class and explain the facts children should know about drugs.

Resource Options
■ Use Activity Book, "Read the Labels," pages 53 and 54.

Drugs in Drinks and Tobacco

Not all drugs are medicines. You know that drugs change the way your body or mind works. Some drugs are in common drinks. **Caffeine** (ka FEEN) is a common drug that speeds up the way the body works. Caffeine is in some soft drinks, coffee, tea, and chocolate. Although a lot of people take in caffeine, too much can be harmful to the body. It can keep a person awake at night or make a person feel nervous.

Alcohol (AL kuh hawl) is a drug that slows down the way the body works. Beer, wine, and liquor have alcohol in them. Alcohol can harm body organs and change the way a person thinks or acts. Alcohol may also make people lose control of their muscles.

What effect does alcohol have on the body?

316

TEACHER RESOURCE MASTERS

Nicotine (NIHK uh teen) is a drug found in tobacco. It is in cigarettes, cigars, and pipe tobacco. It is also found in chewing tobacco. Nicotine speeds up the way the body works and makes the heart beat faster. Nicotine can have the same effects as caffeine.

You can choose not to use harmful drugs. To stay healthy, people choose not to drink caffeine and alcohol. Many people also choose not to smoke or chew tobacco. People who make these choices are working to keep their bodies healthy.

Use Application Activity on pages 363, 364.

317

OPTIONS

■ Bring in labels from products that contain caffeine. Have students read the labels and identify this ingredient.

■ Discuss the alternatives to using products that contain caffeine (such as caffeine-free soft drinks, or fresh fruit).

■ Ask: **What are some of the dangers involved when a person who has been using alcohol loses muscle control?** *A person cannot walk, run, or drive when there is a loss of physical control, therefore the chance of injury increases.*

■ Have students share experiences of being in a room full of cigarette smoke. Discuss how their eyes may have burned, there was an unpleasant smell, and their clothes smelled of smoke after leaving the room.

SOCIAL STUDIES CONNECTION

■ Have interested students report on a vaccine that has had an impact on the world and the person who discovered that vaccine. Choices may include: Jonas Salk—polio, Edward Jenner—smallpox, Albert Sabin—polio, Louis Pasteur—rabies injections, and so on.

● **Enrichment:** Have students find out the three warning label statements that are printed on cigarette wrappers. Discuss why these warnings are vital for good health.

TEACHER RESOURCE MASTERS

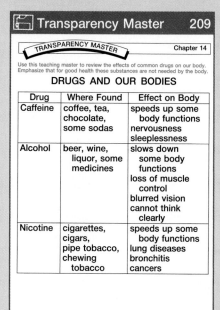

Transparency Master 209

TRANSPARENCY MASTER — Chapter 14

Use this teaching master to review the effects of common drugs on our body. Emphasize that for good health these substances are not needed by the body.

DRUGS AND OUR BODIES

Drug	Where Found	Effect on Body
Caffeine	coffee, tea, chocolate, some sodas	speeds up some body functions nervousness sleeplessness
Alcohol	beer, wine, liquor, some medicines	slows down some body functions loss of muscle control blurred vision cannot think clearly
Nicotine	cigarettes, cigars, pipe tobacco, chewing tobacco	speeds up some body functions lung diseases bronchitis cancers

Health Connection 218

HEALTH CONNECTION — Drugs — Chapter 14

Name _____

DRUGS IN DRINKS AND TOBACCO

In this chapter you learned that there are drugs in drinks, tobacco, and even some foods. These drugs are sometimes used on a regular basis. Many people do not even think of alcohol, nicotine, and caffeine as drugs.

Look at the list of substances on the left. These substances contain either caffeine, nicotine, or alcohol. Put the letter of the drug next to the substance that contains it.

_b_ 1. Chocolate candy bar	**a.** nicotine	
_c_ 2. Beer	**b.** caffeine	
_b_ 3. Cola soft drink	**c.** alcohol	
_c_ 4. Wine		
_a_ 5. Cigarettes		
_b_ 6. Hot chocolate or cocoa		
_a_ 7. Chewing tobacco		
_c_ 8. Liquor		
_b_ 9. Tea		
_a_ 10. Cigars		

11. Which of the substances on the left have you seen advertised? _____
    Answers will vary. Students may have seen all the substances advertised.

OPTIONS

▲ Challenge: Have students work in **cooperative groups** to find out how caffeine is removed from coffee and other beverages, when the processes were developed, and why they were developed. Data can be organized to show how much caffeine is found in regular coffee, decaffeinated coffee, tea, and soft drinks.

LESSON REVIEW ANSWERS

1. You should take medicine only from a parent or doctor. Do not take anyone else's prescription. Follow the directions given on medicine. Notify your parents about any strange effects caused by medicine. Never take medicine from a stranger.

2. A prescription drug is a drug prepared for you after your doctor orders it. An over-the-counter drug can be bought without a doctor's prescription.

3. Caffeine and nicotine speed up the way the body works. Alcohol slows down the way a body works.

Lesson Summary

- A drug is a substance that changes the way your mind or body works. Drugs in medicines may be used to cure diseases, control diseases, or to help people feel better when they are sick.
- Five safety rules should be followed when taking any kind of medicine.
- Caffeine and alcohol are harmful drugs found in drinks. Nicotine is a drug found in tobacco.

Lesson Review

1. What safety rules should you follow if you take medicine?
2. What is the difference between an over-the-counter drug and a prescription drug?
★3. How do caffeine, alcohol, and nicotine affect the body?

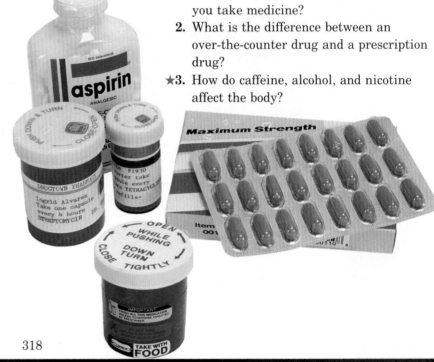

318

TEACHER RESOURCE MASTERS

How do you know which vaccinations you need?

What you need
resource books and pamphlets
pencil and paper

What to do
1. Look at the list of diseases shown in this chart. Make a copy of the chart.
2. Use resource books. Find out which diseases can be prevented by vaccines. Put an X in column 2 next to each disease that has a vaccine.
3. Find out the age(s) at which the vaccines should be given. Fill in column 3.

What did you learn?
1. Which diseases can be prevented by vaccines?
2. Which vaccines do you need more than one time for complete immunity?

Disease	Vaccine Available	Recommended age
Chicken pox		
Common cold		
Diphtheria		
Heart disease		
HIB (bacterial meningitis)		
Measles		
Mumps		
Polio		
Rubella		
Tetanus		
Whooping cough		

Using what you learned
1. States have laws requiring that all students have certain vaccines before they are allowed to attend school. Why?
2. Show the chart to your parents or guardian. Have you had all of your vaccinations?

319

ACTIVITY RESPONSES

What did you learn?
1. diphtheria, HIB, measles, mumps, polio, tetanus, whooping cough, rubella
2. diphtheria, polio, tetanus, whooping cough

Using what you learned
1. If students are not properly immunized, then epidemics of the diseases can occur when they pass the diseases on to their unprotected classmates.
2. Answers will vary; however, most students should have been properly immunized in order to be admitted to school. If anyone is found to be inadequately protected, the school nurse should be alerted.

PREPLAN

Time Allotment: 35 minutes
Process Skills: Communicating/ Interpreting Data/Inferring

Objectives
1. **Determine** which diseases can be prevented by vaccinations.
2. **Infer** why it is important for everyone to be properly immunized.

Setup
■ Gather resource books or pamphlets from the local library; the state, county, or city department of public health; your family doctor; or the school nurse.
■ Have students work through the activity individually.

1 FOCUS

■ Review the different ways the human body can become immune to diseases. Give examples of each way.

2 TEACH

■ Have the school nurse or a local physician talk to the students about the importance of being properly immunized.
■ Have students use the Teacher Resource Master **Activity Worksheet,** pages 213 and 214, to record their data and answers.

3 APPLY

■ Make sure students take their completed charts home. Have them review their own histories of immunizations to be sure they are all current.

Close
■ Discuss the activity and questions.

PREPLAN

Lesson Objectives
8. **Operationally define** *poisons*.
9. **Identify** poison safety rules.
10. **Communicate** the function of the Poison Control Center.

Science Background
■ Poison ivy, poison oak, and poison sumac are even hazardous in the winter when they have dropped their leaves.

■ Among the more common insects that sting people are bees, hornets, wasps, and yellow jackets. These insects are attracted to bright colors, strong perfumes, and meats.

■ Over-the-counter drugs come in tamper-resistant packages. It is important to make sure these packages have not been altered.

Lesson Vocabulary
poisons

1   FOCUS

■ Show students a child-proof medicine bottle. Ask: **Why is it important for this bottle to be difficult to open?** *Child-proof medicine bottles keep small children from accidentally taking medicine.*

■ Use the goals on student page 320 to establish the purpose for studying this lesson.

Poisons

LESSON 4 GOALS
You will learn
● what a poison is.
● important safety rules about poisons.
● what a Poison Control Center does.

"Late at night while you're sleeping
Poison ivy comes a-creeping . . .
You're going to need an ocean of calamine lotion."

Believe it or not, these lines are part of a song sung by a group called The Coasters. If you have ever had a poison ivy rash, you know what they are singing about. Poison ivy is a pretty green plant that has white berries. If you touch this plant, its oil can cause a painful, itchy skin rash.

Other substances called **poisons** (POY zunz) are harmful if they get on or in your body. Poisons may be solids, liquids, or gases. Like poison ivy, a poison may enter your body through contact with the skin, or you might breathe or eat a poison.

320

TEACHER RESOURCE MASTERS

Other plants and some animals are poisonous, too. You can probably think of several insects, spiders, and snakes that inject poisons into a person's body when they bite or sting. Some of these animal poisons can be deadly.

Some gases are poisons and enter our bodies when we breathe them. Gasoline engines produce carbon monoxide, for example. This gas is especially dangerous because it does not have an odor. It could harm you without your knowing it.

Many things that can be poisonous have useful purposes. Often you can find these kinds of poisons in your home. Paint, gasoline, bug spray, and drain cleaner, for example, contain poisons that can be harmful to you. Think of other things that you may have at home that can be poisonous.

TEACHER RESOURCE MASTERS

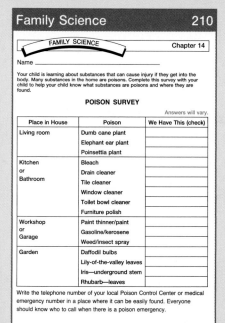

Family Science 210

FAMILY SCIENCE Chapter 14

Name _____

Your child is learning about substances that can cause injury if they get into the body. Many substances in the home are poisons. Complete this survey with your child to help your child know what substances are poisons and where they are found.

POISON SURVEY

Answers will vary.

Place in House	Poison	We Have This (check)
Living room	Dumb cane plant	
	Elephant ear plant	
	Poinsettia plant	
Kitchen or Bathroom	Bleach	
	Drain cleaner	
	Tile cleaner	
	Window cleaner	
	Toilet bowl cleaner	
	Furniture polish	
Workshop or Garage	Paint thinner/paint	
	Gasoline/kerosene	
	Weed/insect spray	
Garden	Daffodil bulbs	
	Lily-of-the-valley leaves	
	Iris—underground stem	
	Rhubarb—leaves	

Write the telephone number of your local Poison Control Center or medical emergency number in a place where it can be easily found. Everyone should know who to call when there is a poison emergency.

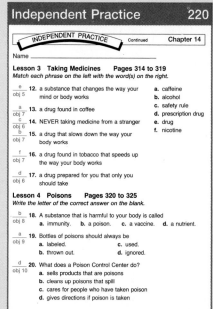

Independent Practice 220

INDEPENDENT PRACTICE Continued Chapter 14

Name _____

Lesson 3   Taking Medicines   Pages 314 to 319
Match each phrase on the left with the word(s) on the right.

_e_ 12. a substance that changes the way your
obj 5   mind or body works

_a_ 13. a drug found in coffee
obj 7

_c_ 14. NEVER taking medicine from a stranger
obj 6

_b_ 15. a drug that slows down the way your
obj 7   body works

_f_ 16. a drug found in tobacco that speeds up
obj 7   the way your body works

_d_ 17. a drug prepared for you that only you
obj 6   should take

a. caffeine
b. alcohol
c. safety rule
d. prescription drug
e. drug
f. nicotine

Lesson 4   Poisons   Pages 320 to 325
Write the letter of the correct answer on the blank.

_b_ 18. A substance that is harmful to your body is called
obj 8   a. immunity.   b. a poison.   c. a vaccine.   d. a nutrient.

_a_ 19. Bottles of poisons should always be
obj 9   a. labeled.   c. used.
           b. thrown out.   d. ignored.

_d_ 20. What does a Poison Control Center do?
obj 10   a. sells products that are poisons
           b. cleans up poisons that spill
           c. cares for people who have taken poison
           d. gives directions if poison is taken

2   TEACH

Point out that some poisonous gases come in aerosol cans or as fumes from household cleaning products such as ammonia or bleach. Make sure your students know where to call for help in their community. Allow students, working in **cooperative groups,** to put on skits showing what they would do in an accidental poisoning situation.

■ Have students make posters listing Poison Safety Rules for their homes.

Guided Practice
■ Check students' understanding of lesson concepts by discussing the Lesson Review questions on student page 324. If necessary, use the **reteaching strategy** in OPTIONS.

Independent Practice
■ Assign the Lesson 4 section of the Teacher Resource Master **Independent Practice,** page 220.

3   APPLY

■ As a class, have students brainstorm to name many of the potential poisons that might be found in their homes.

Close
■ Use Summary statements on student page 324 to review lesson concepts.

OPTIONS

Reteaching Strategy
■ Bring to class a variety of medications with child-proof caps, poisons, and cleaning products. Point out the poison labels and warnings. Discuss reasons for child-proof caps and discuss the reason each product is poisonous.

OPTIONS

LANGUAGE CONNECTION

■ **Writing:** Write the following question regarding the Poison Safety Rules in this lesson on the chalkboard or an overhead transparency. Have students respond in writing.

According to the Poison Safety Rules in this lesson, what should you do before using any product at home? (Read the label.)

♦ **Reinforcement:** Tell students that the words, "Use only in a well-ventilated area," are often found on labels. Ask students why glue used in building models is one item usually marked in this way. Ask them what the word *ventilation* means. Remind students to look for this warning and open windows or doors or go outside when using these products as the vapors they release are dangerous.

People who make substances containing poisons label the materials clearly, but sometimes the label comes off or is not read. Many terrible accidents have occurred because people have not followed poison safety rules. Since poisons are often found in common places like your home, it is important to follow the five safety rules shown here.

Table 3   Poison Safety Rules
1. NEVER taste an unknown substance.
2. Label all poisons.
3. Store poisons where young children cannot reach them.
4. Read the label before using any product at home.
5. Place the telephone number of your doctor or the local Poison Control Center near your telephone.

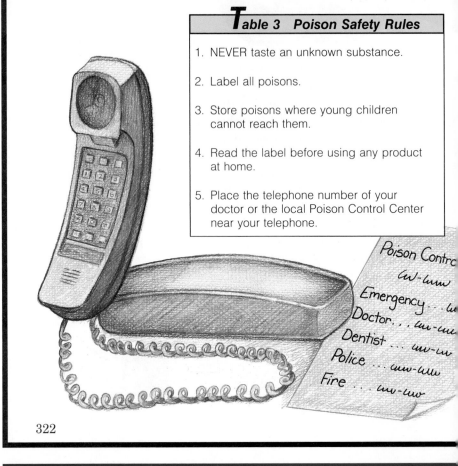

322

TEACHER RESOURCE MASTERS

What would you do if you or someone you know accidentally took a poison? Many communities have Poison Control Centers that give important information about poisons. They will immediately tell you what to do to get the poison out of your body. The directions given will depend on the kind of poison taken. It is important to place the telephone number of the nearest Poison Control Center near the telephone. Make sure each family member knows where to find this phone number.

We live in a world that has lots of wonderful things in it. But it has lots of harmful things, too. Will you be the scientist who finds new vaccines or medicines to help people fight disease? Will you be the doctor who helps people learn how to stay healthy? The choices you make about your health today will affect your health in the future. The decisions you make right now can affect your ability to play a helpful role in the world of the future.

323

OPTIONS

■ Call your community Poison Control Center, fire department, doctor, or a hospital to see if there is a common warning symbol used in your community. Mr. Yuk is one example of a warning symbol.

● **Enrichment:** Ask students to find out when syrup of ipecac is used. Remind students that the Poison Control Center should always be called before this substance is given. Have students obtain literature on common poisons from their local Poison Control Center.

▲ **Challenge:** Using reference books, have students find out which home and garden plants are poisonous. Tell them to prepare a chart that shows a picture of the plant, its name, the part of the plant that is poisonous, and the symptoms it causes.

TEACHER RESOURCE MASTERS

OPTIONS

YOU CAN . . . DESIGN A POISON WARNING SIGN

Process Skill: Communicating

Objective: Design a sign to be used as a warning for poisonous substances.

Setup/Teach

■ posterboard
  paint
  crayons

■ Remind students that small children can't read words, so the illustrations on the signs must also convey the warning.

■ Make a list of all the poisons people may find around their homes. These may include paint thinner, paint, household cleaners, and medicines. Have students discuss with their parents where these dangerous substances are kept. Make sure the telephone numbers of the doctor or the local Poison Control Center is near each household phone.

LESSON REVIEW ANSWERS

1. They have important uses. Paint, gasoline, and lye, for example, are useful as a preservative, a fuel, and a cleaner.

2. Poison Control Center

3. They provide information about what to do if a poison is accidentally ingested or absorbed.

Lesson Summary

• A poison is a substance that is harmful. Poisons may be solids, liquids, or gases.

• The five safety rules can help protect you from the harmful effects of poisons.

• Poison Control Centers provide information about what to do if you accidentally take a poison.

Lesson Review

1. Why is it common to find poisons at home?

2. Where can you call to get help or information about poisons?

★**3.** Why are Poison Control Centers important?

ACTIVITY

You Can...

Design a Poison Warning Sign

Every year many young people become very sick or even die because they tasted something poisonous. You can design a sign that warns people never to taste a poison. Use crayons or paint. Show your sign to the class. How does it warn people about poisons? Where are some good places to display your sign?

324

TEACHER RESOURCE MASTERS

I WANT TO KNOW ABOUT...

Dissolving Away Decay

When was the last time you went to a dentist? Did you have a cavity in a tooth? If it wasn't fixed, you would lose your tooth and probably hurt your gums.

You usually don't know if you have a cavity or not. That's why it's important to go to a dentist every six months. A dentist removes the decayed part of the tooth and replaces it with silver or a white plastic material. Teeth that are properly repaired remain healthy for many years.

Having your teeth drilled can be painful. Some dentists use a special liquid that dissolves decay. The dentist squirts the liquid on a cavity, the decay becomes soft, and then the decay washes away. The dentist may still need to use the drill before the tooth is filled.

It is important to keep your teeth healthy so you will have them for a long time. You keep your teeth healthy when you brush and floss every day. Dentists keep your teeth healthy by checking them every six months and repairing them when needed.

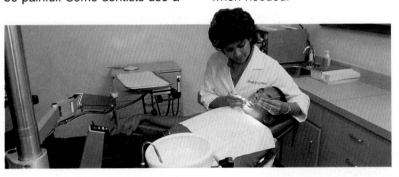

Science and Technology

325

Feature Background

■ Dissolving decay will reduce the amount of healthy tooth often lost with conventional drilling.

■ February is National Children's Dental Health month.

■ Deciduous (baby) teeth that are decayed need to be treated. Some of these teeth will be with the child until age twelve. If allowed to decay, nerve damage will occur. If extracted too early, malocclusion (improper alignment of upper and lower teeth) may occur.

Feature Vocabulary

cavity   decay

Teaching Suggestions

■ Obtain a large model of a decayed tooth from a local dentist. Point out the parts of the tooth and how decay can enter the nerve.

■ Emphasize the importance of keeping teeth clean, of having regular checkups, and of brushing after eating.

■ Have children think about how many times a day they eat. Three meals? Snacks? How often should brushing take place?

■ Have students suggest ways to keep teeth clean while at school.

TEACHER RESOURCE MASTERS

Summary

Chapter Closure: Have students locate the text section in which each summary statement's idea is introduced. Tell them to use the information to complete a chart giving statement number, page number, and paragraph number. Allow students to check their own work by having the appropriate sections read orally. Discuss the information they contain to review the summary statements.

Science Words

Use the science words to play "Hangman" with students. Each completed word must be used in an original sentence by the student who supplies the last letter.

Student Responses

1. poisons
2. disease
3. nicotine
4. immunity
5. over-the-counter drug
6. vaccine
7. caffeine
8. drug
9. prescription drug
10. alcohol

CHAPTER REVIEW 14

Summary

Lesson 1
- Healthful foods repair cells.
- Healthful foods have nutrients you need.

Lesson 2
- The body makes substances that kill germs.
- Liquids, healthful foods, and rest are important when sick.

Lesson 3
- Drugs may be used to cure or control diseases.

- Follow safety rules for medicine.
- Caffeine and alcohol are found in some drinks. Nicotine is in tobacco.

Lesson 4
- Poisons are harmful substances.
- Follow five poison safety rules.
- A Poison Control Center can give you information about poisons.

Science Words

Fill in the blank with the correct word or words from the list.

disease · caffeine
immunity · alcohol
vaccine · nicotine
drug · poisons
prescription drug
over-the-counter drug

1. Harmful substances are ___ .
2. An illness is a(n) ___ .
3. ___ is found in tobacco.
4. ___ is the body's protection against certain diseases.
5. A drug you can get without a prescription is a(n) ___ .
6. Weak germs are found in a(n) ___ .
7. A drug in some soft drinks is ___ .

326

TEACHER RESOURCE MASTERS

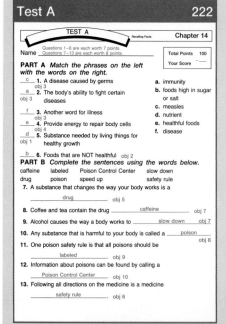

Test A   222

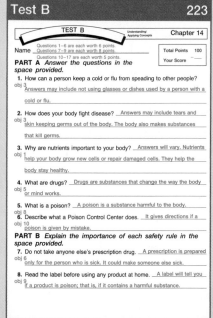

Test B   223

8. A substance that changes the way your body or mind works is a(n) ___.

9. A drug a doctor orders is a(n) ___.

10. Beer contains the drug ___.

Questions

Recalling Ideas
Correctly complete each of the following sentences.

1. Carbon monoxide is a
   (a) disease. (c) nutrient.
   (b) poison. (d) harmless gas.
2. A food from the meat group is
   (a) an egg. (c) soup.
   (b) milk. (d) cereal.
3. A food from the milk group is
   (a) an orange.
   (b) bread.
   (c) cheese.
   (d) peanut butter.

Understanding Ideas
Answer the following questions using complete sentences.

1. How should you take care of yourself when you are sick?
2. List five poison safety rules.
3. List five medicine safety rules.

Thinking Critically
Think about what you have learned in this chapter. Answer the following questions using complete sentences.

1. How do caffeine, alcohol, and nicotine affect the body?
2. Why does the body need healthful foods?

327

TEACHER RESOURCE MASTERS

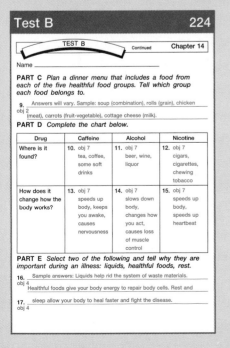

Questions

Recalling Ideas
1. b
2. a
3. c

Understanding Ideas
1. When you are ill, you should drink plenty of fluids, eat healthful foods, and get plenty of rest. These actions help the body heal faster and fight disease.
2. There are five poison safety rules.
   1. Never taste an unknown substance.
   2. Label all poisons.
   3. Store poisons where young children cannot reach them.
   4. Read the label before using any product.
   5. Know the phone number of the Poison Control Center or your doctor. The Center will tell a person what to do in case a poison has been taken accidentally.
3. There are five medicine safety rules.
   1. Take medicine only from your parents, a doctor, or other responsible adult.
   2. Do not take anyone else's prescription drug.
   3. Follow all directions on the medicine.
   4. Tell your parents about any strange effects caused by the medicine.
   5. **NEVER** take medicine from a stranger.

Thinking Critically
1. Caffeine speeds up body activities. It can make you nervous and keep you awake. Alcohol slows down body activities. It changes the way you act and may make you lose control of your muscles. Nicotine speeds up the way the body works. It makes the heart beat faster.
2. Healthful foods are needed by the body to grow new cells and repair damaged ones. They keep your body systems working healthfully. They also control body weight and provide energy for your body.

Checking for Understanding

1. The body makes new cells to replace damaged and dead cells and makes new cells as the body grows.

2. The body's defenses against disease are skin, tears, and substances the body makes to give immunity.

3. The heart, blood, and blood vessels make up the circulatory system.

4. Medicines cure, control, and relieve the distress of disease.

5. Your body gets immunity by having a disease or by getting a vaccine.

6. Muscles contract and relax to move body parts.

7. Answers will vary. Examples of organs are the heart, lungs, kidneys, and brain. Examples of organ systems are the circulatory, skeletal, and nervous systems.

8. (1) Take medicines only from your parents, a doctor, or other responsible adult. (2) Do not take anyone else's prescription drug. (3) Follow all directions on the medicine. (4) Tell your parents if you feel any strange side effects. (5) **Never** take medicine from a stranger.

9. Caffeine and nicotine speed up the way the body works. Alcohol slows down the way the body works.

10. Poisons enter the body through contact with the skin or by inhaling or swallowing them. Plant poisons such as poison ivy enter through contact with the skin. Poisonous gases such as carbon monoxide are inhaled. Poisons such as gasoline or drain cleaner are swallowed.

11. (1) Never taste an unknown substance. (2) Label all poisons. (3) Store poisons out of the reach of young children. (4) Read the label before using any product. (5) Place the phone number of your nearest doctor or Poison Control Center near the telephone.

12. All animal cells contain a nucleus, cytoplasm, and a cell membrane.

13. The nervous system and endocrine system are the control systems of the body.

UNIT REVIEW

4

Checking for Understanding

Write a short answer for each question or statement.

1. Why does your body make new cells all the time?
2. What are your body's defenses against disease?
3. What body parts make up the circulatory system?
4. How are medicines helpful to your body?
5. How does your body get immunity?
6. What do muscles do to make body parts move?
7. Give an example of an organ and an organ system.
8. What are five important medicine safety rules?
9. How do caffeine, alcohol, and nicotine affect the body?
10. How might poisons enter our bodies? Give examples.
11. What are five important poison safety rules?
12. What three different things do all animal cells contain?
13. Which organ systems are the body's control systems?
14. What are tissues and what are some examples of tissue?
15. Name the main functions of the skeletal system.
16. What does the digestive system do?
17. What is the main function of the respiratory system?
18. What happens to your body's liquid wastes?
19. What body parts make up the nervous system?

Recalling Activities

Write a short paragraph for each question or statement.

1. What do different body cells look like?
2. How does your pulse rate change?
3. What healthful foods have you eaten today?
4. How do you know which vaccinations you need?

TEACHER RESOURCE MASTERS

Project Ideas

1. Plan an assembly for your school. Use a play, posters, poems, and music to let students know what you've learned about being healthy.
2. Have a friend help you measure your legs, arms, head, and other parts of your body. Cut bones out of white paper based on your measurements. Assemble them into the shape of a skeleton, and name each bone.

Books to Read

Good Health Fun Book by Gail Aemmer, Carson-Dellosa Publishing Co.: Akron, OH, 1984.

Health & Hygiene by Rae Bains, Troll Associates: Mahwah, NJ, 1985.

The Healthy Habits Handbook by Slim Goodbody, Putnam Publishing Group: New York, 1983.

This interesting book will help you learn about good health.

TEACHER RESOURCE MASTERS

14. Tissue is a group of cells working together. Examples are muscle, bone, skin, nerve, and blood tissue.

15. The skeletal system gives your body shape and support and protects many organs.

16. The digestive system changes the food you eat so that it can be used by your body.

17. The respiratory system brings oxygen into the body to be used by cells and removes carbon dioxide from the body.

18. They are removed by the urinary system.

19. The nervous system includes the brain, the spinal cord, and nerves.

Recalling Activities

1. All animal cells contain a cell membrane, cytoplasm, and a nucleus even though they may be different in size, shape, and function.

2. Pulse rate increases when you do physical activities such as walking and running.

3. Answer should include foods from the five healthful food groups.

4. You can find out which vaccinations you need by checking in resource books and pamphlets. They can tell you the diseases that can be prevented by vaccines and the ages at which the vaccines should be given.

Project Ideas

Have students work individually or in **cooperative groups** to complete one of the projects listed.

Books to Read

♦ *Health & Hygiene*
● *Good Health Fun Book*
▲ *The Healthy Habits Handbook*

330

331

To the Teacher

An appreciation for the nature of science involves an understanding of and experience with a variety of critical thinking process skills because science is not simply an accumulation of scientific facts but is a way of learning how to process information. The Application Activities on the following pages were designed and written specifically to enhance the critical thinking process that is inherent to teaching science and learning in general.

Process Skill Models

The Process Skill Model activities are designed to introduce students to the process skills that are appropriate to the developmental cognitive stage of students within this grade level. The formal activities within the student text further provide students with practice in utilizing these process skills.

Problem Solving Activities

The Problem Solving activities allow students the opportunity to be creative, imaginative, and innovative in finding solutions to problems. Students apply the thinking skills they have learned and are encouraged to have fun proposing, testing, and evaluating their solutions.

Application Activities
Process & Problem Solving Activities

There are many ways to learn about science. You may read or do activities. You use certain thinking skills to observe and record what happens. You use others to explain why something happens. Thinking skills are also used to solve problems. These activities were written to help you practice thinking skills. They were also written so you could use your imagination, to be creative, and to have fun.

TABLE OF CONTENTS

PROCESS SKILL MODELS

332

PROCESS SKILL MODEL

Measuring

Definition Measuring is finding out the size, volume, mass, weight, or temperature of an object. It is also finding out how long it takes for an event to happen. The object or event is compared to a unit of measure.

Example Mrs. Boyer used a thermometer to measure temperature. She placed the thermometer on a white sheet of paper. Then she shined a lamp at the thermometer as shown below. The bulb was 15 centimeters from the thermometer. She recorded the temperature each minute. This is what she found.

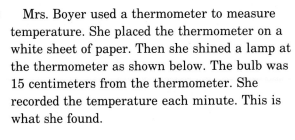

*M*rs. Boyer's Results

Time	Temperature
At start	24°C
1 minute	28°C
2 minutes	30°C
3 minutes	32°C
4 minutes	34°C
5 minutes	35°C

333

PREPLAN

Time Allotment: 45 minutes

Process Skill: Measuring

Objectives
1. Measure and **record** temperature under various conditions.
2. Give examples of situations in which temperature might be measured.

Setup
■ Obtain 6 lamps, 6 thermometers, and 6 sheets of white paper, and a watch with a second hand. Assign one student to be the class timer.

Cooperative Grouping: fives—Assign roles as explained on page T24.

1   FOCUS

■ Bring to class pictures of actual items used to measure temperature in different situations: meat thermometer, indoor/outdoor thermometer, hospital thermometer, laboratory thermometer, car thermostat, and so on. Display each item and ask what its use or purpose must be.

2   TEACH

■ **Safety Considerations:** Remind students to handle glass thermometers with care.
■ Review the demonstration that Mrs. Boyer did. If time permits, do the demonstration and record the results.
■ Demonstrate how to graph the temperature measurements.
 Have students use indoor-outdoor thermometers to measure the temperature of the air in various parts of the classroom. Have them record their measurements.
 Have students make other measurements in the classroom.

pages 333, 334

3 APPLY

■ Discuss the importance of measurements in everyday life. Include measurements other than temperature, such as length, area, volume, and weight.

Close

■ Discuss with students their answers for each question. Have several students explain why they think the temperature readings were lower under the slanted light source. Remind students that measurements help to explain or describe why certain things occur.

Mrs. Boyer asked the class what would happen if the lamp were shined directly over the thermometer from the same distance. The class decided to find out. Their results are shown below.

Class Results

Time	Temperature
At start	24°C
1 minute	31°C
2 minutes	33°C
3 minutes	35°C
4 minutes	37°C
5 minutes	38°C

 Practice

1. How are the measurements taken by the class different from those taken by Mrs. Boyer?
2. What units of measure were used?
3. When might you measure temperature?
4. You can perform this experiment yourself. Make a table like the one below, and record your measurements.

My Results

Time	Temperature
At start	
1 minute	
2 minutes	
3 minutes	
4 minutes	
5 minutes	

334

ACTIVITY RESPONSES

1. The class measurements are higher after one, two, three, four, and five minutes.
2. minutes and degrees Celsius
3. Answers will vary. Sample answers: when I want to go outside (air temperature); when I am sick (body temperature).
4. Answers will vary depending on distance.

PROCESS SKILL MODEL

Using Numbers

 Definition Using numbers includes ordering, counting, adding, subtracting, multiplying, and dividing numbers.

 Example Mrs. Butler's class had a popcorn contest. Each student started with 50 kernels, which were allowed to pop for three minutes. Timing began when the first kernel popped. Jason found that 45 of his kernels popped. Erica found that 47 of her kernels popped. Here are some more results:

*P*opcorn Popping Contest

Student	Kernels That Popped	Kernels That Did Not Pop
Erica	47	3
Faith	48	2
Jason	45	5
Jodi	46	4
José	40	10
Joseph	46	4
Leroy	39	11
Sarah	38	12

The students looked at the chart. They decided that Faith won. She popped 48 kernels.

335

PREPLAN

Time Allotment: 45 minutes

Process Skill: Using Numbers

Objectives

1. **Describe** various everyday objects or events using numbers.
2. **Count, add,** and **subtract** numbers.

Setup

■ Obtain two or three hot-air popcorn poppers and three bags of popcorn. Butter, salt, and napkins are optional.

Cooperative Grouping: fives—Assign roles as explained on page T24.

1 FOCUS

Prior to the activity, review with students the process skill of using numbers. Focus on counting. For example, have students count the number of blue eyes in the class, the number of brown eyes, and the number of eyes that are neither blue nor brown. Students can then determine by subtraction how many more brown eyes there are than blue eyes. Or how many more (or less) other-colored eyes there are than either blue or brown eyes.

2 TEACH

■ **Safety Consideration:** Caution students not to touch the hot poppers.

Have each group count out 50 kernels. You may wish to have them count out more kernels, just as long as the amount is the same for each group. Check over each group's pile for the correct amount.

Have students order the results in Mrs. Butler's class from the most kernels popped to the least kernels popped. Or have them order the results and determine a winner in your class.

3   APPLY

■ Discuss the importance of using numbers in everyday activities. Examples include getting the correct change when shopping; keeping score in sporting events; giving a person a telephone number; weighing oneself.

Close

■ Be sure each student has prepared a substantial list for question 4. Point out that scientists often use numbers to describe objects and communicate results, such as how many ducks they observed flying in formation.

 **Practice**   Look at the names and numbers in the table on the last page. Answer these questions. Show your work.

1. How many kernels did Leroy and Jodi pop altogether?
2. How many more kernels did Joseph pop than Sarah?
3. Study the information given in the table, then answer this question: How many kernels of popcorn did not pop during the contest?
4. Give examples of how you use numbers at home.

ACTIVITY RESPONSES

1. 39 + 46 = 85
2. 46 − 38 = 8
3. 51
4. Answers may include buying groceries, counting change, setting the table.

PROCESS SKILL MODEL
Predicting

Definition   Predicting is proposing possible outcomes of an event or experiment. Predictions are based on earlier observations and inferences.

Example   When Justin took a bath, he put hot and cold water into the tub. He knew that the mixture would be warm. If he put in more hot water, the mixture got warmer. If he put in more cold water, the mixture got cooler.

This led Justin to make this prediction. When equal amounts of hot and cold water are mixed, the temperature of the mixture will be halfway between the temperatures of the hot and cold water. To find out if his prediction was correct, Justin made mixtures of hot and cold water. His results are shown in the table.

337

PREPLAN

Time Allotment: 45 minutes

Process Skill: Predicting

Objectives
1. Apply the process of predicting to everyday occurrences.
2. Predict the temperature of a mixture of hot and cold water.

Setup
■ For group activities, obtain the following items per group: cold water, warm water, 2 thermometers, 1 large container, 2 small containers and 1 stirrer.
■ For your demonstration, obtain a baseball, a tennis ball, a table tennis ball, and a meter stick.

Cooperative Grouping: fives—Assign roles as explained on page T24.

1   FOCUS

■ Bring a baseball, a tennis ball, and a table tennis ball to class. Show students the three balls and ask them to predict which will bounce highest, next highest, and lowest if all are dropped from the same height. After students have made their predictions, ask them on what past observations or inferences their predictions are based. Distinguish this kind of reasoning from "guessing," for which there is no logical support. Drop the balls and determine the height to which each bounces. Discuss what led to both correct and incorrect predictions.

2   TEACH

One of the thermometers should be transferred quickly from one of the small containers to the large one after the two samples of water are combined. The mixture should be stirred gently.

3   APPLY

■ Ask students to explain why Justin's idea was a prediction and not a guess. Relate this scenario to your students: You hear footsteps outside your closed bedroom door. Your mother, father, and sister are home. It is 8:00 a.m. Whose footsteps do you hear? Have students give examples of a guess: simply choosing one out of three possibilities. A prediction, however, might be based on the fact that your mother wakes you up every morning at 8:00.

Close

■ Review the observations and inferences that led to the predictions in each activity. Have each group think of other daily activities in which they make predictions based on observations and inferences.

Mixing Warm and Cool Water

Temperature of Warm Water	Temperature of Cool Water	Temperature of Mixture
52°C	16°C	35°C
46°C	14°C	29°C
42°C	20°C	31°C
40°C	24°C	33°C
38°C	22°C	30°C

 Practice

1. Was Justin's prediction correct? Explain.
2. Suppose you mixed equal amounts of warm water at 36°C and cool water at 20°C. Predict what the temperature of the mixture would be.
3. Test your prediction. How close did you come to your prediction?
4. Do your results support your prediction? Explain.

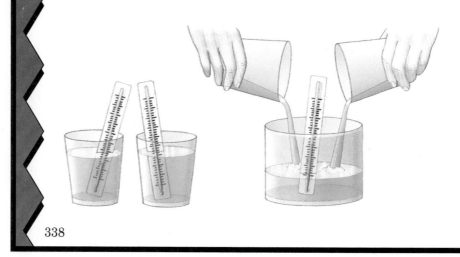

338

ACTIVITY RESPONSES

1. Yes. The temperatures of the mixtures were at or close to halfway between the temperatures of the warm and cool water.
2. at or near 28°C
3. Answers will vary but should be within a range of 25°–31°C.
4. The results should be near the halfway point between the two starting temperatures, which would support the prediction.

Interpreting Data

Definition   Interpreting data is explaining the meaning of information that has been collected.

Example   Mr. Hart's students were studying earthworms. They found that earthworms do not have eyes. The students wondered if earthworms react to light.

The students darkened the room. One student shined a flashlight on an earthworm. The earthworm moved out of the circle of light. The same thing happened with each of ten earthworms. The students interpreted this data to mean that earthworms react to light by moving away.

The students then covered the end of the flashlight with different colors of cellophane. Each color was shined on ten earthworms.

339

---

pages 339, 340

PREPLAN

Time Allotment: 45 minutes

Process Skill: Interpreting Data

Objectives
1. Interpret data that has been collected.
2. Identify everyday situations in which data is interpreted.

Setup
■ Obtain newspaper or magazine advertisements, various product labels, copies of charts and tables from science books or magazines.

Cooperative Grouping: whole class—no role assignments

1   FOCUS

■ Show students various ads and other items you have collected that must be interpreted by or for someone in order for them to be meaningful. Ask students to explain, or interpret, the data in one or two of the ads. Keep the materials for use in the APPLY section below.

2   TEACH

Have interested students devise an experiment to find out whether earthworms are more or less attracted to various kinds of soil: dry vs. wet, sandy vs. top soil, cool vs. warm, and so on. Have students report their data to the class. Have the class interpret the data.
■ Discuss student responses to each question. Point out that the earthworms behaved differently under each type of light. The reason the earthworms moved under all but the red light is that earthworms are not sensitive to red light.

3 APPLY

- Discuss with students how data are collected in scientific experiments. Remind students how scientists interpret the data they collect.
- Bring out the materials that you had students interpret during the FOCUS section. Ask how they might interpret the data differently now that they have done the activity.

Close

- Point out that data about how earthworms respond to light of different colors do not become meaningful until they are interpreted. For example, the fact that no worms moved away from red light leads to the meaningful interpretation that the worms perceive red light as darkness.

Earthworm Response to Light of Different Colors

Color	Response
Red	no worms moved away
Yellow	6 worms moved away immediately; 2 moved away later; 2 did not move away
Green	8 worms moved away immediately; 2 moved away later
Blue	no worms moved away immediately; all 10 later moved away

 Practice

1. Look at the table. Which two colors did the earthworms seem to prefer least? Explain.
2. Based on the example and the table, which color did the worms most likely sense as the darkest? Explain your answer.
3. Give examples of the kinds of data you interpret at home or in school.

340

ACTIVITY RESPONSES

1. Green and blue. More worms moved away from these colors than from either yellow or red.
2. Red. The example shows that earthworms move away from light and toward darkness. Since the earthworms did not move away from the red light they must have sensed it as being dark.
3. Answers will vary. Some possible answers may be temperature, wind speed, speed a storm is moving in a weather report, amount of different ingredients listed on a cereal box, the numbers or letters on a report card, the batting averages of baseball players.

Definition Controlling variables is making sure that everything in an experiment stays the same except for one factor.

Example Christopher watched a sugar cube dissolve in water. He wondered if the temperature of the water affected how fast the sugar dissolved.

To find out, Christopher filled two identical cups with the same amount of water. The water in one cup was warm. The water in the second cup was cold. Christopher put identical sugar cubes into each cup. He used identical spoons and began to stir the water in each cup. Christopher stirred each cup exactly the same way. Using a watch, he found out how long it took for the sugar to dissolve in each cup. His results are shown below.

Dissolving a Sugar Cube

Temperature of Water	Time Required
Cold	45 seconds
Warm	20 seconds

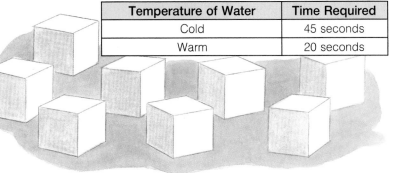

341

PREPLAN

Time Allotment: 45 minutes

Process Skill: Controlling Variables

Objectives
1. **Identify** the variables that are changed and the variable that is controlled in an experiment.
2. **Design** an experiment in which one variable is changed.

Setup
■ Obtain the following materials per group: 2 clear plastic cups, warm water, cold water, 2 sugar cubes, spoon, plastic sandwich bag and tie, watch or timer.
■ For the FOCUS, obtain 2 clear plastic cups, milk, water, lemon juice, and salt.

Cooperative Grouping: fives—Assign roles as explained on page T24.

1 FOCUS

■ Display a lemon, salt, and one clear cup partly filled with a mixture of milk and water. Ask students to observe the contents of the cup and describe. Next, simultaneously squeeze lemon juice and pour salt into the cup. Again ask students to describe the cup's contents. (The milk will have curdled.)

2 TEACH

Tell students that one of the substances will cause the mixture to curdle. Ask them to suggest which substance was responsible for the change. Salt should be added to each of two cups of water and milk mixture and lemon juice to only one of the cups. Ask: **Which variable is being controlled?** *salt* Ask: **Which variable is being tested?** *the lemon juice*

3 APPLY

■ You can relate this activity to the everyday experiences of making cold lemonade and hot tea. Sugar dissolves more readily in the tea than in the lemonade.

Close

■ Point out that in an experiment all the possible causes, or variables, must be controlled except one. For example, in the sugar-cube experiment all the variables were controlled except temperature.

 Practice 1. Which variables did Christopher control or keep the same?
2. Which variable did Christopher test or change?
3. What did Christopher discover from his experiment?
4. Design and perform an experiment to see if crushing a sugar cube affects the time required for the sugar to dissolve. Make a table like the one below. What were your results?

Dissolving Sugar

Variables Kept the Same	Variable Changed

342

ACTIVITY RESPONSES

1. the amount of sugar and water, the kind of cups, the form and size of the sugar (cube), and the speed of stirring
2. the temperature of the water
3. He found that sugar dissolves faster in warm water than in cold water.
4.   **Dissolving Sugar**

Variables kept the same

water temperature
amount of sugar
amount of water
kind of cup
speed of stirring

Variables changed

One sugar cube was crushed; the other was not. The crushed cube dissolved faster than the uncrushed cube.

Hypothesizing

Definition Hypothesizing is making an educated guess about how or why something happens. A hypothesis can be tested to see if it is correct.

Example Jonathan found some small animals called isopods. He found them under leaves in the flower bed. He also found them under rocks near the fence. He did not find any on the sidewalk or patio.

Jonathan formed a hypothesis based on his observations. He suggested that "Isopods like moist places." Jonathan decided to test his hypothesis.

He put ten isopods in the middle of a shoe box. Jonathan sprinkled water on one side of the shoe box to make it moist. The other side was dry. He waited five minutes and then recorded where he found the isopods. Jonathan repeated this experiment four more times.

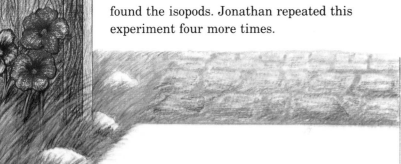

343

PREPLAN

Time Allotment: 45 minutes
Process Skill: Hypothesizing

Objectives
1. **Distinguish** between a hypothesis and an observation.
2. **Formulate** a hypothesis that can be tested.

Setup
Cooperative Grouping: whole class—no role assignments

1 FOCUS

■ Relate the following story: While working with certain frogs, a scientist injured the skin of the frogs. The scientist expected that the injuries would become infected. When this did not happen, the scientist became very curious. The scientist thought of a number of possible explanations, or hypotheses. One hypothesis was that when the frogs' skin was injured, a chemical was given off by the skin that prevented an infection from happening. Ask: **What observation led to the scientist's hypothesis?** *When injured, the frog did not become infected as might be expected.* Tell students that the hypothesis was later supported by experiments performed by the scientist.

2 TEACH

■ Inform students that isopods are also called sow bugs and may be referred to as such in other books.
■ Discuss the difference between a hypothesis and a guess. Point out that a hypothesis is an educated guess. That is, there is some basis for the guess, and the guess can be tested to see if it is correct. In this case, the word *correct* means that it is supported by data or results.

3 APPLY

■ You might want to explain to students the role a hypothesis plays in scientific activities by relating such activities to a detective story. To solve a mystery (a problem), a detective looks for and gathers clues (makes observations). From the clues, the detective makes an educated guess (a hypothesis) as to the solution of the mystery. The detective may then collect data such as fingerprints and other evidence (experiment) that may support or reject the educated guess (hypothesis).

Close

■ Discuss with students their answers for questions 3 and 4. Have several students explain how they formulated their hypothesis and how they would test their hypothesis.

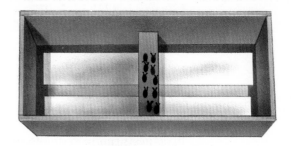

Location of Isopods

Test	Dry Side	Moist Side
1	2	8
2	1	9
3	3	7
4	1	9
5	2	8

 Practice

1. What observations did Jonathan make about isopods before he formed his hypothesis?
2. Look at Jonathan's results. Based on these results, was his hypothesis correct? Explain.
3. What other hypotheses can you make about where isopods live?
4. Describe how you would test your hypotheses from question 3.

ACTIVITY RESPONSES

1. He found isopods under leaves and rocks but not on the sidewalk or patio.
2. Yes, Jonathan found more isopods on the moist side of the shoe box than on the dry side.
3. Answers will vary. Based on the example, students could logically hypothesize that isopods live in dark, moist places.
4. Answers will vary. Students might use a shoe box and cover half the box. Students might place the box in a lighted location so the uncovered half receives light. They might place the isopods in the middle of the shoe box. After five minutes, they might record the location of the isopods. The experiment might be repeated four times.

Who Will Stop the Rust?

Use after page 63.

Background   Rust is a reddish-brown compound that forms when iron or steel combines with oxygen. Rust is formed when the surface of the iron or steel is exposed to water and air. One way to prevent the formation of rust is to keep these objects dry. Water and oxygen must be kept from combining with the iron or steel.

Problem   Your class has been discussing the problem of rust. You have begun to list objects that could be damaged by rust, such as cars, bicycles, toys, nails, and tools. The list seems to go on forever! Your teacher has challenged you to devise at least three methods of preventing rust. You are to test each method and decide which is best.

Materials   objects that will rust, such as washers or paper clips • materials of your choice to stop these objects from rusting • plant mister

345

PREPLAN

Time Allotment: 40 minutes total; 5 minutes each day for 5 days, then 15 minutes to compare results

Process Skills: Controlling Variables, Predicting

Objectives
1. **Design** a method to prevent the formation of rust.
2. **Test** a method to prevent rust, and **compare** that method with a control.
3. **Compare** class results to determine the best method of preventing rust.

Setup
■ Obtain some objects made of iron, such as washers or paper clips. Galvanized or painted objects will not work.
■ Obtain materials such as paints, oil, masking tape, and plastic wrap.
Cooperative Grouping: twos—Assign roles as explained on page T24.

1   FOCUS

■ Display a common household object that has rusted. Explain the process of rust formation. Have students give examples of objects that can rust.

2   TEACH

■ **Safety Consideration:** Have students wear smocks.
■ Have students devise methods of rust prevention before providing them with the materials.
Make sure students spray each of the objects with equal amounts of water. They should make sure the objects remain moist. The surfaces of the objects should be exposed to air.
If students paint their objects or add oil, stress the importance of completely covering the object.

3 APPLY

■ Ask: **Why might bridges rust easily if they are not protected?** *Bridges are usually built over water or low areas where they stay moist. They also have a lot of surface area exposed to air.*

Close

■ Compare results of the entire class. Identify which class members prevented rust and acknowledge their methods. Discuss why preventing rust is important in everyday life.

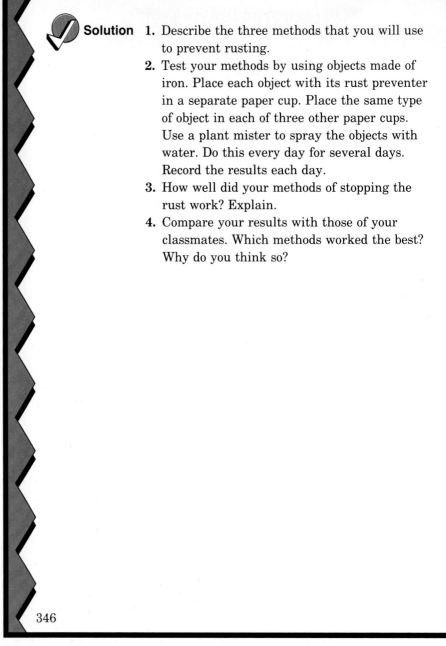

Solution

1. Describe the three methods that you will use to prevent rusting.
2. Test your methods by using objects made of iron. Place each object with its rust preventer in a separate paper cup. Place the same type of object in each of three other paper cups. Use a plant mister to spray the objects with water. Do this every day for several days. Record the results each day.
3. How well did your methods of stopping the rust work? Explain.
4. Compare your results with those of your classmates. Which methods worked the best? Why do you think so?

346

ACTIVITY RESPONSES

1. Students may suggest painting objects with an oil-based paint, coating the objects with oil, using masking tape or plastic wrap, and so on.

2. Answers may include that the objects not protected with a rust preventer should show more evidence of rust.

3. Answers will vary, but students will probably find that using an oil-based paint works best.

4. Answers will vary but should show that students have used good reasoning in their comparisons.

A Balancing Act

Use after page 104.

 Background Every scientist needs basic tools to use for observing and experimenting. One of the basic pieces of equipment is a balance for measuring mass. There are many different types of balances. A simple balance with a pan on each side is one of them.

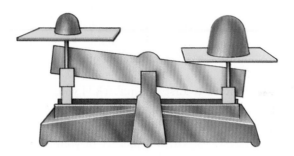

 Problem You are conducting a science experiment. Your experiment involves measuring the mass of some items in grams. Your balance is broken and there is not enough time to go out and buy a new one. You must build a new balance. Your balance must contain at least two of the following simple machines: lever, inclined plane, wedge, pulley, and wheel and axle.

347

---

pages 347, 348

PREPLAN

Time Allotment: 40 minutes

Process Skills: Measuring/Observing/ Classifying

Objectives
1. **Construct** a simple balance for measuring mass.
2. **Use** two or more simple machines in the construction of the balance.

Setup
■ Provide a variety of materials, such as gram masses, triangular blocks of wood, pans or cups, string, paper clips, drinking straws, toothpicks, clothespins, and screws.
■ Obtain a pan balance.

Cooperative Grouping: threes— Assign roles as explained on page T24.

1 FOCUS

■ Display the pan balance and recall with students how this scale is used to measure mass. Find the mass of some common items in the classroom.

2 TEACH

■ **Safety Considerations:** Remind students that toothpicks may be sharp.
When students are creating the pan balance, they may need assistance in fixing a fulcrum to the arm of the lever. A toothpick pushed through the center of a drinking straw could serve as a fulcrum.
Once students have made their balances, help them determine how to measure mass using the gram masses.

pages 347, 348

3 APPLY

■ Ask: **Could you use other units such as washers, coins, and so on, as units of mass?** Students would be able to determine relative mass, but would not be able to determine exact mass.

Close

■ Have students display their balances. Have them discuss the various simple machines, such as the lever, the inclined plane, the wedge, the pulley, and the wheel and axle, and how they are used in their balances.

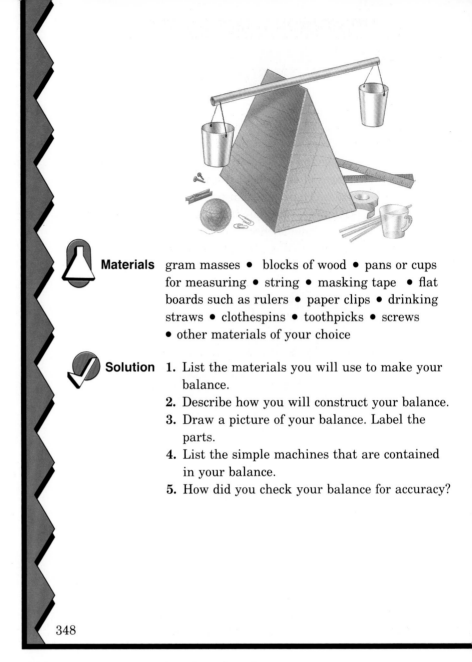

Materials gram masses • blocks of wood • pans or cups for measuring • string • masking tape • flat boards such as rulers • paper clips • drinking straws • clothespins • toothpicks • screws • other materials of your choice

Solution
1. List the materials you will use to make your balance.
2. Describe how you will construct your balance.
3. Draw a picture of your balance. Label the parts.
4. List the simple machines that are contained in your balance.
5. How did you check your balance for accuracy?

348

ACTIVITY RESPONSES

1. Students may use drinking straws, paper clips, string, paper cups, and triangular blocks of wood as materials.

3. Students may push a straightened paper clip through the middle of a straw, then bend the ends of the paper clip into a "U" shape. The ends of the clip may then be taped to the opposite sides of a triangular block.

3. Labeled parts should include stand, arm, fulcrum, and balance pans.

4. Sample answers: a lever may be used for the balancing arm and pivot, a wedge for the stand, and so on. Accept any creative solution to the problem.

5. Students could use a commercial balance to verify that the number of gram masses needed to balance objects is accurate.

PROBLEM SOLVING ACTIVITY
An Age-old Problem

Use after page 127.

 Background   Fossils are formed when parts of dead plants or animals become buried in sediments. Over many years, these sediments become sedimentary rock. Sometimes a plant or an animal leaves an imprint in the sedimentary rock. We can study such fossil prints to better understand the features of plants and animals that lived long ago.

Problem   You have found an unusually large leaf. You would like to keep it but know that the leaf will become dry and crumble over a period of time. You decide to use natural materials to make a print of the leaf. You wonder which materials will work best.

349

PREPLAN

Time Allotment: 40 minutes for activity; 15 minutes to conclude

Process Skills: Interpreting Data, Controlling Variables

Objectives
1. **Determine** the best type of sedimentary material in which fossils may form.
2. **Explain** why certain kinds of sedimentary rocks are better for fossil formation.

Setup
- Obtain 4 aluminum pie pans per group.
- Obtain 2 kg of each of the following materials: sand, silt, clay, gravel, leaf mulch (fine) and sawdust from a local nursery.

Cooperative Grouping: fours—Assign roles as explained on page T24.

1   FOCUS

- Show students some fossils or pictures of fossils. Explain how parts of plants or animals must be buried quickly to prevent decay. These parts must remain undisturbed for a long period of time. During this time, the sediments are cemented together to form sedimentary rock. The quality of the fossil prints varies depending on the type of sedimentary particles in which the fossil is formed.

2   TEACH

Direct students to work together to predict and experiment to find out which materials will work best making leaf prints. Assist any students who are having trouble preparing their mixtures. Make sure the same amount of water is added to each mixture.
- Allow prints to dry overnight. Allow students to compare their observations.

3 APPLY

■ Talk about how fossils are important in helping scientists learn about life long ago. Obtain a copy of *A Golden Guide on Fossils* for interested students.

Close

■ Have students display their leaf prints and discuss their observations.

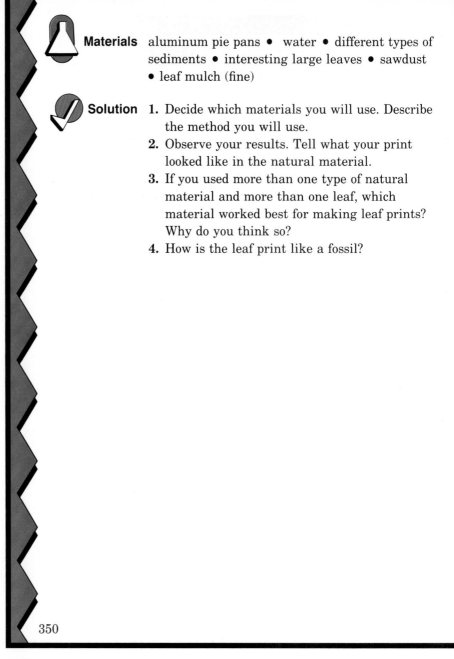

Materials aluminum pie pans • water • different types of sediments • interesting large leaves • sawdust • leaf mulch (fine)

Solution 1. Decide which materials you will use. Describe the method you will use.
2. Observe your results. Tell what your print looked like in the natural material.
3. If you used more than one type of natural material and more than one leaf, which material worked best for making leaf prints? Why do you think so?
4. How is the leaf print like a fossil?

350

ACTIVITY RESPONSES

1. Students may list sediments and/or plant materials (sawdust, mulch).
2. Prints made with fine-grained sediments will probably resemble clay molds. Prints made with plant materials will be coarser in appearance.
3. Students should conclude that the finer the sediment, the better the imprint that will be made.
4. Leaf prints and fossil prints are both made from natural materials. Both have prints of leaf embedded in hardened material.

Build a Shelter

Use after page 118.

Background Many rocks and minerals are used for building. Different types of rocks may be used, depending on the environment. Different environments require different types of rocks.

Many modern buildings are made from stones taken from stone quarries. The stones are crushed or cut into smaller pieces. Then they are cemented together over an inner wall of brick or concrete block.

In all cases, buildings made from rocks or minerals must be able to withstand weathering caused by wind, rain, or sand.

Problem Your problem is to build a model shelter. The shelter must be able to withstand wind, rain, sand, and any other elements in the environment.

351

pages 351, 352

PREPLAN

Time Allotment: 40 minutes for projects; one week to test them; 20 minutes for questions 3 and 4

Process Skills: Observing, Interpreting Data

Objectives
1. Construct a protective shelter using rock materials.
2. Test the shelter and **interpret** the results.

Setup
■ Obtain a variety of rocks, clay, and sand.

Cooperative Grouping: fives—Assign roles as explained on page T24.

1 FOCUS

■ Display some pictures of buildings that are constructed from rocks and minerals. Pictures of adobe houses, pyramids, and stone and brick houses can be found in most encyclopedias. Discuss the type of environment in which each type of building is found. Talk about the differences and similarities of the environments. Compare and contrast the materials used in each of the structures and their respective environments.

2 TEACH

■ **Safety Consideration:** You may wish to have students wear smocks or old clothes when constructing the shelters.
■ Choose a location for the shelters that will be free from animals.

3 APPLY

■ Have students plan to build a house in the area and discuss which materials would be most suitable for construction.

Close

■ After a week has passed, have students examine their shelters to see if they withstood the elements of the environment. Have students discuss which materials worked best and why.

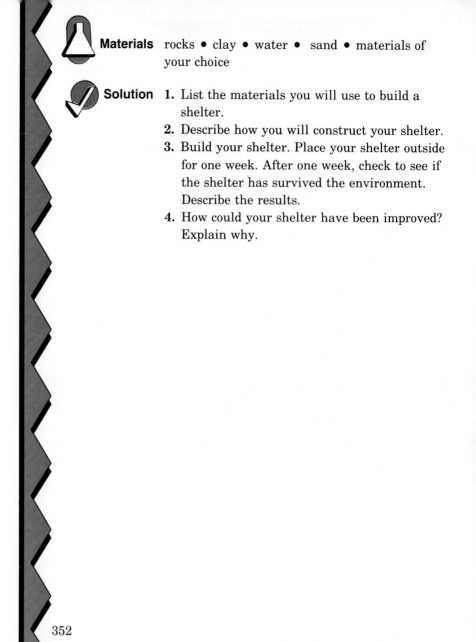

Materials   rocks • clay • water • sand • materials of your choice

Solution
1. List the materials you will use to build a shelter.
2. Describe how you will construct your shelter.
3. Build your shelter. Place your shelter outside for one week. After one week, check to see if the shelter has survived the environment. Describe the results.
4. How could your shelter have been improved? Explain why.

352

ACTIVITY RESPONSES

1. Answers will vary. Students should suggest a variety of building materials, such as rocks, clay, sand, straw, or wood; a bonding material; and so on.
2. Answers will vary depending on students' constructions.
3. Answers will vary depending on students' constructions.
4. Answers will vary depending on students' constructions.

PROBLEM SOLVING ACTIVITY
Soil Savers!

Use after page 142.

Background Soil is important for the growth of crops. Sometimes soil is blown away by wind or washed away by water. Erosion of soil can be prevented in many ways.

Problem Your family has just moved into a house that is on a hill. You want to plant a garden, but the rest of your family thinks it will be impossible. They think the soil will erode when it rains. Your job is to build a model of a soil saver to show that erosion near the house can be controlled. You may use natural materials only. No glue or cement is allowed.

Materials aluminum pan • soil • water • pan balance • books • paper cups • gram masses • natural materials of your choice

353

PREPLAN

Time Allotment: 40 minutes to build soil savers; 15 minutes to conclude

Process Skills: Predicting, Measuring

Objectives
1. Determine the materials necessary to build the best soil saver.
2. Measure the results in order to determine the least amount of soil eroded.

Setup
■ Have each student group use the same number and types of books for the slope.
■ Obtain a watering can, several long aluminum baking pans, and about 0.5 kg of soil for each group of students.
■ Provide a variety of materials such as rocks, twigs, leaves, plants, mosses, soil samples, or any other natural objects.
■ Provide a heat source, such as a hair dryer, for drying the soil samples.
⬚ **Cooperative Grouping:** fives—Assign roles as explained on page T24.

1   FOCUS

■ Bring in pictures of the "Dust Bowl" or badly eroded landscapes. Discuss how wind and water can cause erosion.

2   TEACH

■ **Safety Considerations:** Only you should use the heat source. Have students wear smocks.
⬚ Tell students they must construct a soil saver using natural materials.
■ Assist students in collecting the soil deposits at the base of their pans and determining the mass. The group with the least amount of erosion is the winner.

pages 353, 354

3 APPLY

■ Have students explain how their models are designed to prevent erosion.

Close

■ Ask students to be alert for signs of erosion in the community.

Solution 1. Prepare an aluminum pan of soil as shown:

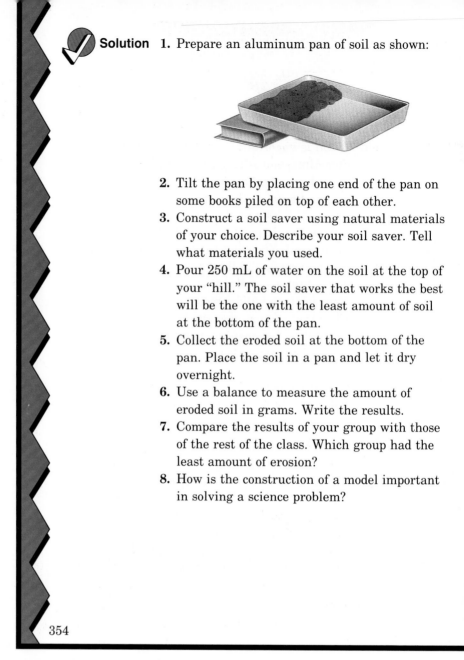

2. Tilt the pan by placing one end of the pan on some books piled on top of each other.
3. Construct a soil saver using natural materials of your choice. Describe your soil saver. Tell what materials you used.
4. Pour 250 mL of water on the soil at the top of your "hill." The soil saver that works the best will be the one with the least amount of soil at the bottom of the pan.
5. Collect the eroded soil at the bottom of the pan. Place the soil in a pan and let it dry overnight.
6. Use a balance to measure the amount of eroded soil in grams. Write the results.
7. Compare the results of your group with those of the rest of the class. Which group had the least amount of erosion?
8. How is the construction of a model important in solving a science problem?

354

ACTIVITY RESPONSES

1. Soil should be mounded at one end of the pan.
2. Books should be placed under the end with the soil.
3. Materials may include rocks, twigs, plants, ferns, mosses, and leaves.
4. Students should pour water slowly.
5. Collected soil will probably contain some of the soil saver.
6. & 7. Answers will vary depending on each group's soil saver.
8. A model can demonstrate if a solution to a problem is workable.

Who Will Stop the Rain?

Use after page 162.

Background   People who live in climates with much rainfall must be prepared for precipitation. They must have plenty of protective clothing. Raincoats, hats, and boots are important to them.

Many different types of materials are used to make weatherproof clothing. Sometimes materials such as plastic or vinyl are used to make this clothing. Also, fabric can be treated with chemicals to make it weatherproof.

Problem   You have gone on an overnight hike with the Outing Club. You have forgotten your raincoat, and a rainstorm is approaching. You need to protect yourself from the rain. All you have is a cotton poncho. There is a supply store nearby that sells things such as candles, plastic wrap, suntan oil, and so on. What can you do to the cloth to make it weatherproof? You may purchase any items of your choice at the supply store.

355

PREPLAN

Time Allotment: 40 minutes

Process Skills: Observing, Inferring, Controlling Variables, Interpreting Data

Objectives

1. Devise three methods of weatherproofing cotton cloth.

2. Test the methods to see which is the most effective.

Setup

■ Obtain some cotton cloth and cut the cloth into small squares (about 64 square centimeters).

■ Obtain some pans for students to catch the water as they spray it over the pieces of "weatherproofed" cloth.

Cooperative Grouping: fives—Assign roles as explained on page T24.

1   FOCUS

■ Ask some students to describe what type of rain gear they have. Make a list of their responses on the chalkboard. Point out the similarities and differences in the various types of rain gear. Lead students to discover that many types of materials are treated with chemicals to make them weatherproof.

2   TEACH

■ **Safety Consideration:** Caution students that materials, especially aerosol sprays, should be used only with adult supervision.

■ Work individually with each group to help students brainstorm about some methods of weatherproofing. Encourage students to express all their ideas.

3 APPLY

Relate this activity to the actual weatherproofing of fabrics. For example, some silicone sprays are used at dry-cleaning establishments to weatherproof overcoats.

Close

■ Have students present the results of their testing. Have each group demonstrate the method that worked best. Discuss the reasons some methods may have worked better than others. Encourage students to interpret their results based on their experimentation.

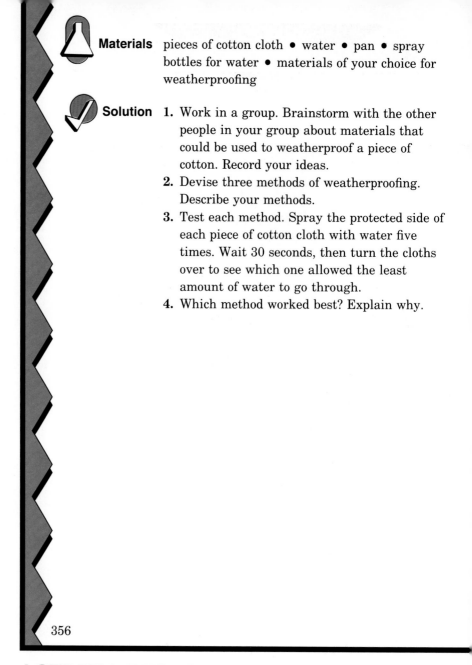

Materials pieces of cotton cloth • water • pan • spray bottles for water • materials of your choice for weatherproofing

Solution 1. Work in a group. Brainstorm with the other people in your group about materials that could be used to weatherproof a piece of cotton. Record your ideas.
2. Devise three methods of weatherproofing. Describe your methods.
3. Test each method. Spray the protected side of each piece of cotton cloth with water five times. Wait 30 seconds, then turn the cloths over to see which one allowed the least amount of water to go through.
4. Which method worked best? Explain why.

356

ACTIVITY RESPONSES

1. Answers will vary but may include candle wax, transparent wrap, salves such as petroleum jelly, and so on.
2. Students' solutions will vary. Students may suggest spraying the pieces of cotton with a water-repellent spray; coating the cotton with a water-repellent spray; coating the cotton with a water-repellent lotion, oil, or cream; rubbing the material with wax from candles; covering the material with plastic wrap or waterproof tape; and so on.
3. Test results will vary depending on the materials chosen.
4. Answers will vary. The method that prevents the most water from soaking into the cotton works the best.

PROBLEM SOLVING ACTIVITY
Protect Yourself

Use after page 240.

 Background   Many plants and animals live in only one kind of habitat. People are able to adapt to many different kinds of habitats. One of the things people can do to adapt to certain habitats is to dress differently. It is necessary for people to protect themselves from many different types of conditions within a habitat.

Problem   You have received an award for becoming the Junior Scientist of the Year. You and four other Junior Scientists have been chosen to go with a group of five scientists to study some animals in five different habitats. Each Junior Scientist will go to one of the following habitats: grassland, temperate forest, desert, tundra, and rain forest. You will need to wear the proper clothing and any additional protection necessary to adapt to living out in the open in the habitat you will be studying.

357

PREPLAN

Time Allotment: 20 minutes the first day; 30 minutes the next day; allow one or two days for gathering materials

Process Skills: Observing, Inferring

Objectives
1. **Observe** environmental conditions for a particular habitat.
2. **Infer** the types of clothing necessary to adapt to a particular environment.

Setup
■ Obtain photographs or artwork representative of each habitat.

Cooperative Grouping: fives—Assign roles as explained on page T24.

1   FOCUS

■ List the following habitats on the chalkboard and review the characteristics of each: grassland, temperate forest, coniferous forest, polar regions, desert, tundra, and rain forest.

2   TEACH

■ You may suggest that students study a particular animal that lives in that environment and mimic how that animal is adapted to the particular habitat.

■ If there is more than one season in a particular habitat, remind students to account for the changes in seasons when designing their clothing.

3 APPLY

■ Have students tell how the clothing is suitable for their habitat. Students might explain the purpose of each item of clothing.

Close
■ Have students compare and contrast the clothing they have chosen to wear in each of the habitats.

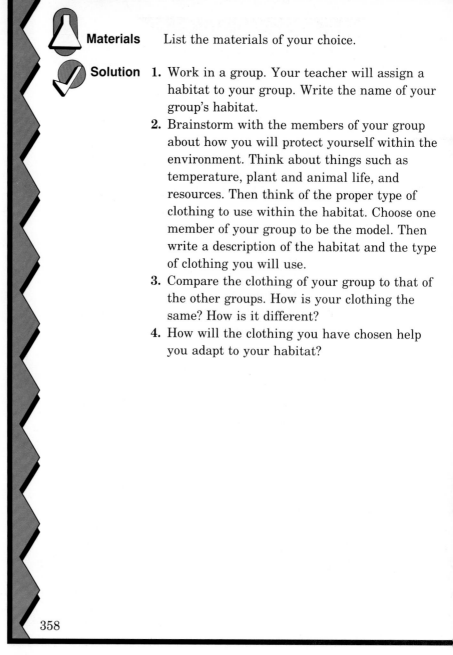

Materials   List the materials of your choice.

Solution
1. Work in a group. Your teacher will assign a habitat to your group. Write the name of your group's habitat.
2. Brainstorm with the members of your group about how you will protect yourself within the environment. Think about things such as temperature, plant and animal life, and resources. Then think of the proper type of clothing to use within the habitat. Choose one member of your group to be the model. Then write a description of the habitat and the type of clothing you will use.
3. Compare the clothing of your group to that of the other groups. How is your clothing the same? How is it different?
4. How will the clothing you have chosen help you adapt to your habitat?

358

ACTIVITY RESPONSES

1. Possible answers are grassland, temperate forest, coniferous forest, polar region, desert, tundra, rain forest.
2. Answers will depend on the habitat of each individual group.
3. Answers will depend on the habitat of each individual group.
4. Students should suggest that the clothing they have chosen will help protect them from extremes in temperature and precipitation and hazards of the environment, such as strong sunlight, brush, and so on.

Blending Right In

PROBLEM SOLVING ACTIVITY

Use after page 252.

 Background Some animals blend into their environment so well they can hardly be seen. The ability to hide in this way is called camouflage. Camouflage is an adaptation that helps animals to survive by blending into the environment. Probably the best example of camouflage is the chameleon. This lizard-like creature can change its skin color to blend into different environments.

Problem Several flying saucers have landed at the edge of your school grounds. Small creatures have come out of the saucers. You are not sure whether or not these creatures are friendly. In order to get a better look at them, you decide to camouflage yourself in the bushes or trees nearest the school building. How can you dress so that you will not be seen by the space creatures?

359

PREPLAN

Time Allotment: several days to gather materials; 60 minutes for the activity

Process Skills: Observing, Inferring, Measuring, Interpreting Data

Objectives
1. **Determine** how camouflage can be used in the environment.
2. **Create** effective camouflage clothing.

Setup
■ A few days before this activity, have students bring in various pieces of different colored clothing and old white shirts, sheets, or pieces of cloth.

🏠 **Cooperative Grouping:** fives—Assign roles as explained on page T24.

1 FOCUS

■ Have students observe the color of the wall or chalkboard at the front of the classroom. Ask two students to come forward, one whose clothing is the same color as the wall and one whose clothing is radically different in color from the wall. Ask which person shows up more clearly and why.

2 TEACH

■ If your school is in the city and has no trees or bushes on the grounds, you may wish to conduct this activity in a nearby park. Otherwise, challenge students to blend in with the color of the school building or other structures.

3 APPLY

■ Show students a picture or live specimen of a chameleon. Talk about how the chameleon changes its color. Ask: **How is a slow-moving chameleon helped by its ability to change color?** *It becomes hidden from predators and prey.*

Close
■ Have groups of students interact with each other by taking turns evaluating the effectiveness of each other's camouflage.

Materials old clothing of different colors ● pieces of cloth that are disposable ● scissors ● string ● materials of your choice

Solution
1. Examine the area near your school building. List the areas in which you can hide.
2. Describe the color clothing you would need to blend in with these surroundings.
3. Create your camouflage clothing. Describe it.
4. Make the table shown below. Then hide in the area you have chosen. Ask several classmates to determine whether or not you are visible at the distances shown in the table. Describe the results of these observations.

Visibility of Camouflaged Students

Distances	Results
a. the edge of the school grounds	
b. several hundred meters	
c. less than one hundred meters	
d. less than ten meters	

5. Do you think you could safely observe the space creatures? Explain why. If not, what changes would you make in your camouflage?

360

ACTIVITY RESPONSES
1–5. Answers will vary depending on the environment of your school grounds.

What's For Lunch?

Use after page 308.

 Background Your body needs nutrients that come from the healthful food groups. Children through the age of 12 should eat the following servings from each of these food groups: milk group: 3 servings, meat group: 2 servings, fruit-vegetable group: 4 servings, and grain group: 4 servings. Each meal that you eat for breakfast, lunch, and dinner should have a combination of servings from these food groups.

Problem You forgot to bring your lunch to school. You have only $1.50 in your pocket. You want to have a healthful lunch. Look at the cafeteria menu on the next page. Choose a lunch that is healthful and does not cost more than $1.50.

361

PREPLAN

Time Allotment: 25 minutes

Process Skills: Classifying, Using Numbers, Measuring, Interpreting Data

Objectives
1. Select healthful foods from a given list of foods.
2. Create a lunch menu within a specific price range.
3. Group foods within food groups.
4. Determine whether a lunch is healthful and tell why it is or is not.

Setup
■ Obtain some old magazines with pictures of a variety of foods.

Cooperative Grouping: fives—Assign roles as explained on page T24.

1 FOCUS

■ Write the names of the four healthful food groups on the board: milk, meat, fruit/vegetable, grain. Then provide pictures obtained from magazines of the following foods: milk, peanut, hot dog, chicken, carrot, apple, bread, sugar-coated cereal. Have students classify the foods under the appropriate food groups. Then lead a discussion on why some of the food choices are healthful and why some are not. (The sugar-coated cereal should not be considered a healthful food.)

2 TEACH

Students will find it helpful to use play money to find the total amount spent on lunch.

3 APPLY

■ Have students look at the school lunch menu for the week and classify the foods under the appropriate food groups. You may want to have them plan a balanced meal and determine the cost of lunch for the week.

Close

■ Have students discuss their various combinations of food. Make sure students understand that they should have selected a lunch with at least one serving from each of the four food groups. Have students tell why they think their choices are healthful.

Materials play money

Solution 1. List what you will buy for lunch. Make sure you do not spend more than $1.50.

Daily Menu

carton of milk	$0.35
yogurt	$0.49
cheese slice	$0.10
hard-boiled egg	$0.25
tuna fish sandwich	$0.40
chicken drumstick	$0.39
carton of juice	$0.35
fruit cup	$0.59
vegetable soup	$0.49
roll	$0.10
biscuit	$0.15
spaghetti	$0.45
chocolate cake	$0.25
apple	$0.25
vanilla pudding	$0.25
brownie	$0.25

2. Next to each choice you listed in #1, write the name of the food group to which the item belongs.
3. How can you decide whether or not you had a healthful lunch?

362

ACTIVITY RESPONSES

1. Answers will vary. Sample answer:

carton of milk	$0.35
vegetable soup	$0.49
tuna fish sandwich	$0.40
brownie	$0.25

2. Answers will vary. Sample answer:
milk—milk group
vegetable soup—fruit/vegetable group
tuna fish sandwich—meat group, grain group
brownie—"others" group

3. Answers will vary. Students should suggest checking each food chosen to determine if its ingredients are contained in one or more of the healthful food groups. In the case of the sample lunch listed in step 1, all choices were healthful except the brownie.

Read the Labels

Use after page 317.

 Background   Many people buy over-the-counter medicines when they have coughs or colds. The medicines can help them feel better. They must read the label carefully to find out how much of the medicine to take. They must also find out how often to take the medicine.

Problem   You are helping your mother clean out the medicine cabinet. There are several bottles of cold and cough medicines on the shelf. Your mother asks you to read the labels on the bottles and keep only the bottles of cold and cough medicines that you know can be used for all members of the family, including your 3-year-old sister. You are to throw all the other bottles away. Look at the dosage information from the five medicine labels in the table.

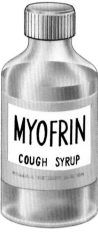

363

PREPLAN

Time Allotment: 35 minutes

Process Skills: Interpreting Data, Using Numbers, Measuring

Objectives
1. Interpret data to determine the proper medicine dosage that should be administered by an adult.
2. State a conclusion based on the data interpreted.

Setup
■ Obtain copies of several medicine labels with which students may be familiar.
■ Provide actual medicine labels or copy dosages and warning labels for students.
■ Arrange for a pediatrician to visit the class at the conclusion of the activity to discus the importance of reading and following carefully all directions on medicines.
Cooperative Grouping: fives—Assign roles as explained on page T24.

1   FOCUS

■ Describe the following scene for students: A student in the class feels ill. He or she has a fever and an upset stomach. What should the student do? Elicit responses from students. If any students suggest taking medicines, tell them it is important to read medicine labels and always have a responsible adult give them the right amount of medicine.

2   TEACH

■ **Safety Considerations:** Note that not all medicines are suitable for children.
■ Remind students *never* to take medicine from a stranger.
■ Show students how to read and interpret medicine labels.

3 APPLY

■ Have a class discussion on students' experiences with various medicines. Discuss the importance of seeing a doctor if one still feels ill after three or four days of taking over-the-counter drugs.

Close

■ Help students realize that medicines help cure or suppress symptoms but should be taken only when actually needed.

Materials medicine labels

Medicines—Dosage for 24 Hours

Age	A	B	C	D	E
0-1	Consult Doctor	Don't take	Consult Doctor	Consult Doctor	Consult Doctor
2-3	Consult Doctor	Consult Doctor	5 mL	1 tbs.	Consult Doctor
4-5	Consult Doctor	Consult Doctor	7.5 mL	2 tbs.	Consult Doctor
6-8	2 tablets	1 tsp.	10 mL	2 tbs.	1 tsp.
9-10	2.5 tablets	2 tsp.	12.5 mL	3 tbs.	1 tsp.
11	3 tablets	2 tsp.	15 mL	3 tbs.	1 tsp.
12+	4 tablets	2 tbs.	20 mL	4tbs.	1 tsp.

Solution

1. List the bottles of medicine that you will keep.
2. List the bottles of medicine that you will throw away.
3. What dosage of each medicine could you now take safely?

   Medicine A   Medicine D

   Medicine B   Medicine E

   Medicine C

4. Choose a medicine label from those that your teacher has given to you.
5. What is the name of the medicine?
6. How often should someone your age take the medicine?
7. What is the medicine for?
8. When reading the medicine label, what warnings did you notice?

364

ACTIVITY RESPONSES

1. Keep bottles C and D.
2. Throw away bottles A, B, and E.
3. For an eight-year-old child answers would be as follows:

Medicine A—2 tablets

Medicine B—1 tsp.

Medicine C—10 mL

Medicine D—2 tbs.

Medicine E—1 tsp.

4. No answer is needed.

5–8. Answers will vary but should reflect information from the labels provided.

Glossary

This book has words you may not have read before. Many of these words are science words. Some science words may be hard for you to read. You will find the science words in **bold print.** These words may appear two ways. The first way shows how the word is spelled. The second way shows how the word sounds. The list below shows the sounds each letter or group of letters makes.

Look at the word **energy** (EN ur jee). The second spelling shows the letters "ee." Find these letters in the list. The "ee" has the sound of "ea" in the word "leaf." Anytime you see "ee," you know what sound to say.

The capitalized syllable is the accented syllable.

a . . . back (BAK)
er . . . care, fair (KER, FER)
ay . . . day (DAY)
ah . . . father (FAHTH ur)
ar . . . car (KAR)
ow . . . flower, loud (FLOW ur, LOWD)
e . . . less (LES)
ee . . . leaf (LEEF)
ih . . . trip (TRIHP)
i (or i + consonant + e) . . . idea, life (i DEE uh, LIFE)
oh . . . go (GOH)
aw . . . soft (SAWFT)
or . . . orbit (OR but)
oy . . . coin (KOYN)

oo . . . foot (FOOT)
yoo . . . pure (PYOOR)
ew . . . food (FEWD)
yew . . . few (FYEW)
uh (or u + consonant) . . . comma, mother (KAHM uh, MUTH ur)
sh . . . shelf (SHELF)
ch . . . nature (NAY chur)
g . . . gift (GIHFT)
j . . . gem, edge (JEM, EJ)
ing . . . sing (SING)
zh . . . vision (VIHZH un)
k . . . cake (KAYK)
s . . . seed, cent (SEED, SENT)
z . . . zone, raise (ZOHN, RAYZ)

365

Using the Glossary

The glossary provides definitions of the key science words presented in the text. These words are also listed in the *Science Words* at the end of each chapter.

Phonetic respellings are included for words that may be difficult to pronounce.

You may use this glossary to teach or sharpen the dictionary skills of students.

Read the directions with the class. They tell students how to use the glossary to learn about their science words.

A

adaptation (ad ap TAY shun): anything that helps an animal live in its environment

alcohol (AL kuh hawl): a drug that slows down the way the body works

atmosphere (AT muh sfihr): all the air that surrounds Earth

atom (AT um): the smallest part of any kind of matter

B

behavior (bih HAY vyur): a living thing's response to something in its environment

C

caffeine (ka FEEN): a drug that speeds up the way the body works

cell (SEL): the smallest unit of living matter

chemical change: a change that takes place when a compound forms

circulatory (SUR kyuh luh tor ee) **system:** moves blood throughout your body

cirrus (SIHR us) **clouds:** thin clouds formed high in the atmosphere and made of ice

climate (KLI mut): the usual weather in an area year after year

clouds: formed from millions of water droplets, tiny pieces of ice, or both ice and water

community (kuh MYEW nut ee): a group of producers and consumers living together in one area

compound (KAHM pownd): a kind of matter formed from two or more elements

compound machine: a machine made of two or more simple machines

condensation (kahn den SAY shun): the change from a gas to a liquid

coniferous (kuh NIHF rus) **forest:** a forest habitat found in northern regions

consumer (kun SEW mur): a living thing that cannot make its own food

control (kun TROL): something that shows what happens when no changes are made in an experiment

core (KOR): the innermost part of Earth

crust (KRUST): the top layer of Earth

cumulus (KYEW myuh lus) **clouds:** large, puffy clouds

D

decomposer (dee kum POH zur): a living thing that breaks down dead plants and animals into simpler matter

desert (DEZ urt): a hot or cold habitat that has very little moisture

dew: water that condenses on objects near the ground

366

digestive (di JES tihv) **system:** changes the food you eat so that it can be used by your body

disease (dihz EEZ): an illness

drug: a substance that changes the way a body or mind works

E

element (EL uh munt): matter that is made of one kind of atom

endocrine (EN duh krun) **system:** is made of organs that make chemicals that control your body; some chemicals are important for growth

energy (EN ur jee): the ability to do work

erosion (ih ROH zhun): the movement of soil and rocks to new places

evaporation (ih vap uh RAY shun): the change from a liquid to a gas

F

feathers: strong, lightweight outer coverings of birds

food chain: the transfer of energy in a community

food web: all the feeding relationships in a community

force: a push or a pull

freshwater habitats: water habitat such as ponds, bogs, swamps, lakes, and rivers

friction (FRIHK shun): a force that slows down or stops moving objects

frost (FRAWST): ice that forms directly from water vapor

fur: a thick covering of soft hair on an animal's body

G

gas: matter that has no shape or size of its own

glacier (GLAY shur): a large mass of ice that moves

gram: a unit used to measure small amounts of mass

grassland: a habitat where most of the plants are grasses

gravity (GRAV ut ee): the pulling force between objects

groundwater: water that soaks into the ground

H

habitat (HAB uh tat): an area that supports the life needs of a plant or animal

hypothesis (hi PAHTH uh sus): an idea that has not been proved but is stated to be true for purposes of study and testing

367

I

igneous (IHG nee us) **rock:** rock that forms from cooled magma or lava

immunity (ihm YEW nut ee): the body's protection against certain diseases

inclined (IHN klind) **plane:** a simple machine with a sloped surface used to move objects

instinct (IHN stingt): a complex type of behavior an animal is born with

K

kilograms (Kee luh grams): units used to measure large amounts of mass; one kilogram equals 1000 grams

L

lava (LAHV uh): magma at Earth's surface

learned behavior: behavior that is caused by experience and can be changed

lever (LEV ur): a simple machine with an arm that rocks on a fulcrum

liquid (LIHK wud): matter that has a certain size but does not have its own shape

M

magma (MAG muh): hot liquid that forms inside Earth

mantle (MANT ul): the layer of Earth between the crust and the core

mass: how much there is of an object

matter: everything that takes up space and has mass

metamorphic (met uh MOR fihk) **rock:** rock that has been changed by heat and pressure

mineral (MIHN uh rul): solid matter found in nature but not made by plants or animals

mixture (MIHKS chur): a combination of two or more different types of matter in which each type of matter keeps its own properties

muscular system: made of muscle tissue and works with bones

N

nervous system: controls all your body actions; your brain, spinal cord, and nerves make up this system

nicotine (NIHK uh teen): a drug that speeds up the way the body works

O

organ: a group of tissues working together

organ system (SIHS tum): a group of organs working together

over-the-counter drug: a drug that can be bought without a doctor's prescription

P

perspiration (pur spuh RAY shun): liquid wastes that are released through sweat glands

physical change: a change in a physical property of matter

poisons (POY zunz): substances that are harmful to the body

polar region (POH lur • REE jun): an area of ice and snow near the poles

polar zones: areas on Earth where the temperatures are always cold

precipitation (prih sihp uh TAY shun): moisture that falls from the atmosphere

predator (PRED ut ur): an animal that hunts and eats other animals

prescription (prih SKRIHP shun) **drug:** a drug prepared after it is ordered by a doctor

prey (PRAY): animals eaten by predators

problem (PRAHB lum): a question for study

producer (pruh DEW sur): a living thing that makes its own food

property (PRAHP urt ee): is a characteristic of an object

pulley (POOL ee): a simple machine that has a rope wrapped around a wheel

R

rain forest: a hot forest habitat that receives large amounts of rainfall each year

reflex: the reaction of an animal to something in its environment

respiratory (RES pruh tor ee) **system:** makes the exchange of gases happen when you breathe

rock cycle (SI kul): the changing of rocks into different kinds of rocks

runoff: water that flows across the ground

S

saltwater habitat: a water habitat found in oceans

scales: small, thin plates that cover the skin of some animals

scavenger (SKAV un jur): an animal that feeds on dead plants and animals

scientific methods (si un TIHF ihk • METH udz): lists of steps that are used to study or explain something

screw: an inclined plane wrapped around a post

sedimentary (sed uh MENT uh ree) **rock:** rock made of sediments that are pressed together

sediments (SED uh munts:) small pieces of Earth material

shelter: a place or object that protects an animal

simple machine: a machine with few or no moving parts

369

skeletal (SKEL ut ul) **system:** gives your body shape and protects many organs

skin: the outer covering of an animal's body

solid (SAHL ud): matter that has a certain size and shape

stratus (STRAT us) **clouds:** clouds that cover the sky

T

temperate (TEM prut) **forest:** a forest habitat with four seasons–spring, summer, autumn, and winter

temperate zones: areas on Earth where the weather changes during four seasons of the year

tissue (TIHSH ewz): a group of cells working together

tropics: area on Earth where the temperatures are always hot

tundra (TUN druh): a cold, dry habitat with a layer of soil that is frozen

U

urethra (yoo REE thruh): releases urine from your body

urinary (YOOR uh ner ee) **system:** is made up of organs that remove liquid wastes from your body

urine (YOOR un): the wastes and water removed from your body

V

vaccine (vak SEEN): dead or weakened germs that give immunity to a disease

variables (VER ee uh bulz): things that change in an experiment

W

water cycle (SI kul): the continuous movement of water through the different stages of evaporation, condensation, precipitation, and storage

water vapor (VAY pur): water as a gas

weathering: the breaking down or wearing away of rock

wedge (WEJ): a simple machine made of two inclined planes

wheel and axle (AK sul): a simple machine with a wheel that turns a post

wildlife conservation (kahn sur VAY shun): the protection of habitats and living things

work: what is done when a force moves an object

Index

A

Adaptations, 246–259; of feet, 254–255; of mouth parts, 256–259; of skin, 248–252; *illus.,* 246–252, 255–259

Alcohol, 316–318

Allen, Bryan, 92

Animals, adaptations of, 246–259; behaviors of, 260–270; cells of, 280–284; feet of, 254–255; and food, 198–212; groups of, 222; habitats of, 218–241; instincts of 266–270; mouthparts of, 256–259; plant eaters, 198–202; predators, 199–200, 202, 210, 233; prey, 199, 210, 221; reflexes of, 264–266, 269; and rocks, 137–138; scavengers, 202, 205; shelters for, 221–222; skin of, 248–253; *act.,* 201, 223, 237, 239

Atmosphere, 148

Atoms, 35–37, 39

Axles, 98, 101–102, *illus.,* 98

B

Bacteria, 203–204; *illus.,* 204

Balloons, hot-air, 45

Behaviors, 260–270; instinctive, 266–270; learned, 261; reflex, 264–266, 269; *act.,* 270; *illus.,* 260–269

Bicycles, 105; *illus.,* 105

Bills, 256–257; *illus.,* 256–257

C

Caffeine, 316–318; *illus.,* 316

California condors, 241

Can openers, 102, 104; *illus.,* 102

Carbon dioxide, 195, 286, 295–296

Cardiopulmonary resuscitation, 301

Cavities, 325

Cells, 280–284, 306; groups of, 284, 286; *act.,* 283; *illus.,* 280–281

Charts, 16–17, 21–22; *act.,* 17

Chemical change, 63

Cigarettes, 317

Circulatory system, 288; *illus.,* 288

Cirrus clouds, 154–156

Climate, 158–162; *act.,* 161

371

Using the Index

The index is an extensive alphabetical listing of topics and science words in the text. A boldface capital letter appears before the first entry of each new letter section. Page references for the topics and science words appear after each entry. Tables, illustrations, and activities are indicated in italics.

Explain the purpose of an index. Help students learn how to use an index as a reference guide to the location of information.

372

374

375

376

377

erosion, 141–142;
evaporation of, 148–150,
169–170; flooding, 175;
groundwater, 176, 183;
habitats, 234–236;
importance of, 168, 194;
pollution, 182–185; runoff,
174–176, 183; storage of,
180–182; and weathering of
rocks, 134–136

Water cycle, 169–173, 177,
182–184; *act.,* 173; *illus.,* 170

Water vapor, 148;
condensation of, 151–152,
154; evaporation of, 148–149

Weather, 148–156; climate,
158–162; clouds, 151,
154–156; precipitation,
155–157, 159–160

Weathering, 134–140; *act.,*
139, 141; *illus.,* 135–137

Wedges, 95–96, 102; *illus.,* 89,
95, 102

Wheels, 83

Wheels and axles, 98,
101–102; *illus.,* 89, 98, 102

Wildlife conservation,
239–241

Wind, and erosion, 141–142;
and evaporation, 150; and
weathering of rocks, 134

Work, 78–82; and machines,
89; *illus.,* 78–79

378

Photo Credits

379